The Collected Writings

of

AMBROSE BIERCE

THE
Collected Writings
OF
AMBROSE BIERCE

With an Introduction by CLIFTON FADIMAN

THE CITADEL PRESS · *New York*

TABLE OF CONTENTS

AMBROSE BIERCE
Portrait of a Misanthrope

As FOR Bierce's life, we know something of its first seventy-one years only. In 1913 he vanished into the revolutionary wilderness of Mexico, and has not, for all the legends and rumors, been heard of since. If at this writing Bierce were still alive, he would be 104 years old. One doubts, however, that these added years could have mellowed his attitude toward the human race. Indeed, the whole conduct of civilized man since Bierce's presumed death in 1914 is happily calculated to confirm his misanthropy. Lidice, Belsen, Dachau, Hiroshima, Nagasaki, Bikini—all would have afforded him a satisfaction deeper and more bitter than that which he drew from the relatively paltry horrors of the nineteenth and early twentieth centuries. If he was killed, as some aver, during the Villa-Carranza fracas, it seems rather a pity. The current scene would have filled him with so pure a pleasure.

WHENEVER and wherever he may have died, Ambrose Gwinett Bierce began life on June 24, 1842 in Meigs County, Ohio. Born in a log cabin, he defied Alger's Law and did not become President. His father was a poor, eccentric farmer who begat nine children, Ambrose being the youngest. He was also the only one of whom the world has heard, thus supplying another bit of evidence to support the by no means fanciful theory that exceptional persons are often the last, or among the later, of a long series of progeny, and the issue, if not of exhausted, certainly of well-exercised loins.

The elder Bierce seems to have suffered an unhappy childhood. This formed the major part of his legacy to Ambrose, for his son hated the home and, except for one brother, Albert, the entire family. The unlovely circumstances of his early life may be in part the source of Bierce's later addiction to aristocratic heroes. Assuredly they played a part in the formation of his misanthropy. A by no means accidentally large number of his horrifying humorous tales turn on patricide and, less often, matricide, with an occasional avunculicide, if that be the word, thrown in for variety. (See, for example, *An Imperfect Conflagration,* with its masterly opening sentence: "Early one June morning in 1872 I murdered my father—an act which made a deep impression on me at the time.") To declare that Bierce's collected works are but a kind of inky revenge on his father is cheap, easy, and false; yet it does not require a Freud to trace in his fierce assault on all forms of authority some evidence of a clouded childhood.

The fact that Bierce wrote like an educated man is hardly explained by his education. When he was seventeen he spent a year at the Kentucky Military Institute. Not long afterward the Civil War broke out and he enlisted as a volunteer with the Union Army. (We have no evidence to indicate that he had any special sympathy with the ideal aims of the North and some slight evidence to show that he felt a mild tenderness for the ante-bellum aristocratic planter-culture of the South.) He began as a drummer-boy with the 9th Indiana Infantry, fought bravely, was wounded at Kenesaw Mountain, and emerged from the war a lieutenant, with the brevet title of major. It is evident that he possessed what military men call "qualities of leadership," that is, qualities of leadership in the stupidest of man's activities. It is no less evident that his Civil War interlude affected him in more important ways. It was directly responsible for some of his most finely felt, least posed stories. It very possibly—for he was but a boy when he played his part in the only genuinely tragic social experience our country in its brief history has lived through—helped to shift his perspective on mankind toward the dark end of the spectrum. And it may have been the spring of a certain military quality in him, for he writes like a conquistador, quick to take offence and to requite insult.

Shortly after the end of the war Bierce removed to San Francisco, the city which, though he lived there only intermittently, was to remain the focal point of his career. His first job was that of night-watchman at the Sub-treasury Building. However, his personality was ill-adapted to the least imaginative of all possible activities: guarding other people's money. He seems to have become vaguely involved in local politics and to have employed his talents as a controversial cartoonist, directing his ire, with characteristic impartiality, against both factions. But now journalism rose to mark him for her own, and in her dubious service he was to continue for many a year, writing well, writing badly, doubtless writing too much. From 1866 to 1872 he contributed various splinters of hackwork to the *Argonaut* and the *News Letter,* of which he finally became editor. In 1871, when he was twenty-nine and old enough to know his own temperament better, he married Mary Ellen Day, the daughter of a '49-er. The years from 1872 to 1876 were spent in London where he engaged in the peculiar slashing journalism that had already won for him the sobriquet "Bitter Bierce." This London period appears to have left little impress on his work.

In 1876, his health having failed, he and the family (there were now two little sons, with a third child on the way) moved back to San Francisco. Bierce contributed again to the *Argonaut,* to the *Wasp,* and from 1887 to 1896 conducted a column in the San Francisco *Sunday Examiner,* a Hearst paper. It is from these fitful contributions and weekly jottings that the contents of several of his books were drawn. The *Examiner* period seems to have constituted his apogee. During the late 'eighties and 'nineties he wielded extraordinary local influence as a kind of West Coast Samuel Johnson. It was, if any place could have been, the right place for him. Then, as it does now, if to a lesser degree, San Francisco tolerated and even encouraged salient personalities. Following the *Examiner* period Bierce worked as Washington correspondent for the *American,* and in later years was a contributor to *Cosmopolitan.*

Dead ends, failures, and tragedies marked his personal life. He was a man, like many, unfit by nature for socialized living, a non-domestic animal. The family pattern of unhappiness repeated itself on a tragic scale. In 1889 his older son was killed in a vulgar shooting-brawl over a girl; two years afterward his wife left him, finally divorcing him, thirty-three years too late, in 1904; in 1901 his younger son died of alcoholism; and at last in 1913 Ambrose Bierce, old, asthmatic, weary, his creative power only an acrid memory, a bitter jester who had outlived his time, made his queer escape from the civilization he had for forty years derided, and somewhere, presumably in Mexico, encountered his favorite character, the figure who, so to speak, animates his finest stories: Death.

DURING Bierce's lifetime his vogue, except in and around San Francisco, stayed within modest bounds, partly through the efforts of his publishers, some of whom possessed a natural talent for bankruptcy. How to "handle" his talent so as to make it yield the maximum public success Bierce never learned nor did he care to learn. The emergence of his reputation was more or less coincidental with the disappearance of himself. The tendency grew to concentrate on the Bierce "legend" and to neglect his books. Nevertheless there has been a constant undercurrent of interest in him as a writer. This is ascribable to our natural fascination by the supernatural, and no less to the equally paradoxical fact that men love to hear themselves scorned and rejected if only the scorn and rejection are sufficiently eloquent. Jeremiah will never be out of a job. Finally, there is a *fin de siècle* aura about Bierce that has these many years recommended him to professional and amateur *épateurs* of the bourgeoisie. He has, for example, furnished considerable inspiration to H. L. Mencken and has been a potent force among the writing men of the West Coast for the past twenty-five years.

Today, over and above the simple fact that he is still generally readable, Bierce solicits our attention because he is a minor prophet of hopelessness. On August 6, 1945, the planet, with the United States in the lead, passed half-unconsciously into an era of despair. With a noiseless flash over Hiroshima *homo sapiens* issued the first dramatic announcement of his inability to make a biological success of himself. The next few years or decades seem almost certain to prove years or decades of planetary wars that will rend and crack and shiver the earth's thin skin, years of wholesale suicide, years that will paralyze the moral and religious sense of mankind. Civilized man—unless he decides to use his reason—will fall forward into a new and almost unimaginable barbarism. The time for the pessimists has come again, whether they be philosophical pessimists, like the French Existentialists, or pessimists in action, like the totalitarians, the managerial state-ers, and the heralds of the American (or Russian) Century. The men and women who do not like men and women are in the saddle and will ride mankind.

What have such matters to do with a dead journalist named Ambrose Bierce? Consider this: the dominating tendency of American literature and social thought, from Benjamin Franklin to Sinclair Lewis, has been optimistic. It has believed in man, it has believed in American man. It has at times been satirical and even bitter—but not negative. It gave the world the positive statements of the Declaration, the Constitution, the Gettysburg Address, Emerson, Whitman, William James, Henry George, John Dewey. This has been the stronger current. But along with it there has coursed a narrower current, the shadowed stream of pessimism. Perhaps its obscure source lies in the southern philosophers of slavery or in the bleak hell-fire morality of early puritan divines like Michael Wigglesworth and Jonathan Edwards. It flows hesitantly in Hawthorne, with fury in "Moby Dick" and "Pierre," with many a subtle meander in the dark symbolisms of Poe. It may appear in part of a writer (the Mark Twain of "The Mysterious Stranger" and "The Man That Corrupted Hadleyburg") and not in the whole of him. It runs through Stephen Crane. You may trace it in an out-of-the-main-stream philosopher such as Thorstein Veblen. You will find it in the thought of H. L. Mencken and the stories of Ring Lardner. And you will see it plain, naked, naive, and powerful, in the strange fables of Ambrose Bierce.

As our planet rolls slowly or rapidly in the direction of its own eclipse, men's minds will darken with it. Losing their faith in themselves, they will look into each other's eyes with hatred, and every man's hand will rest lightly upon his dagger. Even the most sensitive will find it difficult, as the lamps go out, to draw comfort from the words of those who believe in progress. Decline and fall will be the order of the day and night. New philosophies of violence and despair will be contrived, and old nihilisms be exhumed. Among these old nihilisms that of Ambrose Bierce will take its minor place and, for all his weaknesses, he will speak to us with added vehemence.

Those weaknesses are apparent. Bierce's nihilism is as brutal and simple as a blow, and by the same token not too convincing. It has no base in philosophy and, being quite bare of shading or qualification, becomes, if taken in overdoses, a trifle tedious. Except for the skeleton grin that creeps over his face when he has devised in his fiction some peculiarly grotesque death, Bierce never deviates into cheerfulness. His rage is unselective. The great skeptics view human nature without admiration but also without ire. Bierce's misanthropy is too systematic. He is a pessimism-machine. He is a Swift minus true intellectual power, Rochefoucauld with a bludgeon, Voltaire with stomach-ulcers.

Nevertheless he can and will be read with interest in an age which is getting ready to renounce compromise, kindness, and Christianity. The corrosive definitions of "The Devil's Dictionary" will make their appeal to a generation which all over the world is being carefully conditioned to believe in nothing but Force. (And Force is merely Nothing, organized visibly and audibly for the purpose of purposeless destruction.) His cynicism, phrased with really extraordinary concentration, appalled his contemporaries; but it is more likely to attract than to appal us. After a few hours spent with the American (or the British, or the Russian) press, with its almost gloating rehearsal of the day's crimes, tortures, vulgarities, falsehoods and brutalities, the savageries of Bierce have almost a sympathetic quality. His "Fantastic Fables" strike us as neither fantastic nor fabulous. He seems quite a man of our time.

I do not wish to over-state the point, for much of Bierce is oldfashioned. His prose at its worst is flawed with the bad taste of his period; his weakness for melodrama occasionally makes us squirm; he frequently overdoes his effects. Yet it is difficult to forget, for instance, the best of the stories in "In the Midst of Life": *An Occurrence at Owl Creek Bridge,* less interesting as a trick than as a heart-freezing symbolical presentation of the depth of the passion for survival; *Chickamauga,* which, by a device of brilliant originality, rams home the pure and shrieking insanity of war; *One of the Missing,* which, like so many of his tales, shows a completely modern interest in and understanding of abnormal states of consciousness. Bierce, despite his almost Spanish admiration for "honor," was one of the earliest American writers to dismiss the flapdoodle of war and hold up to our gaze something like its true countenance. It is not so much that he hated war; indeed these stories are marked by a sort of agony of joy over war's horrors. Perhaps Bierce took a cold pleasure in war as the perfect justification of his view of mankind. He may even have liked war—no true lover of war (no German, for instance) has ever been so weak-kneed or weakstomached as to attempt to diguise its brutality. But, however complicated Bierce's attitude toward war may have been, what he writes has the bitter-aloes taste of truth. He helped blaze the trail for later and doubtless better realists. (It should be noted in passing that some of his stories of the frontier West performed a similar service in the cause of realism. He had no talent for local or temporal detail but he did seize upon one essential aspect of frontier life—the cheapness with which human life was valued. Bret Harte made lawlessness picturesque and Mark Twain made it humorous. Bierce saw it, though without indignation, for what it was—murder.)

Most of Bierce's other stories (included in this volume under "Can Such Things Be?" and "Negligible Tales") turn upon either the theme of the supernatural or on the humor of horror. In these fields he produced several masterpieces and several minorpieces. Both are to be found in this collection.

It is pertinent that Bierce, who disliked human beings and scoffed at social relationships, should have written so much and on the whole so well about ghosts, apparitions, revenants, were-dogs, animated machines, extra-sensory perception, and action at a distance. It is as though the man's inability to stomach the real world forced him to try to establish citizenship in the country of the occult. (Yet Bierce is no Algernon Blackwood or Arthur Machen, no sensitive in search of "escape." He led a busy life, full of the usual struggle and conflict; there is little of the shrinking esthete about him.) Rather must we think of his interest (not necessarily his belief) in the supernatural as part and parcel of his general misanthropy. He was so obsessed by the horror of real life that he had to call in the aid of another dimension in order to express it. He seems to be saying to us: "You do not have enough sense to shudder at yourselves; by God, I will make you shudder then at spirits which are but yourselves upon another plane! If I cannot make you shrink from life, I will make you shrink from its goal and culmination—death!" Bierce's morbidity is too controlled to have about it any touch of the insane; it merely expresses his fury at our placid healthiness. *"N'importe où, hors du monde."* It is this emotional drive behind his most calculated horrors that makes him much more than an American Monk Lewis. His Gothicism is no hothouse flower but a monstrous orchid. (When he tries to write in the traditional Gothic vein, as in "The Monk and the Hangman's Daughter," he is unconvincing, for he is not using his own voice.)

Among the stories of the impossible that the reader may wish to note with extra care are *The Death of Halpin Frayser*, with its extraordinary utilization of what is now called the Oedipus Complex; *One Summer Night*, a trifle which packs into 500 words a heavy weight of horror; *Moxon's Master*, which inverts La Mettrie's doctrine of man considered as a machine, and which may possibly have been suggested by Poe's wonderful account of Maelzel's Chess-player; *A Resumed Identity*, reflecting Bierce's obsession with the problem of lost, split, or wandering consciousnesses; *The Damned Thing,* a masterpiece in a genre in which Bierce has since been equalled only by H. G. Wells; and *Haïta the Shepherd,* a grave and bitter fable, almost worthy of Poe, expressing the idea—so true and so continually rejected by men—that to seek happiness is to lose it.

Bierce's morbidity was exceptionally fertile—he made it produce humor as well as chills. I should say that in this extremely narrow field of the sardonic, of the ludicrous ghost story and the comical murder, he is unrivaled. He begins by somehow making you accept his basic premise: death is a joke. The rest is deadpan elaboration, with the deadpan occasionally relieved by the rictus of a ghoul trying to laugh. Perhaps the two best examples are *My Favorite Murder* and *Oil of Dog.* (The latter I cannot recommend to the queasy-stomached.) *My Favorite Murder* really creates a new shudder, a shudder in which laughter is grotesquely mingled. It is outrageous, it is frightening,—it is funny. One finishes it in thorough agreement with the narrator that "in point of artistic atrocity" the murder of Uncle William has seldom been excelled. The humor of the unbelievable *Oil of Dog* depends on a careful, indeed beautiful use of ironical understatement, and the exhaustiveness of the technique whereby the macabre is pushed to such an extreme that it falls somehow into the gulf of laughter. One will not easily forget Mr. Boffer Bing's mother who had "a small studio in the shadow of the village church, where she disposed of unwelcome babes." The choice of the word "studio" is one of the happiest thoughts of the unhappy Bierce.

A minor offshoot of Bierce's mastery of the grotesque is the twist he gives to the western "tall tale." In *Curried Cow,* for example, he imparts to it a touch of the gruesome which in its origins it never possessed. He makes a new thing of it.

The nuclear Bierce is to be found in the "Fantastic Fables." One should not read more than a dozen of them at a time, just as one should not read more than a dozen jokes at a time. Their quality lies in their ferocious concentration of extra-double-distilled essential oil of misanthropy. They are so condensed that they take your breath away.

The theme is always the same: mankind is a scoundrel; but the changes rung upon the theme demonstrate an almost abnormal inventiveness. They have no humor—they do not resemble at all, for instance, the fables of George Ade. They have wit but little fancy, they are undecorated, and they sting painfully. The brutal Bierce allows no exceptions. He aims to make mincemeat of all civilized humanity,— lawyers and weather forecasters, doctors and detectives, widows and photographers, editors and insurance agents, anarchists and female journalists, men and women.

Bierce is not, of course, a great writer. He has painful faults of vulgarity and cheapness of imagination. But at his best he is like no one else. He had, for example, a mastery of pared phrasing equalled in our time per- haps only by Wilde and Shaw. When he defines marriage as "The state or condition of a community consisting of a master, a mistress and two slaves, making in all, two" he is saying something that many other un- happy men and women have said—but he is saying it in a way impossible to improve or forget.

His style, for one thing, will preserve him, though for how long no one would care to say; and the purity of his misanthropy, too, will help to keep him alive. It is good that literature should be so catholic and wide-wayed that it affords scope to every emotion and attitude, even the unloveliest. It is fitting that someone should be born and live and die, dedicated to the expression of bitterness. For bitterness is a mood that comes to all intelligent men, though, as they are intelligent, only intermittently. It is proper that there should be at least one man able to give penetrating expression to that mood. Bierce is such a man— limited, wrong-headed, unbalanced, but, in his own constricted way, an artist.

He will remain one of the most interesting and eccentric figures in our literature, one of our great wits, one of our most uncompromising satirists, the perfecter of two or three new, if minor, genres: a writer one cannot casually pass by.

CLIFTON FADIMAN
September 1946

IN THE MIDST OF LIFE

Tales of Soldiers and Civilians

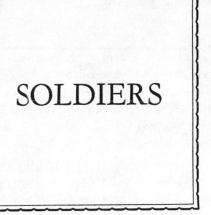

SOLDIERS

A HORSEMAN IN THE SKY

I

ONE sunny afternoon in the autumn of the year 1861 a soldier lay in a clump of laurel by the side of a road in western Virginia. He lay at full length upon his stomach, his feet resting upon the toes, his head upon the left forearm. His extended right hand loosely grasped his rifle. But for the somewhat methodical disposition of his limbs and a slight rhythmic movement of the cartridge-box at the back of his belt he might have been thought to be dead. He was asleep at his post of duty. But if detected he would be dead shortly afterward, death being the just and legal penalty of his crime.

The clump of laurel in which the criminal lay was in the angle of a road which after ascending southward a steep acclivity to that point turned sharply to the west, running along the summit for perhaps one hundred yards. There it turned southward again and went zigzagging downward through the forest. At the salient of that second angle was a large flat rock, jutting out northward, overlooking the deep valley from which the road ascended. The rock capped a high cliff; a stone dropped from its outer edge would have fallen sheer downward one thousand feet to the tops of the pines. The angle where the soldier lay was on an-

3

other spur of the same cliff. Had he been awake he would have commanded a view, not only of the short arm of the road and the jutting rock, but of the entire profile of the cliff below it. It might well have made him giddy to look.

The country was wooded everywhere except at the bottom of the valley to the northward, where there was a small natural meadow, through which flowed a stream scarcely visible from the valley's rim. This open ground looked hardly larger than an ordinary door-yard, but was really several acres in extent. Its green was more vivid than that of the inclosing forest. Away beyond it rose a line of giant cliffs similar to those upon which we are supposed to stand in our survey of the savage scene, and through which the road had somehow made its climb to the summit. The configuration of the valley, indeed, was such that from this point of observation it seemed entirely shut in, and one could but have wondered how the road which found a way out of it had found a way into it, and whence came and whither went the waters of the stream that parted the meadow more than a thousand feet below.

No country is so wild and difficult but men will make it a theatre of war; concealed in the forest at the bottom of that military rat-trap, in which half a hundred men in possession of the exits might have starved an army to submission, lay five regiments of Federal infantry. They had marched all the previous day and night and were resting. At nightfall they would take to the road again, climb to the place where their unfaithful sentinel now slept, and descending the other slope of the ridge fall upon a camp of the enemy at about midnight. Their hope was to surprise it, for the road led to the rear of it. In case of failure, their position would be perilous in the extreme; and fail they surely would should accident or vigilance apprise the enemy of the movement.

II

The sleeping sentinel in the clump of laurel was a young Virginian named Carter Druse. He was the son of wealthy parents, an only child, and had known such ease and cultivation and high living as wealth and taste were able to command in the mountain country of western Virginia. His home was but a few miles from where he now lay. One morning he had risen from the breakfast-table and said, quietly but gravely: "Father, a Union regiment has arrived at Grafton. I am going to join it."

The father lifted his leonine head, looked at the son a moment in silence, and replied: "Well, go, sir, and whatever may occur do what you conceive to be your duty. Virginia, to which you are a traitor, must get on without you. Should we both live to the end of the war, we will speak further of the matter. Your mother, as the physician has informed you, is in a most critical condition; at the best she cannot be with us longer than a few weeks, but that time is precious. It would be better not to disturb her."

So Carter Druse, bowing reverently to his father, who returned the salute with a stately courtesy that masked a breaking heart, left the home of his childhood to go soldiering. By conscience and courage, by deeds of devotion and daring, he soon commended himself to his fellows and his officers; and it was to these qualities and to some knowledge of the country that he owed his selection for his present perilous duty at the extreme outpost. Nevertheless, fatigue had been stronger than resolution and he had fallen asleep. What good or bad angel came in a dream to rouse him from his state of crime, who shall say? Without a movement, without a sound, in the profound silence and the languor of the late afternoon, some invisible messenger of fate touched with unsealing finger the eyes of his consciousness—whispered into the ear of his spirit the mysterious awakening word which no human lips ever have spoken, no human memory ever has recalled. He quietly raised his forehead from his arm and looked between the masking stems of the laurels, instinctively closing his right hand about the stock of his rifle.

His first feeling was a keen artistic delight. On a colossal pedestal, the cliff,—motionless at the extreme edge of the capping rock and sharply outlined against the sky,—was an equestrian statue of impressive dignity. The figure of the man sat the figure of the horse, straight and soldierly, but with the repose of a Grecian god carved in the marble which limits the suggestion of activity. The gray costume harmonized with its aërial background; the metal of accoutrement and caparison was softened and subdued by the shadow; the animal's skin had no points of high light. A carbine strikingly foreshortened lay across the pommel of the saddle, kept in place by the right hand grasping it at the "grip"; the left hand, holding the bridle rein, was invisible. In silhouette against the sky the profile of the horse was cut with the sharpness of a cameo; it looked across the heights of air to the confronting cliffs beyond. The face of the rider, turned slightly away, showed only an outline of temple and beard;

he was looking downward to the bottom of the valley. Magnified by its lift against the sky and by the soldier's testifying sense of the formidableness of a near enemy the group appeared of heroic, almost colossal, size.

For an instant Druse had a strange, half-defined feeling that he had slept to the end of the war and was looking upon a noble work of art reared upon that eminence to commemorate the deeds of an heroic past of which he had been an inglorious part. The feeling was dispelled by a slight movement of the group: the horse, without moving its feet, had drawn its body slightly backward from the verge; the man remained immobile as before. Broad awake and keenly alive to the significance of the situation, Druse now brought the butt of his rifle against his cheek by cautiously pushing the barrel forward through the bushes, cocked the piece, and glancing through the sights covered a vital spot of the horseman's breast. A touch upon the trigger and all would have been well with Carter Druse. At that instant the horseman turned his head and looked in the direction of his concealed foeman—seemed to look into his very face, into his eyes, into his brave, compassionate heart.

Is it then so terrible to kill an enemy in war—an enemy who has surprised a secret vital to the safety of one's self and comrades—an enemy more formidable for his knowledge than all his army for its numbers? Carter Druse grew pale; he shook in every limb, turned faint, and saw the statuesque group before him as black figures, rising, falling, moving unsteadily in arcs of circles in a fiery sky. His hand fell away from his weapon, his head slowly dropped until his face rested on the leaves in which he lay. This courageous gentleman and hardy soldier was near swooning from intensity of emotion.

It was not for long; in another moment his face was raised from earth, his hands resumed their places on the rifle, his forefinger sought the trigger; mind, heart, and eyes were clear, conscience and reason sound. He could not hope to capture that enemy; to alarm him would but send him dashing to his camp with his fatal news. The duty of the soldier was plain: the man must be shot dead from ambush—without warning, without a moment's spiritual preparation, with never so much as an unspoken prayer, he must be sent to his account. But no—there is a hope; he may have discovered nothing—perhaps he is but admiring the sublimity of the landscape. If permitted, he may turn and ride carelessly away in the direction whence he came. Surely it will be possible to judge at the instant of his withdrawing whether he knows. It may well be that his fixity of attention—Druse turned his head and looked through the deeps of air downward, as from the surface to the bottom of a translucent sea. He saw creeping across the green meadow a sinuous line of figures of men and horses—some foolish commander was permitting the soldiers of his escort to water their beasts in the open, in plain view from a dozen summits!

Druse withdrew his eyes from the valley and fixed them again upon the group of man and horse in the sky, and again it was through the sights of his rifle. But this time his aim was at the horse. In his memory, as if they were a divine mandate, rang the words of his father at their parting: "Whatever may occur, do what you conceive to be your duty." He was calm now. His teeth were firmly but not rigidly closed; his nerves were as tranquil as a sleeping babe's—not a tremor affected any muscle of his body; his breathing, until suspended in the act of taking aim, was regular and slow. Duty had conquered; the spirit had said to the body: "Peace, be still." He fired.

III

An officer of the Federal force, who in a spirit of adventure or in quest of knowledge had left the hidden *bivouac* in the valley, and with aimless feet had made his way to the lower edge of a small open space near the foot of the cliff, was considering what he had to gain by pushing his exploration further. At a distance of a quarter-mile before him, but apparently at a stone's throw, rose from its fringe of pines the gigantic face of rock, towering to so great a height above him that it made him giddy to look up to where its edge cut a sharp, rugged line against the sky. It presented a clean, vertical profile against a background of blue sky to a point half the way down, and of distant hills, hardly less blue, thence to the tops of the trees at its base. Lifting his eyes to the dizzy altitude of its summit the officer saw an astonishing sight—a man on horseback riding down into the valley through the air!

Straight upright sat the rider, in military fashion, with a firm seat in the saddle, a strong clutch upon the rein to hold his charger from too impetuous a plunge. From his bare head his long hair streamed upward, waving like a plume. His hands were concealed in the cloud of the horse's lifted mane. The animal's body was as level as if every hoof-stroke encountered the resistant earth. Its motions were those of a wild gallop, but even as the officer looked they ceased, with all the legs thrown sharply forward as in the act of alighting from a leap. But this was a flight!

Filled with amazement and terror by this apparition of a horseman in the sky—half believing himself the chosen scribe of some new Apocalypse, the officer was overcome by the intensity of his emotions; his legs failed him and he fell. Almost at the same instant he heard a crashing sound in the trees—a sound that died without an echo—and all was still.

The officer rose to his feet, trembling. The familiar sensation of an abraded shin recalled his dazed faculties. Pulling himself together he ran rapidly obliquely away from the cliff to a point distant from its foot; thereabout he expected to find his man; and thereabout he naturally failed. In the fleeting instant of his vision his imagination had been so wrought upon by the apparent grace and ease and intention of the marvelous performance that it did not occur to him that the line of march of aërial cavalry is directly downward, and that he could find the objects of his search at the very foot of the cliff. A half-hour later he returned to camp.

This officer was a wise man; he knew better than to tell an incredible truth. He said nothing of what he had seen. But when the commander asked him if in his scout he had learned anything of advantage to the expedition he answered:

"Yes, sir; there is no road leading down into this valley from the southward."

The commander, knowing better, smiled.

IV

After firing his shot, Private Carter Druse reloaded his rifle and resumed his watch. Ten minutes had hardly passed when a Federal sergeant crept cautiously to him on hands and knees. Druse neither turned his head nor looked at him, but lay without motion or sign of recognition.

"Did you fire?" the sergeant whispered.

"Yes."

"At what?"

"A horse. It was standing on yonder rock—pretty far out. You see it is no longer there. It went over the cliff."

The man's face was white, but he showed no other sign of emotion. Having answered, he turned away his eyes and said no more. The sergeant did not understand.

"See here, Druse," he said, after a moment's silence, "it's no use making a mystery. I order you to report. Was there anybody on the horse?"

"Yes."

"Well?"

"My father."

The sergeant rose to his feet and walked away. "Good God!" he said.

AN OCCURRENCE AT OWL CREEK BRIDGE

I

A MAN stood upon a railroad bridge in northern Alabama, looking down into the swift water twenty feet below. The man's hands were behind his back, the wrists bound with a cord. A rope closely encircled his neck. It was attached to a stout cross-timber above his head and the slack fell to the level of his knees. Some loose boards laid upon the sleepers supporting the metals of the railway supplied a footing for him and his executioners—two private soldiers of the Federal army, directed by a sergeant who in civil life may have been a deputy sheriff. At a short remove upon the same temporary platform was an officer in the uniform of his rank, armed. He was a captain. A sentinel at each end of the bridge stood with his rifle in the position known as "support," that is to say, vertical in front of the left shoulder, the hammer resting on the forearm thrown straight across the chest—a formal and unnatural position, enforcing an erect carriage of the body. It did not appear to be the duty of these two men to know what was occurring at the centre of the bridge; they merely blockaded the two ends of the foot planking that traversed it.

Beyond one of the sentinels nobody was in sight; the railroad ran straight away into a forest for a hundred yards, then, curving, was lost to view. Doubtless there was an outpost farther along. The other bank of the stream was open ground—a gentle acclivity topped with a stockade of vertical tree trunks, loop-holed for rifles, with a single embrasure through which protruded the muzzle of a brass cannon commanding the bridge. Midway of the slope between bridge and fort were the spectators—a single company of infantry in line, at "parade rest," the butts of the rifles on the ground, the barrels inclining slightly backward against the right shoulder, the hands crossed upon the stock. A lieutenant stood at the right of the line, the point of his sword upon the ground, his left hand resting upon his right. Excepting the group of four at the centre of the bridge, not a man moved. The company faced the bridge, staring stonily, motionless. The sentinels, facing the banks of the stream, might have been statues to adorn the bridge. The captain stood with folded arms, silent, observing the work of his subordinates, but making no sign. Death is a dignitary who when he comes announced is to be received with formal manifestations of respect, even by those most familiar with him. In the code of military etiquette silence and fixity are forms of deference.

The man who was engaged in being hanged was apparently about thirty-five years of age. He was a civilian, if one might judge from his habit, which was that of a planter. His features were good—a straight nose, firm mouth, broad forehead, from which his long, dark hair was combed straight back, falling behind his ears to the collar of his well-fitting frock-coat. He wore a mustache and pointed beard, but no whiskers; his eyes were large and dark gray, and had a kindly expression which one would hardly have expected in one whose neck was in the hemp. Evidently this was no vulgar assassin. The liberal military code makes provision for hanging many kinds of persons, and gentlemen are not excluded.

The preparations being complete, the two private soldiers stepped aside and each drew away the plank upon which he had been standing. The sergeant turned to the captain, saluted and placed himself immediately behind that officer, who in turn moved apart one pace. These movements left the condemned man and the sergeant standing on the two ends of the same plank, which spanned three of the cross-ties of the bridge. The end upon which the civilian stood almost, but not quite, reached a fourth. This plank had been held in place by the weight of the captain; it was now held by that of the sergeant. At a signal from the former the latter would step aside, the plank would tilt and the condemned man go down between two ties. The arrangement commended itself to his judgment as simple and effective. His face had not been covered nor his eyes bandaged. He looked a moment at his "unsteadfast footing," then let his gaze wander to the swirling water of the stream racing madly beneath his feet. A piece of dancing driftwood caught his attention and his eyes followed it down the current. How slowly it appeared to move! What a sluggish stream!

He closed his eyes in order to fix his last thoughts upon his wife and children. The water, touched to gold by the early sun, the brooding mists under the banks at some distance down the stream, the fort, the soldiers, the piece of drift—all had distracted him. And now he became conscious of a new disturbance. Striking through the thought of his dear ones was a sound which he could neither ignore nor understand, a sharp, distinct, metallic percussion like the stroke of a blacksmith's hammer upon the anvil; it had the same ringing quality. He wondered what it was, and whether immeasurably distant or near by—it seemed both. Its recurrence was regular, but as slow as the tolling of a death knell. He awaited each stroke with impatience and—he knew not why— apprehension. The intervals of silence grew progressively longer; the delays became maddening. With their greater infrequency the sounds increased in strength and sharpness. They hurt his ear like the thrust of a knife; he feared he would shriek. What he heard was the ticking of his watch.

He unclosed his eyes and saw again the water below him. "If I could free my hands," he thought, "I might throw off the noose and spring into the stream. By diving I could evade the bullets and, swimming vigorously, reach the bank, take to the woods and get away home. My home, thank God, is as yet outside their lines; my wife and little ones are still beyond the invader's farthest advance."

As these thoughts, which have here to be set down in words, were flashed into the doomed man's brain rather than evolved from it the captain nodded to the sergeant. The sergeant stepped aside.

II

Peyton Farquhar was a well-to-do planter, of an old and highly respected Alabama family. Being a slave owner and like other slave owners a politician he was naturally an original secessionist and ardently devoted to the Southern cause. Circumstances of an imperious nature, which it is unnecessary to relate here, had prevented him from taking service with the gallant army that had fought the disastrous campaigns ending with the fall of Corinth, and he chafed under the inglorious restraint, longing for the release of his energies, the larger life of the soldier, the opportunity for distinction. That opportunity, he felt, would come, as it comes to all in war time. Meanwhile he did what he could. No service was too humble for him to perform in aid of the South, no adventure too perilous for him to undertake if consistent with the character of a civilian who was at heart a soldier, and who in good faith and without too much qualification assented to at least a part of the frankly villainous dictum that all is fair in love and war.

One evening while Farquhar and his wife were sitting on a rustic bench near the entrance to his grounds, a gray-clad soldier rode up to the gate and asked for a drink of water. Mrs. Farquhar was only too happy to serve him with her own white hands. While she was fetching the water her husband approached the dusty horseman and inquired eagerly for news from the front.

"The Yanks are repairing the railroads," said the man, "and are getting ready for another advance. They have reached the Owl Creek bridge, put it in order and built a stockade on the north bank. The commandant has issued an order, which is posted everywhere, declaring that any civilian caught interfering with the railroad, its bridges, tunnels or trains will be summarily hanged. I saw the order."

"How far is it to the Owl Creek bridge?" Farquhar asked.

"About thirty miles."

"Is there no force on this side the creek?"

"Only a picket post half a mile out, on the railroad, and a single sentinel at this end of the bridge."

"Suppose a man—a civilian and student of hanging—should elude the picket post and perhaps get the better of the sentinel," said Farquhar, smiling, "what could he accomplish?"

The soldier reflected. "I was there a month ago," he replied. "I observed that the flood of last winter had lodged a great quantity of driftwood against the wooden pier at this end of the bridge. It is now dry and would burn like tow."

The lady had now brought the water, which the soldier drank. He thanked her ceremoniously, bowed to her husband and rode away. An hour later, after nightfall, he repassed the plantation, going northward in the direction from which he had come. He was a Federal scout.

III

As Peyton Farquhar fell straight downward through the bridge he lost consciousness and was as one already dead. From this state he was awakened—ages later, it seemed to him—by the pain of a sharp pressure upon his throat, followed by a sense of suffocation. Keen, poignant agonies seemed to shoot from his neck downward through every fibre of his body and limbs. These pains appeared to flash along well-defined lines of ramification and to beat with an inconceivably rapid periodicity. They seemed like streams of pulsating fire heating him to an intolerable temperature. As to his head, he was conscious of nothing but a feeling of fulness—of congestion. These sensations were unaccompanied by thought. The intellectual part of his nature was already effaced; he had power only to feel, and feeling was torment. He was conscious of motion. Encompassed in a luminous cloud, of which he was now merely the fiery heart, without material substance, he swung through unthinkable arcs of oscillation, like a vast pendulum. Then all at once, with terrible suddenness, the light about him shot upward with the noise of a loud plash; a frightful roaring was in his ears, and all was cold and dark. The power of thought was restored; he knew that the rope had broken and he had fallen into the stream. There was no additional strangulation; the noose about his neck was already suffocating him and kept the water from his lungs. To die of hanging at the bottom of a river!—the idea seemed to him ludicrous. He opened his eyes in the darkness and saw above him a gleam of light, but how distant, how inaccessible! He was still sinking, for the light became fainter and fainter until it was a mere glimmer. Then it began to grow and brighten, and he knew that he was rising toward the surface—knew it with reluctance, for he was now very comfortable. "To be hanged and drowned," he thought, "that is not so bad; but I do not wish to be shot. No; I will not be shot; that is not fair."

He was not conscious of an effort, but a sharp pain in his wrist apprised him that he was trying to free his hands. He gave the struggle his attention, as an idler might observe the feat of a juggler, without interest in the outcome. What splendid effort!—what magnificent, what superhuman strength! Ah, that was a fine endeavor! Bravo! The cord fell away; his arms parted and floated upward, the hands dimly seen on each side in the growing light. He watched them with a new interest as first one and then the other pounced upon the noose at his neck. They tore it away and thrust it fiercely aside, its undulations resembling those of a water-snake. "Put it back, put it back!" He thought he shouted these words to his hands, for the undoing of the noose had been succeeded by the direst pang that he had yet experienced. His neck ached horribly; his brain was on fire; his heart, which had been fluttering faintly, gave a great leap, trying to force itself out at his mouth. His whole body was racked and wrenched with an insupportable anguish! But his disobedient hands gave no heed to the command. They beat the water vigorously with quick, downward strokes, forcing him to the surface. He felt his head emerge; his eyes were blinded by the sunlight; his chest expanded convulsively, and with a supreme and crowning agony his lungs engulfed a great draught of air, which instantly he expelled in a shriek!

He was now in full possession of his physical senses. They were, indeed, preternaturally keen and alert. Something in the awful disturbance of his organic system had so exalted and refined them that they made record of things never before perceived. He felt the ripples upon his face and heard their separate sounds as they struck. He looked at the forest on the bank of the stream, saw the individual trees, the leaves and the veining of each leaf—saw the very insects upon them: the locusts, the brilliant-bodied flies, the gray spiders stretching their webs from twig to twig. He noted the prismatic colors in all the dewdrops upon a million blades of grass. The humming of the gnats that danced above the eddies of the stream, the beating of the dragon-flies' wings, the strokes of the water-spiders' legs, like oars which had lifted their boat—all these made audible music. A fish slid along beneath his eyes and he heard the rush of its body parting the water.

He had come to the surface facing down the stream; in a moment the visible world seemed to wheel slowly round, himself the pivotal point, and he saw the bridge, the fort, the soldiers upon the bridge, the captain, the sergeant, the two privates, his executioners. They were in silhouette against the blue sky. They shouted and gesticulated, pointing at him. The captain had drawn his pistol, but did not fire; the others were unarmed. Their movements were grotesque and horrible, their forms gigantic.

Suddenly he heard a sharp report and something struck the water smartly within a few inches of his head, spattering his face with spray. He heard a second report, and saw one of the sentinels with his rifle at his shoulder, a light cloud of blue smoke rising from the muzzle. The man in the water saw the eye of the man on the bridge gazing into his own through the sights of the rifle. He observed that it was a gray eye and remembered having read that gray eyes were keenest, and that all famous markmen had them. Nevertheless, this one had missed.

A counter-swirl had caught Farquhar and turned him half round; he was again looking into the forest on the bank opposite the fort. The sound of a clear, high voice in a monotonous singsong now rang out behind him and came across the water with a distinctness that pierced and subdued all other sounds, even the beating of the ripples in his ears. Although no soldier, he had frequented camps enough to know the dread significance of that deliberate, drawling, aspirated chant; the lieutenant on shore was taking a part in the morning's work. How coldly and pitilessly—with what an even, calm intonation, presaging, and enforcing tranquillity in the men—with what accurately measured intervals fell those cruel words:

"Attention, company! . . . Shoulder arms! . . . Ready! . . . Aim! . . . Fire!"

Farquhar dived—dived as deeply as he could. The water roared in his ears like the voice of Niagara, yet he heard the dulled thunder of the volley and, rising again toward the surface, met shining bits of metal, singularly flattened, oscillating slowly downward. Some of them touched him on the face and hands, then fell away, continuing their descent. One lodged between his collar and neck; it was uncomfortably warm and he snatched it out.

As he rose to the surface, gasping for breath, he saw that he had been a long time under water; he was perceptibly farther down stream— nearer to safety. The soldiers had almost finished reloading; the metal ramrods flashed all at once in the sunshine as they were drawn from the barrels, turned in the air, and thrust into their sockets. The two sentinels fired again, independently and ineffectually.

The hunted man saw all this over his shoulder; he was now swimming vigorously with the current. His brain was as energetic as his arms and legs; he thought with the rapidity of lightning.

"The officer," he reasoned, "will not make that martinet's error a second time. It is as easy to dodge a volley as a single shot. He has probably already given the command to fire at will. God help me, I cannot dodge them all!"

An appalling plash within two yards of him was followed by a loud, rushing sound, *diminuendo,* which seemed to travel back through the air to the fort and died in an explosion which stirred the very river to its deeps! A rising sheet of water curved over him, fell down upon him, blinded him, strangled him! The cannon had taken a hand in the game. As he shook his head free from the commotion of the smitten water he heard the deflected shot humming through the air ahead, and in an instant it was cracking and smashing the branches in the forest beyond.

"They will not do that again," he thought; "the next time they will use a charge of grape. I must keep my eye upon the gun; the smoke will apprise me—the report arrives too late; it lags behind the missile. That is a good gun."

Suddenly he felt himself whirled round and round—spinning like a top. The water, the banks, the forests, the now distant bridge, fort and men—all were commingled and blurred. Objects were represented by their colors only; circular horizontal streaks of color—that was all he saw. He had been caught in a vortex and was being whirled on with a velocity of advance and gyration that made him giddy and sick. In a few moments he was flung upon the gravel at the foot of the left bank of the stream—the southern bank—and behind a projecting point which concealed him from his enemies. The sudden arrest of his motion, the abrasion of one of his hands on the gravel, restored him, and he wept with delight. He dug his fingers into the sand, threw it over himself in handfuls and audibly blessed it. It looked like diamonds, rubies, emeralds; he could think of nothing beautiful which it did not resemble. The trees upon the bank were giant garden plants; he noted a definite order in their arrangement, inhaled the fragrance of their blooms. A strange, roseate light shone through the spaces among their trunks and the wind made in their branches the music of æolian harps. He had no wish to perfect his escape—was content to remain in that enchanting spot until retaken.

A whiz and rattle of grapeshot among the branches high above his head roused him from his dream. The baffled cannoneer had fired him a random farewell. He sprang to his feet, rushed up the sloping bank, and plunged into the forest.

All that day he traveled, laying his course by the rounding sun. The forest seemed interminable; nowhere did he discover a break in it, not even a woodman's road. He had not known that he lived in so wild a region. There was something uncanny in the revelation.

By nightfall he was fatigued, footsore, famishing. The thought of his wife and children urged him on. At last he found a road which led him in what he knew to be the right direction. It was as wide and straight as a city street, yet it seemed untraveled. No fields bordered it, no dwelling anywhere. Not so much as the barking of a dog suggested human habitation. The black bodies of the trees formed a straight wall on both sides, terminating on the horizon in a point, like a diagram in a lesson in perspective. Overhead, as he looked up through this rift in the wood, shone great golden stars looking unfamiliar and grouped in strange constellations. He was sure they were arranged in some order which had a secret and malign significance. The wood on either side was full of singular noises, among which—once, twice, and again—he distinctly heard whispers in an unknown tongue.

His neck was in pain and lifting his hand to it he found it horribly swollen. He knew that it had a circle of black where the rope had bruised it. His eyes felt congested; he could no longer close them. His tongue was swollen with thirst; he relieved its fever by thrusting it forward from between his teeth into the cold air. How softly the turf had carpeted the untraveled avenue—he could no longer feel the roadway beneath his feet!

Doubtless, despite his suffering, he had fallen asleep while walking, for now he sees another scene—perhaps he has merely recovered from a delirium. He stands at the gate of his own home. All is as he left it, and all bright and beautiful in the morning sunshine. He must have traveled the entire night. As he pushes open the gate and passes up the wide white walk, he sees a flutter of female garments; his wife, looking fresh and cool and sweet, steps down from the veranda to meet him. At the bottom of the steps she stands waiting, with a smile of ineffable joy, an attitude of matchless grace and dignity. Ah, how beautiful she is! He springs forward with extended arms. As he is about to clasp her he feels a stunning blow upon the back of the neck; a blinding white light blazes all about him with a sound like the shock of a cannon—then all is darkness and silence!

Peyton Farquhar was dead; his body, with a broken neck, swung gently from side to side beneath the timbers of the Owl Creek bridge.

CHICKAMAUGA

ONE sunny autumn afternoon a child strayed away from its rude home in a small field and entered a forest unobserved. It was happy in a new sense of freedom from control, happy in the opportunity of exploration and adventure; for this child's spirit, in bodies of its ancestors, had for thousands of years been trained to memorable feats of discovery and conquest—victories in battles whose critical moments were centuries, whose victors' camps were cities of hewn stone. From the cradle of its race it had conquered its way through two continents and passing a great sea had penetrated a third, there to be born to war and dominion as a heritage.

The child was a boy aged about six years, the son of a poor planter. In his younger manhood the father had been a soldier, had fought against naked savages and followed the flag of his country into the capital of a civilized race to the far South. In the peaceful life of a planter the warrior-fire survived; once kindled, it is never extinguished. The man loved military books and pictures and the boy had understood enough to make himself a wooden sword, though even the eye of his father would hardly have known it for what it was. This weapon he now bore bravely, as became the son of an heroic race, and pausing now and again in the sunny space of the forest assumed, with some exaggeration, the postures of aggression and defense that he had been taught by the engraver's art. Made reckless by the ease with which he overcame invisible foes attempting to stay his advance, he committed the common enough military error of pushing the pursuit to a dangerous extreme, until he found himself upon the margin of a wide but shallow brook, whose rapid waters barred his direct advance against the flying foe that had crossed with illogical ease. But the intrepid victor was not to be baffled; the spirit of the race which had passed the great sea burned unconquerable in that small breast and would not be denied. Finding a place where some bowlders in the bed of the stream lay but a step or a leap apart, he made his way across and fell again upon the rear-guard of his imaginary foe, putting all to the sword.

Now that the battle had been won, prudence required that he withdraw to his base of operations. Alas; like many a mightier conqueror, and like one, the mightiest, he could not

> curb the lust for war,
> Nor learn that tempted Fate will leave the loftiest star.

Advancing from the bank of the creek he suddenly found himself confronted with a new and more formidable enemy: in the path that he was following, sat, bolt upright, with ears erect and paws suspended before it, a rabbit! With a startled cry the child turned and fled, he knew not in what direction, calling with inarticulate cries for his mother, weeping, stumbling, his tender skin cruelly torn by brambles, his little heart beating hard with terror—breathless, blind with tears—lost in the forest! Then, for more than an hour, he wandered with erring feet through the tangled undergrowth, till at last, overcome by fatigue, he lay down in a narrow space between two rocks, within a few yards of the stream and still grasping his toy sword, no longer a weapon but a companion, sobbed himself to sleep. The wood birds sang merrily above his head; the squirrels, whisking their bravery of tail, ran barking from tree to tree, unconscious of the pity of it, and somewhere far away was a strange, muffled thunder, as if the partridges were drumming in celebration of nature's victory over the son of her immemorial enslavers. And back at the little plantation, where white men and black were hastily searching the fields and hedges in alarm, a mother's heart was breaking for her missing child.

Hours passed, and then the little sleeper rose to his feet. The chill of the evening was in his limbs, the fear of the gloom in his heart. But he had rested, and he no longer wept. With some blind instinct which impelled to action he struggled through the undergrowth about him and came to a more open ground—on his right the brook, to the left a gentle acclivity studded with infrequent trees; over all, the gathering gloom of twilight. A thin, ghostly mist rose along the water. It frightened and repelled him; instead of recrossing, in the direction whence he had come, he turned his back upon it, and went forward toward the dark inclosing wood. Suddenly he saw before him a strange moving object which he took to be some large animal—a dog, a pig—he could not name it; perhaps it was a bear. He had seen pictures of bears, but knew of nothing to their discredit and had vaguely wished to meet one. But something in form or movement of this object—something in the awkwardness of its approach—told him that it was not a bear, and curiosity was stayed by fear. He stood still and as it came slowly on gained courage every moment, for he saw that at least it had not the long, menacing ears of the rabbit. Possibly his impressionable mind was half conscious of something familiar in its shambling, awkward gait. Before it had approached near enough to resolve his doubts he saw that it was followed by another and another. To right and to left were many more; the whole open space about him was alive with them—all moving toward the brook.

They were men. They crept upon their hands and knees. They used their hands only, dragging their legs. They used their knees only, their arms hanging idle at their sides. They strove to rise to their feet, but fell prone in the attempt. They did nothing naturally, and nothing alike, save only to advance foot by foot in the same direction. Singly, in pairs and in little groups, they came on through the gloom, some halting now and again while others crept slowly past them, then resuming their movement. They came by dozens and by hundreds; as far on either hand as one could see in the deepening gloom they extended and the black wood behind them appeared to be inexhaustible. The very ground seemed in motion toward the creek. Occasionally one who had paused did not again go on, but lay motionless. He was dead. Some, pausing, made strange gestures with their hands, erected their arms and lowered them again, clasped their heads; spread their palms upward, as men are sometimes seen to do in public prayer.

Not all of this did the child note; it is what would have been noted by an elder observer; he saw little but that these were men, yet crept like babes. Being men, they were not terrible, though unfamiliarly clad. He moved among them freely, going from one to another and peering into their faces with childish curiosity. All their faces were singularly white and many were streaked and gouted with red. Something in this —something too, perhaps, in their grotesque attitudes and movements

—reminded him of the painted clown whom he had seen last summer in the circus, and he laughed as he watched them. But on and ever on they crept, these maimed and bleeding men, as heedless as he of the dramatic contrast between his laughter and their own ghastly gravity. To him it was a merry spectacle. He had seen his father's Negroes creep upon their hands and knees for his amusement—had ridden them so, "making believe" they were his horses. He now approached one of these crawling figures from behind and with an agile movement mounted it astride. The man sank upon his breast, recovered, flung the small boy fiercely to the ground as an unbroken colt might have done, then turned upon him a face that lacked a lower jaw—from the upper teeth to the throat was a great red gap fringed with hanging shreds of flesh and splinters of bone. The unnatural prominence of nose, the absence of chin, the fierce eyes, gave this man the appearance of a great bird of prey crimsoned in throat and breast by the blood of its quarry. The man rose to his knees, the child to his feet. The man shook his fist at the child; the child, terrified at last, ran to a tree near by, got upon the farther side of it and took a more serious view of the situation. And so the clumsy multitude dragged itself slowly and painfully along in hideous pantomime—moved forward down the slope like a swarm of great black beetles, with never a sound of going—in silence profound, absolute.

Instead of darkening, the haunted landscape began to brighten. Through the belt of trees beyond the brook shone a strange red light, the trunks and branches of the trees making a black lacework against it. It struck the creeping figures and gave them monstrous shadows, which caricatured their movements on the lit grass. It fell upon their faces, touching their whiteness with a ruddy tinge, accentuating the stains with which so many of them were freaked and maculated. It sparkled on buttons and bits of metal in their clothing. Instinctively the child turned toward the growing splendor and moved down the slope with his horrible companions; in a few moments had passed the foremost of the throng—not much of a feat, considering his advantages. He placed himself in the lead, his wooden sword still in hand, and solemnly directed the march, conforming his pace to theirs and occasionally turning as if to see that his forces did not straggle. Surely such a leader never before had such a following.

Scattered about upon the ground now slowly narrowing by the encroachment of this awful march to water, were certain articles to which, in the leader's mind, were coupled no significant associations: an occasional blanket, tightly rolled lengthwise, doubled and the ends bound together with a string; a heavy knapsack here, and there a broken rifle—such things, in short, as are found in the rear of retreating troops, the "spoor" of men flying from their hunters. Everywhere near the creek, which here had a margin of lowland, the earth was trodden into mud by the feet of men and horses. An observer of better experience in the use of his eyes would have noticed that these footprints pointed in both directions; the ground had been twice passed over—in advance and in retreat. A few hours before, these desperate, stricken men, with their more fortunate and now distant comrades, had penetrated the forest in thousands. Their successive battalions, breaking into swarms and reforming in lines, had passed the child on every side—had almost trodden on him as he slept. The rustle and murmur of their march had not awakened him. Almost within a stone's throw of where he lay they had fought a battle; but all unheard by him were the roar of the musketry, the shock of the cannon, "the thunder of the captains and the shouting." He had slept through it all, grasping his little wooden sword with perhaps a tighter clutch in unconscious sympathy with his martial environment, but as heedless of the grandeur of the struggle as the dead who had died to make the glory.

The fire beyond the belt of woods on the farther side of the creek, reflected to earth from the canopy of its own smoke, was now suffusing the whole landscape. It transformed the sinuous line of mist to the vapor of gold. The water gleamed with dashes of red, and red, too, were many of the stones protruding above the surface. But that was blood; the less desperately wounded had stained them in crossing. On them, too, the child now crossed with eager steps; he was going to the fire. As he stood upon the farther bank he turned about to look at the companions of his march. The advance was arriving at the creek. The stronger had already drawn themselves to the brink and plunged their faces into the flood. Three or four who lay without motion appeared to have no heads. At this the child's eyes expanded with wonder; even his hospitable understanding could not accept a phenomenon implying such vitality as that. After slaking their thirst these men had not had the strength to back away from the water, nor to keep their heads above it. They were drowned. In rear of these, the open spaces of the forest showed the leader as many formless figures of his grim command as at first; but not nearly so many were in motion. He waved his cap for their encouragement and smilingly pointed with his weapon in the direction of the guiding light—a pillar of fire to this strange exodus.

Confident of the fidelity of his forces, he now entered the belt of woods, passed through it easily in the red illumination, climbed a fence, ran across a field, turning now and again to coquet with his responsive shadow, and so approached the blazing ruin of a dwelling. Desolation everywhere! In all the wide glare not a living thing was visible. He cared nothing for that; the spectacle pleased, and he danced with glee in imitation of the wavering flames. He ran about, collecting fuel, but every object that he found was too heavy for him to cast in from the distance to which the heat limited his approach. In despair he flung in his sword— a surrender to the superior forces of nature. His military career was at an end.

Shifting his position, his eyes fell upon some outbuildings which had an oddly familiar appearance, as if he had dreamed of them. He stood considering them with wonder, when suddenly the entire plantation, with its inclosing forest, seemed to turn as if upon a pivot. His little world swung half around; the points of the compass were reversed. He recognized the blazing building as his own home!

For a moment he stood stupefied by the power of the revelation, then ran with stumbling feet, making a half-circuit of the ruin. There, conspicuous in the light of the conflagration, lay the dead body of a woman —the white face turned upward, the hands thrown out and clutched full of grass, the clothing deranged, the long dark hair in tangles and full of clotted blood. The greater part of the forehead was torn away, and from the jagged hole the brain protruded, overflowing the temple, a frothy mass of gray, crowned with clusters of crimson bubbles—the work of a shell.

The child moved his little hands, making wild, uncertain gestures. He uttered a series of inarticulate and indescribable cries—something between the chattering of an ape and the gobbling of a turkey—a startling, soulless, unholy sound, the language of a devil. The child was a deaf mute.

Then he stood motionless, with quivering lips, looking down upon the wreck.

A SON OF THE GODS

A Study in the Present Tense

A BREEZY day and a sunny landscape. An open country to right and left and forward; behind, a wood. In the edge of this wood, facing the open but not venturing into it, long lines of troops, halted. The wood is alive with them, and full of confused noises—the occasional rattle of wheels as a battery of artillery goes into position to cover the advance; the hum and murmur of the soldiers talking; a sound of innumerable feet in the dry leaves that strew the interspaces among the trees; hoarse commands of officers. Detached groups of horsemen are well in front —not altogether exposed—many of them intently regarding the crest of a hill a mile away in the direction of the interrupted advance. For this powerful army, moving in battle order through a forest, has met with a formidable obstacle—the open country. The crest of that gentle hill a mile away has a sinister look; it says, Beware! Along it runs a stone wall extending to left and right a great distance. Behind the wall is a hedge; behind the hedge are seen the tops of trees in rather straggling order. Among the trees—what? It is necessary to know.

Yesterday, and for many days and nights previously, we were fighting somewhere; always there was cannonading, with occasional keen rattlings of musketry, mingled with cheers, our own or the enemy's, we seldom knew, attesting some temporary advantage. This morning at daybreak the enemy was gone. We have moved forward across his earthworks, across which we have so often vainly attempted to move before, through the débris of his abandoned camps, among the graves of his fallen, into the woods beyond.

How curiously we had regarded everything! how odd it all had seemed! Nothing had appeared quite familiar; the most commonplace objects—an old saddle, a splintered wheel, a forgotten canteen—everything had related something of the mysterious personality of those strange men who had been killing us. The soldier never becomes wholly familiar with the conception of his foes as men like himself; he cannot divest himself of the feeling that they are another order of beings, dif-

24

ferently conditioned, in an environment not altogether of the earth. The smallest vestiges of them rivet his attention and engage his interest. He thinks of them as inaccessible; and, catching an unexpected glimpse of them, they appear farther away, and therefore larger, than they really are—like objects in a fog. He is somewhat in awe of them.

From the edge of the wood leading up the acclivity are the tracks of horses and wheels—the wheels of cannon. The yellow grass is beaten down by the feet of infantry. Clearly they have passed this way in thousands; they have not withdrawn by the country roads. This is significant—it is the difference between retiring and retreating.

That group of horsemen is our commander, his staff and escort. He is facing the distant crest, holding his field-glass against his eyes with both hands, his elbows needlessly elevated. It is a fashion; it seems to dignify the act; we are all addicted to it. Suddenly he lowers the glass and says a few words to those about him. Two or three aides detach themselves from the group and canter away into the woods, along the lines in each direction. We did not hear his words, but we know them: "Tell General X. to send forward the skirmish line." Those of us who have been out of place resume our positions; the men resting at ease straighten themselves and the ranks are re-formed without a command. Some of us staff officers dismount and look at our saddle girths; those already on the ground remount.

Galloping rapidly along in the edge of the open ground comes a young officer on a snow-white horse. His saddle blanket is scarlet. What a fool! No one who has ever been in action but remembers how naturally every rifle turns toward the man on a white horse; no one but has observed how a bit of red enrages the bull of battle. That such colors are fashionable in military life must be accepted as the most astonishing of all the phenomena of human vanity. They would seem to have been devised to increase the death-rate.

This young officer is in full uniform, as if on parade. He is all agleam with bullion—a blue-and-gold edition of the Poetry of War. A wave of derisive laughter runs abreast of him all along the line. But how handsome he is!—with what careless grace he sits his horse!

He reins up within a respectful distance of the corps commander and salutes. The old soldier nods familiarly; he evidently knows him. A brief colloquy between them is going on; the young man seems to be preferring some request which the elder one is indisposed to grant. Let us ride a little nearer. Ah! too late—it is ended. The young officer salutes again, wheels his horse, and rides straight toward the crest of the hill!

A thin line of skirmishers, the men deployed at six paces or so apart, now pushes from the wood into the open. The commander speaks to his bugler, who claps his instrument to his lips. *Tra-la-la! Tra-la-la!* The skirmishers halt in their tracks.

Meantime the young horseman has advanced a hundred yards. He is riding at a walk, straight up the long slope, with never a turn of the head. How glorious! Gods! what would we not give to be in his place— with his soul! He does not draw his sabre; his right hand hangs easily at his side. The breeze catches the plume in his hat and flutters it smartly. The sunshine rests upon his shoulder-straps, lovingly, like a visible bene- diction. Straight on he rides. Ten thousand pairs of eyes are fixed upon him with an intensity that he can hardly fail to feel; ten thousand hearts keep quick time to the inaudible hoof-beats of his snowy steed. He is not alone—he draws all souls after him. But we remember that we laughed! On and on, straight for the hedge-lined wall, he rides. Not a look backward. O, if he would but turn—if he could but see the love, the adoration, the atonement!

Not a word is spoken; the populous depths of the forest still murmur with their unseen and unseeing swarm, but all along the fringe is silence. The burly commander is an equestrian statue of himself. The mounted staff officers, their field-glasses up, are motionless all. The line of battle in the edge of the wood stands at a new kind of "attention," each man in the attitude in which he was caught by the consciousness of what is going on. All these hardened and impenitent man-killers, to whom death in its awfulest forms is a fact familiar to their every-day observation; who sleep on hills trembling with the thunder of great guns, dine in the midst of streaming missiles, and play at cards among the dead faces of their dearest friends—all are watching with suspended breath and beating hearts the outcome of an act involving the life of one man. Such is the magnetism of courage and devotion.

If now you should turn your head you would see a simultaneous movement among the spectators—a start, as if they had received an electric shock—and looking forward again to the now distant horse- man you would see that he has in that instant altered his direction and is riding at an angle to his former course. The spectators suppose the sudden deflection to be caused by a shot, perhaps a wound; but take this field-glass and you will observe that he is riding toward a break in the wall and hedge. He means, if not killed, to ride through and overlook the country beyond.

You are not to forget the nature of this man's act; it is not permitted to you to think of it as an instance of bravado, nor, on the other hand, a needless sacrifice of self. If the enemy has not retreated he is in force on that ridge. The investigator will encounter nothing less than a line-of-battle; there is no need of pickets, videttes, skirmishers, to give warning of our approach; our attacking lines will be visible, conspicuous, exposed to an artillery fire that will shave the ground the moment they break from cover, and for half the distance to a sheet of rifle bullets in which nothing can live. In short, if the enemy is there, it would be madness to attack him in front; he must be manœuvred out by the immemorial plan of threatening his line of communication, as necessary to his existence as to the diver at the bottom of the sea his air tube. But how ascertain if the enemy is there? There is but one way,—somebody must go and see. The natural and customary thing to do is to send forward a line of skirmishers. But in this case they will answer in the affirmative with all their lives; the enemy, crouching in double ranks behind the stone wall and in cover of the hedge, will wait until it is possible to count each assailant's teeth. At the first volley a half of the questioning line will fall, the other half before it can accomplish the predestined retreat. What a price to pay for gratified curiosity! At what a dear rate an army must sometimes purchase knowledge! "Let me pay all," says this gallant man—this military Christ!

There is no hope except the hope against hope that the crest is clear. True, he might prefer capture to death. So long as he advances, the line will not fire—why should it? He can safely ride into the hostile ranks and become a prisoner of war. But this would defeat his object. It would not answer our question; it is necessary either that he return unharmed or be shot to death before our eyes. Only so shall we know how to act. If captured—why, that might have been done by a half-dozen stragglers.

Now begins an extraordinary contest of intellect between a man and an army. Our horseman, now within a quarter of a mile of the crest, suddenly wheels to the left and gallops in a direction parallel to it. He has caught sight of his antagonist; he knows all. Some slight advantage of ground has enabled him to overlook a part of the line. If he were here he could tell us in words. But that is now hopeless; he must make the best use of the few minutes of life remaining to him, by compelling the enemy himself to tell us as much and as plainly as possible—which, naturally, that discreet power is reluctant to do. Not a rifleman in those crouching ranks, not a cannoneer at those masked and shotted guns, but knows the needs of the situation, the imperative duty of forbearance. Besides, there has been time enough to forbid them all to fire. True, a single rifle-shot might drop him and be no great disclosure. But firing is infectious—and see how rapidly he moves, with never a pause except as he whirls his horse about to take a new direction, never directly backward toward us, never directly forward toward his executioners. All this is visible through the glass; it seems occurring within pistol-shot; we see all but the enemy, whose presence, whose thoughts, whose motives we infer. To the unaided eye there is nothing but a black figure on a white horse, tracing slow zigzags against the slope of a distant hill—so slowly they seem almost to creep.

Now—the glass again—he has tired of his failure, or sees his error, or has gone mad; he is dashing directly forward at the wall, as if to take it at a leap, hedge and all! One moment only and he wheels right about and is speeding like the wind straight down the slope—toward his friends, toward his death! Instantly the wall is topped with a fierce roll of smoke for a distance of hundreds of yards to right and left. This is as instantly dissipated by the wind, and before the rattle of the rifle reaches us he is down. No, he recovers his seat; he has but pulled his horse upon its haunches. They are up and away! A tremendous cheer bursts from our ranks, relieving the insupportable tension of our feelings. And the horse and its rider? Yes, they are up and away. Away, indeed—they are making directly to our left, parallel to the now steadily blazing and smoking wall. The rattle of the musketry is continuous, and every bullet's target is that courageous heart.

Suddenly a great bank of white smoke pushes upward from behind the wall. Another and another—a dozen roll up before the thunder of the explosions and the humming of the missiles reach our ears and the missiles themselves come bounding through clouds of dust into our covert, knocking over here and there a man and causing a temporary distraction, a passing thought of self.

The dust drifts away. Incredible!—that enchanted horse and rider have passed a ravine and are climbing another slope to unveil another conspiracy of silence, to thwart the will of another armed host. Another moment and that crest too is in eruption. The horse rears and strikes the air with its forefeet. They are down at last. But look again—the man has detached himself from the dead animal. He stands erect, motionless, holding his sabre in his right hand straight above his head. His face is toward us. Now he lowers his hand to a level with his face and moves it outward, the blade of the sabre describing a downward curve. It is a sign to us, to the world, to posterity. It is a hero's salute to death and history.

Again the spell is broken; our men attempt to cheer; they are choking with emotion; they utter hoarse, discordant cries; they clutch their weapons and press tumultuously forward into the open. The skirmishers, without orders, against orders, are going forward at a keen run, like hounds unleashed. Our cannon speak and the enemy's now open in full chorus; to right and left as far as we can see, the distant crest, seeming now so near, erects its towers of cloud and the great shot pitch roaring down among our moving masses. Flag after flag of ours emerges from the wood, line after line sweeps forth, catching the sunlight on its burnished arms. The rear battalions alone are in obedience; they preserve their proper distance from the insurgent front.

The commander has not moved. He now removes his field-glass from his eyes and glances to the right and left. He sees the human current flowing on either side of him and his huddled escort, like tide waves parted by a rock. Not a sign of feeling in his face; he is thinking. Again he directs his eyes forward; they slowly traverse that malign and awful crest. He addresses a calm word to his bugler. *Tra-la-la! Tra-la-la!* The injunction has an imperiousness which enforces it. It is repeated by all the bugles of all the subordinate commanders; the sharp metallic notes assert themselves above the hum of the advance and penetrate the sound of the cannon. To halt is to withdraw. The colors move slowly back; the lines face about and sullenly follow, bearing their wounded; the skirmishers return, gathering up the dead.

Ah, those many, many needless dead! That great soul whose beautiful body is lying over yonder, so conspicuous against the sere hillside—could it not have been spared the bitter consciousness of a vain devotion? Would one exception have marred too much the pitiless perfection of the divine, eternal plan?

ONE OF THE MISSING

JEROME SEARING, a private soldier of General Sherman's army, then confronting the enemy at and about Kennesaw Mountain, Georgia, turned his back upon a small group of officers with whom he had been talking in low tones, stepped across a light line of earthworks, and disappeared in a forest. None of the men in line behind the works had said a word to him, nor had he so much as nodded to them in passing, but all who saw understood that this brave man had been intrusted with some perilous duty. Jerome Searing, though a private, did not serve in the ranks; he was detailed for service at division headquarters, being borne upon the rolls as an orderly. "Orderly" is a word covering a multitude of duties. An orderly may be a messenger, a clerk, an officer's servant—anything. He may perform services for which no provision is made in orders and army regulations. Their nature may depend upon his aptitude, upon favor, upon accident. Private Searing, an incomparable marksman, young, hardy, intelligent and insensible to fear, was a scout. The general commanding his division was not content to obey orders blindly without knowing what was in his front, even when his command was not on detached service, but formed a fraction of the line of the army; nor was he satisfied to receive his knowledge of his *vis-à-vis* through the customary channels; he wanted to know more than he was apprised of by the corps commander and the collisions of pickets and skirmishers. Hence Jerome Searing, with his extraordinary daring, his woodcraft, his sharp eyes, and truthful tongue. On this occasion his instructions were simple: to get as near the enemy's lines as possible and learn all that he could.

In a few moments he had arrived at the picket-line, the men on duty there lying in groups of two and four behind little banks of earth scooped out of the slight depression in which they lay, their rifles protruding from the green boughs with which they had masked their small defenses. The forest extended without a break toward the front, so solemn and silent that only by an effort of the imagination could it be conceived as populous with armed men, alert and vigilant—a forest formidable with possibilities of battle. Pausing a moment in one of these rifle-pits to apprise the men of his intention Searing crept stealthily forward on his hands and knees and was soon lost to view in a dense thicket of underbrush.

"That is the last of him," said one of the men; "I wish I had his rifle; those fellows will hurt some of us with it."

Searing crept on, taking advantage of every accident of ground and growth to give himself better cover. His eyes penetrated everywhere, his ears took note of every sound. He stilled his breathing, and at the cracking of a twig beneath his knee stopped his progress and hugged the earth. It was slow work, but not tedious; the danger made it exciting, but by no physical signs was the excitement manifest. His pulse was as regular, his nerves were as steady as if he were trying to trap a sparrow.

"It seems a long time," he thought, "but I cannot have come very far; I am still alive."

He smiled at his own method of estimating distance, and crept forward. A moment later he suddenly flattened himself upon the earth and lay motionless, minute after minute. Through a narrow opening in the bushes he had caught sight of a small mound of yellow clay—one of the enemy's rifle-pits. After some little time he cautiously raised his head, inch by inch, then his body upon his hands, spread out on each side of him, all the while intently regarding the hillock of clay. In another moment he was upon his feet, rifle in hand, striding rapidly forward with little attempt at concealment. He had rightly interpreted the signs, whatever they were; the enemy was gone.

To assure himself beyond a doubt before going back to report upon so important a matter, Searing pushed forward across the line of abandoned pits, running from cover to cover in the more open forest, his eyes vigilant to discover possible stragglers. He came to the edge of a plantation—one of those forlorn, deserted homesteads of the last years of the war, upgrown with brambles, ugly with broken fences and desolate with vacant buildings having blank apertures in place of doors and windows. After a keen reconnoissance from the safe seclusion of a clump of young pines Searing ran lightly across a field and through an orchard to a small structure which stood apart from the other farm buildings, on a slight elevation. This he thought would enable him to overlook a large scope of country in the direction that he supposed the enemy to have taken in withdrawing. This building, which had originally consisted of a single room elevated upon four posts about ten feet high, was now little more than a roof; the floor had fallen away, the joists and planks loosely piled on the ground below or resting on end at various angles, not wholly torn from their fastenings above. The supporting posts were themselves no longer vertical. It looked as if the whole edifice would go down at the touch of a finger.

Concealing himself in the débris of joists and flooring Searing looked across the open ground between his point of view and a spur of Kennesaw Mountain, a half-mile away. A road leading up and across this spur was crowded with troops—the rear-guard of the retiring enemy, their gun-barrels gleaming in the morning sunlight.

Searing had now learned all that he could hope to know. It was his duty to return to his own command with all possible speed and report his discovery. But the gray column of Confederates toiling up the mountain road was singularly tempting. His rifle—an ordinary "Springfield," but fitted with a globe sight and hair-trigger—would easily send its ounce and a quarter of lead hissing into their midst. That would probably not affect the duration and result of the war, but it is the business of a soldier to kill. It is also his habit if he is a good soldier. Searing cocked his rifle and "set" the trigger.

But it was decreed from the beginning of time that Private Searing was not to murder anybody that bright summer morning, nor was the Confederate retreat to be announced by him. For countless ages events had been so matching themselves together in that wondrous mosaic to some parts of which, dimly discernible, we give the name of history, that the acts which he had in will would have marred the harmony of the pattern. Some twenty-five years previously the Power charged with the execution of the work according to the design had provided against that mischance by causing the birth of a certain male child in a little village at the foot of the Carpathian Mountains, had carefully reared it, supervised its education, directed its desires into a military channel, and in due time made it an officer of artillery. By the concurrence of an infinite number of favoring influences and their preponderance over an infinite number of opposing ones, this officer of artillery had been made to commit a breach of discipline and flee from his native country to avoid punishment. He had been directed to New Orleans (instead of New York), where a recruiting officer awaited him on the wharf. He was enlisted and promoted, and things were so ordered that he now commanded a Confederate battery some two miles along the line from where Jerome Searing, the Federal scout, stood cocking his rifle. Nothing had been neglected—at every step in the progress of both these men's lives, and in the lives of their contemporaries and ancestors, and in the lives of the contemporaries of their ancestors, the right thing had been done to bring about the desired result. Had anything in all this vast concatenation been overlooked Private Searing might have fired on the retreating Confederates that morning, and would perhaps have missed. As it fell out, a Confederate captain of artillery, having nothing better to do while awaiting his turn to pull out and be off, amused himself by sighting a field-piece obliquely to his right at what he mistook for some Federal officers on the crest of a hill, and discharged it. The shot flew high of its mark.

As Jerome Searing drew back the hammer of his rifle and with his eyes upon the distant Confederates considered where he could plant his shot with the best hope of making a widow or an orphan or a childless mother,—perhaps all three, for Private Searing, although he had repeatedly refused promotion, was not without a certain kind of ambition,—he heard a rushing sound in the air, like that made by the wings of a great bird swooping down upon its prey. More quickly than he could apprehend the gradation, it increased to a hoarse and horrible roar, as the missile that made it sprang at him out of the sky, striking with a deafening impact one of the posts supporting the confusion of timbers above him, smashing it into matchwood, and bringing down the crazy edifice with a loud clatter, in clouds of blinding dust!

When Jerome Searing recovered consciousness he did not at once understand what had occurred. It was, indeed, some time before he opened his eyes. For a while he believed that he had died and been buried, and he tried to recall some portions of the burial service. He thought that his wife was kneeling upon his grave, adding her weight to that of the earth upon his breast. The two of them, widow and earth, had crushed his coffin. Unless the children should persuade her to go home he would not much longer be able to breathe. He felt a sense of wrong. "I cannot speak to her," he thought; "the dead have no voice; and if I open my eyes I shall get them full of earth."

He opened his eyes. A great expanse of blue sky, rising from a fringe of the tops of trees. In the foreground, shutting out some of the trees, a high, dun mound, angular in outline and crossed by an intricate, patternless system of straight lines; the whole an immeasurable distance away—a distance so inconceivably great that it fatigued him, and he closed his eyes. The moment that he did so he was conscious of an insufferable light. A sound was in his ears like the low, rhythmic thunder of a distant sea breaking in successive waves upon the beach, and out of this noise, seeming a part of it, or possibly coming from beyond it, and intermingled with its ceaseless undertone, came the articulate words: "Jerome Searing, you are caught like a rat in a trap—in a trap, trap, trap."

Suddenly there fell a great silence, a black darkness, an infinite tranquillity, and Jerome Searing, perfectly conscious of his rathood, and well assured of the trap that he was in, remembering all and nowise alarmed, again opened his eyes to reconnoitre, to note the strength of his enemy, to plan his defense.

He was caught in a reclining posture, his back firmly supported by a solid beam. Another lay across his breast, but he had been able to shrink a little away from it so that it no longer oppressed him, though it was immovable. A brace joining it at an angle had wedged him against a pile of boards on his left, fastening the arm on that side. His legs, slightly parted and straight along the ground, were covered upward to the knees with a mass of débris which towered above his narrow horizon. His head was as rigidly fixed as in a vise; he could move his eyes, his chin—no more. Only his right arm was partly free. "You must help us out of this," he said to it. But he could not get it from under the heavy timber athwart his chest, nor move it outward more than six inches at the elbow.

Searing was not seriously injured, nor did he suffer pain. A smart rap on the head from a flying fragment of the splintered post, incurred simultaneously with the frightfully sudden shock to the nervous system, had momentarily dazed him. His term of unconsciousness, including the period of recovery, during which he had had the strange fancies, had probably not exceeded a few seconds, for the dust of the wreck had not wholly cleared away as he began an intelligent survey of the situation.

With his partly free right hand he now tried to get hold of the beam that lay across, but not quite against, his breast. In no way could he do so. He was unable to depress the shoulder so as to push the elbow beyond that edge of the timber which was nearest his knees; failing in that, he could not raise the forearm and hand to grasp the beam. The brace that made an angle with it downward and backward prevented him from doing anything in that direction, and between it and his body the space was not half so wide as the length of his forearm. Obviously he could not get his hand under the beam nor over it; the hand could not, in fact, touch it at all. Having demonstrated his inability, he desisted, and began to think whether he could reach any of the débris piled upon his legs.

In surveying the mass with a view to determining that point, his attention was arrested by what seemed to be a ring of shining metal immediately in front of his eyes. It appeared to him at first to surround some perfectly black substance, and it was somewhat more than a half-inch in diameter. It suddenly occurred to his mind that the blackness was simply shadow and that the ring was in fact the muzzle of his rifle protruding from the pile of débris. He was not long in satisfying himself that this was so—if it was a satisfaction. By closing either eye he could look a little way along the barrel—to the point where it was hidden by the rubbish that held it. He could see the one side, with the corresponding eye, at apparently the same angle as the other side with the other eye. Looking with the right eye, the weapon seemed to be directed at a point to the left of his head, and *vice versa*. He was unable to see the upper surface of the barrel, but could see the under surface of the stock at a slight angle. The piece was, in fact, aimed at the exact centre of his forehead.

In the perception of this circumstance, in the recollection that just previously to the mischance of which this uncomfortable situation was the result he had cocked the rifle and set the trigger so that a touch would discharge it, Private Searing was affected with a feeling of uneasiness. But that was as far as possible from fear; he was a brave man, somewhat familiar with the aspect of rifles from that point of view, and of cannon too. And now he recalled, with something like amusement, an incident of his experience at the storming of Missionary Ridge, where, walking up to one of the enemy's embrasures from which he had seen a heavy gun throw charge after charge of grape among the assailants he had thought for a moment that the piece had been withdrawn; he could see nothing in the opening but a brazen circle. What that was he had understood just in time to step aside as it pitched another peck of iron down that swarming slope. To face firearms is one of the commonest incidents in a soldier's life—firearms, too, with malevolent eyes blazing behind them. That is what a soldier is for. Still, Private

Searing did not altogether relish the situation, and turned away his eyes.

After groping, aimless, with his right hand for a time he made an ineffectual attempt to release his left. Then he tried to disengage his head, the fixity of which was the more annoying from his ignorance of what held it. Next he tried to free his feet, but while exerting the powerful muscles of his legs for that purpose it occurred to him that a disturbance of the rubbish which held them might discharge the rifle; how it could have endured what had already befallen it he could not understand, although memory assisted him with several instances in point. One in particular he recalled, in which in a moment of mental abstraction he had clubbed his rifle and beaten out another gentleman's brains, observing afterward that the weapon which he had been diligently swinging by the muzzle was loaded, capped, and at full cock—knowledge of which circumstance would doubtless have cheered his antagonist to longer endurance. He had always smiled in recalling that blunder of his "green and salad days" as a soldier, but now he did not smile. He turned his eyes again to the muzzle of the rifle and for a moment fancied that it had moved; it seemed somewhat nearer.

Again he looked away. The tops of the distant trees beyond the bounds of the plantation interested him: he had not before observed how light and feathery they were, nor how darkly blue the sky was, even among their branches, where they somewhat paled it with their green; above him it appeared almost black. "It will be uncomfortably hot here," he thought, "as the day advances. I wonder which way I am looking."

Judging by such shadows as he could see, he decided that his face was due north; he would at least not have the sun in his eyes, and north —well, that was toward his wife and children.

"Bah!" he exclaimed aloud, "what have they to do with it?"

He closed his eyes. "As I can't get out I may as well go to sleep. The rebels are gone and some of our fellows are sure to stray out here foraging. They'll find me."

But he did not sleep. Gradually he became sensible of a pain in his forehead—a dull ache, hardly perceptible at first, but growing more and more uncomfortable. He opened his eyes and it was gone—closed them and it returned. "The devil!" he said, irrelevantly, and stared again at the sky. He heard the singing of birds, the strange metallic note of the meadow lark, suggesting the clash of vibrant blades. He fell into pleasant memories of his childhood, played again with his brother and sister, raced across the fields, shouting to alarm the sedentary larks, entered the sombre forest beyond and with timid steps followed the faint path to Ghost Rock, standing at last with audible heart-throbs before the Dead Man's Cave and seeking to penetrate its awful mystery. For the first time he observed that the opening of the haunted cavern was encircled by a ring of metal. Then all else vanished and left him gazing into the barrel of his rifle as before. But whereas before it had seemed nearer, it now seemed an inconceivable distance away, and all the more sinister for that. He cried out and, startled by something in his own voice—the note of fear—lied to himself in denial: "If I don't sing out I may stay here till I die."

He now made no further attempt to evade the menacing stare of the gun barrel. If he turned away his eyes an instant it was to look for as-sistance (although he could not see the ground on either side the ruin), and he permitted them to return, obedient to the imperative fascination. If he closed them it was from weariness, and instantly the poignant pain in his forehead—the prophecy and menace of the bullet—forced him to reopen them.

The tension of nerve and brain was too severe; nature came to his re-lief with intervals of unconsciousness. Reviving from one of these he became sensible of a sharp, smarting pain in his right hand, and when he worked his fingers together, or rubbed his palm with them, he could feel that they were wet and slippery. He could not see the hand, but he knew the sensation; it was running blood. In his delirium he had beaten it against the jagged fragments of the wreck, had clutched it full of splinters. He resolved that he would meet his fate more manly. He was a plain, common soldier, had no religion and not much philosophy; he could not die like a hero, with great and wise last words, even if there had been some one to hear them, but he could die "game," and he would. But if he could only know when to expect the shot!

Some rats which had probably inhabited the shed came sneaking and scampering about. One of them mounted the pile of débris that held the rifle; another followed and another. Searing regarded them at first with indifference, then with friendly interest; then, as the thought flashed into his bewildered mind that they might touch the trigger of his rifle, he cursed them and ordered them to go away. "It is no business of yours," he cried.

The creatures went away; they would return later, attack his face, gnaw away his nose, cut his throat—he knew that, but he hoped by that time to be dead.

Nothing could now unfix his gaze from the little ring of metal with its black interior. The pain in his forehead was fierce and incessant. He felt it gradually penetrating the brain more and more deeply, until at last its progress was arrested by the wood at the back of his head. It grew momentarily more insufferable: he began wantonly beating his lacerated hand against the splinters again to counteract that horrible ache. It seemed to throb with a slow, regular recurrence, each pulsation sharper than the preceding, and sometimes he cried out, thinking he felt the fatal bullet. No thoughts of home, of wife and children, of country, of glory. The whole record of memory was effaced. The world had passed away—not a vestige remained. Here in this confusion of timbers and boards is the sole universe. Here is immortality in time—each pain an everlasting life. The throbs tick off eternities.

Jerome Searing, the man of courage, the formidable enemy, the strong, resolute warrior, was as pale as a ghost. His jaw was fallen; his eyes protruded; he trembled in every fibre; a cold sweat bathed his entire body; he screamed with fear. He was not insane—he was terrified.

In groping about with his torn and bleeding hand he seized at last a strip of board, and, pulling, felt it give way. It lay parallel with his body, and by bending his elbow as much as the contracted space would permit, he could draw it a few inches at a time. Finally it was altogether loosened from the wreckage covering his legs; he could lift it clear of the ground its whole length. A great hope came into his mind: perhaps he could work it upward, that is to say backward, far enough to lift the end and push aside the rifle; or, if that were too tightly wedged, so place the strip of board as to deflect the bullet. With this object he passed it backward inch by inch, hardly daring to breathe lest that act somehow defeat his intent, and more than ever unable to remove his eyes from the rifle, which might perhaps now hasten to improve its waning opportunity. Something at least had been gained: in the occupation of his mind in this attempt at self-defense he was less sensible of the pain in his head and had ceased to wince. But he was still dreadfully frightened and his teeth rattled like castanets.

The strip of board ceased to move to the suasion of his hand. He tugged at it with all his strength, changed the direction of its length all he could, but it had met some extended obstruction behind him and the end in front was still too far away to clear the pile of débris and reach the muzzle of the gun. It extended, indeed, nearly as far as the trigger guard, which, uncovered by the rubbish, he could imperfectly see with his right eye. He tried to break the strip with his hand, but had no leverage. In his defeat, all his terror returned, augmented tenfold. The black aperture of the rifle appeared to threaten a sharper and more imminent death in punishment of his rebellion. The track of the bullet through his head ached with an intenser anguish. He began to tremble again.

Suddenly he became composed. His tremor subsided. He clenched his teeth and drew down his eyebrows. He had not exhausted his means of defense; a new design had shaped itself in his mind—another plan of battle. Raising the front end of the strip of board, he carefully pushed it forward through the wreckage at the side of the rifle until it pressed against the trigger guard. Then he moved the end slowly outward until he could feel that it had cleared it, then, closing his eyes, thrust it against the trigger with all his strength! There was no explosion; the rifle had been discharged as it dropped from his hand when the building fell. But it did its work.

Lieutenant Adrian Searing, in command of the picket-guard on that part of the line through which his brother Jerome had passed on his mission, sat with attentive ears in his breastwork behind the line. Not the faintest sound escaped him; the cry of a bird, the barking of a squirrel, the noise of the wind among the pines—all were anxiously noted by his overstrained sense. Suddenly, directly in front of his line, he heard a faint, confused rumble, like the clatter of a falling building translated by distance. The lieutenant mechanically looked at his watch. Six o'clock and eighteen minutes. At the same moment an officer approached him on foot from the rear and saluted.

"Lieutenant," said the officer, "the colonel directs you to move forward your line and feel the enemy if you find him. If not, continue the advance until directed to halt. There is reason to think that the enemy has retreated."

The lieutenant nodded and said nothing; the other officer retired. In a moment the men, apprised of their duty by the non-commissioned officers in low tones, had deployed from their rifle-pits and were moving forward in skirmishing order, with set teeth and beating hearts.

This line of skirmishers sweeps across the plantation toward the mountain. They pass on both sides of the wrecked building, observing nothing. At a short distance in their rear their commander comes. He casts his eyes curiously upon the ruin and sees a dead body half buried in boards and timbers. It is so covered with dust that its clothing is Confederate gray. Its face is yellowish white; the cheeks are fallen in, the temples sunken, too, with sharp ridges about them, making the forehead forbiddingly narrow; the upper lip, slightly lifted, shows the white teeth, rigidly clenched. The hair is heavy with moisture, the face as wet as the dewy grass all about. From his point of view the officer does not observe the rifle; the man was apparently killed by the fall of the building.

"Dead a week," said the officer curtly, moving on and absently pulling out his watch as if to verify his estimate of time. Six o'clock and forty minutes.

KILLED AT RESACA

THE best soldier of our staff was Lieutenant Herman Brayle, one of the two aides-de-camp. I don't remember where the general picked him up; from some Ohio regiment, I think; none of us had previously known him, and it would have been strange if we had, for no two of us came from the same State, nor even from adjoining States. The general seemed to think that a position on his staff was a distinction that should be so judiciously conferred as not to beget any sectional jealousies and imperil the integrity of that part of the country which was still an integer. He would not even choose officers from his own command, but by some jugglery at department headquarters obtained them from other brigades. Under such circumstances, a man's services had to be very distinguished indeed to be heard of by his family and the friends of his youth; and "the speaking trump of fame" was a trifle hoarse from loquacity, anyhow.

Lieutenant Brayle was more than six feet in height and of splendid proportions, with the light hair and gray-blue eyes which men so gifted usually find associated with a high order of courage. As he was commonly in full uniform, especially in action, when most officers are content to be less flamboyantly attired, he was a very striking and conspicuous figure. As to the rest, he had a gentleman's manners, a scholar's head, and a lion's heart. His age was about thirty.

We all soon came to like Brayle as much as we admired him, and it was with sincere concern that in the engagement at Stone's River—our first action after he joined us—we observed that he had one most objectionable and unsoldierly quality: he was vain of his courage. During all the vicissitudes and mutations of that hideous encounter, whether our troops were fighting in the open cotton fields, in the cedar thickets, or behind the railway embankment, he did not once take cover, except when sternly commanded to do so by the general, who usually had other things to think of than the lives of his staff officers—or those of his men, for that matter.

In every later engagement while Brayle was with us it was the same way. He would sit his horse like an equestrian statue, in a storm of bullets and grape, in the most exposed places—wherever, in fact, duty, requiring him to go, permitted him to remain—when, without trouble and with distinct advantage to his reputation for common sense, he might have been in such security as is possible on a battlefield in the brief intervals of personal inaction.

On foot, from necessity or in deference to his dismounted commander or associates, his conduct was the same. He would stand like a rock in the open when officers and men alike had taken to cover; while men older in service and years, higher in rank and of unquestionable intrepidity, were loyally preserving behind the crest of a hill lives infinitely precious to their country, this fellow would stand, equally idle, on the ridge, facing in the direction of the sharpest fire.

When battles are going on in open ground it frequently occurs that the opposing lines, confronting each other within a stone's throw for hours, hug the earth as closely as if they loved it. The line officers in their proper places flatten themselves no less, and the field officers, their horses all killed or sent to the rear, crouch beneath the infernal canopy of hissing lead and screaming iron without a thought of personal dignity.

In such circumstances the life of a staff officer of a brigade is distinctly "not a happy one," mainly because of its precarious tenure and the unnerving alternations of emotion to which he is exposed. From a position of that comparative security from which a civilian would ascribe his escape to a "miracle," he may be despatched with an order to some commander of a prone regiment in the front line—a person for the moment inconspicuous and not always easy to find without a deal of search among men somewhat preoccupied, and in a din in which question and answer alike must be imparted in the sign language. It is customary in such cases to duck the head and scuttle away on a keen run, an object of lively interest to some thousands of admiring marksmen. In returning—well, it is not customary to return.

Brayle's practice was different. He would consign his horse to the care of an orderly,—he loved his horse,—and walk quietly away on his perilous errand with never a stoop of the back, his splendid figure, accentuated by his uniform, holding the eye with a strange fascination. We watched him with suspended breath, our hearts in our mouths. On one occasion of this kind, indeed, one of our number, an impetuous stammerer, was so possessed by his emotion that he shouted at me:

"I'll b-b-bet you t-two d-d-dollars they d-drop him b-b-before he g-gets to that d-d-ditch!"

I did not accept the brutal wager; I thought they would.

Let me do justice to a brave man's memory; in all these needless exposures of life there was no visible bravado nor subsequent narration. In the few instances when some of us had ventured to remonstrate, Brayle had smiled pleasantly and made some light reply, which, however, had not encouraged a further pursuit of the subject. Once he said:

"Captain, if ever I come to grief by forgetting your advice, I hope my last moments will be cheered by the sound of your beloved voice breathing into my ear the blessed words, 'I told you so.' "

We laughed at the captain—just why we could probably not have explained—and that afternoon when he was shot to rags from an ambuscade Brayle remained by the body for some time, adjusting the limbs with needless care—there in the middle of a road swept by gusts of grape and canister! It is easy to condemn this kind of thing, and not very difficult to refrain from imitation, but it is impossible not to respect, and Brayle was liked none the less for the weakness which had so heroic an expression. We wished he were not a fool, but he went on that way to the end, sometimes hard hit, but always returning to duty about as good as new.

Of course, it came at last; he who ignores the law of probabilities challenges an adversary that is seldom beaten. It was at Resaca, in Georgia, during the movement that resulted in the taking of Atlanta. In front of our brigade the enemy's line of earthworks ran through open fields along a slight crest. At each end of this open ground we were close up to him in the woods, but the clear ground we could not hope to occupy until night, when darkness would enable us to burrow like moles and throw up earth. At this point our line was a quarter-mile away in the edge of a wood. Roughly, we formed a semicircle, the enemy's fortified line being the chord of the arc.

"Lieutenant, go tell Colonel Ward to work up as close as he can get cover, and not to waste much ammunition in unnecessary firing. You may leave your horse."

When the general gave this direction we were in the fringe of the forest, near the right extremity of the arc. Colonel Ward was at the left. The suggestion to leave the horse obviously enough meant that Brayle was to take the longer line, through the woods and among the men. Indeed, the suggestion was needless; to go by the short route meant absolutely certain failure to deliver the message. Before anybody could interpose, Brayle had cantered lightly into the field and the enemy's works were in crackling conflagration.

"Stop that damned fool!" shouted the general.

A private of the escort, with more ambition than brains, spurred forward to obey, and within ten yards left himself and his horse dead on the field of honor.

Brayle was beyond recall, galloping easily along, parallel to the enemy and less than two hundred yards distant. He was a picture to see! His hat had been blown or shot from his head, and his long, blond hair rose and fell with the motion of his horse. He sat erect in the saddle, holding the reins lightly in his left hand, his right hanging carelessly at his side. An occasional glimpse of his handsome profile as he turned his head one way or the other proved that the interest which he took in what was going on was natural and without affectation.

The picture was intensely dramatic, but in no degree theatrical. Successive scores of rifles spat at him viciously as he came within range, and our own line in the edge of the timber broke out in visible and audible defense. No longer regardful of themselves or their orders, our fellows sprang to their feet, and swarming into the open sent broad sheets of bullets against the blazing crest of the offending works, which poured an answering fire into their unprotected groups with deadly effect. The artillery on both sides joined the battle, punctuating the rattle and roar with deep, earth-shaking explosions and tearing the air with storms of screaming grape, which from the enemy's side splintered the trees and spattered them with blood, and from ours defiled the smoke of his arms with banks and clouds of dust from his parapet.

My attention had been for a moment drawn to the general combat, but now, glancing down the unobscured avenue between these two thunderclouds, I saw Brayle, the cause of the carnage. Invisible now from either side, and equally doomed by friend and foe, he stood in the shot-swept space, motionless, his face toward the enemy. At some little distance lay his horse. I instantly saw what had stopped him.

As topographical engineer I had, early in the day, made a hasty examination of the ground, and now remembered that at that point was a deep and sinuous gully, crossing half the field from the enemy's line, its general course at right angles to it. From where we now were it was invisible, and Brayle had evidently not known about it. Clearly, it was impassable. Its salient angles would have afforded him absolute security if he had chosen to be satisfied with the miracle already wrought in his favor and leapt into it. He could not go forward, he would not turn back; he stood awaiting death. It did not keep him long waiting.

By some mysterious coincidence, almost instantaneously as he fell, the firing ceased, a few desultory shots at long intervals serving rather to accentuate than break the silence. It was as if both sides had suddenly repented of their profitless crime. Four stretcher-bearers of ours, following a sergeant with a white flag, soon afterward moved unmolested into the field, and made straight for Brayle's body. Several Confederate officers and men came out to meet them, and with uncovered heads assisted them to take up their sacred burden. As it was borne toward us we heard beyond the hostile works fifes and a muffled drum—a dirge. A generous enemy honored the fallen brave.

Amongst the dead man's effects was a soiled Russia-leather pocket-book. In the distribution of mementoes of our friend, which the general, as administrator, decreed, this fell to me.

A year after the close of the war, on my way to California, I opened and idly inspected it. Out of an overlooked compartment fell a letter without envelope or address. It was in a woman's handwriting, and began with words of endearment, but no name.

It had the following date line: "San Francisco, Cal., July 9, 1862." The signature was "Darling," in marks of quotation. Incidentally, in the body of the text, the writer's full name was given—Marian Mendenhall.

The letter showed evidence of cultivation and good breeding, but it was an ordinary love letter, if a love letter can be ordinary. There was not much in it, but there was something. It was this:

"Mr. Winters, whom I shall always hate for it, has been telling that at some battle in Virginia, where he got his hurt, you were seen crouching behind a tree. I think he wants to injure you in my regard, which he knows the story would do if I believed it. I could bear to hear of my soldier lover's death, but not of his cowardice."

These were the words which on that sunny afternoon, in a distant region, had slain a hundred men. Is woman weak?

One evening I called on Miss Mendenhall to return the letter to her. I intended, also, to tell her what she had done—but not that she did it. I found her in a handsome dwelling on Rincon Hill. She was beautiful, well bred—in a word, charming.

"You knew Lieutenant Herman Brayle," I said, rather abruptly. "You know, doubtless, that he fell in battle. Among his effects was found this letter from you. My errand here is to place it in your hands."

She mechanically took the letter, glanced through it with deepening color, and then, looking at me with a smile, said:

"It is very good of you, though I am sure it was hardly worth while." She started suddenly and changed color. "This stain," she said, "is it—surely it is not—"

"Madam," I said, "pardon me, but that is the blood of the truest and bravest heart that ever beat."

She hastily flung the letter on the blazing coals. "Uh! I cannot bear the sight of blood!" she said. "How did he die?"

I had involuntarily risen to rescue that scrap of paper, sacred even to me, and now stood partly behind her. As she asked the question she turned her face about and slightly upward. The light of the burning letter was reflected in her eyes and touched her cheek with a tinge of crimson like the stain upon its page. I had never seen anything so beautiful as this detestable creature.

"He was bitten by a snake," I replied.

THE AFFAIR AT COULTER'S NOTCH

"DO you think, Colonel, that your brave Coulter would like to put one of his guns in here?" the general asked.

He was apparently not altogether serious; it certainly did not seem a place where any artillerist, however brave, would like to put a gun. The colonel thought that possibly his division commander meant good-humoredly to intimate that in a recent conversation between them Captain Coulter's courage had been too highly extolled.

"General," he replied warmly, "Coulter would like to put a gun anywhere within reach of those people," with a motion of his hand in the direction of the enemy.

"It is the only place," said the general. He was serious, then.

The place was a depression, a "notch," in the sharp crest of a hill. It was a pass, and through it ran a turnpike, which reaching this highest point in its course by a sinuous ascent through a thin forest made a similar, though less steep, descent toward the enemy. For a mile to the left and a mile to the right, the ridge, though occupied by Federal infantry lying close behind the sharp crest and appearing as if held in place by atmospheric pressure, was inaccessible to artillery. There was no place but the bottom of the notch, and that was barely wide enough for the roadbed. From the Confederate side this point was commanded by two batteries posted on a slightly lower elevation beyond a creek, and a half-mile away. All the guns but one were masked by the trees of an orchard; that one—it seemed a bit of impudence—was on an open lawn directly in front of a rather grandiose building, the planter's dwelling. The gun was safe enough in its exposure—but only because the Federal infantry had been forbidden to fire. Coulter's Notch—it came to be called so—was not, that pleasant summer afternoon, a place where one would "like to put a gun."

Three or four dead horses lay there sprawling in the road, three or four dead men in a trim row at one side of it, and a little back, down the hill. All but one were cavalrymen belonging to the Federal advance. One was a quartermaster. The general commanding the division and

46

the colonel commanding the brigade, with their staffs and escorts, had ridden into the notch to have a look at the enemy's guns—which had straightway obscured themselves in towering clouds of smoke. It was hardly profitable to be curious about guns which had the trick of the cuttlefish, and the season of observation had been brief. At its conclusion —a short remove backward from where it began—occurred the conversation already partly reported. "It is the only place," the general repeated thoughtfully, "to get at them."

The colonel looked at him gravely. "There is room for only one gun, General—one against twelve."

"That is true—for only one at a time," said the commander with something like, yet not altogether like, a smile. "But then, your brave Coulter —a whole battery in himself."

The tone of irony was now unmistakable. It angered the colonel, but he did not know what to say. The spirit of military subordination is not favorable to retort, nor even to deprecation.

At this moment a young officer of artillery came riding slowly up the road attended by his bugler. It was Captain Coulter. He could not have been more than twenty-three years of age. He was of medium height, but very slender and lithe, and sat his horse with something of the air of a civilian. In face he was of a type singularly unlike the men about him; thin, high-nosed, gray-eyed, with a slight blond mustache, and long, rather straggling hair of the same color. There was an apparent negligence in his attire. His cap was worn with the visor a trifle askew; his coat was buttoned only at the sword-belt, showing a considerable expanse of white shirt, tolerably clean for that stage of the campaign. But the negligence was all in his dress and bearing; in his face was a look of intense interest in his surroundings. His gray eyes, which seemed occasionally to strike right and left across the landscape, like search-lights, were for the most part fixed upon the sky beyond the Notch; until he should arrive at the summit of the road there was nothing else in that direction to see. As he came opposite his division and brigade commanders at the roadside he saluted mechanically and was about to pass on. The colonel signed to him to halt.

"Captain Coulter," he said, "the enemy has twelve pieces over there on the next ridge. If I rightly understand the general, he directs that you bring up a gun and engage them."

There was a blank silence; the general looked stolidly at a distant regiment swarming slowly up the hill through rough undergrowth, like a torn and draggled cloud of blue smoke; the captain appeared not to have observed him. Presently the captain spoke, slowly and with apparent effort:

"On the next ridge, did you say, sir? Are the guns near the house?"

"Ah, you have been over this road before. Directly at the house."

"And it is—necessary—to engage them? The order is imperative?"

His voice was husky and broken. He was visibly paler. The colonel was astonished and mortified. He stole a glance at the commander. In that set, immobile face was no sign; it was as hard as bronze. A moment later the general rode away, followed by his staff and escort. The colonel, humiliated and indignant, was about to order Captain Coulter in arrest, when the latter spoke a few words in a low tone to his bugler, saluted, and rode straight forward into the Notch, where, presently, at the summit of the road, his field-glass at his eyes, he showed against the sky, he and his horse, sharply defined and statuesque. The bugler had dashed down the speed and disappeared behind a wood. Presently his bugle was heard singing in the cedars, and in an incredibly short time a single gun with its caisson, each drawn by six horses and manned by its full complement of gunners, came bounding and banging up the grade in a storm of dust, unlimbered under cover, and was run forward by hand to the fatal crest among the dead horses. A gesture of the captain's arm, some strangely agile movements of the men in loading, and almost before the troops along the way had ceased to hear the rattle of the wheels, a great white cloud sprang forward down the slope, and with a deafening report the affair at Coulter's Notch had begun.

It is not intended to relate in detail the progress and incidents of that ghastly contest—a contest without vicissitudes, its alternations only different degrees of despair. Almost at the instant when Captain Coulter's gun blew its challenging cloud twelve answering clouds rolled upward from among the trees about the plantation house, a deep multiple report roared back like a broken echo, and thenceforth to the end the Federal cannoneers fought their hopeless battle in an atmosphere of living iron whose thoughts were lightnings and whose deeds were death.

Unwilling to see the efforts which he could not aid and the slaughter which he could not stay, the colonel ascended the ridge at a point a quarter of a mile to the left, whence the Notch, itself invisible, but pushing up successive masses of smoke, seemed the crater of a volcano in thundering eruption. With his glass he watched the enemy's guns, noting as he could the effects of Coulter's fire—if Coulter still lived to direct it. He saw that the Federal gunners, ignoring those of the enemy's pieces whose positions could be determined by their smoke only, gave their whole attention to the one that maintained its place in the open— the lawn in front of the house. Over and about that hardy piece the shells exploded at intervals of a few seconds. Some exploded in the house, as could be seen by thin ascensions of smoke from the breached roof. Figures of prostrate men and horses were plainly visible.

"If our fellows are doing so good work with a single gun," said the colonel to an aide who happened to be nearest, "they must be suffering like the devil from twelve. Go down and present the commander of that piece with my congratulations on the accuracy of his fire."

Turning to his adjutant-general he said, "Did you observe Coulter's damned reluctance to obey orders?"

"Yes, sir, I did."

"Well, say nothing about it, please. I don't think the general will care to make any accusations. He will probably have enough to do in explaining his own connection with this uncommon way of amusing the rearguard of a retreating enemy."

A young officer approached from below, climbing breathless up the acclivity. Almost before he had saluted, he gasped out:

"Colonel, I am directed by Colonel Harmon to say that the enemy's guns are within easy reach of our rifles, and most of them visible from several points along the ridge."

The brigade commander looked at him without a trace of interest in his expression. "I know it," he said quietly.

The young adjutant was visibly embarrassed. "Colonel Harmon would like to have permission to silence those guns," he stammered.

"So should I," the colonel said in the same tone. "Present my compliments to Colonel Harmon and say to him that the general's orders for the infantry not to fire are still in force."

The adjutant saluted and retired. The colonel ground his heel into the earth and turned to look again at the enemy's guns.

"Colonel," said the adjutant-general, "I don't know that I ought to say anything, but there is something wrong in all this. Do you happen to know that Captain Coulter is from the South?"

"No; *was* he, indeed?"

"I heard that last summer the division which the general then commanded was in the vicinity of Coulter's home—camped there for weeks, and—"

"Listen!" said the colonel, interrupting with an upward gesture. "Do you hear *that?*"

"That" was the silence of the Federal gun. The staff, the orderlies, the lines of infantry behind the crest—all had "heard," and were looking curiously in the direction of the crater, whence no smoke now ascended except desultory cloudlets from the enemy's shells. Then came the blare of a bugle, a faint rattle of wheels; a minute later the sharp reports recommenced with double activity. The demolished gun had been replaced with a sound one.

"Yes," said the adjutant-general, resuming his narrative, "the general made the acquaintance of Coulter's family. There was trouble—I don't know the exact nature of it—something about Coulter's wife. She is a red-hot Secessionist, as they all are, except Coulter himself, but she is a good wife and high-bred lady. There was a complaint to army headquarters. The general was transferred to this division. It is odd that Coulter's battery should afterward have been assigned to it."

The colonel had risen from the rock upon which they had been sitting. His eyes were blazing with a generous indignation.

"See here, Morrison," said he, looking his gossiping staff officer straight in the face, "did you get that story from a gentleman or a liar?"

"I don't want to say how I got it, Colonel, unless it is necessary"—he was blushing a trifle—"but I'll stake my life upon its truth in the main."

The colonel turned toward a small knot of officers some distance away. "Lieutenant Williams!" he shouted.

One of the officers detached himself from the group and coming forward saluted, saying: "Pardon me, Colonel, I thought you had been informed. Williams is dead down there by the gun. What can I do, sir?"

Lieutenant Williams was the aide who had had the pleasure of conveying to the officer in charge of the gun his brigade commander's congratulations.

"Go," said the colonel, "and direct the withdrawal of that gun instantly. No—I'll go myself."

He strode down the declivity toward the rear of the Notch at a breakneck pace, over rocks and through brambles, followed by his little retinue in tumultuous disorder. At the foot of the declivity they mounted their waiting animals and took to the road at a lively trot, round a bend and into the Notch. The spectacle which they encountered there was appalling!

Within that defile, barely broad enough for a single gun, were piled the wrecks of no fewer than four. They had noted the silencing of only the last one disabled—there had been a lack of men to replace it quickly with another. The débris lay on both sides of the road; the men had managed to keep an open way between, through which the fifth piece was now firing. The men?—they looked like demons of the pit! All were hatless, all stripped to the waist, their reeking skins black with blotches of powder and spattered with gouts of blood. They worked like madmen, with rammer and cartridge, lever and lanyard. They set their swollen shoulders and bleeding hands against the wheels at each recoil and heaved the heavy gun back to its place. There were no commands; in that awful environment of whooping shot, exploding shells, shrieking fragments of iron, and flying splinters of wood, none could have been heard. Officers, if officers there were, were indistinguishable; all worked together—each while he lasted—governed by the eye. When the gun was sponged, it was loaded; when loaded, aimed and fired. The colonel observed something new to his military experience—something horrible and unnatural: the gun was bleeding at the mouth! In temporary default of water, the man sponging had dipped his sponge into a pool of comrade's blood. In all this work there was no clashing; the duty of the instant was obvious. When one fell, another, looking a trifle cleaner, seemed to rise from the earth in the dead man's tracks, to fall in his turn.

With the ruined guns lay the ruined men—alongside the wreckage, under it and atop of it; and back down the road—a ghastly procession!— crept on hands and knees such of the wounded as were able to move. The colonel—he had compassionately sent his cavalcade to the right about—had to ride over those who were entirely dead in order not to crush those who were partly alive. Into that hell he tranquilly held his way, rode up alongside the gun, and, in the obscurity of the last discharge, tapped upon the cheek the man holding the rammer—who straightway fell, thinking himself killed. A fiend seven times damned sprang out of the smoke to take his place, but paused and gazed up at the mounted officer with an unearthly regard, his teeth flashing between his black lips, his eyes, fierce and expanded, burning like coals beneath his bloody brow. The colonel made an authoritative gesture and pointed to the rear. The fiend bowed in token of obedience. It was Captain Coulter.

Simultaneously with the colonel's arresting sign, silence fell upon the whole field of action. The procession of missiles no longer streamed into that defile of death, for the enemy also had ceased firing. His army had been gone for hours, and the commander of his rear-guard, who had held his position perilously long in hope to silence the Federal fire, at that strange moment had silenced his own. "I was not aware of the breadth of my authority," said the colonel to anybody, riding forward to the crest to see what had really happened.

An hour later his brigade was in bivouac on the enemy's ground, and its idlers were examining, with something of awe, as the faithful inspect a saint's relics, a score of straddling dead horses and three disabled guns, all spiked. The fallen men had been carried away; their torn and broken bodies would have given too great satisfaction.

Naturally, the colonel established himself and his military family in the plantation house. It was somewhat shattered, but it was better than the open air. The furniture was greatly deranged and broken. Walls and ceilings were knocked away here and there, and a lingering odor of powder smoke was everywhere. The beds, the closets of women's clothing, the cupboards were not greatly damaged. The new tenants for a night made themselves comfortable, and the virtual effacement of Coulter's battery supplied them with an interesting topic.

During supper an orderly of the escort showed himself into the dining-room and asked permission to speak to the colonel.

"What is it, Barbour?" said that officer pleasantly, having overheard the request.

"Colonel, there is something wrong in the cellar; I don't know what —somebody there. I was down there rummaging about."

"I will go down and see," said a staff officer, rising.

"So will I," the colonel said; "let the others remain. Lead on, orderly."

They took a candle from the table and descended the cellar stairs, the orderly in visible trepidation. The candle made but a feeble light, but presently, as they advanced, its narrow circle of illumination revealed a human figure seated on the ground against the black stone wall which they were skirting, its knees elevated, its head bowed sharply forward. The face, which should have been seen in profile, was invisible, for the man was bent so far forward that his long hair concealed it; and, strange to relate, the beard, of a much darker hue, fell in a great tangled mass and lay along the ground at his side. They involuntarily paused; then the colonel, taking the candle from the orderly's shaking hand, approached the man and attentively considered him. The long dark beard was the hair of a woman—dead. The dead woman clasped in her arms a dead babe. Both were clasped in the arms of the man, pressed against his breast, against his lips. There was blood in the hair of the woman; there was blood in the hair of the man. A yard away, near an irregular depression in the beaten earth which formed the cellar's floor—a fresh excavation with a convex bit of iron, having jagged edges, visible in one of the sides—lay an infant's foot. The colonel held the light as high as he could. The floor of the room above was broken through, the splinters pointing at all angles downward. "This casemate is not bomb-proof," said the colonel gravely. It did not occur to him that his summing up of the matter had any levity in it.

They stood about the group awhile in silence; the staff officer was thinking of his unfinished supper, the orderly of what might possibly be in one of the casks on the other side of the cellar. Suddenly the man whom they had thought dead raised his head and gazed tranquilly into their faces. His complexion was coal black; the cheeks were apparently tattooed in irregular sinuous lines from the eyes downward. The lips, too, were white, like those of a stage Negro. There was blood upon his forehead.

The staff officer drew back a pace, the orderly two paces.

"What are you doing here, my man?" said the colonel, unmoved.

"This house belongs to me, sir," was the reply, civilly delivered.

"To you? Ah, I see! And these?"

"My wife and child. I am Captain Coulter."

THE COUP DE GRÂCE

THE fighting had been hard and continuous; that was attested by all the senses. The very taste of battle was in the air. All was now over; it remained only to succor the wounded and bury the dead—to "tidy up a bit," as the humorist of a burial squad put it. A good deal of "tidying up" was required. As far as one could see through the forests, among the splintered trees, lay wrecks of men and horses. Among them moved the stretcher-bearers, gathering and carrying away the few who showed signs of life. Most of the wounded had died of neglect while the right to minister to their wants was in dispute. It is an army regulation that the wounded must wait; the best way to care for them is to win the battle. It must be confessed that victory is a distinct advantage to a man requiring attention, but many do not live to avail themselves of it.

The dead were collected in groups of a dozen or a score and laid side by side in rows while the trenches were dug to receive them. Some, found at too great a distance from these rallying points, were buried where they lay. There was little attempt at identification, though in most cases, the burial parties being detailed to glean the same ground which they had assisted to reap, the names of the victorious dead were known and listed. The enemy's fallen had to be content with counting. But of that they got enough: many of them were counted several times, and the total, as given afterward in the official report of the victorious commander, denoted rather a hope than a result.

At some little distance from the spot where one of the burial parties had established its "bivouac of the dead," a man in the uniform of a Federal officer stood leaning against a tree. From his feet upward to his neck his attitude was that of weariness reposing; but he turned his head uneasily from side to side; his mind was apparently not at rest. He was perhaps uncertain in which direction to go; he was not likely to remain long where he was, for already the level rays of the setting sun straggled redly through the open spaces of the wood and the weary soldiers were quitting their task for the day. He would hardly make a night of it alone there among the dead. Nine men in ten whom you meet after a battle inquire the way to some fraction of the army—as if any one could know. Doubtless this officer was lost. After resting himself a moment he would presumably follow one of the retiring burial squads.

When all were gone he walked straight away into the forest toward the red west, its light staining his face like blood. The air of confidence with which he now strode along showed that he was on familiar ground; he had recovered his bearings. The dead on his right and on his left were unregarded as he passed. An occasional low moan from some sorely-stricken wretch whom the relief-parties had not reached, and who would have to pass a comfortless night beneath the stars with his thirst to keep him company, was equally unheeded. What, indeed, could the officer have done, being no surgeon and having no water?

At the head of a shallow ravine, a mere depression of the ground, lay a small group of bodies. He saw, and swerving suddenly from his course walked rapidly toward them. Scanning each one sharply as he passed, he stopped at last above one which lay at a slight remove from the others, near a clump of small trees. He looked at it narrowly. It seemed to stir. He stooped and laid his hand upon its face. It screamed.

The officer was Captain Downing Madwell, of a Massachusetts regiment of infantry, a daring and intelligent soldier, an honorable man.

In the regiment were two brothers named Halcrow—Caffal and Creede Halcrow. Caffal Halcrow was a sergeant in Captain Madwell's company, and these two men, the sergeant and the captain, were devoted friends. In so far as disparity of rank, difference in duties and considerations of military discipline would permit they were commonly together. They had, indeed, grown up together from childhood. A habit of the heart is not easily broken off. Caffal Halcrow had nothing military in his taste nor disposition, but the thought of separation from his friend was disagreeable; he enlisted in the company in which Madwell was second-lieutenant. Each had taken two steps upward in rank, but between the highest non-commissioned and the lowest commissioned officer the gulf is deep and wide and the old relation was maintained with difficulty and a difference.

Creede Halcrow, the brother of Caffal, was the major of the regiment —a cynical, saturnine man, between whom and Captain Madwell there was a natural antipathy which circumstances had nourished and strengthened to an active animosity. But for the restraining influence of their mutual relation to Caffal these two patriots would doubtless have endeavored to deprive their country of each other's services.

At the opening of the battle that morning the regiment was performing outpost duty a mile away from the main army. It was attacked and nearly surrounded in the forest, but stubbornly held its ground. During a lull in the fighting, Major Halcrow came to Captain Madwell. The two exchanged formal salutes, and the major said: "Captain, the colonel directs that you push your company to the head of this ravine and hold your place there until recalled. I need hardly apprise you of the dangerous character of the movement, but if you wish, you can, I suppose, turn over the command to your first-lieutenant. I was not, however, directed to authorize the substitution; it is merely a suggestion of my own, unofficially made."

To this deadly insult Captain Madwell coolly replied:

"Sir, I invite you to accompany the movement. A mounted officer would be a conspicuous mark, and I have long held the opinion that it would be better if you were dead."   .

The art of repartee was cultivated in military circles as early as 1862.

A half-hour later Captain Madwell's company was driven from its position at the head of the ravine, with a loss of one-third its number. Among the fallen was Sergeant Halcrow. The regiment was soon afterward forced back to the main line, and at the close of the battle was miles away. The captain was now standing at the side of his subordinate and friend.

Sergeant Halcrow was mortally hurt. His clothing was deranged; it seemed to have been violently torn apart, exposing the abdomen. Some of the buttons of his jacket had been pulled off and lay on the ground beside him and fragments of his other garments were strewn about. His leather belt was parted and had apparently been dragged from beneath him as he lay. There had been no great effusion of blood. The only visible wound was a wide, ragged opening in the abdomen. It was defiled with earth and dead leaves. Protruding from it was a loop of small intestine. In all his experience Captain Madwell had not seen a wound like this. He could neither conjecture how it was made nor explain the attendant circumstances—the strangely torn clothing, the parted belt, the besmirching of the white skin. He knelt and made a closer examination. When he rose to his feet, he turned his eyes in different directions as if looking for an enemy. Fifty yards away, on the crest of a low, thinly wooded hill, he saw several dark objects moving about among the fallen men—a herd of swine. One stood with its back to him, its shoulders sharply elevated. Its forefeet were upon a human body, its head was depressed and invisible. The bristly ridge of its chine showed black against the red west. Captain Madwell drew away his eyes and fixed them again upon the thing which had been his friend.

The man who had suffered these monstrous mutilations was alive. At intervals he moved his limbs; he moaned at every breath. He stared blankly into the face of his friend and if touched screamed. In his giant agony he had torn up the ground on which he lay; his clenched hands were full of leaves and twigs and earth. Articulate speech was beyond his power; it was impossible to know if he were sensible to anything but pain. The expression of his face was an appeal; his eyes were full of prayer. For what?

There was no misreading that look; the captain had too frequently seen it in eyes of those whose lips had still the power to formulate it by an entreaty for death. Consciously or unconsciously, this writhing fragment of humanity, this type and example of acute sensation, this handiwork of man and beast, this humble, unheroic Prometheus, was imploring everything, all, the whole non-ego, for the boon of oblivion. To the earth and the sky alike, to the trees, to the man, to whatever took form in sense or consciousness, this incarnate suffering addressed that silent plea.

For what, indeed? For that which we accord to even the meanest creature without sense to demand it, denying it only to the wretched of our own race: for the blessed release, the rite of uttermost compassion, the *coup de grâce*.

Captain Madwell spoke the name of his friend. He repeated it over and over without effect until emotion choked his utterance. His tears plashed upon the livid face beneath his own and blinded himself. He saw nothing but a blurred and moving object, but the moans were more distinct than ever, interrupted at briefer intervals by sharper shrieks. He turned away, struck his hand upon his forehead, and strode from the spot. The swine, catching sight of him, threw up their crimson muzzles, regarding him suspiciously a second, and then with a gruff, concerted grunt, raced away out of sight. A horse, its foreleg splintered by a cannon-shot, lifted its head sidewise from the ground and neighed piteously. Madwell stepped forward, drew his revolver and shot the poor beast between the eyes, narrowly observing its death-struggle, which, contrary to his expectation, was violent and long; but at last it lay still. The tense muscles of its lips, which had uncovered the teeth in a horrible grin, relaxed; the sharp, clean-cut profile took on a look of profound peace and rest.

Along the distant, thinly wooded crest to westward the fringe of sunset fire had now nearly burned itself out. The light upon the trunks of the trees had faded to a tender gray; shadows were in their tops, like great dark birds aperch. Night was coming and there were miles of haunted forest between Captain Madwell and camp. Yet he stood there at the side of the dead animal, apparently lost to all sense of his surroundings. His eyes were bent upon the earth at his feet; his left hand hung loosely at his side, his right still held the pistol. Presently he lifted his face, turned it toward his dying friend and walked rapidly back to his side. He knelt upon one knee, cocked the weapon, placed the muzzle against the man's forehead, and turning away his eyes pulled the trigger. There was no report. He had used his last cartridge for the horse.

The sufferer moaned and his lips moved convulsively. The froth that ran from them had a tinge of blood.

Captain Madwell rose to his feet and drew his sword from the scabbard. He passed the fingers of his left hand along the edge from hilt to point. He held it out straight before him, as if to test his nerves. There was no visible tremor of the blade; the ray of bleak skylight that it reflected was steady and true. He stooped and with his left hand tore away the dying man's shirt, rose and placed the point of the sword just over the heart. This time he did not withdraw his eyes. Grasping the hilt with both hands, he thrust downward with all his strength and weight. The blade sank into the man's body—through his body into the earth; Captain Madwell came near falling forward upon his work. The dying man drew up his knees and at the same time threw his right arm across his breast and grasped the steel so tightly that the knuckles of the hand visibly whitened. By a violent but vain effort to withdraw the blade the wound was enlarged; a rill of blood escaped, running sinuously down into the deranged clothing. At that moment three men stepped silently forward from behind the clump of young trees which had concealed their approach. Two were hospital attendants and carried a stretcher.

The third was Major Creede Halcrow.

PARKER ADDERSON, PHILOSOPHER

"Prisoner, what is your name?"

"As I am to lose it at daylight to-morrow morning it is hardly worth while concealing it. Parker Adderson."

"Your rank?"

"A somewhat humble one; commissioned officers are too precious to be risked in the perilous business of a spy. I am a sergeant."

"Of what regiment?"

"You must excuse me; my answer might, for anything I know, give you an idea of whose forces are in your front. Such knowledge as that is what I came into your lines to obtain, not to impart."

"You are not without wit."

"If you have the patience to wait you will find me dull enough to-morrow."

"How do you know that you are to die to-morrow morning?"

"Among spies captured by night that is the custom. It is one of the nice observances of the profession."

The general so far laid aside the dignity appropriate to a Confederate officer of high rank and wide renown as to smile. But no one in his power and out of his favor would have drawn any happy augury from that outward and visible sign of approval. It was neither genial nor infectious; it did not communicate itself to the other persons exposed to it—the caught spy who had provoked it and the armed guard who had brought him into the tent and now stood a little apart, watching his prisoner in the yellow candle-light. It was no part of that warrior's duty to smile; he had been detailed for another purpose. The conversation was resumed; it was in character a trial for a capital offense.

"You admit, then, that you are a spy—that you came into my camp, disguised as you are in the uniform of a Confederate soldier, to obtain information secretly regarding the numbers and disposition of my troops."

"Regarding, particularly, their numbers. Their disposition I already knew. It is morose."

The general brightened again; the guard, with a severer sense of his responsibility, accentuated the austerity of his expression and stood a trifle more erect than before. Twirling his gray slouch hat round and round upon his forefinger, the spy took a leisurely survey of his surroundings. They were simple enough. The tent was a common "wall tent," about eight feet by ten in dimensions, lighted by a single tallow candle stuck into the haft of a bayonet, which was itself stuck into a pine table at which the general sat, now busily writing and apparently forgetful of his unwilling guest. An old rag carpet covered the earthen floor; an older leather trunk, a second chair and a roll of blankets were about all else that the tent contained; in General Clavering's command Confederate simplicity and penury of "pomp and circumstance" had attained their highest development. On a large nail driven into the tent pole at the entrance was suspended a sword-belt supporting a long sabre, a pistol in its holster and, absurdly enough, a bowie-knife. Of that most unmilitary weapon it was the general's habit to explain that it was a souvenir of the peaceful days when he was a civilian.

It was a stormy night. The rain cascaded upon the canvas in torrents, with the dull, drum-like sound familiar to dwellers in tents. As the whooping blasts charged upon it the frail structure shook and swayed and strained at its confining stakes and ropes.

The general finished writing, folded the half-sheet of paper and spoke to the soldier guarding Adderson: "Here, Tassman, take that to the adjutant-general; then return."

"And the prisoner, General?" said the soldier, saluting, with an inquiring glance in the direction of that unfortunate.

"Do as I said," replied the officer, curtly.

The soldier took the note and ducked himself out of the tent. General Clavering turned his handsome face toward the Federal spy, looked him in the eyes, not unkindly, and said: "It is a bad night, my man."

"For me, yes."

"Do you guess what I have written?"

"Something worth reading, I dare say. And—perhaps it is my vanity— I venture to suppose that I am mentioned in it."

"Yes; it is a memorandum for an order to be read to the troops at *reveille* concerning your execution. Also some notes for the guidance of the provost-marshal in arranging the details of that event."

"I hope, General, the spectacle will be intelligently arranged, for I shall attend it myself."

"Have you any arrangements of your own that you wish to make? Do you wish to see a chaplain, for example?"

"I could hardly secure a longer rest for myself by depriving him of some of his."

"Good God, man! do you mean to go to your death with nothing but jokes upon your lips? Do you know that this is a serious matter?"

"How can I know that? I have never been dead in all my life. I have heard that death is a serious matter, but never from any of those who have experienced it."

The general was silent for a moment; the man interested, perhaps amused him—a type not previously encountered.

"Death," he said, "is at least a loss—a loss of such happiness as we have, and of opportunities for more."

"A loss of which we shall never be conscious can be borne with composure and therefore expected without apprehension. You must have observed, General, that of all the dead men with whom it is your soldierly pleasure to strew your path none shows signs of regret."

"If the being dead is not a regrettable condition, yet the becoming so —the act of dying—appears to be distinctly disagreeable to one who has not lost the power to feel."

"Pain is disagreeable, no doubt. I never suffer it without more or less discomfort. But he who lives longest is most exposed to it. What you call dying is simply the last pain—there is really no such thing as dying. Suppose, for illustration, that I attempt to escape. You lift the revolver that you are courteously concealing in your lap, and—"

The general blushed like a girl, then laughed softly, disclosing his brilliant teeth, made a slight inclination of his handsome head and said nothing. The spy continued: "You fire, and I have in my stomach what I did not swallow. I fall, but am not dead. After a half-hour of agony I am dead. But at any given instant of that half-hour I was either alive or dead. There is no transition period.

"When I am hanged to-morrow morning it will be quite the same; while conscious I shall be living; when dead, unconscious. Nature appears to have ordered the matter quite in my interest—the way that I should have ordered it myself. It is so simple," he added with a smile, "that it seems hardly worth while to be hanged at all."

At the finish of his remarks there was a long silence. The general sat impassive, looking into the man's face, but apparently not attentive to what had been said. It was as if his eyes had mounted guard over the prisoner while his mind concerned itself with other matters. Presently he drew a long, deep breath, shuddered, as one awakened from a dreadful dream, and exclaimed almost inaudibly: "Death is horrible!"—this man of death.

"It was horrible to our savage ancestors," said the spy, gravely, "because they had not enough intelligence to dissociate the idea of consciousness from the idea of the physical forms in which it is manifested—as an even lower order of intelligence, that of the monkey, for example, may be unable to imagine a house without inhabitants, and seeing a ruined hut fancies a suffering occupant. To us it is horrible because we have inherited the tendency to think it so, accounting for the notion by wild and fanciful theories of another world—as names of places give rise to legends explaining them and reasonless conduct to philosophies in justification. You can hang me, General, but there your power of evil ends; you cannot condemn me to heaven."

The general appeared not to have heard; the spy's talk had merely turned his thoughts into an unfamiliar channel, but there they pursued their will independently to conclusions of their own. The storm had ceased, and something of the solemn spirit of the night had imparted itself to his reflections, giving them the sombre tinge of a supernatural dread. Perhaps there was an element of prescience in it. "I should not like to die," he said—"not to-night."

He was interrupted—if, indeed, he had intended to speak further— by the entrance of an officer of his staff, Captain Hasterlick, the provost-marshal. This recalled him to himself; the absent look passed away from his face.

"Captain," he said, acknowledging the officer's salute, "this man is a Yankee spy captured inside our lines with incriminating papers on him. He has confessed. How is the weather?"

"The storm is over, sir, and the moon shining."

"Good; take a file of men, conduct him at once to the parade ground, and shoot him."

A sharp cry broke from the spy's lips. He threw himself forward, thrust out his neck, expanded his eyes, clenched his hands.

"Good God!" he cried hoarsely, almost inarticulately; "you do not mean that! You forget—I am not to die until morning."

"I have said nothing of morning," replied the general, coldly; "that was an assumption of your own. You die now."

"But, General, I beg—I implore you to remember; I am to hang! It will take some time to erect the gallows—two hours—an hour. Spies are hanged; I have rights under military law. For Heaven's sake, General, consider how short—"

"Captain, observe my directions."

The officer drew his sword and fixing his eyes upon the prisoner pointed silently to the opening of the tent. The prisoner hesitated; the officer grasped him by the collar and pushed him gently forward. As he approached the tent pole the frantic man sprang to it and with cat-like agility seized the handle of the bowie-knife, plucked the weapon from the scabbard and thrusting the captain aside leaped upon the general with the fury of a madman, hurling him to the ground and falling headlong upon him as he lay. The table was overturned, the candle extinguished and they fought blindly in the darkness. The provost-marshal sprang to the assistance of his superior officer and was himself prostrated upon the struggling forms. Curses and inarticulate cries of rage and pain came from the welter of limbs and bodies; the tent came down upon them and beneath its hampering and enveloping folds the struggle went on. Private Tassman, returning from his errand and dimly conjecturing the situation, threw down his rifle and laying hold of the flouncing canvas at random vainly tried to drag it off the men under it; and the sentinel who paced up and down in front, not daring to leave his beat though the skies should fall, discharged his rifle. The report alarmed the camp; drums beat the long roll and bugles sounded the assembly, bringing swarms of half-clad men into the moonlight, dressing as they ran, and falling into line at the sharp commands of their officers. This was well; being in line the men were under control; they stood at arms while the general's staff and the men of his escort brought order out of confusion by lifting off the fallen tent and pulling apart the breathless and bleeding actors in that strange contention.

Breathless, indeed, was one: the captain was dead; the handle of the bowie-knife, protruding from his throat, was pressed back beneath his chin until the end had caught in the angle of the jaw and the hand that delivered the blow had been unable to remove the weapon. In the dead man's hand was his sword, clenched with a grip that defied the strength of the living. Its blade was streaked with red to the hilt.

Lifted to his feet, the general sank back to the earth with a moan and fainted. Besides his bruises he had two sword-thrusts—one through the thigh, the other through the shoulder.

The spy had suffered the least damage. Apart from a broken right arm, his wounds were such only as might have been incurred in an ordinary combat with nature's weapons. But he was dazed and seemed hardly to know what had occurred. He shrank away from those attending him, cowered upon the ground and uttered unintelligible remonstrances. His face, swollen by blows and stained with gouts of blood, nevertheless showed white beneath his disheveled hair—as white as that of a corpse.

"The man is not insane," said the surgeon, preparing bandages and replying to a question; "he is suffering from fright. Who and what is he?"

Private Tassman began to explain. It was the opportunity of his life; he omitted nothing that could in any way accentuate the importance of his own relation to the night's events. When he had finished his story and was ready to begin it again nobody gave him any attention.

The general had now recovered consciousness. He raised himself upon his elbow, looked about him, and, seeing the spy crouching by a camp-fire, guarded, said simply:

"Take that man to the parade ground and shoot him."

"The general's mind wanders," said an officer standing near.

"His mind does *not* wander," the adjutant-general said. "I have a memorandum from him about this business; he had given that same order to Hasterlick"—with a motion of the hand toward the dead provost-marshal—"and, by God! it shall be executed."

Ten minutes later Sergeant Parker Adderson, of the Federal army, philosopher and wit, kneeling in the moonlight and begging incoherently for his life, was shot to death by twenty men. As the volley rang out upon the keen air of the midnight, General Clavering, lying white and still in the red glow of the camp-fire, opened his big blue eyes, looked pleasantly upon those about him and said: "How silent it all is!"

The surgeon looked at the adjutant-general, gravely and significantly. The patient's eyes slowly closed, and thus he lay for a few moments; then, his face suffused with a smile of ineffable sweetness, he said, faintly: "I suppose this must be death," and so passed away.

AN AFFAIR OF OUTPOSTS

I

CONCERNING THE WISH TO BE DEAD

TWO men sat in conversation. One was the Governor of the State. The year was 1861; the war was on and the Governor already famous for the intelligence and zeal with which he directed all the powers and resources of his State to the service of the Union.

"What! *you?*" the Governor was saying in evident surprise—"you too want a military commission? Really, the fifing and drumming must have effected a profound alteration in your convictions. In my character of recruiting sergeant I suppose I ought not to be fastidious, but"—there was a touch of irony in his manner—"well, have you forgotten that an oath of allegiance is required?"

"I have altered neither my convictions nor my sympathies," said the other, tranquilly. "While my sympathies are with the South, as you do me the honor to recollect, I have never doubted that the North was in the right. I am a Southerner in fact and in feeling, but it is my habit in matters of importance to act as I think, not as I feel."

The Governor was absently tapping his desk with a pencil; he did not immediately reply. After a while he said: "I have heard that there are all kinds of men in the world, so I suppose there are some like that, and doubtless you think yourself one. I've known you a long time and— pardon me—I don't think so."

"Then I am to understand that my application is denied?"

"Unless you can remove my belief that your Southern sympathies are in some degree a disqualification, yes. I do not doubt your good faith, and I know you to be abundantly fitted by intelligence and special train-ing for the duties of an officer. Your convictions, you say, favor the Union cause, but I prefer a man with his heart in it. The heart is what men fight with."

"Look here, Governor," said the younger man, with a smile that had more light than warmth: "I have something up my sleeve—a qualifica-tion which I had hoped it would not be necessary to mention. A great military authority has given a simple recipe for being a good soldier: 'Try always to get yourself killed.' It is with that purpose that I wish to enter the service. I am not, perhaps, much of a patriot, but I wish to be dead."

The Governor looked at him rather sharply, then a little coldly. "There is a simpler and franker way," he said.

"In my family, sir," was the reply, "we do not do that—no Armisted has ever done that."

A long silence ensued and neither man looked at the other. Presently the Governor lifted his eyes from the pencil, which had resumed its tapping, and said:

"Who is she?"

"My wife."

The Governor tossed the pencil into the desk, rose and walked two or three times across the room. Then he turned to Armisted, who also had risen, looked at him more coldly than before and said: "But the man—would it not be better that he—could not the country spare him better than it can spare you? Or are the Armisteds opposed to 'the unwritten law'?"

The Armisteds, apparently, could feel an insult: the face of the younger man flushed, then paled, but he subdued himself to the service of his purpose.

"The man's identity is unknown to me," he said, calmly enough.

"Pardon me," said the Governor, with even less of visible contrition than commonly underlies those words. After a moment's reflection he added: "I shall send you to-morrow a captain's commission in the Tenth Infantry, now at Nashville, Tennessee. Good night."

"Good night, sir. I thank you."

Left alone, the Governor remained for a time motionless, leaning against his desk. Presently he shrugged his shoulders as if throwing off a burden. "This is a bad business," he said.

Seating himself at a reading-table before the fire, he took up the book nearest his hand, absently opening it. His eyes fell upon this sentence:

"When God made it necessary for an unfaithful wife to lie about her husband in justification of her own sins He had the tenderness to endow men with the folly to believe her."

He looked at the title of the book; it was, *His Excellency the Fool.*

He flung the volume into the fire.

II
HOW TO SAY WHAT IS WORTH HEARING

The enemy, defeated in two days of battle at Pittsburg Landing, had sullenly retired to Corinth, whence he had come. For manifest incompetence Grant, whose beaten army had been saved from destruction and capture by Buell's soldierly activity and skill, had been relieved of his command, which nevertheless had not been given to Buell, but to Halleck, a man of unproved powers, a theorist, sluggish, irresolute. Foot by foot his troops, always deployed in line-of-battle to resist the enemy's bickering skirmishers, always entrenching against the columns that never came, advanced across the thirty miles of forest and swamp toward an antagonist prepared to vanish at contact, like a ghost at cock-crow. It was a campaign of "excursions and alarums," of reconnoissances and counter-marches, of cross-purposes and countermanded orders. For weeks the solemn farce held attention, luring distinguished civilians from fields of political ambition to see what they safely could of the horrors of war. Among these was our friend the Governor. At the headquarters of the army and in the camps of the troops from his State he was a familiar figure, attended by the several members of his personal staff, showily horsed, faultlessly betailored and bravely silk-hatted. Things of charm they were, rich in suggestions of peaceful lands beyond a sea of strife. The bedraggled soldier looked up from his trench as they passed, leaned upon his spade and audibly damned them to signify his sense of their ornamental irrelevance to the austerities of his trade.

"I think, Governor," said General Masterson one day, going into informal session atop of his horse and throwing one leg across the pommel of his saddle, his favorite posture—"I think I would not ride any farther in that direction if I were you. We've nothing out there but a line of skirmishers. That, I presume, is why I was directed to put these siege guns here: if the skirmishers are driven in the enemy will die of dejection at being unable to haul them away—they're a trifle heavy."

There is reason to fear that the unstrained quality of this military humor dropped not as the gentle rain from heaven upon the place beneath the civilian's silk hat. Anyhow he abated none of his dignity in recognition.

"I understand," he said, gravely, "that some of my men are out there—

a company of the Tenth, commanded by Captain Armisted. I should like to meet him if you do not mind."

"He is worth meeting. But there's a bad bit of jungle out there, and I should advise that you leave your horse and"—with a look at the Governor's retinue—"your other impedimenta."

The Governor went forward alone and on foot. In a half-hour he had pushed through a tangled undergrowth covering a boggy soil and entered upon firm and more open ground. Here he found a half-company of infantry lounging behind a line of stacked rifles. The men wore their accoutrements—their belts, cartridge-boxes, haversacks and canteens. Some lying at full length on the dry leaves were fast asleep: others in small groups gossiped idly of this and that; a few played at cards; none was far from the line of stacked arms. To the civilian's eye the scene was one of carelessness, confusion, indifference; a soldier would have observed expectancy and readiness.

At a little distance apart an officer in fatigue uniform, armed, sat on a fallen tree noting the approach of the visitor, to whom a sergeant, rising from one of the groups, now came forward.

"I wish to see Captain Armisted," said the Governor.

The sergeant eyed him narrowly, saying nothing, pointed to the officer, and taking a rifle from one of the stacks, accompanied him.

"This man wants to see you, sir," said the sergeant, saluting. The officer rose.

It would have been a sharp eye that would have recognized him. His hair, which but a few months before had been brown, was streaked with gray. His face, tanned by exposure, was seamed as with age. A long livid scar across the forehead marked the stroke of a sabre; one cheek was drawn and puckered by the work of a bullet. Only a woman of the loyal North would have thought the man handsome.

"Armisted—Captain," said the Governor, extending his hand, "do you not know me?"

"I know you, sir, and I salute you—as the Governor of my State."

Lifting his right hand to the level of his eyes he threw it outward and downward. In the code of military etiquette there is no provision for shaking hands. That of the civilian was withdrawn. If he felt either surprise or chagrin his face did not betray it.

"It is the hand that signed your commission," he said.

"And it is the hand—"

The sentence remains unfinished. The sharp report of a rifle came from the front, followed by another and another. A bullet hissed through the forest and struck a tree near by. The men sprang from the ground and even before the captain's high, clear voice was done intoning the command "At-ten-tion!" had fallen into line in rear of the stacked arms. Again—and now through the din of a crackling fusillade—sounded the strong, deliberate sing-song of authority: "Take . . . arms!" followed by the rattle of unlocking bayonets.

Bullets from the unseen enemy were now flying thick and fast, though mostly well spent and emitting the humming sound which signified interference by twigs and rotation in the plane of flight. Two or three of the men in the line were already struck and down. A few wounded men came limping awkwardly out of the undergrowth from the skirmish line in front; most of them did not pause, but held their way with white faces and set teeth to the rear.

Suddenly there was a deep, jarring report in front, followed by the startling rush of a shell, which passing overhead exploded in the edge of a thicket, setting afire the fallen leaves. Penetrating the din—seeming to float above it like the melody of a soaring bird—rang the slow, aspirated monotones of the captain's several commands, without emphasis, without accent, musical and restful as an evensong under the harvest moon. Familiar with this tranquilizing chant in moments of imminent peril, these raw soldiers of less than a year's training yielded themselves to the spell, executing its mandates with the composure and precision of veterans. Even the distinguished civilian behind his tree, hesitating between pride and terror, was accessible to its charm and suasion. He was conscious of a fortified resolution and ran away only when the skirmishers, under orders to rally on the reserve, came out of the woods like hunted hares and formed on the left of the stiff little line, breathing hard and thankful for the boon of breath.

III
THE FIGHTING OF ONE WHOSE HEART WAS NOT IN THE QUARREL

Guided in his retreat by that of the fugitive wounded, the Governor struggled bravely to the rear through the "bad bit of jungle." He was well winded and a trifle confused. Excepting a single rifle-shot now and again, there was no sound of strife behind him; the enemy was pulling himself together for a new onset against an antagonist of whose numbers and tactical disposition he was in doubt. The fugitive felt that he would probably be spared to his country, and only commended the arrangements of Providence to that end, but in leaping a small brook in more open ground one of the arrangements incurred the mischance of a disabling sprain at the ankle. He was unable to continue his flight, for he was too fat to hop, and after several vain attempts, causing intolerable pain, seated himself on the earth to nurse his ignoble disability and deprecate the military situation.

A brisk renewal of the firing broke out and stray bullets came flitting and droning by. Then came the crash of two clean, definite volleys, followed by a continuous rattle, through which he heard the yells and cheers of the combatants, punctuated by thunderclaps of cannon. All this told him that Armisted's little command was bitterly beset and fighting at close quarters. The wounded men whom he had distanced began to straggle by on either hand, their numbers visibly augmented by new levies from the line. Singly and by twos and threes, some supporting comrades more desperately hurt than themselves, but all deaf to his appeals for assistance, they sifted through the underbrush and disappeared. The firing was increasingly louder and more distinct, and presently the ailing fugitives were succeeded by men who strode with a firmer tread, occasionally facing about and discharging their pieces, then doggedly resuming their retreat, reloading as they walked. Two or three fell as he looked, and lay motionless. One had enough of life left in him to make a pitiful attempt to drag himself to cover. A passing comrade paused beside him long enough to fire, appraised the poor devil's disability with a look and moved sullenly on, inserting a cartridge in his weapon.

In all this was none of the pomp of war—no hint of glory. Even in his distress and peril the helpless civilian could not forbear to contrast it with the gorgeous parades and reviews held in honor of himself—with the brilliant uniforms, the music, the banners, and the marching. It was an ugly and sickening business: to all that was artistic in his nature, revolting, brutal, in bad taste.

"Ugh!" he grunted, shuddering—"this is beastly! Where is the charm of it all? Where are the elevated sentiments, the devotion, the heroism, the—"

From a point somewhere near, in the direction of the pursuing enemy, rose the clear, deliberate sing-song of Captain Armisted.

"Stead-y, men—stead-y. Halt! Commence fir-ing."

The rattle of fewer than a score of rifles could be distinguished through the general uproar, and again that penetrating falsetto:

"Cease fir-ing. In re-treat . . . maaarch!"

In a few moments this remnant had drifted slowly past the Governor, all to the right of him as they faced in retiring, the men deployed at intervals of a half-dozen paces. At the extreme left and a few yards behind came the captain. The civilian called out his name, but he did not hear. A swarm of men in gray now broke out of cover in pursuit, making directly for the spot where the Governor lay—some accident of the ground had caused them to converge upon that point: their line had become a crowd. In a last struggle for life and liberty the Governor attempted to rise, and looking back the captain saw him. Promptly, but with the same slow precision as before, he sang his commands:

"Skirm-ish-ers, halt!" The men stopped and according to rule turned to face the enemy.

"Ral-ly on the right!"—and they came in at a run, fixing bayonets and forming loosely on the man at that end of the line.

"Forward . . . to save the Gov-ern-or of your State . . . doub-le quick . . . maaarch!"

Only one man disobeyed this astonishing command! He was dead. With a cheer they sprang forward over the twenty or thirty paces between them and their task. The captain having a shorter distance to go arrived first—simultaneously with the enemy. A half-dozen hasty shots were fired at him, and the foremost man—a fellow of heroic stature, hatless and bare-breasted—made a vicious sweep at his head with a clubbed rifle. The officer parried the blow at the cost of a broken arm and drove his sword to the hilt into the giant's breast. As the body fell the weapon was wrenched from his hand and before he could pluck his revolver from the scabbard at his belt another man leaped upon him like a tiger, fastening both hands upon his throat and bearing him backward upon the prostrate Governor, still struggling to rise. This man was promptly spitted upon the bayonet of a Federal sergeant and his death-gripe on the captain's throat loosened by a kick upon each wrist. When the captain had risen he was at the rear of his men, who had all passed over and around him and were thrusting fiercely at their more numerous but less coherent antagonists. Nearly all the rifles on both sides were empty and in the crush there was neither time nor room to reload. The Confederates were at a disadvantage in that most of them lacked bayonets; they fought by bludgeoning—and a clubbed rifle is a formidable arm. The sound of the conflict was a clatter like that of the interlocking horns of battling bulls—now and then the pash of a crushed skull, an oath, or a grunt caused by the impact of a rifle's muzzle against the abdomen transfixed by its bayonet. Through an opening made by the fall of one of his men Captain Armisted sprang, with his dangling left arm; in his right hand a full-charged revolver, which he fired with rapidity and terrible effect into the thick of the gray crowd: but across the bodies of the slain the survivors in the front were pushed forward by their comrades in the rear till again they breasted the tireless bayonets. There were fewer bayonets now to breast—a beggarly half-dozen, all told. A few minutes more of this rough work—a little fighting back to back—and all would be over.

Suddenly a lively firing was heard on the right and the left: a fresh line of Federal skirmishers came forward at a run, driving before them those parts of the Confederate line that had been separated by staying the advance of the centre. And behind these new and noisy combatants, at a distance of two or three hundred yards, could be seen, indistinct among the trees a line-of-battle!

Instinctively before retiring, the crowd in gray made a tremendous rush upon its handful of antagonists, overwhelming them by mere momentum and, unable to use weapons in the crush, trampled them, stamped savagely on their limbs, their bodies, their necks, their faces; then retiring with bloody feet across its own dead it joined the general rout and the incident was at an end.

IV

THE GREAT HONOR THE GREAT

The Governor, who had been unconscious, opened his eyes and stared about him, slowly recalling the day's events. A man in the uniform of a major was kneeling beside him; he was a surgeon. Grouped about were the civilian members of the Governor's staff, their faces expressing a natural solicitude regarding their offices. A little apart stood General Masterson addressing another officer and gesticulating with a cigar.

He was saying: "It was the beautifulest fight ever made—by God, sir, it was great!"

The beauty and greatness were attested by a row of dead, trimly disposed, and another of wounded, less formally placed, restless, half-naked, but bravely bebandaged.

"How do you feel, sir?" said the surgeon. "I find no wound."

"I think I am all right," the patient replied, sitting up. "It is that ankle."

The surgeon transferred his attention to the ankle, cutting away the boot. All eyes followed the knife.

In moving the leg a folded paper was uncovered. The patient picked it up and carelessly opened it. It was a letter three months old, signed "Julia." Catching sight of his name in it he read it. It was nothing very remarkable—merely a weak woman's confession of unprofitable sin— the penitence of a faithless wife deserted by her betrayer. The letter had fallen from the pocket of Captain Armisted; the reader quietly transferred it to his own.

An aide-de-camp rode up and dismounted. Advancing to the Governor he saluted.

"Sir," he said, "I am sorry to find you wounded—the Commanding General has not been informed. He presents his compliments and I am directed to say that he has ordered for to-morrow a grand review of the reserve corps in your honor. I venture to add that the General's carriage is at your service if you are able to attend."

"Be pleased to say to the Commanding General that I am deeply touched by his kindness. If you have the patience to wait a few moments you shall convey a more definite reply."

He smiled brightly and glancing at the surgeon and his assistants added: "At present—if you will permit an allusion to the horrors of peace —I am 'in the hands of my friends.'"

The humor of the great is infectious; all laughed who heard.

"Where is Captain Armisted?" the Governor asked, not altogether carelessly.

The surgeon looked up from his work, pointing silently to the nearest body in the row of dead, the features discreetly covered with a handkerchief. It was so near that the great man could have laid his hand upon it, but he did not. He may have feared that it would bleed.

THE STORY OF A CONSCIENCE

I

CAPTAIN PARROL HARTROY stood at the advanced post of his picket-guard, talking in low tones with the sentinel. This post was on a turnpike which bisected the captain's camp, a half-mile in rear, though the camp was not in sight from that point. The officer was apparently giving the soldier certain instructions—was perhaps merely inquiring if all were quiet in front. As the two stood talking a man approached them from the direction of the camp, carelessly whistling, and was promptly halted by the soldier. He was evidently a civilian—a tall person, coarsely clad in the home-made stuff of yellow gray, called "butternut," which was men's only wear in the latter days of the Confederacy. On his head was a slouch felt hat, once white, from beneath which hung masses of uneven hair, seemingly unacquainted with either scissors or comb. The man's face was rather striking; a broad forehead, high nose, and thin cheeks, the mouth invisible in the full dark beard, which seemed as neglected as the hair. The eyes were large and had that steadiness and fixity of attention which so frequently mark a considering intelligence and a will not easily turned from its purpose—so say those physiognomists who have that kind of eyes. On the whole, this was a man whom one would be likely to observe and be observed by. He carried a walking-stick freshly cut from the forest and his ailing cowskin boots were white with dust.

"Show your pass," said the Federal soldier, a trifle more imperiously perhaps than he would have thought necessary if he had not been under the eye of his commander, who with folded arms looked on from the roadside.

" 'Lowed you'd rec'lect me, Gineral," said the wayfarer tranquilly, while producing the paper from the pocket of his coat. There was something in his tone—perhaps a faint suggestion of irony—which made his elevation of his obstructor to exalted rank less agreeable to that worthy warrior than promotion is commonly found to be. "You-all have to be purty pertickler, I reckon," he added, in a more conciliatory tone, as if in half-apology for being halted.

Having read the pass, with his rifle resting on the ground, the soldier handed the document back without a word, shouldered his weapon, and returned to his commander. The civilian passed on in the middle of the road, and when he had penetrated the circumjacent Confederacy a few yards resumed his whistling and was soon out of sight beyond an angle in the road, which at that point entered a thin forest. Suddenly the officer undid his arms from his breast, drew a revolver from his belt and sprang forward at a run in the same direction, leaving his sentinel in gaping astonishment at his post. After making to the various visible forms of nature a solemn promise to be damned, that gentleman resumed the air of stolidity which is supposed to be appropriate to a state of alert military attention.

II

Captain Hartroy held an independent command. His force consisted of a company of infantry, a squadron of cavalry, and a section of artillery, detached from the army to which they belonged, to defend an important defile in the Cumberland Mountains in Tennessee. It was a field officer's command held by a line officer promoted from the ranks, where he had quietly served until "discovered." His post was one of exceptional peril; its defense entailed a heavy responsibility and he had wisely been given corresponding discretionary powers, all the more necessary because of his distance from the main army, the precarious nature of his communications and the lawless character of the enemy's irregular troops infesting that region. He had strongly fortified his little camp, which embraced a village of a half-dozen dwellings and a country store, and had collected a considerable quantity of supplies. To a few resident civilians of known loyalty, with whom it was desirable to trade, and of whose services in various ways he sometimes availed himself, he had given written passes admitting them within his lines. It is easy to understand that an abuse of this privilege in the interest of the enemy might entail serious consequences. Captain Hartroy had made an order to the effect that any one so abusing it would be summarily shot.

While the sentinel had been examining the civilian's pass the captain had eyed the latter narrowly. He thought his appearance familiar and had at first no doubt of having given him the pass which had satisfied the sentinel. It was not until the man had got out of sight and hearing that his identity was disclosed by a revealing light from memory. With soldierly promptness of decision the officer had acted on the revelation.

III

To any but a singularly self-possessed man the apparition of an officer of the military forces, formidably clad, bearing in one hand a sheathed sword and in the other a cocked revolver, and rushing in furious pursuit, is no doubt disquieting to a high degree; upon the man to whom the pursuit was in this instance directed it appeared to have no other effect than somewhat to intensify his tranquillity. He might easily enough have escaped into the forest to the right or the left, but chose another course of action—turned and quietly faced the captain, saying as he came up: "I reckon ye must have something to say to me, which ye disremembered. What mout it be, neighbor?"

But the "neighbor" did not answer, being engaged in the unneighborly act of covering him with a cocked pistol.

"Surrender," said the captain as calmly as a slight breathlessness from exertion would permit, "or you die."

There was no menace in the manner of this demand; that was all in the matter and in the means of enforcing it. There was, too, something not altogether reassuring in the cold gray eyes that glanced along the barrel of the weapon. For a moment the two men stood looking at each other in silence; then the civilian, with no appearance of fear—with as great apparent unconcern as when complying with the less austere demand of the sentinel—slowly pulled from his pocket the paper which had satisfied that humble functionary and held it out, saying:

"I reckon this 'ere parss from Mister Hartroy is—"

"The pass is a forgery," the officer said, interrupting. "I am Captain Hartroy—and you are Dramer Brune."

It would have required a sharp eye to observe the slight pallor of the civilian's face at these words, and the only other manifestation attesting their significance was a voluntary relaxation of the thumb and fingers holding the dishonored paper, which, falling to the road, unheeded, was rolled by a gentle wind and then lay still, with a coating of dust, as in humiliation for the lie that it bore. A moment later the civilian, still looking unmoved into the barrel of the pistol, said:

"Yes, I am Dramer Brune, a Confederate spy, and your prisoner. I have on my person, as you will soon discover, a plan of your fort and its armament, a statement of the distribution of your men and their number, a map of the approaches, showing the positions of all your outposts. My life is fairly yours, but if you wish it taken in a more formal way than by your own hand, and if you are willing to spare me the indignity of marching into camp at the muzzle of your pistol, I promise you that I will neither resist, escape, nor remonstrate, but will submit to whatever penalty may be imposed."

The officer lowered his pistol, uncocked it, and thrust it into its place in his belt. Brune advanced a step, extending his right hand.

"It is the hand of a traitor and a spy," said the officer coldly, and did not take it. The other bowed.

"Come," said the captain, "let us go to camp; you shall not die until to-morrow morning."

He turned his back upon his prisoner, and these two enigmatical men retraced their steps and soon passed the sentinel, who expressed his general sense of things by a needless and exaggerated salute to his commander.

IV

Early on the morning after these events the two men, captor and captive, sat in the tent of the former. A table was between them on which lay, among a number of letters, official and private, which the captain had written during the night, the incriminating papers found upon the spy. That gentleman had slept through the night in an adjoining tent, unguarded. Both, having breakfasted, were now smoking.

"Mr. Brune," said Captain Hartroy, "you probably do not understand why I recognized you in your disguise, nor how I was aware of your name."

"I have not sought to learn, Captain," the prisoner said with quiet dignity.

"Nevertheless I should like you to know—if the story will not offend. You will perceive that my knowledge of you goes back to the autumn of 1861. At that time you were a private in an Ohio regiment—a brave and trusted soldier. To the surprise and grief of your officers and comrades you deserted and went over to the enemy. Soon afterward you were captured in a skirmish, recognized, tried by court-martial and sentenced to be shot. Awaiting the execution of the sentence you were confined, unfettered, in a freight car standing on a side track of a railway."

"At Grafton, Virginia," said Brune, pushing the ashes from his cigar with the little finger of the hand holding it, and without looking up.

"At Grafton, Virginia," the captain repeated. "One dark and stormy night a soldier who had just returned from a long, fatiguing march was put on guard over you. He sat on a cracker box inside the car, near the door, his rifle loaded and the bayonet fixed. You sat in a corner and his orders were to kill you if you attempted to rise."

"But if I *asked* to rise he might call the corporal of the guard."

"Yes. As the long silent hours wore away the soldier yielded to the demands of nature: he himself incurred the death penalty by sleeping at his post of duty."

"You did."

"What! you recognize me? you have known me all along?"

The captain had risen and was walking the floor of his tent, visibly excited. His face was flushed, the gray eyes had lost the cold, pitiless look which they had shown when Brune had seen them over the pistol barrel; they had softened wonderfully.

"I knew you," said the spy, with his customary tranquillity, "the moment you faced me, demanding my surrender. In the circumstances it would have been hardly becoming in me to recall these matters. I am perhaps a traitor, certainly a spy; but I should not wish to seem a suppliant."

The captain had paused in his walk and was facing his prisoner. There was a singular huskiness in his voice as he spoke again.

"Mr. Brune, whatever your conscience may permit you to be, you saved my life at what you must have believed the cost of your own. Until I saw you yesterday when halted by my sentinel I believed you dead— thought that you had suffered the fate which through my own crime you might easily have escaped. You had only to step from the car and leave me to take your place before the firing-squad. You had a divine compassion. You pitied my fatigue. You let me sleep, watched over me, and as the time drew near for the relief-guard to come and detect me in my crime, you gently waked me. Ah, Brune, Brune, that was well done—that was great—that—"

The captain's voice failed him; the tears were running down his face and sparkled upon his beard and his breast. Resuming his seat at the table, he buried his face in his arms and sobbed. All else was silence.

Suddenly the clear warble of a bugle was heard sounding the "assembly." The captain started and raised his wet face from his arms; it had turned ghastly pale. Outside, in the sunlight, were heard the stir of the men falling into line; the voices of the sergeants calling the roll; the tapping of the drummers as they braced their drums. The captain spoke again:

"I ought to have confessed my fault in order to relate the story of your magnanimity; it might have procured you a pardon. A hundred times I resolved to do so, but shame prevented. Besides, your sentence was just and righteous. Well, Heaven forgive me! I said nothing, and my regiment was soon afterward ordered to Tennessee and I never heard about you."

"It was all right, sir," said Brune, without visible emotion; "I escaped and returned to my colors—the Confederate colors. I should like to add that before deserting from the Federal service I had earnestly asked a discharge, on the ground of altered convictions. I was answered by punishment."

"Ah, but if I had suffered the penalty of my crime—if you had not generously given me the life that I accepted without gratitude you would not be again in the shadow and imminence of death."

The prisoner started slightly and a look of anxiety came into his face. One would have said, too, that he was surprised. At that moment a lieutenant, the adjutant, appeared at the opening of the tent and saluted. "Captain," he said, "the battalion is formed."

Captain Hartroy had recovered his composure. He turned to the officer and said: "Lieutenant, go to Captain Graham and say that I direct him to assume command of the battalion and parade it outside the parapet. This gentleman is a deserter and a spy; he is to be shot to death in the presence of the troops. He will accompany you, unbound and unguarded."

While the adjutant waited at the door the two men inside the tent rose and exchanged ceremonious bows, Brune immediately retiring.

Half an hour later an old Negro cook, the only person left in camp except the commander, was so startled by the sound of a volley of musketry that he dropped the kettle that he was lifting from a fire. But for his consternation and the hissing which the contents of the kettle made among the embers, he might also have heard, nearer at hand, the single pistol shot with which Captain Hartroy renounced the life which in conscience he could no longer keep.

In compliance with the terms of a note that he left for the officer who succeeded him in command, he was buried, like the deserter and spy, without military honors; and in the solemn shadow of the mountain which knows no more of war the two sleep well in long-forgotten graves.

ONE KIND OF OFFICER

I

OF THE USES OF CIVILITY

"CAPTAIN RANSOME, it is not permitted to you to know *anything*. It is sufficient that you obey my order—which permit me to repeat. If you perceive any movement of troops in your front you are to open fire, and if attacked hold this position as long as you can. Do I make myself understood, sir?"

"Nothing could be plainer. Lieutenant Price,"—this to an officer of his own battery, who had ridden up in time to hear the order—"the general's meaning is clear, is it not?"

"Perfectly."

The lieutenant passed on to his post. For a moment General Cameron and the commander of the battery sat in their saddles, looking at each other in silence. There was no more to say; apparently too much had already been said. Then the superior officer nodded coldly and turned his horse to ride away. The artillerist saluted slowly, gravely, and with extreme formality. One acquainted with the niceties of military etiquette would have said that by his manner he attested a sense of the rebuke that he had incurred. It is one of the important uses of civility to signify resentment.

When the general had joined his staff and escort, awaiting him at a little distance, the whole cavalcade moved off toward the right of the guns and vanished in the fog. Captain Ransome was alone, silent, motionless as an equestrian statue. The gray fog, thickening every moment, closed in about him like a visible doom.

II

UNDER WHAT CIRCUMSTANCES MEN DO NOT WISH TO BE SHOT

The fighting of the day before had been desultory and indecisive. At the points of collision the smoke of battle had hung in blue sheets among the branches of the trees till beaten into nothing by the falling rain. In the softened earth the wheels of cannon and ammunition wagons cut deep, ragged furrows, and movements of infantry seemed impeded by the mud that clung to the soldiers' feet as, with soaken garments and rifles imperfectly protected by capes of overcoats they went dragging in sinuous lines hither and thither through dripping forest and flooded field. Mounted officers, their heads protruding from rubber ponchos that glittered like black armor, picked their way, singly and in loose groups, among the men, coming and going with apparent aimlessness and commanding attention from nobody but one another. Here and there a dead man, his clothing defiled with earth, his face covered with a blanket or showing yellow and claylike in the rain, added his dispiriting influence to that of the other dismal features of the scene and augmented the general discomfort with a particular dejection. Very repulsive these wrecks looked—not at all heroic, and nobody was accessible to the infection of their patriotic example. Dead upon the field of honor, yes; but the field of honor was so very wet! It makes a difference.

The general engagement that all expected did not occur, none of the small advantages accruing, now to this side and now to that, in isolated and accidental collisions being followed up. Half-hearted attacks provoked a sullen resistance which was satisfied with mere repulse. Orders were obeyed with mechanical fidelity; no one did any more than his duty.

"The army is cowardly to-day," said General Cameron, the commander of a Federal brigade, to his adjutant-general.

"The army is cold," replied the officer addressed, "and—yes, it doesn't wish to be like that."

He pointed to one of the dead bodies, lying in a thin pool of yellow water, its face and clothing bespattered with mud from hoof and wheel.

The army's weapons seemed to share its military delinquency. The rattle of rifles sounded flat and contemptible. It had no meaning and scarcely roused to attention and expectancy the unengaged parts of the line-of-battle and the waiting reserves. Heard at a little distance, the reports of cannon were feeble in volume and *timbre:* they lacked sting and resonance. The guns seemed to be fired with light charges, unshotted. And so the futile day wore on to its dreary close, and then to a night of discomfort succeeded a day of apprehension.

An army has a personality. Beneath the individual thoughts and emotions of its component parts it thinks and feels as a unit. And in this large, inclusive sense of things lies a wiser wisdom than the mere sum of all that it knows. On that dismal morning this great brute force, groping at the bottom of a white ocean of fog among trees that seemed as sea weeds, had a dumb consciousness that all was not well; that a day's manœuvring had resulted in a faulty disposition of its parts, a blind diffusion of its strength. The men felt insecure and talked among themselves of such tactical errors as with their meager military vocabulary they were able to name. Field and line officers gathered in groups and spoke more learnedly of what they apprehended with no greater clearness. Commanders of brigades and divisions looked anxiously to their connections on the right and on the left, sent staff officers on errands of inquiry and pushed skirmish lines silently and cautiously forward into the dubious region between the known and the unknown. At some points on the line the troops, apparently of their own volition, constructed such defenses as they could without the silent spade and the noisy ax.

One of these points was held by Captain Ransome's battery of six guns. Provided always with intrenching tools, his men had labored with diligence during the night, and now his guns thrust their black muzzles through the embrasures of a really formidable earthwork. It crowned a slight acclivity devoid of undergrowth and providing an unobstructed fire that would sweep the ground for an unknown distance in front. The position could hardly have been better chosen. It had this peculiarity, which Captain Ransome, who was greatly addicted to the use of the compass, had not failed to observe: it faced northward, whereas he knew that the general line of the army must face eastward. In fact, that part of the line was "refused"—that is to say, bent backward, away from the enemy. This implied that Captain Ransome's battery was somewhere near the left flank of the army; for an army in line of battle retires its flanks if the nature of the ground will permit, they being its vulnerable points. Actually, Captain Ransome appeared to hold the extreme left of the line, no troops being visible in that direction beyond his own. Immediately in rear of his guns occurred that conversation between him and his brigade commander, the concluding and more picturesque part of which is reported above.

III
HOW TO PLAY THE CANNON WITHOUT NOTES

Captain Ransome sat motionless and silent on horseback. A few yards away his men were standing at their guns. Somewhere—everywhere within a few miles—were a hundred thousand men, friends and enemies. Yet he was alone. The mist had isolated him as completely as if he had been in the heart of a desert. His world was a few square yards of wet and trampled earth about the feet of his horse. His comrades in that ghostly domain were invisible and inaudible. These were conditions favorable to thought, and he was thinking. Of the nature of his thoughts his clear-cut handsome features yielded no attesting sign. His face was as inscrutable as that of the sphinx. Why should it have made a record which there was none to observe? At the sound of a footstep he merely turned his eyes in the direction whence it came; one of his sergeants, looking a giant in stature in the false perspective of the fog, approached, and when clearly defined and reduced to his true dimensions by propinquity, saluted and stood at attention.

"Well, Morris," said the officer, returning his subordinate's salute.

"Lieutenant Price directed me to tell you, sir, that most of the infantry has been withdrawn. We have not sufficient support."

"Yes, I know."

"I am to say that some of our men have been out over the works a hundred yards and report that our front is not picketed."

"Yes."

"They were so far forward that they heard the enemy."

"Yes."

"They heard the rattle of the wheels of artillery and the commands of officers."

"Yes."

"The enemy is moving toward our works."

Captain Ransome, who had been facing to the rear of his line—toward the point where the brigade commander and his cavalcade had been swallowed up by the fog—reined his horse about and faced the other way. Then he sat motionless as before.

"Who are the men who made that statement?" he inquired, without looking at the sergeant; his eyes were directed straight into the fog over the head of his horse.

"Corporal Hassman and Gunner Manning."

Captain Ransome was a moment silent. A slight pallor came into his face, a slight compression affected the lines of his lips, but it would have required a closer observer than Sergeant Morris to note the change. There was none in the voice.

"Sergeant, present my compliments to Lieutenant Price and direct him to open fire with all the guns. Grape."

The sergeant saluted and vanished in the fog.

IV

TO INTRODUCE GENERAL MASTERSON

Searching for his division commander, General Cameron and his escort had followed the line of battle for nearly a mile to the right of Ransome's battery, and there learned that the division commander had gone in search of the corps commander. It seemed that everybody was looking for his immediate superior—an ominous circumstance. It meant that nobody was quite at ease. So General Cameron rode on for another half-mile, where by good luck he met General Masterson, the division commander, returning.

"Ah, Cameron," said the higher officer, reining up, and throwing his right leg across the pommel of his saddle in a most unmilitary way—"anything up? Found a good position for your battery, I hope—if one place is better than another in a fog."

"Yes, general," said the other, with the greater dignity appropriate to his less exalted rank, "my battery is very well placed. I wish I could say that it is as well commanded."

"Eh, what's that? Ransome? I think him a fine fellow. In the army we should be proud of him."

It was customary for officers of the regular army to speak of it as "the army." As the greatest cities are most provincial, so the self-complacency of aristocracies is most frankly plebeian.

"He is too fond of his opinion. By the way, in order to occupy the hill that he holds I had to extend my line dangerously. The hill is on my left—that is to say the left flank of the army."

"Oh, no, Hart's brigade is beyond. It was ordered up from Drytown during the night and directed to hook on to you. Better go and—"

The sentence was unfinished: a lively cannonade had broken out on the left, and both officers, followed by their retinues of aides and orderlies making a great jingle and clank, rode rapidly toward the spot. But they were soon impeded, for they were compelled by the fog to keep within sight of the line-of-battle, behind which were swarms of men, all in motion across their way. Everywhere the line was assuming a sharper and harder definition, as the men sprang to arms and the officers, with drawn swords, "dressed" the ranks. Color-bearers unfurled the flags, buglers blew the "assembly," hospital attendants appeared with stretchers. Field officers mounted and sent their impedimenta to the rear in care of Negro servants. Back in the ghostly spaces of the forest could be heard the rustle and murmur of the reserves, pulling themselves together.

Nor was all this preparation vain, for scarcely five minutes had passed since Captain Ransome's guns had broken the truce of doubt before the whole region was aroar: the enemy had attacked nearly everywhere.

V

HOW SOUNDS CAN FIGHT SHADOWS

Captain Ransome walked up and down behind his guns, which were firing rapidly but with steadiness. The gunners worked alertly, but without haste or apparent excitement. There was really no reason for excitement; it is not much to point a cannon into a fog and fire it. Anybody can do as much as that.

The men smiled at their noisy work, performing it with a lessening alacrity. They cast curious regards upon their captain, who had now mounted the banquette of the fortification and was looking across the parapet as if observing the effect of his fire. But the only visible effect was the substitution of wide, low-lying sheets of smoke for their bulk of fog. Suddenly out of the obscurity burst a great sound of cheering, which filled the intervals between the reports of the guns with startling distinctness! To the few with leisure and opportunity to observe, the sound was inexpressibly strange—so loud, so near, so menacing, yet nothing seen! The men who had smiled at their work smiled no more, but performed it with a serious and feverish activity.

From his station at the parapet Captain Ransome now saw a great multitude of dim gray figures taking shape in the mist below him and swarming up the slope. But the work of the guns was now fast and furious. They swept the populous declivity with gusts of grape and canister, the whirring of which could be heard through the thunder of the explosions. In this awful tempest of iron the assailants struggled forward foot by foot across their dead, firing into the embrasures, reloading, firing again, and at last falling in their turn, a little in advance of those who had fallen before. Soon the smoke was dense enough to cover all. It settled down upon the attack and, drifting back, involved the defense. The gunners could hardly see to serve their pieces, and when occasional figures of the enemy appeared upon the parapet—having had the good luck to get near enough to it, between two embrasures, to be protected from the guns—they looked so unsubstantial that it seemed hardly worth while for the few infantrymen to go to work upon them with the bayonet and tumble them back into the ditch.

As the commander of a battery in action can find something better to do than cracking individual skulls, Captain Ransome had retired from the parapet to his proper post in rear of his guns, where he stood with folded arms, his bugler beside him. Here, during the hottest of the fight, he was approached by Lieutenant Price, who had just sabred a daring assailant inside the work. A spirited colloquy ensued between the two officers—spirited, at least, on the part of the lieutenant, who gesticulated with energy and shouted again and again into his commander's ear in the attempt to make himself heard above the infernal din of the guns. His gestures, if coolly noted by an actor, would have been pronounced to be those of protestation: one would have said that he was opposed to the proceedings. Did he wish to surrender?

Captain Ransome listened without a change of countenance or attitude, and when the other man had finished his harangue, looked him coldly in the eyes and during a seasonable abatement of the uproar said:

"Lieutenant Price, it is not permitted to you to know *anything*. It is sufficient that you obey my orders."

The lieutenant went to his post, and the parapet being now apparently clear Captain Ransome returned to it to have a look over. As he mounted the banquette a man sprang upon the crest, waving a great brilliant flag. The captain drew a pistol from his belt and shot him dead. The body, pitching forward, hung over the inner edge of the embankment, the arms straight downward, both hands still grasping the flag. The man's few followers turned and fled down the slope. Looking over the parapet, the captain saw no living thing. He observed also that no bullets were coming into the work.

He made a sign to the bugler, who sounded the command to cease firing. At all other points the action had already ended with a repulse of the Confederate attack; with the cessation of this cannonade the silence was absolute.

VI

WHY, BEING AFFRONTED BY A, IT IS NOT BEST TO AFFRONT B

General Masterson rode into the redoubt. The men, gathered in groups, were talking loudly and gesticulating. They pointed at the dead, running from one body to another. They neglected their foul and heated guns and forgot to resume their outer clothing. They ran to the parapet and looked over, some of them leaping down into the ditch. A score were gathered about a flag rigidly held by a dead man.

"Well, my men," said the general cheerily, "you have had a pretty fight of it."

They stared; nobody replied; the presence of the great man seemed to embarrass and alarm.

Getting no response to his pleasant condescension, the easy-mannered officer whistled a bar or two of a popular air, and riding forward to the parapet, looked over at the dead. In an instant he had whirled his horse about and was spurring along in rear of the guns, his eyes everywhere at once. An officer sat on the trail of one of the guns, smoking a cigar. As the general dashed up he rose and tranquilly saluted.

"Captain Ransome!"—the words fell sharp and harsh, like the clash of steel blades—"you have been fighting our own men—our own men, sir; do you hear? Hart's brigade!"

"General, I know that."

"You know it—you know that, and you sit here smoking? Oh, damn it, Hamilton, I'm losing my temper,"—this to his provost-marshal. "Sir —Captain Ransome, be good enough to say—to say why you fought our own men."

"That I am unable to say. In my orders that information was withheld."

Apparently the general did not comprehend.

"Who was the aggressor in this affair, you or General Hart?" he asked.

"I was."

"And could you not have known—could you not see, sir, that you were attacking our own men?"

The reply was astounding!

"I knew that, general. It appeared to be none of my business."

Then, breaking the dead silence that followed his answer, he said:

"I must refer you to General Cameron."

"General Cameron is dead, sir—as dead as he can be—as dead as any man in this army. He lies back yonder under a tree. Do you mean to say that he had anything to do with this horrible business?"

Captain Ransome did not reply. Observing the altercation his men had gathered about to watch the outcome. They were greatly excited. The fog, which had been partly dissipated by the firing, had again closed in so darkly about them that they drew more closely together till the judge on horseback and the accused standing calmly before him had but a narrow space free from intrusion. It was the most informal of courts-martial, but all felt that the formal one to follow would but affirm its judgment. It had no jurisdiction, but it had the significance of prophecy.

"Captain Ransome," the general cried impetuously, but with something in his voice that was almost entreaty, "if you can say anything to put a better light upon your incomprehensible conduct I beg you will do so."

Having recovered his temper this generous soldier sought for something to justify his naturally sympathetic attitude toward a brave man in the imminence of a dishonorable death.

"Where is Lieutenant Price?" the captain said.

That officer stood forward, his dark saturnine face looking somewhat forbidding under a bloody handkerchief bound about his brow. He understood the summons and needed no invitation to speak. He did not look at the captain, but addressed the general:

"During the engagement I discovered the state of affairs, and apprised the commander of the battery. I ventured to urge that the firing cease. I was insulted and ordered to my post."

"Do you know anything of the orders under which I was acting?" asked the captain.

"Of any orders under which the commander of the battery was acting," the lieutenant continued, still addressing the general, "I know nothing."

Captain Ransome felt his world sink away from his feet. In those cruel words he heard the murmur of the centuries breaking upon the shore of eternity. He heard the voice of doom; it said, in cold, mechanical, and measured tones: "Ready, aim, fire!" and he felt the bullets tear his heart to shreds. He heard the sound of the earth upon his coffin and (if the good God was so merciful) the song of a bird above his forgotten grave. Quietly detaching his sabre from its supports, he handed it up to the provost-marshal.

ONE OFFICER, ONE MAN

CAPTAIN GRAFFENREID stood at the head of his company. The regiment was not engaged. It formed a part of the front line-of-battle, which stretched away to the right with a visible length of nearly two miles through the open ground. The left flank was veiled by woods; to the right also the line was lost to sight, but it extended many miles. A hundred yards in rear was a second line; behind this, the reserve brigades and divisions in column. Batteries of artillery occupied the spaces between and crowned the low hills. Groups of horsemen—generals with their staffs and escorts, and field officers of regiments behind the colors —broke the regularity of the lines and columns. Numbers of these figures of interest had field-glasses at their eyes and sat motionless, stolidly scanning the country in front; others came and went at a slow canter, bearing orders. There were squads of stretcher-bearers, ambulances, wagon-trains with ammunition, and officers' servants in rear of all—of all that was visible—for still in rear of these, along the roads, extended for many miles all that vast multitude of non-combatants who with their various impedimenta are assigned to the inglorious but important duty of supplying the fighters' many needs.

An army in line-of-battle awaiting attack, or prepared to deliver it, presents strange contrasts. At the front are precision, formality, fixity, and silence. Toward the rear these characteristics are less and less conspicuous, and finally, in point of space, are lost altogether in confusion, motion and noise. The homogeneous becomes heterogeneous. Definition is lacking; repose is replaced by an apparently purposeless activity; harmony vanishes in hubbub, form in disorder. Commotion everywhere and ceaseless unrest. The men who do not fight are never ready.

From his position at the right of his company in the front rank, Captain Graffenreid had an unobstructed outlook toward the enemy. A half-mile of open and nearly level ground lay before him, and beyond it an irregular wood, covering a slight acclivity; not a human being anywhere visible. He could imagine nothing more peaceful than the appearance of that pleasant landscape with its long stretches of brown fields over which the atmosphere was beginning to quiver in the heat of the morning sun. Not a sound came from forest or field—not even the barking of a dog or the crowing of a cock at the half-seen plantation house on the crest among the trees. Yet every man in those miles of men knew that he and death were face to face.

Captain Graffenreid had never in his life seen an armed enemy, and the war in which his regiment was one of the first to take the field was two years old. He had had the rare advantage of a military education, and when his comrades had marched to the front he had been detached for administrative service at the capital of his State, where it was thought that he could be most useful. Like a bad soldier he protested, and like a good one obeyed. In close official and personal relations with the governor of his State, and enjoying his confidence and favor, he had firmly refused promotion and seen his juniors elevated above him. Death had been busy in his distant regiment; vacancies among the field officers had occurred again and again; but from a chivalrous feeling that war's rewards belonged of right to those who bore the storm and stress of battle he had held his humble rank and generously advanced the fortunes of others. His silent devotion to principle had conquered at last: he had been relieved of his hateful duties and ordered to the front, and now, untried by fire, stood in the van of battle in command of a company of hardy veterans, to whom he had been only a name, and that name a byword. By none—not even by those of his brother officers in whose favor he had waived his rights—was his devotion to duty understood. They were too busy to be just; he was looked upon as one who had shirked his duty, until forced unwillingly into the field. Too proud to explain, yet not too insensible to feel, he could only endure and hope.

Of all the Federal Army on that summer morning none had accepted battle more joyously than Anderton Graffenreid. His spirit was buoyant, his faculties were riotous. He was in a state of mental exaltation and scarcely could endure the enemy's tardiness in advancing to the attack. To him this was opportunity—for the result he cared nothing. Victory or defeat, as God might will; in one or in the other he should prove himself a soldier and a hero; he should vindicate his right to the respect of his men and the companionship of his brother officers—to the consideration of his superiors. How his heart leaped in his breast as the bugle sounded the stirring notes of the "assembly"! With what a light tread, scarcely conscious of the earth beneath his feet, he strode forward at the head of his company, and how exultingly he noted the tactical dispositions which placed his regiment in the front line! And if perchance some memory came to him of a pair of dark eyes that might take on a tenderer light in reading the account of that day's doings, who shall blame him for the unmartial thought or count it a debasement of soldierly ardor?

Suddenly, from the forest a half-mile in front—apparently from among the upper branches of the trees, but really from the ridge beyond—rose a tall column of white smoke. A moment later came a deep, jarring explosion, followed—almost attended—by a hideous rushing sound that seemed to leap forward across the intervening space with inconceivable rapidity, rising from whisper to roar with too quick a gradation for attention to note the successive stages of its horrible progression! A visible tremor ran along the lines of men; all were startled into motion. Captain Graffenreid dodged and threw up his hands to one side of his head, palms outward. As he did so he heard a keen, ringing report, and saw on a hillside behind the line a fierce roll of smoke and dust—the shell's explosion. It had passed a hundred feet to his left! He heard, or fancied he heard, a low, mocking laugh and turning in the direction whence it came saw the eyes of his first lieutenant fixed upon him with an unmistakable look of amusement. He looked along the line of faces in the front ranks. The men were laughing. At him? The thought restored the color to his bloodless face—restored too much of it. His cheeks burned with a fever of shame.

The enemy's shot was not answered: the officer in command at that exposed part of the line had evidently no desire to provoke a cannonade. For the forbearance Captain Graffenreid was conscious of a sense of gratitude. He had not known that the flight of a projectile was a phenomenon of so appalling character. His conception of war had already undergone a profound change, and he was conscious that his new feeling was manifesting itself in visible perturbation. His blood was boiling in his veins; he had a choking sensation and felt that if he had a command to give it would be inaudible, or at least unintelligible. The hand in which he held his sword trembled; the other moved automatically, clutching at various parts of his clothing. He found a difficulty in standing still and fancied that his men observed it. Was it fear? He feared it was.

From somewhere away to the right came, as the wind served, a low, intermittent murmur like that of ocean in a storm—like that of a distant railway train—like that of wind among the pines—three sounds so nearly alike that the ear, unaided by the judgment, cannot distinguish them one from another. The eyes of the troops were drawn in that direction; the mounted officers turned their field-glasses that way. Mingled with the sound was an irregular throbbing. He thought it, at first, the beating of his fevered blood in his ears; next, the distant tapping of a bass drum.

"The ball is opened on the right flank," said an officer.

Captain Graffenreid understood: the sounds were musketry and artillery. He nodded and tried to smile. There was apparently nothing infectious in the smile.

Presently a light line of blue smoke-puffs broke out along the edge of the wood in front, succeeded by a crackle of rifles. There were keen, sharp hissings in the air, terminating abruptly with a thump near by. The man at Captain Graffenreid's side dropped his rifle; his knees gave way and he pitched awkwardly forward, falling upon his face. Somebody shouted "Lie down!" and the dead man was hardly distinguishable from the living. It looked as if those few rifle-shots had slain ten thousand men. Only the field officers remained erect; their concession to the emergency consisted in dismounting and sending their horses to the shelter of the low hills immediately in rear.

Captain Graffenreid lay alongside the dead man, from beneath whose breast flowed a little rill of blood. It had a faint, sweetish odor that sickened him. The face was crushed into the earth and flattened. It looked yellow already, and was repulsive. Nothing suggested the glory of a soldier's death nor mitigated the loathsomeness of the incident. He could not turn his back upon the body without facing away from his company.

He fixed his eyes upon the forest, where all again was silent. He tried to imagine what was going on there—the lines of troops forming to attack, the guns being pushed forward by hand to the edge of the open. He fancied he could see their black muzzles protruding from the undergrowth, ready to deliver their storm of missiles—such missiles as the one whose shriek had so unsettled his nerves. The distension of his eyes became painful; a mist seemed to gather before them; he could no longer see across the field, yet would not withdraw his gaze lest he see the dead man at his side.

The fire of battle was not now burning very brightly in this warrior's soul. From inaction had come introspection. He sought rather to analyze his feelings than distinguish himself by courage and devotion. The result was profoundly disappointing. He covered his face with his hands and groaned aloud.

The hoarse murmur of battle grew more and more distinct upon the right; the murmur had, indeed, become a roar, the throbbing, a thunder. The sounds had worked round obliquely to the front; evidently the enemy's left was being driven back, and the propitious moment to move against the salient angle of his line would soon arrive. The silence and mystery in front were ominous; all felt that they boded evil to the assailants.

Behind the prostrate lines sounded the hoof-beats of galloping horses; the men turned to look. A dozen staff officers were riding to the various brigade and regimental commanders, who had remounted. A moment more and there was a chorus of voices, all uttering out of time the same words—"Attention, battalion!" The men sprang to their feet and were aligned by the company commanders. They awaited the word "forward"—awaited, too, with beating hearts and set teeth the gusts of lead and iron that were to smite them at their first movement in obedience to that word. The word was not given; the tempest did not break out. The delay was hideous, maddening! It unnerved like a respite at the guillotine.

Captain Graffenreid stood at the head of his company, the dead man at his feet. He heard the battle on the right—rattle and crash of musketry, ceaseless thunder of cannon, desultory cheers of invisible combatants. He marked ascending clouds of smoke from distant forests. He noted the sinister silence of the forest in front. These contrasting extremes affected the whole range of his sensibilities. The strain upon his nervous organization was insupportable. He grew hot and cold by turns. He panted like a dog, and then forgot to breathe until reminded by vertigo.

Suddenly he grew calm. Glancing downward, his eyes had fallen upon his naked sword, as he held it, point to earth. Foreshortened to his view, it resembled somewhat, he thought, the short heavy blade of the ancient Roman. The fancy was full of suggestion, malign, fateful, heroic!

The sergeant in the rear rank, immediately behind Captain Graffenreid, now observed a strange sight. His attention drawn by an uncommon movement made by the captain—a sudden reaching forward of the hands and their energetic withdrawal, throwing the elbows out, as in pulling an oar—he saw spring from between the officer's shoulders a bright point of metal which prolonged itself outward, nearly a half-arm's length—a blade! It was faintly streaked with crimson, and its point approached so near to the sergeant's breast, and with so quick a movement, that he shrank backward in alarm. That moment Captain Graffenreid pitched heavily forward upon the dead man and died.

A week later the major-general commanding the left corps of the Federal Army submitted the following official report:

"Sir: I have the honor to report, with regard to the action of the 19th inst., that owing to the enemy's withdrawal from my front to reinforce his beaten left, my command was not seriously engaged. My loss was as follows: Killed, one officer, one man."

GEORGE THURSTON
Three Incidents in the Life of a Man

GEORGE THURSTON was a first lieutenant and aide-de-camp on the staff of Colonel Brough, commanding a Federal brigade. Colonel Brough was only temporarily in command, as senior colonel, the brigadier-general having been severely wounded and granted a leave of absence to recover. Lieutenant Thurston was, I believe, of Colonel Brough's regiment, to which, with his chief, he would naturally have been relegated had he lived till our brigade commander's recovery. The aide whose place Thurston took had been killed in battle; Thurston's advent among us was the only change in the *personnel* of our staff consequent upon the change in commanders. We did not like him; he was unsocial. This, however, was more observed by others than by me. Whether in camp or on the march, in barracks, in tents, or *en bivouac,* my duties as topographical engineer kept me working like a beaver—all day in the saddle and half the night at my drawing-table, platting my surveys. It was hazardous work; the nearer to the enemy's lines I could penetrate, the more valuable were my field notes and the resulting maps. It was a business in which the lives of men counted as nothing against the chance of defining a road or sketching a bridge. Whole squadrons of cavalry escort had sometimes to be sent thundering against a powerful infantry outpost in order that the brief time between the charge and the inevitable retreat might be utilized in sounding a ford or determining the point of intersection of two roads.

In some of the dark corners of England and Wales they have an immemorial custom of "beating the bounds" of the parish. On a certain day of the year the whole population turns out and travels in procession from one landmark to another on the boundary line. At the most important points lads are soundly beaten with rods to make them remember the place in after life. They become authorities. Our frequent engagements with the Confederate outposts, patrols, and scouting parties had, incidentally, the same educating value; they fixed in my memory a vivid and apparently imperishable picture of the locality—a picture serving instead of accurate field notes, which, indeed, it was not always convenient to take, with carbines cracking, sabers clashing, and horses plunging all about. These spirited encounters were observations entered in red.

One morning as I set out at the head of my escort on an expedition of more than the usual hazard Lieutenant Thurston rode up alongside and asked if I had any objection to his accompanying me, the colonel commanding having given him permission.

"None whatever," I replied rather gruffly; "but in what capacity will you go? You are not a topographical engineer, and Captain Burling commands my escort."

"I will go as a spectator," he said. Removing his sword-belt and taking the pistols from his holsters he handed them to his servant, who took them back to headquarters. I realized the brutality of my remark, but not clearly seeing my way to an apology, said nothing.

That afternoon we encountered a whole regiment of the enemy's cavalry in line and a field-piece that dominated a straight mile of the turnpike by which we had approached. My escort fought deployed in the woods on both sides, but Thurston remained in the center of the road, which at intervals of a few seconds was swept by gusts of grape and canister that tore the air wide open as they passed. He had dropped the rein on the neck of his horse and sat bolt upright in the saddle, with folded arms. Soon he was down, his horse torn to pieces. From the side of the road, my pencil and field book idle, my duty forgotten, I watched him slowly disengaging himself from the wreck and rising. At that instant, the cannon having ceased firing, a burly Confederate trooper on a spirited horse dashed like a thunderbolt down the road with drawn saber. Thurston saw him coming, drew himself up to his full height, and again folded his arms. He was too brave to retreat before the sword, and my uncivil words had disarmed him. He was a spectator. Another moment and he would have been split like a mackerel, but a blessed bullet tumbled his assailant into the dusty road so near that the impetus sent the body rolling to Thurston's feet. That evening, while platting my hasty survey, I found time to frame an apology, which I think took the rude, primitive form of a confession that I had spoken like a malicious idiot.

A few weeks later a part of our army made an assault upon the enemy's left. The attack, which was made upon an unknown position and across unfamiliar ground, was led by our brigade. The ground was so broken and the underbrush so thick that all mounted officers and men were compelled to fight on foot—the brigade commander and his staff included. In the *mêlée* Thurston was parted from the rest of us, and we found him, horribly wounded, only when we had taken the enemy's last defense. He was some months in hospital at Nashville, Tennessee, but finally rejoined us. He said little about his misadventure, except that he had been bewildered and had strayed into the enemy's lines and been shot down; but from one of his captors, whom we in turn had captured, we learned the particulars. "He came walking right upon us as we lay in line," said this man. "A whole company of us instantly sprang up and leveled our rifles at his breast, some of them almost touching him. 'Throw down that sword and surrender, you damned Yank!' shouted some one in authority. The fellow ran his eyes along the line of rifle barrels, folded his arms across his breast, his right hand still clutching his sword, and deliberately replied, 'I will not.' If we had all fired he would have been torn to shreds. Some of us didn't. I didn't, for one; nothing could have induced me."

When one is tranquilly looking death in the eye and refusing him any concession one naturally has a good opinion of one's self. I don't know if it was this feeling that in Thurston found expression in a stiffish attitude and folded arms; at the mess table one day, in his absence, another explanation was suggested by our quartermaster, an irreclaimable stammerer when the wine was in: "It's h—is w—ay of m-m-mastering a c-c-consti-t-tu-tional t-tendency to r—un aw—ay."

"What!" I flamed out, indignantly rising; "you intimate that Thurston is a coward—and in his absence?"

"If he w—ere a cow—wow-ard h—e w—wouldn't t-try to m-m-master it; and if he w—ere p-present I w—wouldn't d-d-dare to d-d-discuss it," was the mollifying reply.

This intrepid man, George Thurston, died an ignoble death. The brigade was in camp, with headquarters in a grove of immense trees. To an upper branch of one of these a venturesome climber had attached the two ends of a long rope and made a swing with a length of not less than one hundred feet. Plunging downward from a height of fifty feet, along the arc of a circle with such a radius, soaring to an equal altitude, pausing for one breathless instant, then sweeping dizzily backward—no one who has not tried it can conceive the terrors of such sport to the novice. Thurston came out of his tent one day and asked for instruction in the mystery of propelling the swing—the art of rising and sitting, which every boy has mastered. In a few moments he had acquired the trick and was swinging higher than the most experienced of us had dared. We shuddered to look at his fearful flights.

"St-t-top him," said the quartermaster, snailing lazily along from the mess-tent, where he had been lunching; "h—e d-doesn't know that if h—e g-g-goes c-clear over h—e'll w—ind up the sw—ing."

With such energy was that strong man cannonading himself through the air that at each extremity of his increasing arc his body, standing in the swing, was almost horizontal. Should he once pass above the level of the rope's attachment he would be lost; the rope would slacken and he would fall vertically to a point as far below as he had gone above, and then the sudden tension of the rope would wrest it from his hands. All saw the peril—all cried out to him to desist, and gesticulated at him as, indistinct and with a noise like the rush of a cannon shot in flight, he swept past us through the lower reaches of his hideous oscillation. A woman standing at a little distance away fainted and fell unobserved. Men from the camp of a regiment near by ran in crowds to see, all shouting. Suddenly, as Thurston was on his upward curve, the shouts all ceased.

Thurston and the swing had parted—that is all that can be known; both hands at once had released the rope. The impetus of the light swing exhausted, it was falling back; the man's momentum was carrying him, almost erect, upward and forward, no longer in his arc, but with an outward curve. It could have been but an instant, yet it seemed an age. I cried out, or thought I cried out: "My God! will he never stop going up?" He passed close to the branch of a tree. I remember a feeling of delight as I thought he would clutch it and save himself. I speculated on the possibility of it sustaining his weight. He passed above it, and from my point of view was sharply outlined against the blue. At this distance of many years I can distinctly recall that image of a man in the sky, its head erect, its feet close together, its hands—I do not see its hands. All at once, with astonishing suddenness and rapidity, it turns clear over and pitches downward. There is another cry from the crowd, which has rushed instinctively forward. The man has become merely a whirling object, mostly legs. Then there is an indescribable sound—the sound of an impact that shakes the earth, and these men, familiar with death in its most awful aspects, turn sick. Many walk unsteadily away from the spot; others support themselves against the trunks of trees or sit at the roots. Death has taken an unfair advantage; he has struck with an unfamiliar weapon; he has executed a new and disquieting stratagem. We did not know that he had so ghastly resources, possibilities of terror so dismal.

Thurston's body lay on its back. One leg, bent beneath, was broken above the knee and the bone driven into the earth. The abdomen had burst; the bowels protruded. The neck was broken.

The arms were folded tightly across the breast.

THE MOCKING-BIRD

THE time, a pleasant Sunday afternoon in the early autumn of 1861. The place, a forest's heart in the mountain region of southwestern Virginia. Private Grayrock of the Federal Army is discovered seated comfortably at the root of a great pine tree, against which he leans, his legs extended straight along the ground, his rifle lying across his thighs, his hands (clasped in order that they may not fall away to his sides) resting upon the barrel of the weapon. The contact of the back of his head with the tree has pushed his cap downward over his eyes, almost concealing them; one seeing him would say that he slept.

Private Grayrock did not sleep; to have done so would have imperiled the interests of the United States, for he was a long way outside the lines and subject to capture or death at the hands of the enemy. Moreover, he was in a frame of mind unfavorable to repose. The cause of his perturbation of spirit was this: during the previous night he had served on the picket-guard, and had been posted as a sentinel in this very forest. The night was clear, though moonless, but in the gloom of the wood the darkness was deep. Grayrock's post was at a considerable distance from those to right and left, for the pickets had been thrown out a needless distance from the camp, making the line too long for the force detailed to occupy it. The war was young, and military camps entertained the error that while sleeping they were better protected by thin lines a long way out toward the enemy than by thicker ones close in. And surely they needed as long notice as possible of an enemy's approach, for they were at that time addicted to the practice of undressing—than which nothing could be more unsoldierly. On the morning of the memorable 6th of April, at Shiloh, many of Grant's men when spitted on Confederate bayonets were as naked as civilians; but it should be allowed that this was not because of any defect in their picket line. Their error was of another sort: they had no pickets. This is perhaps a vain digression. I should not care to undertake to interest the reader in the fate of an army; what we have here to consider is that of Private Grayrock.

For two hours after he had been left at his lonely post that Saturday night he stood stockstill, leaning against the trunk of a large tree, staring into the darkness in his front and trying to recognize known objects; for he had been posted at the same spot during the day. But all was now different; he saw nothing in detail, but only groups of things, whose shapes, not observed when there was something more of them to observe, were now unfamiliar. They seemed not to have been there before. A landscape that is all trees and undergrowth, moreover, lacks definition, is confused and without accentuated points upon which attention can gain a foothold. Add the gloom of a moonless night, and something more than great natural intelligence and a city education is required to preserve one's knowledge of direction. And that is how it occurred that Private Grayrock, after vigilantly watching the spaces in his front and then imprudently executing a circumspection of his whole dimly visible environment (silently walking around his tree to accomplish it) lost his bearings and seriously impaired his usefulness as a sentinel. Lost at his post—unable to say in which direction to look for an enemy's approach, and in which lay the sleeping camp for whose security he was accountable with his life—conscious, too, of many another awkward feature of the situation and of considerations affecting his own safety, Private Grayrock was profoundly disquieted. Nor was he given time to recover his tranquillity, for almost at the moment that he realized his awkward predicament he heard a stir of leaves and a snap of fallen twigs, and turning with a stilled heart in the direction whence it came, saw in the gloom the indistinct outlines of a human figure.

"Halt!" shouted Private Grayrock, peremptorily as in duty bound, backing up the command with the sharp metallic snap of his cocking rifle—"who goes there?"

There was no answer; at least there was an instant's hesitation, and the answer, if it came, was lost in the report of the sentinel's rifle. In the silence of the night and the forest the sound was deafening, and hardly had it died away when it was repeated by the pieces of the pickets to right and left, a sympathetic fusillade. For two hours every unconverted civilian of them had been evolving enemies from his imagination, and peopling the woods in his front with them, and Grayrock's shot had started the whole encroaching host into visible existence. Having fired, all retreated, breathless, to the reserves—all but Grayrock, who did not know in what direction to retreat. When, no enemy appearing, the roused camp two miles away had undressed and got itself into bed again, and the picket line was cautiously re-established, he was discovered bravely holding his ground, and was complimented by the officer of the guard as the one soldier of that devoted band who could rightly be considered the moral equivalent of that uncommon unit of value, "a whoop in hell."

In the mean time, however, Grayrock had made a close but unavailing search for the mortal part of the intruder at whom he had fired, and whom he had a marksman's intuitive sense of having hit; for he was one of those born experts who shoot without aim by an instinctive sense of direction, and are nearly as dangerous by night as by day. During a full half of his twenty-four years he had been a terror to the targets of all the shooting-galleries in three cities. Unable now to produce his dead game he had the discretion to hold his tongue, and was glad to observe in his officer and comrades the natural assumption that not having run away he had seen nothing hostile. His "honorable mention" had been earned by not running away anyhow.

Nevertheless, Private Grayrock was far from satisfied with the night's adventure, and when the next day he made some fair enough pretext to apply for a pass to go outside the lines, and the general commanding promptly granted it in recognition of his bravery the night before, he passed out at the point where that had been displayed. Telling the sentinel then on duty there that he had lost something,—which was true enough—he renewed the search for the person whom he supposed himself to have shot, and whom if only wounded he hoped to trail by the blood. He was no more successful by daylight than he had been in the darkness, and after covering a wide area and boldly penetrating a long distance into "the Confederacy" he gave up the search, somewhat fatigued, seated himself at the root of the great pine tree, where we have seen him, and indulged his disappointment.

It is not to be inferred that Grayrock's was the chagrin of a cruel nature balked of its bloody deed. In the clear large eyes, finely wrought lips, and broad forehead of that young man one could read quite another story, and in point of fact his character was a singularly felicitous compound of boldness and sensibility, courage and conscience.

"I find myself disappointed," he said to himself, sitting there at the bottom of the golden haze submerging the forest like a subtler sea— "disappointed in failing to discover a fellow-man dead by my hand! Do I then really wish that I had taken life in the performance of a duty as well performed without? What more could I wish? If any danger threatened, my shot averted it; that is what I was there to do. No, I am glad indeed if no human life was needlessly extinguished by me. But I am in a false position. I have suffered myself to be complimented by my officers and envied by my comrades. The camp is ringing with praise of my courage. That is not just; I know myself courageous, but this praise is for specific acts which I did not perform, or performed—otherwise. It is believed that I remained at my post bravely, without firing, whereas it was I who began the fusillade, and I did not retreat in the general alarm because bewildered. What, then, shall I do? Explain that I saw an enemy and fired? They have all said that of themselves, yet none believes it. Shall I tell a truth which, discrediting my courage, will have the effect of a lie? Ugh! it is an ugly business altogether. I wish to God I could find my man!"

And so wishing, Private Grayrock, overcome at last by the languor of the afternoon and lulled by the stilly sounds of insects droning and prosing in certain fragrant shrubs, so far forgot the interests of the United States as to fall asleep and expose himself to capture. And sleeping he dreamed.

He thought himself a boy, living in a far, fair land by the border of a great river upon which the tall steamboats moved grandly up and down beneath their towering evolutions of black smoke, which announced them long before they had rounded the bends and marked their movements when miles out of sight. With him always, at his side as he watched them, was one to whom he gave his heart and soul in love—a twin brother. Together they strolled along the banks of the stream; together explored the fields lying farther away from it, and gathered pungent mints and sticks of fragrant sassafras in the hills overlooking all—beyond which lay the Realm of Conjecture, and from which, looking southward across the great river, they caught glimpses of the Enchanted Land. Hand in hand and heart in heart they two, the only children of a widowed mother, walked in paths of light through valleys of peace, seeing new things under a new sun. And through all the golden days floated one unceasing sound—the rich, thrilling melody of a mocking-bird in a cage by the cottage door. It pervaded and possessed all the spiritual intervals of the dream, like a musical benediction. The joyous bird was always in song; its infinitely various notes seemed to flow from its throat, effortless, in bubbles and rills at each heart-beat, like the waters of a pulsing spring. That fresh, clear melody seemed, indeed, the spirit of the scene, the meaning and interpretation to sense of the mysteries of life and love.

But there came a time when the days of the dream grew dark with sorrow in a rain of tears. The good mother was dead, the meadowside home by the great river was broken up, and the brothers were parted between two of their kinsmen. William (the dreamer) went to live in a populous city in the Realm of Conjecture, and John, crossing the river into the Enchanted Land, was taken to a distant region whose people in their lives and ways were said to be strange and wicked. To him, in the distribution of the dead mother's estate, had fallen all that they deemed of value—the mocking-bird. They could be divided, but it could not, so it was carried away into the strange country, and the world of William knew it no more forever. Yet still through the aftertime of his loneliness its song filled all the dream, and seemed always sounding in his ear and in his heart.

The kinsmen who had adopted the boys were enemies, holding no communication. For a time letters full of boyish bravado and boastful narratives of the new and larger experience—grotesque descriptions of their widening lives and the new worlds they had conquered—passed between them; but these gradually became less frequent, and with William's removal to another and greater city ceased altogether. But ever through it all ran the song of the mocking-bird, and when the dreamer opened his eyes and stared through the vistas of the pine forest the cessation of its music first apprised him that he was awake.

The sun was low and red in the west; the level rays projected from the trunk of each giant pine a wall of shadow traversing the golden haze to eastward until light and shade were blended in undistinguishable blue.

Private Grayrock rose to his feet, looked cautiously about him, shouldered his rifle and set off toward camp. He had gone perhaps a half-mile, and was passing a thicket of laurel, when a bird rose from the midst of it and perching on the branch of a tree above, poured from its joyous breast so inexhaustible floods of song as but one of all God's creatures can utter in His praise. There was little in that—it was only to open the bill and breathe; yet the man stopped as if struck—stopped and let fall his rifle, looked upward at the bird, covered his eyes with his hands and wept like a child! For the moment he was, indeed, a child, in spirit and in memory, dwelling again by the great river, over-against the Enchanted Land! Then with an effort of the will he pulled himself together, picked up his weapon and audibly damning himself for an idiot strode on. Passing an opening that reached into the heart of the little thicket he looked in, and there, supine upon the earth, its arms all abroad, its gray uniform stained with a single spot of blood upon the breast, its white face turned sharply upward and backward, lay the image of himself!—the body of John Grayrock, dead of a gunshot wound, and still warm! He had found his man.

As the unfortunate soldier knelt beside that masterwork of civil war the shrilling bird upon the bough overhead stilled her song and, flushed with sunset's crimson glory, glided silently away through the solemn spaces of the wood. At roll-call that evening in the Federal camp the name William Grayrock brought no response, nor ever again thereafter.

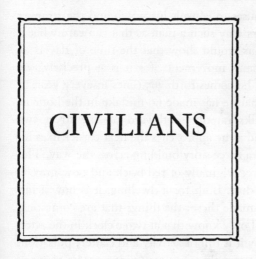

CIVILIANS

THE MAN OUT OF THE NOSE

AT the intersection of two certain streets in that part of San Francisco known by the rather loosely applied name of North Beach, is a vacant lot, which is rather more nearly level than is usually the case with lots, vacant or otherwise, in that region. Immediately at the back of it, to the south, however, the ground slopes steeply upward, the acclivity broken by three terraces cut into the soft rock. It is a place for goats and poor persons, several families of each class having occupied it jointly and amicably "from the foundation of the city." One of the humble habitations of the lowest terrace is noticeable for its rude resemblance to the human face, or rather to such a simulacrum of it as a boy might cut out of a hollowed pumpkin, meaning no offense to his race. The eyes are two circular windows, the nose is a door, the mouth an aperture caused by removal of a board below. There are no doorsteps. As a face, this house is too large; as a dwelling, too small. The blank, unmeaning stare of its lidless and browless eyes is uncanny.

Sometimes a man steps out of the nose, turns, passes the place where the right ear should be and making his way through the throng of children and goats obstructing the narrow walk between his neighbors' doors and the edge of the terrace gains the street by descending a flight of rickety stairs. Here he pauses to consult his watch and the stranger who happens to pass wonders why such a man as that can care what is the hour. Longer observations would show that the time of day is an important element in the man's movements, for it is at precisely two o'clock in the afternoon that he comes forth 365 times in every year.

Having satisfied himself that he has made no mistake in the hour he replaces the watch and walks rapidly southward up the street two squares, turns to the right and as he approaches the next corner fixes his eyes on an upper window in a three-story building across the way. This is a somewhat dingy structure, originally of red brick and now gray. It shows the touch of age and dust. Built for a dwelling, it is now a factory. I do not know what is made there; the things that are commonly made in a factory, I suppose. I only know that at two o'clock in the afternoon of every day but Sunday it is full of activity and clatter; pulsations of some great engine shake it and there are recurrent screams of wood tormented by the saw. At the window on which the man fixes an intensely expectant gaze nothing ever appears; the glass, in truth, has such a coating of dust that it has long ceased to be transparent. The man looks at it without stopping; he merely keeps turning his head more and more backward as he leaves the building behind. Passing along to the next corner, he turns to the left, goes round the block, and comes back till he reaches the point diagonally across the street from the factory—a point on his former course, which he then retraces, looking frequently backward over his right shoulder at the window while it is in sight. For many years he has not been known to vary his route nor to introduce a single innovation into his action. In a quarter of an hour he is again at the mouth of his dwelling, and a woman, who has for some time been standing in the nose, assists him to enter. He is seen no more until two o'clock the next day.

The woman is his wife. She supports herself and him by washing for the poor people among whom they live, at rates which destroy Chinese and domestic competition.

This man is about fifty-seven years of age, though he looks greatly older. His hair is dead white. He wears no beard, and is always newly shaven. His hands are clean, his nails well kept. In the matter of dress he is distinctly superior to his position, as indicated by his surroundings and the business of his wife. He is, indeed, very neatly, if not quite fashionably, clad. His silk hat has a date no earlier than the year before the last, and his boots, scrupulously polished, are innocent of patches. I am told that the suit which he wears during his daily excursions of fifteen minutes is not the one that he wears at home. Like everything else that he has, this is provided and kept in repair by the wife, and is renewed as frequently as her scanty means permit.

Thirty years ago John Hardshaw and his wife lived on Rincon Hill in one of the finest residences of that once aristocratic quarter. He had once been a physician, but having inherited a considerable estate from his father concerned himself no more about the ailments of his fellow-creatures and found as much work as he cared for in managing his own affairs. Both he and his wife were highly cultivated persons, and their house was frequented by a small set of such men and women as persons of their tastes would think worth knowing. So far as these knew, Mr. and Mrs. Hardshaw lived happily together; certainly the wife was devoted to her handsome and accomplished husband and exceedingly proud of him.

Among their acquaintances were the Barwells—man, wife and two young children—of Sacramento. Mr. Barwell was a civil and mining engineer, whose duties took him much from home and frequently to San Francisco. On these occasions his wife commonly accompanied him and passed much of her time at the house of her friend, Mrs. Hardshaw, always with her two children, of whom Mrs. Hardshaw, childless herself, grew fond. Unluckily, her husband grew equally fond of their mother—a good deal fonder. Still more unluckily, that attractive lady was less wise than weak.

At about three o'clock one autumn morning Officer No. 13 of the Sacramento police saw a man stealthily leaving the rear entrance of a gentleman's residence and promptly arrested him. The man—who wore a slouch hat and shaggy overcoat—offered the policeman one hundred, then five hundred, then one thousand dollars to be released. As he had less than the first mentioned sum on his person the officer treated his proposal with virtuous contempt. Before reaching the station the prisoner agreed to give him a check for ten thousand dollars and remain ironed in the willows along the river bank until it should be paid. As this only provoked new derision he would say no more, merely giving an obviously fictitious name. When he was searched at the station nothing of value was found on him but a miniature portrait of Mrs. Barwell—the lady of the house at which he was caught. The case was set with costly diamonds; and something in the quality of the man's linen sent a pang of unavailing regret through the severely incorruptible bosom of Officer No. 13. There was nothing about the prisoner's clothing nor person to identify him and he was booked for burglary under the name that he had given, the honorable name of John K. Smith. The K. was an inspiration upon which, doubtless, he greatly prided himself.

In the mean time the mysterious disappearance of John Hardshaw was agitating the gossips of Rincon Hill in San Francisco, and was even mentioned in one of the newspapers. It did not occur to the lady whom that journal considerately described as his "widow," to look for him in the city prison at Sacramento—a town which he was not known ever to have visited. As John K. Smith he was arraigned and, waiving examination, committed for trial.

About two weeks before the trial, Mrs. Hardshaw, accidentally learning that her husband was held in Sacramento under an assumed name on a charge of burglary, hastened to that city without daring to mention the matter to any one and presented herself at the prison, asking for an interview with her husband, John K. Smith. Haggard and ill with anxiety, wearing a plain traveling wrap which covered her from neck to foot, and in which she had passed the night on the steamboat, too anxious to sleep, she hardly showed for what she was, but her manner pleaded for her more strongly than anything that she chose to say in evidence of her right to admittance. She was permitted to see him alone.

What occurred during that distressing interview has never transpired; but later events prove that Hardshaw had found means to subdue her will to his own. She left the prison, a broken-hearted woman, refusing to answer a single question, and returning to her desolate home renewed, in a half-hearted way, her inquiries for her missing husband. A week later she was herself missing: she had "gone back to the States"— nobody knew any more than that.

On his trial the prisoner pleaded guilty—"by advice of his counsel," so his counsel said. Nevertheless, the judge, in whose mind several unusual circumstances had created a doubt, insisted on the district attorney placing Officer No. 13 on the stand, and the deposition of Mrs. Barwell, who was too ill to attend, was read to the jury. It was very brief: she knew nothing of the matter except that the likeness of herself was her property, and had, she thought, been left on the parlor table when she had retired on the night of the arrest. She had intended it as a present to her husband, then and still absent in Europe on business for a mining company.

This witness's manner when making the deposition at her residence was afterward described by the district attorney as most extraordinary. Twice she had refused to testify, and once, when the deposition lacked nothing but her signature, she had caught it from the clerk's hands and torn it in pieces. She had called her children to the bedside and embraced them with streaming eyes, then suddenly sending them from the room, she verified her statement by oath and signature, and fainted— "slick away," said the district attorney. It was at that time that her physician, arriving upon the scene, took in the situation at a glance and grasping the representative of the law by the collar chucked him into the street and kicked his assistant after him. The insulted majesty of the law was not vindicated; the victim of the indignity did not even mention anything of all this in court. He was ambitious to win his case, and the circumstances of the taking of that deposition were not such as would give it weight if related; and after all, the man on trial had committed an offense against the law's majesty only less heinous than that of the irascible physician.

By suggestion of the judge the jury rendered a verdict of guilty; there was nothing else to do, and the prisoner was sentenced to the penitentiary for three years. His counsel, who had objected to nothing and had made no plea for lenity—had, in fact, hardly said a word—wrung his client's hand and left the room. It was obvious to the whole bar that he had been engaged only to prevent the court from appointing counsel who might possibly insist on making a defense.

John Hardshaw served out his term at San Quentin, and when discharged was met at the prison gates by his wife, who had returned from "the States" to receive him. It is thought they went straight to Europe; anyhow, a general power-of-attorney to a lawyer still living among us— from whom I have many of the facts of this simple history—was executed in Paris. This lawyer in a short time sold everything that Hardshaw owned in California, and for years nothing was heard of the unfortunate couple; though many to whose ears had come vague and inaccurate intimations of their strange story, and who had known them, recalled their personality with tenderness and their misfortunes with compassion.

Some years later they returned, both broken in fortune and spirits and he in health. The purpose of their return I have not been able to ascertain. For some time they lived, under the name of Johnson, in a respectable enough quarter south of Market Street, pretty well out, and were never seen away from the vicinity of their dwelling. They must have had a little money left, for it is not known that the man had any occupation, the state of his health probably not permitting. The woman's devotion to her invalid husband was matter of remark among their neighbors; she seemed never absent from his side and always supporting and cheering him. They would sit for hours on one of the benches in a little public park, she reading to him, his hand in hers, her light touch occasionally visiting his pale brow, her still beautiful eyes frequently lifted from the book to look into his as she made some comment on the text, or closed the volume to beguile his mood with talk of—what? Nobody ever overheard a conversation between these two. The reader who has had the patience to follow their history to this point may possibly find a pleasure in conjecture: there was probably something to be avoided. The bearing of the man was one of profound dejection; indeed, the unsympathetic youth of the neighborhood, with that keen sense for visible characteristics which ever distinguishes the young male of our species, sometimes mentioned him among themselves by the name of Spoony Glum.

It occurred one day that John Hardshaw was possessed by the spirit of unrest. God knows what led him whither he went, but he crossed Market Street and held his way northward over the hills, and downward into the region known as North Beach. Turning aimlessly to the left he followed his toes along an unfamiliar street until he was opposite what for that period was a rather grand dwelling, and for this is a rather shabby factory. Casting his eyes casually upward he saw at an open window what it had been better that he had not seen—the face and figure of Elvira Barwell. Their eyes met. With a sharp exclamation, like the cry of a startled bird, the lady sprang to her feet and thrust her body half out of the window, clutching the casing on each side. Arrested by the cry, the people in the street below looked up. Hardshaw stood motionless, speechless, his eyes two flames. "Take care!" shouted some one in the crowd, as the woman strained further and further forward, defying the silent, implacable law of gravitation, as once she had defied that other law which God thundered from Sinai. The suddenness of her movements had tumbled a torrent of dark hair down her shoulders, and now it was blown about her cheeks, almost concealing her face. A moment so, and then—! A fearful cry rang through the street, as, losing her balance, she pitched headlong from the window, a confused and whirling mass of skirts, limbs, hair, and white face, and struck the pavement with a horrible sound and a force of impact that was felt a hundred feet away. For a moment all eyes refused their office and turned from the sickening spectacle on the sidewalk. Drawn again to that horror, they saw it strangely augmented. A man, hatless, seated flat upon the paving stones, held the broken, bleeding body against his breast, kissing the mangled cheeks and streaming mouth through tangles of wet hair, his own features indistinguishably crimson with the blood that half-strangled him and ran in rills from his soaken beard.

The reporter's task is nearly finished. The Barwells had that very morning returned from a two years' absence in Peru. A week later the widower, now doubly desolate, since there could be no missing the significance of Hardshaw's horrible demonstration, had sailed for I know not what distant port; he has never come back to stay. Hardshaw—as Johnson no longer—passed a year in the Stockton asylum for the insane, where also, through the influence of pitying friends, his wife was admitted to care for him. When he was discharged, not cured but harmless, they returned to the city; it would seem ever to have had some dreadful fascination for them. For a time they lived near the Mission Dolores, in poverty only less abject than that which is their present lot; but it was too far away from the objective point of the man's daily pilgrimage. They could not afford car fare. So that poor devil of an angel from Heaven—wife to this convict and lunatic—obtained, at a fair enough rental, the blank-faced shanty on the lower terrace of Goat Hill. Thence to the structure that was a dwelling and is a factory the distance is not so great; it is, in fact, an agreeable walk, judging from the man's eager and cheerful look as he takes it. The return journey appears to be a trifle wearisome.

AN ADVENTURE AT BROWNVILLE *

I TAUGHT a little country school near Brownville, which, as every one knows who has had the good luck to live there, is the capital of a considerable expanse of the finest scenery in California. The town is somewhat frequented in summer by a class of persons whom it is the habit of the local journal to call "pleasure seekers," but who by a juster classification would be known as "the sick and those in adversity." Brownville itself might rightly enough be described, indeed, as a summer place of last resort. It is fairly well endowed with boarding-houses, at the least pernicious of which I performed twice a day (lunching at the schoolhouse) the humble rite of cementing the alliance between soul and body. From this "hostelry" (as the local journal preferred to call it when it did not call it a "caravanserai") to the schoolhouse the distance by the wagon road was about a mile and a half; but there was a trail, very little used, which led over an intervening range of low, heavily wooded hills, considerably shortening the distance. By this trail I was returning one evening later than usual. It was the last day of the term and I had been detained at the schoolhouse until almost dark, preparing an account of my stewardship for the trustees—two of whom, I proudly reflected, would be able to read it, and the third (an instance of the dominion of mind over matter) would be overruled in his customary antagonism to the schoolmaster of his own creation.

I had gone not more than a quarter of the way when, finding an interest in the antics of a family of lizards which dwelt thereabout and seemed full of reptilian joy for their immunity from the ills incident to life at the Brownville House, I sat upon a fallen tree to observe them. As I leaned wearily against a branch of the gnarled old trunk the twilight deepened in the somber woods and the faint new moon began casting visible shadows and gilding the leaves of the trees with a tender but ghostly light.

I heard the sound of voices—a woman's, angry, impetuous, rising

* This story was written in collaboration with Miss Ina Lillian Peterson, to whom is rightly due the credit for whatever merit it may have.

against deep masculine tones, rich and musical. I strained my eyes, peering through the dusky shadows of the wood, hoping to get a view of the intruders on my solitude, but could see no one. For some yards in each direction I had an uninterrupted view of the trail, and knowing of no other within a half mile thought the persons heard must be approaching from the wood at one side. There was no sound but that of the voices, which were now so distinct that I could catch the words. That of the man gave me an impression of anger, abundantly confirmed by the matter spoken.

"I will have no threats; you are powerless, as you very well know. Let things remain as they are or, by God! you shall both suffer for it."

"What do you mean?"—this was the voice of the woman, a cultivated voice, the voice of a lady. "You would not—murder us."

There was no reply, at least none that was audible to me. During the silence I peered into the wood in hope to get a glimpse of the speakers, for I felt sure that this was an affair of gravity in which ordinary scruples ought not to count. It seemed to me that the woman was in peril; at any rate the man had not disavowed a willingness to murder. When a man is enacting the rôle of potential assassin he has not the right to choose his audience.

After some little time I saw them, indistinct in the moonlight among the trees. The man, tall and slender, seemed clothed in black; the woman wore, as nearly as I could make out, a gown of gray stuff. Evidently they were still unaware of my presence in the shadow, though for some reason when they renewed their conversation they spoke in lower tones and I could no longer understand. As I looked the woman seemed to sink to the ground and raise her hands in supplication, as is frequently done on the stage and never, so far as I knew, anywhere else, and I am now not altogether sure that it was done in this instance. The man fixed his eyes upon her; they seemed to glitter bleakly in the moonlight with an expression that made me apprehensive that he would turn them upon me. I do not know by what impulse I was moved, but I sprang to my feet out of the shadow. At that instant the figures vanished. I peered in vain through the spaces among the trees and clumps of undergrowth. The night wind rustled the leaves; the lizards had retired early, reptiles of exemplary habits. The little moon was already slipping behind a black hill in the west.

I went home, somewhat disturbed in mind, half doubting that I had heard or seen any living thing excepting the lizards. It all seemed a trifle odd and uncanny. It was as if among the several phenomena, objective and subjective, that made the sum total of the incident there had been an uncertain element which had diffused its dubious character over all—had leavened the whole mass with unreality. I did not like it.

At the breakfast table the next morning there was a new face; opposite me sat a young woman at whom I merely glanced as I took my seat. In speaking to the high and mighty female personage who condescended to seem to wait upon us, this girl soon invited my attention by the sound of her voice, which was like, yet not altogether like, the one still murmuring in my memory of the previous evening's adventure. A moment later another girl, a few years older, entered the room and sat at the left of the other, speaking to her a gentle "good morning." By *her* voice I was startled: it was without doubt the one of which the first girl's had reminded me. Here was the lady of the sylvan incident sitting bodily before me, "in her habit as she lived."

Evidently enough the two were sisters. With a nebulous kind of apprehension that I might be recognized as the mute inglorious hero of an adventure which had in my consciousness and conscience something of the character of eavesdropping, I allowed myself only a hasty cup of the lukewarm coffee thoughtfully provided by the prescient waitress for the emergency, and left the table. As I passed out of the house into the grounds I heard a rich, strong male voice singing an aria from "Rigoletto." I am bound to say that it was exquisitely sung, too, but there was something in the performance that displeased me, I could say neither what nor why, and I walked rapidly away.

Returning later in the day I saw the elder of the two young women standing on the porch and near her a tall man in black clothing—the man whom I had expected to see. All day the desire to know something of these persons had been uppermost in my mind and I now resolved to learn what I could of them in any way that was neither dishonorable nor low.

The man was talking easily and affably to his companion, but at the sound of my footsteps on the gravel walk he ceased, and turning about looked me full in the face. He was apparently of middle age, dark and uncommonly handsome. His attire was faultless, his bearing easy and graceful, the look which he turned upon me open, free, and devoid of any suggestion of rudeness. Nevertheless it affected me with a distinct

emotion which on subsequent analysis in memory appeared to be compounded of hatred and dread— I am unwilling to call it fear. A second
later the man and woman had disappeared. They seemed to have a trick
of disappearing. On entering the house, however, I saw them through
the open doorway of the parlor as I passed; they had merely stepped
through a window which opened down to the floor.

Cautiously "approached" on the subject of her new guests my landlady
proved not ungracious. Restated with, I hope, some small reverence for
English grammar the facts were these: the two girls were Pauline and
Eva Maynard of San Francisco; the elder was Pauline. The man was
Richard Benning, their guardian, who had been the most intimate friend
of their father, now deceased. Mr. Benning had brought them to Brownville in the hope that the mountain climate might benefit Eva, who was
thought to be in danger of consumption.

Upon these short and simple annals the landlady wrought an em-
broidery of eulogium which abundantly attested her faith in Mr. Benning's will and ability to pay for the best that her house afforded. That
he had a good heart was evident to her from his devotion to his two
beautiful wards and his really touching solicitude for their comfort. The
evidence impressed me as insufficient and I silently found the Scotch
verdict, "Not proven."

Certainly Mr. Benning was most attentive to his wards. In my strolls
about the country I frequently encountered them—sometimes in company with other guests of the hotel—exploring the gulches, fishing, rifle
shooting, and otherwise wiling away the monotony of country life; and
although I watched them as closely as good manners would permit I
saw nothing that would in any way explain the strange words that I
had overheard in the wood. I had grown tolerably well acquainted with
the young ladies and could exchange looks and even greetings with their
guardian without actual repugnance.

A month went by and I had almost ceased to interest myself in their
affairs when one night our entire little community was thrown into
excitement by an event which vividly recalled my experience in the
forest.

This was the death of the elder girl, Pauline.

The sisters had occupied the same bedroom on the third floor of the
house. Waking in the gray of the morning Eva had found Pauline dead
beside her. Later, when the poor girl was weeping beside the body amid

a throng of sympathetic if not very considerate persons, Mr. Benning entered the room and appeared to be about to take her hand. She drew away from the side of the dead and moved slowly toward the door.

"It is you," she said—"you who have done this. You—you—you!"

"She is raving," he said in a low voice. He followed her, step by step, as she retreated, his eyes fixed upon hers with a steady gaze in which there was nothing of tenderness nor of compassion. She stopped; the hand that she had raised in accusation fell to her side, her dilated eyes contracted visibly, the lids slowly dropped over them, veiling their strange wild beauty, and she stood motionless and almost as white as the dead girl lying near. The man took her hand and put his arm gently about her shoulders, as if to support her. Suddenly she burst into a passion of tears and clung to him as a child to its mother. He smiled with a smile that affected me most disagreeably—perhaps any kind of smile would have done so—and led her silently out of the room.

There was an inquest—and the customary verdict: the deceased, it appeared, came to her death through "heart disease." It was before the invention of heart *failure,* though the heart of poor Pauline had indubitably failed. The body was embalmed and taken to San Francisco by some one summoned thence for the purpose, neither Eva nor Benning accompanying it. Some of the hotel gossips ventured to think that very strange, and a few hardy spirits went so far as to think it very strange indeed; but the good landlady generously threw herself into the breach, saying it was owing to the precarious nature of the girl's health. It is not of record that either of the two persons most affected and apparently least concerned made any explanation.

One evening about a week after the death I went out upon the veranda of the hotel to get a book that I had left there. Under some vines shutting out the moonlight from a part of the space I saw Richard Benning, for whose apparition I was prepared by having previously heard the low, sweet voice of Eva Maynard, whom also I now discerned, standing before him with one hand raised to his shoulder and her eyes, as nearly as I could judge, gazing upward into his. He held her disengaged hand and his head was bent with a singular dignity and grace. Their attitude was that of lovers, and as I stood in deep shadow to observe I felt even guiltier than on that memorable night in the wood. I was about to retire, when the girl spoke, and the contrast between her words and her attitude was so surprising that I remained, because I had merely forgotten to go away.

"You will take my life," she said, "as you did Pauline's. I know your intention as well as I know your power, and I ask nothing, only that you finish your work without needless delay and let me be at peace."

He made no reply—merely let go the hand that he was holding, removed the other from his shoulder, and turning away descended the steps leading to the garden and disappeared in the shrubbery. But a moment later I heard, seemingly from a great distance, his fine clear voice in a barbaric chant, which as I listened brought before some inner spiritual sense a consciousness of some far, strange land peopled with beings having forbidden powers. The song held me in a kind of spell, but when it had died away I recovered and instantly perceived what I thought an opportunity. I walked out of my shadow to where the girl stood. She turned and stared at me with something of the look, it seemed to me, of a hunted hare. Possibly my intrusion had frightened her.

"Miss Maynard," I said, "I beg you to tell me who that man is and the nature of his power over you. Perhaps this is rude in me, but it is not a matter for idle civilities. When a woman is in danger any man has a right to act."

She listened without visible emotion—almost I thought without interest, and when I had finished she closed her big blue eyes as if unspeakably weary.

"You can do nothing," she said.

I took hold of her arm, gently shaking her as one shakes a person falling into a dangerous sleep.

"You must rouse yourself," I said; "something must be done and you must give me leave to act. You have said that that man killed your sister, and I believe it—that he will kill you, and I believe that."

She merely raised her eyes to mine.

"Will you not tell me all?" I added.

"There is nothing to be done, I tell you—nothing. And if I could do anything I would not. It does not matter in the least. We shall be here only two days more; we go away then, oh, so far! If you have observed anything, I beg you to be silent."

"But this is madness, girl." I was trying by rough speech to break the deadly repose of her manner. "You have accused him of murder.

Unless you explain these things to me I shall lay the matter before the authorities."

This roused her, but in a way that I did not like. She lifted her head proudly and said: "Do not meddle, sir, in what does not concern you. This is my affair, Mr. Moran, not yours."

"It concerns every person in the country—in the world," I answered, with equal coldness. "If you had no love for your sister I, at least, am concerned for you."

"Listen," she interrupted, leaning toward me. "I loved her, yes, God knows! But more than that—beyond all, beyond expression, I love *him*. You have overheard a secret, but you shall not make use of it to harm him. I shall deny all. Your word against mine—it will be that. Do you think your 'authorities' will believe you?"

She was now smiling like an angel and, God help me! I was heels over head in love with her! Did she, by some of the many methods of divination known to her sex, read my feelings? Her whole manner had altered.

"Come," she said, almost coaxingly, "promise that you will not be impolite again." She took my arm in the most friendly way. "Come, I will walk with you. He will not know—he will remain away all night."

Up and down the veranda we paced in the moonlight, she seemingly forgetting her recent bereavement, cooing and murmuring girl-wise of every kind of nothing in all Brownville; I silent, consciously awkward and with something of the feeling of being concerned in an intrigue. It was a revelation—this most charming and apparently blameless creature coolly and confessedly deceiving the man for whom a moment before she had acknowledged and shown the supreme love which finds even death an acceptable endearment.

"Truly," I thought in my inexperience, "here is something new under the moon."

And the moon must have smiled.

Before we parted I had exacted a promise that she would walk with me the next afternoon—before going away forever—to the Old Mill, one of Brownville's revered antiquities, erected in 1860.

"If he is not about," she added gravely, as I let go the hand she had given me at parting, and of which, may the good saints forgive me, I strove vainly to repossess myself when she had said it—so charming, as the wise Frenchman has pointed out, do we find woman's infidelity when we are its objects, not its victims. In apportioning his benefactions that night the Angel of Sleep overlooked me.

The Brownville House dined early, and after dinner the next day Miss Maynard, who had not been at table, came to me on the veranda, attired in the demurest of walking costumes, saying not a word. "He" was evidently "not about." We went slowly up the road that led to the Old Mill. She was apparently not strong and at times took my arm, relinquishing it and taking it again rather capriciously, I thought. Her mood, or rather her succession of moods, was as mutable as skylight in a rippling sea. She jested as if she had never heard of such a thing as death, and laughed on the lightest incitement, and directly afterward would sing a few bars of some grave melody with such tenderness of expression that I had to turn away my eyes lest she should see the evidence of her success in art, if art it was, not artlessness, as then I was compelled to think it. And she said the oddest things in the most unconventional way, skirting sometimes unfathomable abysms of thought, where I had hardly the courage to set foot. In short, she was fascinating in a thousand and fifty different ways, and at every step I executed a new and profounder emotional folly, a hardier spiritual indiscretion, incurring fresh liability to arrest by the constabulary of conscience for infractions of my own peace.

Arriving at the mill, she made no pretense of stopping, but turned into a trail leading through a field of stubble toward a creek. Crossing by a rustic bridge we continued on the trail, which now led uphill to one of the most picturesque spots in the country. The Eagle's Nest, it was called —the summit of a cliff that rose sheer into the air to a height of hundreds of feet above the forest at its base. From this elevated point we had a noble view of another valley and of the opposite hills flushed with the last rays of the setting sun. As we watched the light escaping to higher and higher planes from the encroaching flood of shadow filling the valley we heard footsteps, and in another moment were joined by Richard Benning.

"I saw you from the road," he said carelessly; "so I came up."

Being a fool, I neglected to take him by the throat and pitch him into the treetops below, but muttered some polite lie instead. On the girl the effect of his coming was immediate and unmistakable. Her face was suffused with the glory of love's transfiguration: the red light of the sunset had not been more obvious in her eyes than was now the lovelight that replaced it.

"I am so glad you came!" she said, giving him both her hands; and, God help me! it was manifestly true.

Seating himself upon the ground he began a lively dissertation upon the wild flowers of the region, a number of which he had with him. In the middle of a facetious sentence he suddenly ceased speaking and fixed his eyes upon Eva, who leaned against the stump of a tree, absently plaiting grasses. She lifted her eyes in a startled way to his, as if she had *felt* his look. She then rose, cast away her grasses, and moved slowly away from him. He also rose, continuing to look at her. He had still in his hand the bunch of flowers. The girl turned, as if to speak, but said nothing. I recall clearly now something of which I was but half-conscious then —the dreadful contrast between the smile upon her lips and the terrified expression in her eyes as she met his steady and imperative gaze. I know nothing of how it happened, nor how it was that I did not sooner understand; I only know that with the smile of an angel upon her lips and that look of terror in her beautiful eyes Eva Maynard sprang from the cliff and shot crashing into the tops of the pines below!

How and how long afterward I reached the place I cannot say, but Richard Benning was already there, kneeling beside the dreadful thing that had been a woman.

"She is dead—quite dead," he said coldly. "I will go to town for assistance. Please do me the favor to remain."

He rose to his feet and moved away, but in a moment had stopped and turned about.

"You have doubtless observed, my friend," he said, "that this was entirely her own act. I did not rise in time to prevent it, and you, not knowing her mental condition—you could not, of course, have suspected."

His manner maddened me.

"You are as much her assassin," I said, "as if your damnable hands had cut her throat."

He shrugged his shoulders without reply and, turning, walked away. A moment later I heard, through the deepening shadows of the wood into which he had disappeared, a rich, strong, baritone voice singing *"La donna e mobile,"* from "Rigoletto."

THE FAMOUS GILSON BEQUEST

It was rough on Gilson. Such was the terse, cold, but not altogether unsympathetic judgment of the better public opinion at Mammon Hill— the dictum of respectability. The verdict of the opposite, or rather the opposing, element—the element that lurked red-eyed and restless about Moll Gurney's "deadfall," while respectability took it with sugar at Mr. Jo. Bentley's gorgeous "saloon"—was to pretty much the same general effect, though somewhat more ornately expressed by the use of picturesque expletives, which it is needless to quote. Virtually, Mammon Hill was a unit on the Gilson question. And it must be confessed that in a merely temporal sense all was not well with Mr. Gilson. He had that morning been led into town by Mr. Brentshaw and publicly charged with horse stealing; the sheriff meantime busying himself about The Tree with a new manila rope and Carpenter Pete being actively employed between drinks upon a pine box about the length and breadth of Mr. Gilson. Society having rendered its verdict, there remained between Gilson and eternity only the decent formality of a trial.

These are the short and simple annals of the prisoner: He had recently been a resident of New Jerusalem, on the north fork of the Little Stony, but had come to the newly discovered placers of Mammon Hill immediately before the "rush" by which the former place was depopulated. The discovery of the new diggings had occurred opportunely for Mr. Gilson, for it had only just before been intimated to him by a New Jerusalem vigilance committee that it would better his prospects in, and for, life to go somewhere; and the list of places to which he could safely go did not include any of the older camps; so he naturally established himself at Mammon Hill. Being eventually followed thither by all his judges, he ordered his conduct with considerable circumspection, but as he had never been known to do an honest day's work at any industry sanctioned by the stern local code of morality except draw poker he was still an object of suspicion. Indeed, it was conjectured that he was the author of the many daring depredations that had recently been committed with pan and brush on the sluice boxes.

Prominent among those in whom this suspicion had ripened into a steadfast conviction was Mr. Brentshaw. At all seasonable and unseasonable times Mr. Brentshaw avowed his belief in Mr. Gilson's connection with these unholy midnight enterprises, and his own willingness to prepare a way for the solar beams through the body of any one who might think it expedient to utter a different opinion—which, in his presence, no one was more careful not to do than the peace-loving person most concerned. Whatever may have been the truth of the matter, it is certain that Gilson frequently lost more "clean dust" at Jo. Bentley's faro table than it was recorded in local history that he had ever honestly earned at draw poker in all the days of the camp's existence. But at last Mr. Bentley—fearing, it may be, to lose the more profitable patronage of Mr. Brentshaw—peremptorily refused to let Gilson copper the queen, intimating at the same time, in his frank, forthright way, that the privilege of losing money at "this bank" was a blessing appertaining to, proceeding logically from, and coterminous with, a condition of notorious commercial righteousness and social good repute.

The Hill thought it high time to look after a person whom its most honored citizen had felt it his duty to rebuke at a considerable personal sacrifice. The New Jerusalem contingent, particularly, began to abate something of the toleration begotten of amusement at their own blunder in exiling an objectionable neighbor from the place which they had left to the place whither they had come. Mammon Hill was at last of one mind. Not much was said, but that Gilson must hang was "in the air." But at this critical juncture in his affairs he showed signs of an altered life if not a changed heart. Perhaps it was only that "the bank" being closed against him he had no further use for gold dust. Anyhow the sluice boxes were molested no more forever. But it was impossible to repress the abounding energies of such a nature as his, and he continued, possibly from habit, the tortuous courses which he had pursued for profit of Mr. Bentley. After a few tentative and resultless undertakings in the way of highway robbery—if one may venture to designate road-agency by so harsh a name—he made one or two modest essays in horse-herding, and it was in the midst of a promising enterprise of this character, and just as he had taken the tide in his affairs at its flood, that he made shipwreck. For on a misty, moonlight night Mr. Brentshaw rode up alongside a person who was evidently leaving that part of the country, laid a hand upon the halter connecting Mr. Gilson's wrist with

Mr. Harper's bay mare, tapped him familiarly on the cheek with the barrel of a navy revolver and requested the pleasure of his company in a direction opposite to that in which he was traveling.

It was indeed rough on Gilson.

On the morning after his arrest he was tried, convicted, and sentenced. It only remains, so far as concerns his earthly career, to hang him, reserving for more particular mention his last will and testament, which, with great labor, he contrived in prison, and in which, probably from some confused and imperfect notion of the rights of captors, he bequeathed everything he owned to his "lawfle execketer," Mr. Brentshaw. The bequest, however, was made conditional on the legatee taking the testator's body from The Tree and "planting it white."

So Mr. Gilson was—I was about to say "swung off," but I fear there has been already something too much of slang in this straightforward statement of facts; besides, the manner in which the law took its course is more accurately described in the terms employed by the judge in passing sentence: Mr. Gilson was "strung up."

In due season Mr. Brentshaw, somewhat touched, it may well be, by the empty compliment of the bequest, repaired to The Tree to pluck the fruit thereof. When taken down the body was found to have in its waistcoat pocket a duly attested codicil to the will already noted. The nature of its provisions accounted for the manner in which it had been withheld, for had Mr. Brentshaw previously been made aware of the conditions under which he was to succeed to the Gilson estate he would indubitably have declined the responsibility. Briefly stated, the purport of the codicil was as follows:

Whereas, at divers times and in sundry places, certain persons had asserted that during his life the testator had robbed their sluice boxes; therefore, if during the five years next succeeding the date of this instrument any one should make proof of such assertion before a court of law, such person was to receive as reparation the entire personal and real estate of which the testator died seized and possessed, minus the expenses of court and a stated compensation to the executor, Henry Clay Brentshaw; provided, that if more than one person made such proof the estate was to be equally divided between or among them. But in case none should succeed in so establishing the testator's guilt, then the whole property, minus court expenses, as aforesaid, should go to the said Henry Clay Brentshaw for his own use, as stated in the will.

The syntax of this remarkable document was perhaps open to critical objection, but that was clearly enough the meaning of it. The orthography conformed to no recognized system, but being mainly phonetic it was not ambiguous. As the probate judge remarked, it would take five aces to beat it. Mr. Brentshaw smiled good-humoredly, and after performing the last sad rites with amusing ostentation, had himself duly sworn as executor and conditional legatee under the provisions of a law hastily passed (at the instance of the member from the Mammon Hill district) by a facetious legislature; which law was afterward discovered to have created also three or four lucrative offices and authorized the expenditure of a considerable sum of public money for the construction of a certain railway bridge that with greater advantage might perhaps have been erected on the line of some actual railway.

Of course Mr. Brentshaw expected neither profit from the will nor litigation in consequence of its unusual provisions; Gilson, although frequently "flush," had been a man whom assessors and tax collectors were well satisfied to lose no money by. But a careless and merely formal search among his papers revealed title deeds to valuable estates in the East and certificates of deposit for incredible sums in banks less severely scrupulous than that of Mr. Jo. Bentley.

The astounding news got abroad directly, throwing the Hill into a fever of excitement. The Mammon Hill *Patriot*, whose editor had been a leading spirit in the proceedings that resulted in Gilson's departure from New Jerusalem, published a most complimentary obituary notice of the deceased, and was good enough to call attention to the fact that his degraded contemporary, the Squaw Gulch *Clarion*, was bringing virtue into contempt by beslavering with flattery the memory of one who in life had spurned the vile sheet as a nuisance from his door. Undeterred by the press, however, claimants under the will were not slow in presenting themselves with their evidence; and great as was the Gilson estate it appeared conspicuously paltry considering the vast number of sluice boxes from which it was averred to have been obtained. The country rose as one man!

Mr. Brentshaw was equal to the emergency. With a shrewd application of humble auxiliary devices, he at once erected above the bones of his benefactor a costly monument, overtopping every rough headboard in the cemetery, and on this he judiciously caused to be inscribed an epitaph of his own composing, eulogizing the honesty, public spirit and cognate virtues of him who slept beneath, "a victim to the unjust aspersions of Slander's viper brood."

Moreover, he employed the best legal talent in the Territory to defend the memory of his departed friend, and for five long years the Territorial courts were occupied with litigation growing out of the Gilson bequest. To fine forensic abilities Mr. Brentshaw opposed abilities more finely forensic; in bidding for purchasable favors he offered prices which utterly deranged the market; the judges found at his hospitable board entertainment for man and beast, the like of which had never been spread in the Territory; with mendacious witnesses he confronted witnesses of superior mendacity.

Nor was the battle confined to the temple of the blind goddess—it invaded the press, the pulpit, the drawing-room. It raged in the mart, the exchange, the school; in the gulches, and on the street corners. And upon the last day of the memorable period to which legal action under the Gilson will was limited, the sun went down upon a region in which the moral sense was dead, the social conscience callous, the intellectual capacity dwarfed, enfeebled, and confused! But Mr. Brentshaw was victorious all along the line.

On that night it so happened that the cemetery in one corner of which lay the now honored ashes of the late Milton Gilson, Esq., was partly under water. Swollen by incessant rains, Cat Creek had spilled over its banks an angry flood which, after scooping out unsightly hollows wherever the soil had been disturbed, had partly subsided, as if ashamed of the sacrilege, leaving exposed much that had been piously concealed. Even the famous Gilson monument, the pride and glory of Mammon Hill, was no longer a standing rebuke to the "viper brood"; succumbing to the sapping current it had toppled prone to earth. The ghoulish flood had exhumed the poor, decayed pine coffin, which now lay half-exposed, in pitiful contrast to the pompous monolith which, like a giant note of admiration, emphasized the disclosure.

To this depressing spot, drawn by some subtle influence he had sought neither to resist nor analyze, came Mr. Brentshaw. An altered man was Mr. Brentshaw. Five years of toil, anxiety, and wakefulness had dashed his black locks with streaks and patches of gray, bowed his fine figure, drawn sharp and angular his face, and debased his walk to a doddering shuffle. Nor had this lustrum of fierce contention wrought less upon his heart and intellect. The careless good humor that had prompted him to accept the trust of the dead man had given place to a fixed habit of melancholy. The firm, vigorous intellect had overripened into the mental mellowness of second childhood. His broad understanding had narrowed to the accommodation of a single idea; and in place of the quiet, cynical incredulity of former days, there was in him a haunting faith in the supernatural, that flitted and fluttered about his soul, shadowy, batlike, ominous of insanity. Unsettled in all else, his understanding clung to one conviction with the tenacity of a wrecked intellect. That was an unshaken belief in the entire blamelessness of the dead Gilson. He had so often sworn to this in court and asserted it in private conversation—had so frequently and so triumphantly established it by testimony that had come expensive to him (for that very day he had paid the last dollar of the Gilson estate to Mr. Jo. Bentley, the last witness to the Gilson good character)—that it had become to him a sort of religious faith. It seemed to him the one great central and basic truth of life—the sole serene verity in a world of lies.

On that night, as he seated himself pensively upon the prostrate monument, trying by the uncertain moonlight to spell out the epitaph which five years before he had composed with a chuckle that memory had not recorded, tears of remorse came into his eyes as he remembered that he had been mainly instrumental in compassing by a false accusation this good man's death; for during some of the legal proceedings, Mr. Harper, for a consideration (forgotten) had come forward and sworn that in the little transaction with his bay mare the deceased had acted in strict accordance with the Harperian wishes, confidentially communicated to the deceased and by him faithfully concealed at the cost of his life. All that Mr. Brentshaw had since done for the dead man's memory seemed pitifully inadequate—most mean, paltry, and debased with selfishness!

As he sat there, torturing himself with futile regrets, a faint shadow fell across his eyes. Looking toward the moon, hanging low in the west, he saw what seemed a vague, watery cloud obscuring her; but as it moved so that her beams lit up one side of it he perceived the clear, sharp outline of a human figure. The apparition became momentarily more distinct, and grew, visibly; it was drawing near. Dazed as were his senses, half locked up with terror and confounded with dreadful imaginings, Mr. Brentshaw yet could but perceive, or think he perceived, in this unearthly shape a strange similitude to the mortal part of the late Milton Gilson, as that person had looked when taken from The

Tree five years before. The likeness was indeed complete, even to the full, stony eyes, and a certain shadowy circle about the neck. It was without coat or hat, precisely as Gilson had been when laid in his poor, cheap casket by the not ungentle hands of Carpenter Pete—for whom some one had long since performed the same neighborly office. The spectre, if such it was, seemed to bear something in its hands which Mr. Brentshaw could not clearly make out. It drew nearer, and paused at last beside the coffin containing the ashes of the late Mr. Gilson, the lid of which was awry, half disclosing the uncertain interior. Bending over this, the phantom seemed to shake into it from a basin some dark substance of dubious consistency, then glided stealthily back to the lowest part of the cemetery. Here the retiring flood had stranded a number of open coffins, about and among which it gurgled with low sobbings and stilly whispers. Stooping over one of these, the apparition carefully brushed its contents into the basin, then returning to its own casket, emptied the vessel into that, as before. This mysterious operation was repeated at every exposed coffin, the ghost sometimes dipping its laden basin into the running water, and gently agitating it to free it of the baser clay, always hoarding the residuum in its own private box. In short, the immortal part of the late Milton Gilson was cleaning up the dust of its neighbors and providently adding the same to its own.

Perhaps it was a phantasm of a disordered mind in a fevered body. Perhaps it was a solemn farce enacted by pranking existences that throng the shadows lying along the border of another world. God knows; to us is permitted only the knowledge that when the sun of another day touched with a grace of gold the ruined cemetery of Mammon Hill his kindliest beam fell upon the white, still face of Henry Brentshaw, dead among the dead.

THE APPLICANT

PUSHING his adventurous shins through the deep snow that had fallen overnight, and encouraged by the glee of his little sister, following in the open way that he made, a sturdy small boy, the son of Grayville's most distinguished citizen, struck his foot against something of which there was no visible sign on the surface of the snow. It is the purpose of this narrative to explain how it came to be there.

No one who has had the advantage of passing through Grayville by day can have failed to observe the large stone building crowning the low hill to the north of the railway station—that is to say, to the right in going toward Great Mowbray. It is a somewhat dull-looking edifice, of the Early Comatose order, and appears to have been designed by an architect who shrank from publicity, and although unable to conceal his work—even compelled, in this instance, to set it on an eminence in the sight of men—did what he honestly could to insure it against a second look. So far as concerns its outer and visible aspect, the Abersush Home for Old Men is unquestionably inhospitable to human attention. But it is a building of great magnitude, and cost its benevolent founder the profit of many a cargo of the teas and silks and spices that his ships brought up from the under-world when he was in trade in Boston; though the main expense was its endowment. Altogether, this reckless person had robbed his heirs-at-law of no less a sum than half a million dollars and flung it away in riotous giving. Possibly it was with a view to get out of sight of the silent big witness to his extravagance that he shortly afterward disposed of all his Grayville property that remained to him, turned his back upon the scene of his prodigality and went off across the sea in one of his own ships. But the gossips who got their inspiration most directly from Heaven declared that he went in search of a wife—a theory not easily reconciled with that of the village humorist, who solemnly averred that the bachelor philanthropist had departed this life (left Grayville, to wit) because the marriageable maidens had made it too hot to hold him. However this may have been, he had not returned, and although at long intervals there had come to Grayville, in a desultory way, vague rumors of his wanderings in strange lands, no one seemed certainly to know about him, and to the new generation he was no more than a name. But from above the portal of the Home for Old Men the name shouted in stone.

Despite its unpromising exterior, the Home is a fairly commodious place of retreat from the ills that its inmates have incurred by being poor and old and men. At the time embraced in this brief chronicle they were in number about a score, but in acerbity, querulousness, and general ingratitude they could hardly be reckoned at fewer than a hundred; at least that was the estimate of the superintendent, Mr. Silas Tilbody. It was Mr. Tilbody's steadfast conviction that always, in admitting new old men to replace those who had gone to another and a better Home, the trustees had distinctly in will the infraction of his peace, and the trial of his patience. In truth, the longer the institution was connected with him, the stronger was his feeling that the founder's scheme of benevolence was sadly impaired by providing any inmates at all. He had not much imagination, but with what he had he was addicted to the reconstruction of the Home for Old Men into a kind of "castle in Spain," with himself as castellan, hospitably entertaining about a score of sleek and prosperous middle-aged gentlemen, consummately good-humored and civilly willing to pay for their board and lodging. In this revised project of philanthropy the trustees, to whom he was indebted for his office and responsible for his conduct, had not the happiness to appear. As to them, it was held by the village humorist aforementioned that in their management of the great charity Providence had thoughtfully supplied an incentive to thrift. With the inference which he expected to be drawn from that view we have nothing to do; it had neither support nor denial from the inmates, who certainly were most concerned. They lived out their little remnant of life, crept into graves neatly numbered, and were succeeded by other old men as like them as could be desired by the Adversary of Peace. If the Home was a place of punishment for the sin of unthrift the veteran offenders sought justice with a persistence that attested the sincerity of their penitence. It is to one of these that the reader's attention is now invited.

In the matter of attire this person was not altogether engaging. But for this season, which was midwinter, a careless observer might have looked upon him as a clever device of the husbandman indisposed to share the fruits of his toil with the crows that toil not, neither spin—an error that might not have been dispelled without longer and closer observation than he seemed to court; for his progress up Abersush Street, toward the Home in the gloom of the winter evening, was not visibly faster than what might have been expected of a scarecrow blessed with youth, health, and discontent. The man was indisputably ill-clad, yet not without a certain fitness and good taste, withal; for he was obviously an applicant for admittance to the Home, where poverty was a qualification. In the army of indigence the uniform is rags; they serve to distinguish the rank and file from the recruiting officers.

As the old man, entering the gate of the grounds, shuffled up the broad walk, already white with the fast-falling snow, which from time to time he feebly shook from its various coigns of vantage on his person, he came under inspection of the large globe lamp that burned always by night over the great door of the building. As if unwilling to incur its revealing beams, he turned to the left and, passing a considerable distance along the face of the building, rang at a smaller door emitting a dimmer ray that came from within, through the fanlight, and expended itself incuriously overhead. The door was opened by no less a personage than the great Mr. Tilbody himself. Observing his visitor, who at once uncovered, and somewhat shortened the radius of the permanent curvature of his back, the great man gave visible token of neither surprise nor displeasure. Mr. Tilbody was, indeed, in an uncommonly good humor, a phenomenon ascribable doubtless to the cheerful influence of the season; for this was Christmas Eve, and the morrow would be that blessed 365th part of the year that all Christian souls set apart for mighty feats of goodness and joy. Mr. Tilbody was so full of the spirit of the season that his fat face and pale blue eyes, whose ineffectual fire served to distinguish it from an untimely summer squash, effused so genial a glow that it seemed a pity that he could not have lain down in it, basking in the consciousness of his own identity. He was hatted, booted, overcoated, and umbrellaed, as became a person who was about to expose himself to the night and the storm on an errand of charity; for Mr. Tilbody had just parted from his wife and children to go "down town" and purchase the wherewithal to confirm the annual falsehood about the hunch-bellied saint who frequents the chimneys to reward little boys and girls who are good, and especially truthful. So he did not invite the old man in, but saluted him cheerily:

"Hello! just in time; a moment later and you would have missed me. Come, I have no time to waste; we'll walk a little way together."

"Thank you," said the old man, upon whose thin and white but not ignoble face the light from the open door showed an expression that was perhaps disappointment; "but if the trustees—if my application—"

"The trustees," Mr. Tilbody said, closing more doors than one, and cutting off two kinds of light, "have agreed that your application disagrees with them."

Certain sentiments are inappropriate to Christmastide, but Humor, like Death, has all seasons for his own.

"Oh, my God!" cried the old man, in so thin and husky a tone that the invocation was anything but impressive, and to at least one of his two auditors sounded, indeed, somewhat ludicrous. To the Other—but that is a matter which laymen are devoid of the light to expound.

"Yes," continued Mr. Tilbody, accommodating his gait to that of his companion, who was mechanically, and not very successfully, retracing the track that he had made through the snow; "they have decided that, under the circumstances—under the very peculiar circumstances, you understand—it would be inexpedient to admit you. As superintendent and *ex officio* secretary of the honorable board"—as Mr. Tilbody "read his title clear" the magnitude of the big building, seen through its veil of falling snow, appeared to suffer somewhat in comparison—"it is my duty to inform you that, in the words of Deacon Byram, the chairman, your presence in the Home would—under the circumstances—be peculiarly embarrassing. I felt it my duty to submit to the honorable board the statement that you made to me yesterday of your needs, your physical condition, and the trials which it has pleased Providence to send upon you in your very proper effort to present your claims in person; but, after careful, and I may say prayerful, consideration of your case—with something too, I trust, of the large charitableness appropriate to the season—it was decided that we would not be justified in doing anything likely to impair the usefulness of the institution intrusted (under Providence) to our care."

They had now passed out of the grounds; the street lamp opposite the gate was dimly visible through the snow. Already the old man's former track was obliterated, and he seemed uncertain as to which way he should go. Mr. Tilbody had drawn a little away from him, but paused

and turned half toward him, apparently reluctant to forego the continuing opportunity.

"Under the circumstances," he resumed, "the decision—"

But the old man was inaccessible to the suasion of his verbosity; he had
crossed the street into a vacant lot and was going forward, rather deviously toward nowhere in particular—which, he having nowhere in particular to go to, was not so reasonless a proceeding as it looked.

And that is how it happened that the next morning, when the church
bells of all Grayville were ringing with an added unction appropriate to
the day, the sturdy little son of Deacon Byram, breaking a way through
the snow to the place of worship, struck his foot against the body of
Amasa Abersush, philanthropist.

A WATCHER BY THE DEAD

I

IN an upper room of an unoccupied dwelling in the part of San
Francisco known as North Beach lay the body of a man, under a sheet.
The hour was near nine in the evening; the room was dimly lighted by
a single candle. Although the weather was warm, the two windows, contrary to the custom which gives the dead plenty of air, were closed and
the blinds drawn down. The furniture of the room consisted of but three
pieces—an arm-chair, a small reading-stand supporting the candle, and
a long kitchen table, supporting the body of the man. All these, as also
the corpse, seemed to have been recently brought in, for an observer,
had there been one, would have seen that all were free from dust, whereas
everything else in the room was pretty thickly coated with it, and there
were cobwebs in the angles of the walls.

Under the sheet the outlines of the body could be traced, even the
features, these having that unnaturally sharp definition which seems to
belong to faces of the dead, but is really characteristic of those only that
have been wasted by disease. From the silence of the room one would

rightly have inferred that it was not in the front of the house, facing a street. It really faced nothing but a high breast of rock, the rear of the building being set into a hill.

As a neighboring church clock was striking nine with an indolence which seemed to imply such an indifference to the flight of time that one could hardly help wondering why it took the trouble to strike at all, the single door of the room was opened and a man entered, advancing toward the body. As he did so the door closed, apparently of its own volition; there was a grating, as of a key turned with difficulty, and the snap of the lock bolt as it shot into its socket. A sound of retiring footsteps in the passage outside ensued, and the man was to all appearance a prisoner. Advancing to the table, he stood a moment looking down at the body; then with a slight shrug of the shoulders walked over to one of the windows and hoisted the blind. The darkness outside was absolute, the panes were covered with dust, but by wiping this away he could see that the window was fortified with strong iron bars crossing it within a few inches of the glass and imbedded in the masonry on each side. He examined the other window. It was the same. He manifested no great curiosity in the matter, did not even so much as raise the sash. If he was a prisoner he was apparently a tractable one. Having completed his examination of the room, he seated himself in the arm-chair, took a book from his pocket, drew the stand with its candle alongside and began to read.

The man was young—not more than thirty—dark in complexion, smooth-shaven, with brown hair. His face was thin and high-nosed, with a broad forehead and a "firmness" of the chin and jaw which is said by those having it to denote resolution. The eyes were gray and steadfast, not moving except with definitive purpose. They were now for the greater part of the time fixed upon his book, but he occasionally withdrew them and turned them to the body on the table, not, apparently, from any dismal fascination which under such circumstances it might be supposed to exercise upon even a courageous person, nor with a conscious rebellion against the contrary influence which might dominate a timid one. He looked at it as if in his reading he had come upon something recalling him to a sense of his surroundings. Clearly this watcher by the dead was discharging his trust with intelligence and composure, as became him.

After reading for perhaps a half-hour he seemed to come to the end of a chapter and quietly laid away the book. He then rose and taking the reading-stand from the floor carried it into a corner of the room near one of the windows, lifted the candle from it and returned to the empty fireplace before which he had been sitting.

A moment later he walked over to the body on the table, lifted the sheet and turned it back from the head, exposing a mass of dark hair and a thin face-cloth, beneath which the features showed with even sharper definition than before. Shading his eyes by interposing his free hand between them and the candle, he stood looking at his motionless companion with a serious and tranquil regard. Satisfied with his inspection, he pulled the sheet over the face again and returning to the chair, took some matches off the candlestick, put them in the side pocket of his sack-coat and sat down. He then lifted the candle from its socket and looked at it critically, as if calculating how long it would last. It was barely two inches long; in another hour he would be in darkness. He replaced it in the candlestick and blew it out.

II

In a physician's office in Kearny Street three men sat about a table, drinking punch and smoking. It was late in the evening, almost midnight, indeed, and there had been no lack of punch. The gravest of the three, Dr. Helberson, was the host—it was in his rooms they sat. He was about thirty years of age; the others were even younger; all were physicians.

"The superstitious awe with which the living regard the dead," said Dr. Helberson, "is hereditary and incurable. One needs no more be ashamed of it than of the fact that he inherits, for example, an incapacity for mathematics, or a tendency to lie."

The others laughed. "Oughtn't a man to be ashamed to lie?" asked the youngest of the three, who was in fact a medical student not yet graduated.

"My dear Harper, I said nothing about that. The tendency to lie is one thing; lying is another."

"But do you think," said the third man, "that this superstitious feeling, this fear of the dead, reasonless as we know it to be, is universal? I am myself not conscious of it."

"Oh, but it is 'in your system' for all that," replied Helberson; "it needs only the right conditions—what Shakespeare calls the 'confederate season'—to manifest itself in some very disagreeable way that will open your eyes. Physicians and soldiers are of course more nearly free from it than others."

"Physicians and soldiers!—why don't you add hangmen and headsmen? Let us have in all the assassin classes."

"No, my dear Mancher; the juries will not let the public executioners acquire sufficient familiarity with death to be altogether unmoved by it."

Young Harper, who had been helping himself to a fresh cigar at the sideboard, resumed his seat. "What would you consider conditions under which any man of woman born would become insupportably conscious of his share of our common weakness in this regard?" he asked, rather verbosely.

"Well, I should say that if a man were locked up all night with a corpse—alone—in a dark room—of a vacant house—with no bed covers to pull over his head—and lived through it without going altogether mad, he might justly boast himself not of woman born, nor yet, like Macduff, a product of Cæsarean section."

"I thought you never would finish piling up conditions," said Harper, "but I know a man who is neither a physician nor a soldier who will accept them all, for any stake you like to name."

"Who is he?"

"His name is Jarette—a stranger here; comes from my town in New York. I have no money to back him, but he will back himself with loads of it."

"How do you know that?"

"He would rather bet than eat. As for fear—I dare say he thinks it some cutaneous disorder, or possibly a particular kind of religious heresy."

"What does he look like?" Helberson was evidently becoming interested.

"Like Mancher, here—might be his twin brother."

"I accept the challenge," said Helberson, promptly.

"Awfully obliged to you for the compliment, I'm sure," drawled Mancher, who was growing sleepy. "Can't I get into this?"

"Not against me," Helberson said. "I don't want *your* money."

"All right," said Mancher; "I'll be the corpse."

The others laughed.

The outcome of this crazy conversation we have seen.

III

In extinguishing his meagre allowance of candle Mr. Jarette's object was to preserve it against some unforeseen need. He may have thought, too, or half thought, that the darkness would be no worse at one time than another, and if the situation became insupportable it would be better to have a means of relief, or even release. At any rate it was wise to have a little reserve of light, even if only to enable him to look at his watch.

No sooner had he blown out the candle and set it on the floor at his side than he settled himself comfortably in the arm-chair, leaned back and closed his eyes, hoping and expecting to sleep. In this he was disappointed; he had never in his life felt less sleepy, and in a few minutes he gave up the attempt. But what could he do? He could not go groping about in absolute darkness at the risk of bruising himself—at the risk, too, of blundering against the table and rudely disturbing the dead. We all recognize their right to lie at rest, with immunity from all that is harsh and violent. Jarette almost succeeded in making himself believe that considerations of this kind restrained him from risking the collision and fixed him to the chair.

While thinking of this matter he fancied that he heard a faint sound in the direction of the table—what kind of sound he could hardly have explained. He did not turn his head. Why should he—in the darkness? But he listened—why should he not? And listening he grew giddy and grasped the arms of the chair for support. There was a strange ringing in his ears; his head seemed bursting; his chest was oppressed by the constriction of his clothing. He wondered why it was so, and whether these were symptoms of fear. Then, with a long and strong expiration, his chest appeared to collapse, and with the great gasp with which he refilled his exhausted lungs the vertigo left him and he knew that so intently had he listened that he had held his breath almost to suffocation. The revelation was vexatious; he arose, pushed away the chair with his foot and strode to the centre of the room. But one does not stride far in darkness; he began to grope, and finding the wall followed it to an angle, turned, followed it past the two windows and there in another corner came into violent contact with the reading-stand, overturning it. It made a clatter that startled him. He was annoyed. "How the devil could

I have forgotten where it was?" he muttered, and groped his way along the third wall to the fireplace. "I must put things to rights," said he, feeling the floor for the candle.

Having recovered that, he lighted it and instantly turned his eyes to the table, where, naturally, nothing had undergone any change. The reading-stand lay unobserved upon the floor: he had forgotten to "put it to rights." He looked all about the room, dispersing the deeper shadows by movements of the candle in his hand, and crossing over to the door tested it by turning and pulling the knob with all his strength. It did not yield and this seemed to afford him a certain satisfaction; indeed, he secured it more firmly by a bolt which he had not before observed. Returning to his chair, he looked at his watch; it was half-past nine. With a start of surprise he held the watch at his ear. It had not stopped. The candle was now visibly shorter. He again extinguished it, placing it on the floor at his side as before.

Mr. Jarette was not at his ease; he was distinctly dissatisfied with his surroundings, and with himself for being so. "What have I to fear?" he thought. "This is ridiculous and disgraceful; I will not be so great a fool." But courage does not come of saying, "I will be courageous," nor of recognizing its appropriateness to the occasion. The more Jarette condemned himself, the more reason he gave himself for condemnation; the greater the number of variations which he played upon the simple theme of the harmlessness of the dead, the more insupportable grew the discord of his emotions. "What!" he cried aloud in the anguish of his spirit, "what! shall I, who have not a shade of superstition in my nature—I, who have no belief in immortality—I, who know (and never more clearly than now) that the after-life is the dream of a desire—shall I lose at once my bet, my honor and my self-respect, perhaps my reason, because certain savage ancestors dwelling in caves and burrows conceived the monstrous notion that the dead walk by night?—that—" Distinctly, unmistakably, Mr. Jarette heard behind him a light, soft sound of footfalls, deliberate, regular, successively nearer!

IV

Just before daybreak the next morning Dr. Helberson and his young friend Harper were driving slowly through the streets of North Beach in the doctor's coupé.

"Have you still the confidence of youth in the courage or stolidity of your friend?" said the elder man. "Do you believe that I have lost this wager?"

"I *know* you have," replied the other, with enfeebling emphasis.

"Well, upon my soul, I hope so."

It was spoken earnestly, almost solemnly. There was a silence for a few moments.

"Harper," the doctor resumed, looking very serious in the shifting half-lights that entered the carriage as they passed the street lamps, "I don't feel altogether comfortable about this business. If your friend had not irritated me by the contemptuous manner in which he treated my doubt of his endurance—a purely physical quality—and by the cool incivility of his suggestion that the corpse be that of a physician, I should not have gone on with it. If anything should happen we are ruined, as I fear we deserve to be."

"What can happen? Even if the matter should be taking a serious turn, of which I am not at all afraid, Mancher has only to 'resurrect' himself and explain matters. With a genuine 'subject' from the dissecting room, or one of your late patients, it might be different."

Dr. Mancher, then, had been as good as his promise; he was the "corpse."

Dr. Helberson was silent for a long time, as the carriage, at a snail's pace, crept along the same street it had traveled two or three times already. Presently he spoke: "Well, let us hope that Mancher, if he has had to rise from the dead, has been discreet about it. A mistake in that might make matters worse instead of better."

"Yes," said Harper, "Jarette would kill him. But, Doctor"—looking at his watch as the carriage passed a gas lamp—"It is nearly four o'clock at last."

A moment later the two had quitted the vehicle and were walking briskly toward the long-unoccupied house belonging to the doctor in which they had immured Mr. Jarette in accordance with the terms of the mad wager. As they neared it they met a man running. "Can you tell me," he cried, suddenly checking his speed, "where I can find a doctor?"

"What's the matter?" Helberson asked, non-committal.

"Go and see for yourself," said the man, resuming his running.

They hastened on. Arrived at the house, they saw several persons entering in haste and excitement. In some of the dwellings near by and across the way the chamber windows were thrown up, showing a protrusion of heads. All heads were asking questions, none heeding the questions of the others. A few of the windows with closed blinds were illuminated; the inmates of those rooms were dressing to come down. Exactly opposite the door of the house that they sought a street lamp threw a yellow, insufficient light upon the scene, seeming to say that it could disclose a good deal more if it wished. Harper paused at the door and laid a hand upon his companion's arm. "It is all up with us, Doctor," he said in extreme agitation, which contrasted strangely with his free-and-easy words; "the game has gone against us all. Let's not go in there; I'm for lying low."

"I'm a physician," said Dr. Helberson, calmly; "there may be need of one."

They mounted the doorsteps and were about to enter. The door was open; the street lamp opposite lighted the passage into which it opened. It was full of men. Some had ascended the stairs at the farther end, and, denied admittance above, waited for better fortune. All were talking, none listening. Suddenly, on the upper landing there was a great commotion; a man had sprung out of a door and was breaking away from those endeavoring to detain him. Down through the mass of affrighted idlers he came, pushing them aside, flattening them against the wall on one side, or compelling them to cling to the rail on the other, clutching them by the throat, striking them savagely, thrusting them back down the stairs and walking over the fallen. His clothing was in disorder, he was without a hat. His eyes, wild and restless, had in them something more terrifying than his apparently superhuman strength. His face, smooth-shaven, was bloodless, his hair frost-white.

As the crowd at the foot of the stairs, having more freedom, fell away to let him pass Harper sprang forward. "Jarette! Jarette!" he cried.

Dr. Helberson seized Harper by the collar and dragged him back. The man looked into their faces without seeming to see them and sprang through the door, down the steps, into the street, and away. A stout policeman, who had had inferior success in conquering his way down the stairway, followed a moment later and started in pursuit, all the heads in the windows—those of women and children now—screaming in guidance.

The stairway being now partly cleared, most of the crowd having rushed down to the street to observe the flight and pursuit, Dr. Helberson mounted to the landing, followed by Harper. At a door in the upper passage an officer denied them admittance. "We are physicians," said the doctor, and they passed in. The room was full of men, dimly seen, crowded about a table. The newcomers edged their way forward and looked over the shoulders of those in the front rank. Upon the table, the lower limbs covered with a sheet, lay the body of a man, brilliantly illuminated by the beam of a bull's-eye lantern held by a policeman standing at the feet. The others, excepting those near the head—the officer himself—all were in darkness. The face of the body showed yellow, repulsive, horrible! The eyes were partly open and upturned and the jaw fallen; traces of froth defiled the lips, the chin, the cheeks. A tall man, evidently a doctor, bent over the body with his hand thrust under the shirt front. He withdrew it and placed two fingers in the open mouth. "This man has been about six hours dead," said he. "It is a case for the coroner."

He drew a card from his pocket, handed it to the officer and made his way toward the door.

"Clear the room—out, all!" said the officer, sharply, and the body disappeared as if it had been snatched away, as shifting the lantern he flashed its beam of light here and there against the faces of the crowd. The effect was amazing! The men, blinded, confused, almost terrified, made a tumultuous rush for the door, pushing, crowding, and tumbling over one another as they fled, like the hosts of Night before the shafts of Apollo. Upon the struggling, trampling mass the officer poured his light without pity and without cessation. Caught in the current, Helberson and Harper were swept out of the room and cascaded down the stairs into the street.

"Good God, Doctor! did I not tell you that Jarette would kill him?" said Harper, as soon as they were clear of the crowd.

"I believe you did," replied the other, without apparent emotion.

They walked on in silence, block after block. Against the graying east the dwellings of the hill tribes showed in silhouette. The familiar milk wagon was already astir in the streets; the baker's man would soon come upon the scene; the newspaper carrier was abroad in the land.

"It strikes me, youngster," said Helberson, "that you and I have been having too much of the morning air lately. It is unwholesome; we need a change. What do you say to a tour in Europe?"

"When?"

"I'm not particular. I should suppose that four o'clock this afternoon would be early enough."

"I'll meet you at the boat," said Harper.

V

Seven years afterward these two men sat upon a bench in Madison Square, New York, in familiar conversation. Another man, who had been observing them for some time, himself unobserved, approached and, courteously lifting his hat from locks as white as frost, said: "I beg your pardon, gentlemen, but when you have killed a man by coming to life, it is best to change clothes with him, and at the first opportunity make a break for liberty."

Helberson and Harper exchanged significant glances. They were obviously amused. The former then looked the stranger kindly in the eye and replied:

"That has always been my plan. I entirely agree with you as to its advant—"

He stopped suddenly, rose and went white. He stared at the man, open-mouthed; he trembled visibly.

"Ah!" said the stranger, "I see that you are indisposed, Doctor. If you cannot treat yourself Dr. Harper can do something for you, I am sure."

"Who the devil are you?" said Harper, bluntly.

The stranger came nearer and, bending toward them, said in a whisper: "I call myself Jarette sometimes, but I don't mind telling you, for old friendship, that I am Dr. William Mancher."

The revelation brought Harper to his feet. "Mancher!" he cried; and Helberson added: "It is true, by God!"

"Yes," said the stranger, smiling vaguely, "it is true enough, no doubt."

He hesitated and seemed to be trying to recall something, then began humming a popular air. He had apparently forgotten their presence.

"Look here, Mancher," said the elder of the two, "tell us just what occurred that night—to Jarette, you know."

"Oh, yes, about Jarette," said the other. "It's odd I should have neglected to tell you— I tell it so often. You see I knew, by overhearing him talking to himself, that he was pretty badly frightened. So I couldn't resist the temptation to come to life and have a bit of fun out of him— I couldn't really. That was all right, though certainly I did not think he would take it so seriously; I did not, truly. And afterward—well, it was a tough job changing places with him, and then—damn you! you didn't let me out!"

Nothing could exceed the ferocity with which these last words were delivered. Both men stepped back in alarm.

"We?—why—why," Helberson stammered, losing his self-possession utterly, "we had nothing to do with it."

"Didn't I say you were Drs. Hell-born and Sharper?" inquired the man, laughing.

"My name is Helberson, yes; and this gentleman is Mr. Harper," replied the former, reassured by the laugh. "But we are not physicians now; we are—well, hang it, old man, we are gamblers."

And that was the truth.

"A very good profession—very good, indeed; and, by the way, I hope Sharper here paid over Jarette's money like an honest stakeholder. A very good and honorable profession," he repeated, thoughtfully, moving carelessly away; "but I stick to the old one. I am High Supreme Medical Officer of the Bloomingdale Asylum; it is my duty to cure the superintendent."

THE MAN AND THE SNAKE

It is of veritabyll report, and attested of so many that there be nowe of wyse and learned none to gaynsaye it, that yᵉ serpente hys eye hath a magnetick propertie that whosoe falleth into its svasion is drawn forwards in despyte of his wille, and perisheth miserabyll by yᵉ creature hys byte.

STRETCHED at ease upon a sofa, in gown and slippers, Harker Brayton smiled as he read the foregoing sentence in old Morryster's *Marvells of Science*. "The only marvel in the matter," he said to himself, "is that the wise and learned in Morryster's day should have believed such nonsense as is rejected by most of even the ignorant in ours."

A train of reflection followed—for Brayton was a man of thought—and he unconsciously lowered his book without altering the direction of his eyes. As soon as the volume had gone below the line of sight, something in an obscure corner of the room recalled his attention to his surroundings. What he saw, in the shadow under his bed, was two small points of light, apparently about an inch apart. They might have been reflections of the gas jet above him, in metal nail heads; he gave them but little thought and resumed his reading. A moment later something—some impulse which it did not occur to him to analyze—impelled him to lower the book again and seek for what he saw before. The points of light were still there. They seemed to have become brighter than before, shining with a greenish lustre that he had not at first observed. He thought, too, that they might have moved a trifle—were somewhat nearer. They were still too much in shadow, however, to reveal their nature and origin to an indolent attention, and again he resumed his reading. Suddenly something in the text suggested a thought that made him start and drop the book for the third time to the side of the sofa, whence, escaping from his hand, it fell sprawling to the floor, back upward. Brayton, half-risen, was staring intently into the obscurity beneath the bed, where the points of light shone with, it seemed to him, an added fire. His attention was now fully aroused, his gaze eager and imperative. It disclosed, almost directly under the foot-rail of the bed, the coils of a large serpent—the points of light were its eyes! Its horrible head, thrust flatly forth from the innermost coil and resting upon the outermost, was directed straight toward him, the definition of the wide, brutal jaw and the idiot-like forehead serving to show the direction of its malevolent gaze. The eyes were no longer merely luminous points; they looked into his own with a meaning, a malign significance.

II

A snake in a bedroom of a modern city dwelling of the better sort is, happily, not so common a phenomenon as to make explanation altogether needless. Harker Brayton, a bachelor of thirty-five, a scholar, idler and something of an athlete, rich, popular and of sound health, had returned to San Francisco from all manner of remote and unfamiliar countries. His tastes, always a trifle luxurious, had taken on an added exuberance from long privation; and the resources of even the Castle Hotel being inadequate to their perfect gratification, he had gladly accepted the hospitality of his friend, Dr. Druring, the distinguished scientist. Dr. Druring's house, a large, old-fashioned one in what is now an obscure quarter of the city, had an outer and visible aspect of proud reserve. It plainly would not associate with the contiguous elements of its altered environment, and appeared to have developed some of the eccentricities which come of isolation. One of these was a "wing," conspicuously irrelevant in point of architecture, and no less rebellious in matter of purpose; for it was a combination of laboratory, menagerie and museum. It was here that the doctor indulged the scientific side of his nature in the study of such forms of animal life as engaged his interest and comforted his taste—which, it must be confessed, ran rather to the lower types. For one of the higher nimbly and sweetly to recommend itself unto his gentle senses it had at least to retain certain rudimentary characteristics allying it to such "dragons of the prime" as toads and snakes. His scientific sympathies were distinctly reptilian; he loved nature's vulgarians and described himself as the Zola of zoölogy. His wife and daughters not having the advantage to share his enlightened curiosity regarding the works and ways of our ill-starred fellow-creatures, were with needless austerity excluded from what he called the Snakery and doomed to companionship with their own kind, though to soften the rigors of their lot he had permitted them out of his great wealth to outdo the reptiles in the gorgeousness of their surroundings and to shine with a superior splendor.

Architecturally and in point of "furnishing" the Snakery had a severe simplicity befitting the humble circumstances of its occupants, many of whom, indeed, could not safely have been intrusted with the liberty that is necessary to the full enjoyment of luxury, for they had the troublesome peculiarity of being alive. In their own apartments, however, they were under as little personal restraint as was compatible with their protection from the baneful habit of swallowing one another; and, as Brayton had thoughtfully been apprised, it was more than a tradition that some of them had at divers times been found in parts of the premises where it would have embarrassed them to explain their presence. Despite the Snakery and its uncanny associations—to which, indeed, he gave little attention—Brayton found life at the Druring mansion very much to his mind.

III

Beyond a smart shock of surprise and a shudder of mere loathing Mr. Brayton was not greatly affected. His first thought was to ring the call bell and bring a servant; but although the bell cord dangled within easy reach he made no movement toward it; it had occurred to his mind that the act might subject him to the suspicion of fear, which he certainly did not feel. He was more keenly conscious of the incongruous nature of the situation than affected by its perils; it was revolting, but absurd.

The reptile was of a species with which Brayton was unfamiliar. Its length he could only conjecture; the body at the largest visible part seemed about as thick as his forearm. In what way was it dangerous, if in any way? Was it venomous? Was it a constrictor? His knowledge of nature's danger signals did not enable him to say; he had never deciphered the code.

If not dangerous the creature was at least offensive. It was *de trop*— "matter out of place"—an impertinence. The gem was unworthy of the setting. Even the barbarous taste of our time and country, which had loaded the walls of the room with pictures, the floor with furniture and the furniture with bric-a-brac, had not quite fitted the place for this bit of the savage life of the jungle. Besides—insupportable thought!—the exhalations of its breath mingled with the atmosphere which he himself was breathing.

These thoughts shaped themselves with greater or less definition in Brayton's mind and begot action. The process is what we call consideration and decision. It is thus that we are wise and unwise. It is thus that the withered leaf in an autumn breeze shows greater or less intelligence than its fellows, falling upon the land or upon the lake. The secret of human action is an open one: something contracts our muscles. Does it matter if we give to the preparatory molecular changes the name of will?

Brayton rose to his feet and prepared to back softly away from the snake, without disturbing it if possible, and through the door. Men retire so from the presence of the great, for greatness is power and power is a menace. He knew that he could walk backward without error. Should the monster follow, the taste which had plastered the walls with paintings had consistently supplied a rack of murderous Oriental weapons from which he could snatch one to suit the occasion. In the mean time the snake's eyes burned with a more pitiless malevolence than before.

Brayton lifted his right foot free of the floor to step backward. That moment he felt a strong aversion to doing so.

"I am accounted brave," he thought; "is bravery, then, no more than pride? Because there are none to witness the shame shall I retreat?"

He was steadying himself with his right hand upon the back of a chair, his foot suspended.

"Nonsense!" he said aloud; "I am not so great a coward as to fear to seem to myself afraid."

He lifted the foot a little higher by slightly bending the knee and thrust it sharply to the floor—an inch in front of the other! He could not think how that occurred. A trial with the left foot had the same result; it was again in advance of the right. The hand upon the chair back was grasping it; the arm was straight, reaching somewhat backward. One might have said that he was reluctant to lose his hold. The snake's malignant head was still thrust forth from the inner coil as before, the neck level. It had not moved, but its eyes were now electric sparks, radiating an infinity of luminous needles.

The man had an ashy pallor. Again he took a step forward, and another, partly dragging the chair, which when finally released fell upon the floor with a crash. The man groaned; the snake made neither sound nor motion, but its eyes were two dazzling suns. The reptile itself was wholly concealed by them. They gave off enlarging rings of rich and vivid colors, which at their greatest expansion successively vanished like soap-bubbles; they seemed to approach his very face, and anon were an immeasurable distance away. He heard, somewhere, the continuous throbbing of a great drum, with desultory bursts of far music, inconceivably sweet, like the tones of an æolian harp. He knew it for the sunrise melody of Memnon's statue, and thought he stood in the Nileside reeds hearing with exalted sense that immortal anthem through the silence of the centuries.

The music ceased; rather, it became by insensible degrees the distant roll of a retreating thunder-storm. A landscape, glittering with sun and rain, stretched before him, arched with a vivid rainbow framing in its giant curve a hundred visible cities. In the middle distance a vast serpent, wearing a crown, reared its head out of its voluminous convolutions and looked at him with his dead mother's eyes. Suddenly this enchanting landscape seemed to rise swiftly upward like the drop scene at a theatre, and vanished in a blank. Something struck him a hard blow upon the face and breast. He had fallen to the floor; the blood ran from his broken nose and his bruised lips. For a time he was dazed and stunned, and lay with closed eyes, his face against the floor. In a few moments he had recovered, and then knew that this fall, by withdrawing his eyes, had broken the spell that held him. He felt that now, by keeping his gaze averted, he would be able to retreat. But the thought of the serpent within a few feet of his head, yet unseen—perhaps in the very act of springing upon him and throwing its coils about his throat—was too horrible! He lifted his head, stared again into those baleful eyes and was again in bondage.

The snake had not moved and appeared somewhat to have lost its power upon the imagination; the gorgeous illusions of a few moments before were not repeated. Beneath that flat and brainless brow its black, beady eyes simply glittered as at first with an expression unspeakably malignant. It was as if the creature, assured of its triumph, had determined to practise no more alluring wiles.

Now ensued a fearful scene. The man, prone upon the floor, within a yard of his enemy, raised the upper part of his body upon his elbows, his head thrown back, his legs extended to their full length. His face was white between its stains of blood; his eyes were strained open to their uttermost expansion. There was froth upon his lips; it dropped off in flakes. Strong convulsions ran through his body, making almost serpentile undulations. He bent himself at the waist, shifting his legs from side to side. And every movement left him a little nearer to the snake. He thrust his hands forward to brace himself back, yet constantly advanced upon his elbows.

IV

Dr. Druring and his wife sat in the library. The scientist was in rare good humor.

"I have just obtained by exchange with another collector," he said, "a splendid specimen of the *ophiophagus*."

"And what may that be?" the lady inquired with a somewhat languid interest.

"Why, bless my soul, what profound ignorance! My dear, a man who ascertains after marriage that his wife does not know Greek is entitled to a divorce. The *ophiophagus* is a snake that eats other snakes."

"I hope it will eat all yours," she said, absently shifting the lamp. "But how does it get the other snakes? By charming them, I suppose."

"That is just like you, dear," said the doctor, with an affectation of petulance. "You know how irritating to me is any allusion to that vulgar superstition about a snake's power of fascination."

The conversation was interrupted by a mighty cry, which rang through the silent house like the voice of a demon shouting in a tomb! Again and yet again it sounded, with terrible distinctness. They sprang to their feet, the man confused, the lady pale and speechless with fright. Almost before the echoes of the last cry had died away the doctor was out of the room, springing up the stairs two steps at a time. In the corridor in front of Brayton's chamber he met some servants who had come from the upper floor. Together they rushed at the door without knocking. It was unfastened and gave way. Brayton lay upon his stomach on the floor, dead. His head and arms were partly concealed under the foot rail of the bed. They pulled the body away, turning it upon the back. The face was daubed with blood and froth, the eyes were wide open, staring— a dreadful sight!

"Died in a fit," said the scientist, bending his knee and placing his hand upon the heart. While in that position, he chanced to look under the bed. "Good God!" he added, "how did this thing get in here?"

He reached under the bed, pulled out the snake and flung it, still coiled, to the center of the room, whence with a harsh, shuffling sound it slid across the polished floor till stopped by the wall, where it lay without motion. It was a stuffed snake; its eyes were two shoe buttons.

A HOLY TERROR

I

THERE was an entire lack of interest in the latest arrival at Hurdy-Gurdy. He was not even christened with the picturesquely descriptive nick-name which is so frequently a mining camp's word of welcome to the newcomer. In almost any other camp thereabout this circumstance would of itself have secured him some such appellation as "The White-headed Conundrum," or "No Sarvey"—an expression naïvely supposed to suggest to quick intelligences the Spanish *quien sabe*. He came without provoking a ripple of concern upon the social surface of Hurdy-Gurdy—a place which to the general Californian contempt of men's personal history superadded a local indifference of its own. The time was long past when it was of any importance who came there, or if anybody came. No one was living at Hurdy-Gurdy.

Two years before, the camp had boasted a stirring population of two or three thousand males and not fewer than a dozen females. A majority of the former had done a few weeks' earnest work in demonstrating, to the disgust of the latter, the singularly mendacious character of the person whose ingenious tales of rich gold deposits had lured them thither—work, by the way, in which there was as little mental satisfaction as pecuniary profit; for a bullet from the pistol of a public-spirited citizen had put that imaginative gentleman beyond the reach of aspersion on the third day of the camp's existence. Still, his fiction had a certain foundation in fact, and many had lingered a considerable time in and about Hurdy-Gurdy, though now all had been long gone.

But they had left ample evidence of their sojourn. From the point where Injun Creek falls into the Rio San Juan Smith, up along both banks of the former into the cañon whence it emerges, extended a double row of forlorn shanties that seemed about to fall upon one another's neck to bewail their desolation; while about an equal number appeared to have straggled up the slope on either hand and perched themselves upon commanding eminences, whence they craned forward to get a good view of the affecting scene. Most of these habitations were emaciated as by famine to the condition of mere skeletons, about which clung unlovely tatters of what might have been skin, but was really canvas. The little valley itself, torn and gashed by pick and shovel, was unhandsome with long, bending lines of decaying flume resting here and there upon the summits of sharp ridges, and stilting awkwardly across the intervals upon unhewn poles. The whole place presented that raw and forbidding aspect of arrested development which is a new country's substitute for the solemn grace of ruin wrought by time. Wherever there remained a patch of the original soil a rank overgrowth of weeds and brambles had spread upon the scene, and from its dank, unwholesome

shades the visitor curious in such matters might have obtained number-
less souvenirs of the camp's former glory—fellowless boots mantled with
green mould and plethoric of rotting leaves; an occasional old felt hat;
desultory remnants of a flannel shirt; sardine boxes inhumanly mutilated and a surprising profusion of black bottles distributed with a truly
catholic impartiality, everywhere.

II

The man who had now rediscovered Hurdy-Gurdy was evidently not
curious as to its archæology. Nor, as he looked about him upon the dismal evidences of wasted work and broken hopes, their dispiriting significance accentuated by the ironical pomp of a cheap gilding by the
rising sun, did he supplement his sigh of weariness by one of sensibility.
He simply removed from the back of his tired burro a miner's outfit a
trifle larger than the animal itself, picketed that creature and selecting a
hatchet from his kit moved off at once across the dry bed of Injun Creek
to the top of a low, gravelly hill beyond.

Stepping across a prostrate fence of brush and boards he picked up
one of the latter, split it into five parts and sharpened them at one end.
He then began a kind of search, occasionally stooping to examine something with close attention. At last his patient scrutiny appeared to be
rewarded with success, for he suddenly erected his figure to its full
height, made a gesture of satisfaction, pronounced the word "Scarry"
and at once strode away with long, equal steps, which he counted. Then
he stopped and drove one of his stakes into the earth. He then looked
carefully about him, measured off a number of paces over a singularly
uneven ground and hammered in another. Pacing off twice the distance
at a right angle to his former course he drove down a third, and repeating the process sank home the fourth, and then a fifth. This he split at
the top and in the cleft inserted an old letter envelope covered with an
intricate system of pencil tracks. In short, he staked off a hill claim in
strict accordance with the local mining laws of Hurdy-Gurdy and put
up the customary notice.

It is necessary to explain that one of the adjuncts to Hurdy-Gurdy—
one to which that metropolis became afterward itself an adjunct—was
a cemetery. In the first week of the camp's existence this had been
thoughtfully laid out by a committee of citizens. The day after had been

signalized by a debate between two members of the committee, with reference to a more eligible site, and on the third day the necropolis was inaugurated by a double funeral. As the camp had waned the cemetery had waxed; and long before the ultimate inhabitant, victorious alike over the insidious malaria and the forthright revolver, had turned the tail of his pack-ass upon Injun Creek the outlying settlement had become a populous if not popular suburb. And now, when the town was fallen into the sere and yellow leaf of an unlovely senility, the graveyard— though somewhat marred by time and circumstance, and not altogether exempt from innovations in grammar and experiments in orthography, to say nothing of the devastating coyote—answered the humble needs of its denizens with reasonable completeness. It comprised a generous two acres of ground, which with commendable thrift but needless care had been selected for its mineral unworth, contained two or three skeleton trees (one of which had a stout lateral branch from which a weather-wasted rope still significantly dangled), half a hundred gravelly mounds, a score of rude headboards displaying the literary peculiarities above mentioned and a struggling colony of prickly pears. Altogether, God's Location, as with characteristic reverence it had been called, could justly boast of an indubitably superior quality of desolation. It was in the most thickly settled part of this interesting demesne that Mr. Jefferson Doman staked off his claim. If in the prosecution of his design he should deem it expedient to remove any of the dead they would have the right to be suitably reinterred.

III

This Mr. Jefferson Doman was from Elizabethtown, New Jersey, where six years before he had left his heart in the keeping of a golden-haired, demure-mannered young woman named Mary Matthews, as collateral security for his return to claim her hand.

"I just *know* you'll never get back alive—you never do succeed in anything," was the remark which illustrated Miss Matthews's notion of what constituted success and, inferentially, her view of the nature of encouragement. She added: "If you don't I'll go to California too. I can put the coins in little bags as you dig them out."

This characteristically feminine theory of auriferous deposits did not commend itself to the masculine intelligence: it was Mr. Doman's belief that gold was found in a liquid state. He deprecated her intent with considerable enthusiasm, suppressed her sobs with a light hand upon her mouth, laughed in her eyes as he kissed away her tears, and with a cheerful "Ta-ta" went to California to labor for her through the long, loveless years, with a strong heart, an alert hope and a steadfast fidelity that never for a moment forgot what it was about. In the mean time, Miss Matthews had granted a monopoly of her humble talent for sacking up coins to Mr. Jo. Seeman, of New York, gambler, by whom it was better appreciated than her commanding genius for unsacking and bestowing them upon his local rivals. Of this latter aptitude, indeed, he manifested his disapproval by an act which secured him the position of clerk of the laundry in the State prison, and for her the *sobriquet* of "Split-faced Moll." At about this time she wrote to Mr. Doman a touching letter of renunciation, inclosing her photograph to prove that she had no longer a right to indulge the dream of becoming Mrs. Doman, and recounting so graphically her fall from a horse that the staid "plug" upon which Mr. Doman had ridden into Red Dog to get the letter made vicarious atonement under the spur all the way back to camp. The letter failed in a signal way to accomplish its object; the fidelity which had before been to Mr. Doman a matter of love and duty was thenceforth a matter of honor also; and the photograph, showing the once pretty face sadly disfigured as by the slash of a knife, was duly instated in his affections and its more comely predecessor treated with contumelious neglect. On being informed of this, Miss Matthews, it is only fair to say, appeared less surprised than from the apparently low estimate of Mr. Doman's generosity which the tone of her former letter attested one would naturally have expected her to be. Soon after, however, her letters grew infrequent, and then ceased altogether.

But Mr. Doman had another correspondent, Mr. Barney Bree, of Hurdy-Gurdy, formerly of Red Dog. This gentleman, although a notable figure among miners, was not a miner. His knowledge of mining consisted mainly in a marvelous command of its slang, to which he made copious contributions, enriching its vocabulary with a wealth of uncommon phrases more remarkable for their aptness than their refinement, and which impressed the unlearned "tenderfoot" with a lively sense of the profundity of their inventor's acquirements. When not entertaining a circle of admiring auditors from San Francisco or the East he could commonly be found pursuing the comparatively obscure industry of sweeping out the various dance houses and purifying the cuspidors.

Barney had apparently but two passions in life—love of Jefferson Doman, who had once been of some service to him, and love of whisky, which certainly had not. He had been among the first in the rush to Hurdy-Gurdy, but had not prospered, and had sunk by degrees to the position of grave digger. This was not a vocation, but Barney in a desultory way turned his trembling hand to it whenever some local misunderstanding at the card table and his own partial recovery from a prolonged debauch occurred coincidently in point of time. One day Mr. Doman received, at Red Dog, a letter with the simple postmark, "Hurdy, Cal.," and being occupied with another matter, carelessly thrust it into a chink of his cabin for future perusal. Some two years later it was accidentally dislodged and he read it. It ran as follows:—

Hurdy, June 6.
Friend Jeff: I've hit her hard in the boneyard. She's blind and lousy. I'm on the divvy—that's me, and mum's my lay till you toot. Yours,
Barney.
P. S.—I've clayed her with Scarry.

With some knowledge of the general mining camp *argot* and of Mr. Bree's private system for the communication of ideas Mr. Doman had no difficulty in understanding by this uncommon epistle that Barney while performing his duty as grave digger had uncovered a quartz ledge with no outcroppings; that it was visibly rich in free gold; that, moved by considerations of friendship, he was willing to accept Mr. Doman as a partner and awaiting that gentleman's declaration of his will in the matter would discreetly keep the discovery a secret. From the postscript it was plainly inferable that in order to conceal the treasure he had buried above it the mortal part of a person named Scarry.

From subsequent events, as related to Mr. Doman at Red Dog, it would appear that before taking this precaution Mr. Bree must have had the thrift to remove a modest competency of the gold; at any rate, it was at about that time that he entered upon that memorable series of potations and treatings which is still one of the cherished traditions of the San Juan Smith country, and is spoken of with respect as far away as Ghost Rock and Lone Hand. At its conclusion some former citizens of Hurdy-Gurdy, for whom he had performed the last kindly office at the cemetery, made room for him among them, and he rested well.

IV

Having finished staking off his claim Mr. Doman walked back to the centre of it and stood again at the spot where his search among the graves had expired in the exclamation, "Scarry." He bent again over the head-board that bore that name and as if to reinforce the senses of sight and hearing ran his forefinger along the rudely carved letters. Re-erecting himself he appended orally to the simple inscription the shockingly forthright epitaph, "She was a holy terror!"

Had Mr. Doman been required to make these words good with proof —as, considering their somewhat censorious character, he doubtless should have been—he would have found himself embarrassed by the absence of reputable witnesses, and hearsay evidence would have been the best he could command. At the time when Scarry had been prevalent in the mining camps thereabout—when, as the editor of the *Hurdy Herald* would have phrased it, she was "in the plenitude of her power"—Mr. Doman's fortunes had been at a low ebb, and he had led the vagrantly laborious life of a prospector. His time had been mostly spent in the mountains, now with one companion, now with another. It was from the admiring recitals of these casual partners, fresh from the various camps, that his judgment of Scarry had been made up; he himself had never had the doubtful advantage of her acquaintance and the precarious distinction of her favor. And when, finally, on the termination of her perverse career at Hurdy-Gurdy he had read in a chance copy of the *Herald* her column-long obituary (written by the local humorist of that lively sheet in the highest style of his art) Doman had paid to her memory and to her historiographer's genius the tribute of a smile and chivalrously forgotten her. Standing now at the grave-side of this mountain Messalina he recalled the leading events of her turbulent career, as he had heard them celebrated at his several camp-fires, and perhaps with an unconscious attempt at self-justification repeated that she was a holy terror, and sank his pick into her grave up to the handle. At that moment a raven, which had silently settled upon a branch of the blasted tree above his head, solemnly snapped its beak and uttered its mind about the matter with an approving croak.

Pursuing his discovery of free gold with great zeal, which he probably credited to his conscience as a grave digger, Mr. Barney Bree had made an unusually deep sepulcher, and it was near sunset before Mr. Doman, laboring with the leisurely deliberation of one who has "a dead sure thing" and no fear of an adverse claimant's enforcement of a prior right, reached the coffin and uncovered it. When he had done so he was confronted by a difficulty for which he had made no provision; the coffin— a mere flat shell of not very well-preserved redwood boards, apparently— had no handles, and it filled the entire bottom of the excavation. The best he could do without violating the decent sanctities of the situation was to make the excavation sufficiently longer to enable him to stand at the head of the casket and getting his powerful hands underneath erect it upon its narrower end; and this he proceeded to do. The approach of night quickened his efforts. He had no thought of abandoning his task at this stage to resume it on the morrow under more advantageous conditions. The feverish stimulation of cupidity and the fascination of terror held him to his dismal work with an iron authority. He no longer idled, but wrought with a terrible zeal. His head uncovered, his outer garments discarded, his shirt opened at the neck and thrown back from his breast, down which ran sinuous rills of perspiration, this hardy and impenitent gold-getter and grave-robber toiled with a giant energy that almost dignified the character of his horrible purpose; and when the sun fringes had burned themselves out along the crest line of the western hills, and the full moon had climbed out of the shadows that lay along the purple plain, he had erected the coffin upon its foot, where it stood propped against the end of the open grave. Then, standing up to his neck in the earth at the opposite extreme of the excavation, as he looked at the coffin upon which the moonlight now fell with a full illumination he was thrilled with a sudden terror to observe upon it the startling apparition of a dark human head—the shadow of his own. For a moment this simple and natural circumstance unnerved him. The noise of his labored breathing frightened him, and he tried to still it, but his bursting lungs would not be denied. Then, laughing half-audibly and wholly without spirit, he began making movements of his head from side to side, in order to compel the apparition to repeat them. He found a comforting reassurance in asserting his command over his own shadow. He was temporizing, making, with unconscious prudence, a dilatory opposition to an impending catastrophe. He felt that invisible forces of evil were closing in upon him, and he parleyed for time with the Inevitable.

He now observed in succession several unusual circumstances. The surface of the coffin upon which his eyes were fastened was not flat; it presented two distinct ridges, one longitudinal and the other transverse. Where these intersected at the widest part there was a corroded metallic plate that reflected the moonlight with a dismal lustre. Along the outer edges of the coffin, at long intervals, were rust-eaten heads of nails. This frail product of the carpenter's art had been put into the grave the wrong side up!

Perhaps it was one of the humors of the camp—a practical manifestation of the facetious spirit that had found literary expression in the topsy-turvy obituary notice from the pen of Hurdy-Gurdy's great humorist. Perhaps it had some occult personal signification impenetrable to understandings uninstructed in local traditions. A more charitable hypothesis is that it was owing to a misadventure on the part of Mr. Barney Bree, who, making the interment unassisted (either by choice for the conservation of his golden secret, or through public apathy), had committed a blunder which he was afterward unable or unconcerned to rectify. However it had come about, poor Scarry had indubitably been put into the earth face downward.

When terror and absurdity make alliance, the effect is frightful. This strong-hearted and daring man, this hardy night worker among the dead, this defiant antagonist of darkness and desolation, succumbed to a ridiculous surprise. He was smitten with a thrilling chill—shivered, and shook his massive shoulders as if to throw off an icy hand. He no longer breathed, and the blood in his veins, unable to abate its impetus, surged hotly beneath his cold skin. Unleavened with oxygen, it mounted to his head and congested his brain. His physical functions had gone over to the enemy; his very heart was arrayed against him. He did not move; he could not have cried out. He needed but a coffin to be dead—as dead as the death that confronted him with only the length of an open grave and the thickness of a rotting plank between.

Then, one by one, his senses returned; the tide of terror that had overwhelmed his faculties began to recede. But with the return of his senses he became singularly unconscious of the object of his fear. He saw the moonlight gilding the coffin, but no longer the coffin that it gilded. Raising his eyes and turning his head, he noted, curiously and with surprise, the black branches of the dead tree, and tried to estimate the length of the weather-worn rope that dangled from its ghostly hand. The monotonous barking of distant coyotes affected him as something he had heard years ago in a dream. An owl flapped awkwardly above him on noiseless wings, and he tried to forecast the direction of its flight when it should encounter the cliff that reared its illuminated front a mile away. His hearing took account of a gopher's stealthy tread in the shadow of the cactus. He was intensely observant; his senses were all alert; but he saw not the coffin. As one can gaze at the sun until it looks black and then vanishes, so his mind, having exhausted its capacities of dread, was no longer conscious of the separate existence of anything dreadful. The Assassin was cloaking the sword.

It was during this lull in the battle that he became sensible of a faint, sickening odor. At first he thought it was that of a rattle-snake, and involuntarily tried to look about his feet. They were nearly invisible in the gloom of the grave. A hoarse, gurgling sound, like the death-rattle in a human throat, seemed to come out of the sky, and a moment later a great, black, angular shadow, like the same sound made visible, dropped curving from the topmost branch of the spectral tree, fluttered for an instant before his face and sailed fiercely away into the mist along the creek. It was the raven. The incident recalled him to a sense of the situation, and again his eyes sought the upright coffin, now illuminated by the moon for half its length. He saw the gleam of the metallic plate and tried without moving to decipher the inscription. Then he fell to speculating upon what was behind it. His creative imagination presented him a vivid picture. The planks no longer seemed an obstacle to his vision and he saw the livid corpse of the dead woman, standing in grave-clothes, and staring vacantly at him, with lidless, shrunken eyes. The lower jaw was fallen, the upper lip drawn away from the uncovered teeth. He could make out a mottled pattern on the hollow cheeks—the maculations of decay. By some mysterious process his mind reverted for the first time that day to the photograph of Mary Matthews. He contrasted its blonde beauty with the forbidding aspect of this dead face— the most beloved object that he knew with the most hideous that he could conceive.

The Assassin now advanced and displaying the blade laid it against the victim's throat. That is to say, the man became at first dimly, then definitely, aware of an impressive coincidence—a relation—a parallel between the face on the card and the name on the headboard. The one was disfigured, the other described a disfiguration. The thought took hold of him and shook him. It transformed the face that his imagination had created behind the coffin lid; the contrast became a resemblance; the resemblance grew to identity. Remembering the many descriptions of Scarry's personal appearance that he had heard from the gossips of his camp-fire he tried with imperfect success to recall the exact nature of the disfiguration that had given the woman her ugly name; and what was lacking in his memory fancy supplied, stamping it with the validity of conviction. In the maddening attempt to recall such scraps of the woman's history as he had heard, the muscles of his arms and hands were strained to a painful tension, as by an effort to lift a great weight. His body writhed and twisted with the exertion. The tendons of his neck stood out as tense as whip-cords, and his breath came in short, sharp gasps. The catastrophe could not be much longer delayed, or the agony of anticipation would leave nothing to be done by the *coup de grâce* of verification. The scarred face behind the lid would slay him through the wood.

A movement of the coffin diverted his thought. It came forward to within a foot of his face, growing visibly larger as it approached. The rusted metallic plate, with an inscription illegible in the moonlight, looked him steadily in the eye. Determined not to shrink, he tried to brace his shoulders more firmly against the end of the excavation, and nearly fell backward in the attempt. There was nothing to support him; he had unconsciously moved upon his enemy, clutching the heavy knife that he had drawn from his belt. The coffin had not advanced and he smiled to think it could not retreat. Lifting his knife he struck the heavy hilt against the metal plate with all his power. There was a sharp, ringing percussion, and with a dull clatter the whole decayed coffin lid broke in pieces and came away, falling about his feet. The quick and the dead were face to face—the frenzied, shrieking man—the woman standing tranquil in her silences. She was a holy terror!

V

Some months later a party of men and women belonging to the highest social circles of San Francisco passed through Hurdy-Gurdy on their way to the Yosemite Valley by a new trail. They halted for dinner and during its preparation explored the desolate camp. One of the party had been at Hurdy-Gurdy in the days of its glory. He had, indeed, been one of its prominent citizens; and it used to be said that more money passed over his faro table in any one night than over those of all his competitors in a week; but being now a millionaire engaged in greater enterprises, he did not deem these early successes of sufficient importance to merit the distinction of remark. His invalid wife, a lady famous in San Francisco for the costly nature of her entertainments and her exacting rigor with regard to the social position and "antecedents" of those who attended them, accompanied the expedition. During a stroll among the shanties of the abandoned camp Mr. Porfer directed the attention of his wife and friends to a dead tree on a low hill beyond Injun Creek.

"As I told you," he said, "I passed through this camp in 1852, and was told that no fewer than five men had been hanged here by vigilantes at different times, and all on that tree. If I am not mistaken, the rope is dangling from it yet. Let us go over and see the place."

Mr. Porfer did not add that the rope in question was perhaps the very one from whose fatal embrace his own neck had once had an escape so narrow that an hour's delay in taking himself out of that region would have spanned it.

Proceeding leisurely down the creek to a convenient crossing, the party came upon the cleanly picked skeleton of an animal which Mr. Porfer after due examination pronounced to be that of an ass. The distinguishing ears were gone, but much of the inedible head had been spared by the beasts and birds, and the stout bridle of horsehair was intact, as was the riata, of similar material, connecting it with a picket pin still firmly sunken in the earth. The wooden and metallic elements of a miner's kit lay near by. The customary remarks were made, cynical on the part of the men, sentimental and refined by the lady. A little later they stood by the tree in the cemetery and Mr. Porfer sufficiently unbent from his dignity to place himself beneath the rotten rope and confidently lay a coil of it about his neck, somewhat, it appeared, to his own satisfaction, but greatly to the horror of his wife, to whose sensibilities the performance gave a smart shock.

An exclamation from one of the party gathered them all about an open grave, at the bottom of which they saw a confused mass of human bones and the broken remnants of a coffin. Coyotes and buzzards had performed the last sad rites for pretty much all else. Two skulls were visible and in order to investigate this somewhat unusual redundancy one of the younger men had the hardihood to spring into the grave and hand them up to another before Mrs. Porfer could indicate her marked disapproval of so shocking an act, which, nevertheless, she did with considerable feeling and in very choice words. Pursuing his search among the dismal débris at the bottom of the grave the young man next handed up a rusted coffin plate, with a rudely cut inscription, which with difficulty Mr. Porfer deciphered and read aloud with an earnest and not altogether unsuccessful attempt at the dramatic effect which he deemed befitting to the occasion and his rhetorical abilities:

> MANUELITA MURPHY.
> Born at the Mission San Pedro—Died in
> Hurdy-Gurdy,
> Aged 47.
> Hell's full of such.

In deference to the piety of the reader and the nerves of Mrs. Porfer's fastidious sisterhood of both sexes let us not touch upon the painful impression produced by this uncommon inscription, further than to say that the elocutionary powers of Mr. Porfer had never before met with so spontaneous and overwhelming recognition.

The next morsel that rewarded the ghoul in the grave was a long tangle of black hair defiled with clay: but this was such an anticlimax that it received little attention. Suddenly, with a short exclamation and a gesture of excitement, the young man unearthed a fragment of grayish rock, and after a hurried inspection handed it up to Mr. Porfer. As the sunlight fell upon it it glittered with a yellow luster—it was thickly studded with gleaming points. Mr. Porfer snatched it, bent his head over it a moment and threw it lightly away with the simple remark:

"Iron pyrites—fool's gold."

The young man in the discovery shaft was a trifle disconcerted, apparently.

Meanwhile, Mrs. Porfer, unable longer to endure the disagreeable business, had walked back to the tree and seated herself at its root. While rearranging a tress of golden hair which had slipped from its confinement she was attracted by what appeared to be and really was the fragment of an old coat. Looking about to assure herself that so unladylike an act was not observed, she thrust her jeweled hand into the exposed breast pocket and drew out a mouldy pocket-book. Its contents were as follows:

One bundle of letters, postmarked "Elizabethtown, New Jersey."
One circle of blonde hair tied with a ribbon.
One photograph of a beautiful girl.
One ditto of same, singularly disfigured.
One name on back of photograph—"Jefferson Doman."

A few moments later a group of anxious gentlemen surrounded Mrs. Porfer as she sat motionless at the foot of the tree, her head dropped forward, her fingers clutching a crushed photograph. Her husband raised her head, exposing a face ghastly white, except the long, deforming cicatrice, familiar to all her friends, which no art could ever hide, and which now traversed the pallor of her countenance like a visible curse.

Mary Matthews Porfer had the bad luck to be dead.

THE SUITABLE SURROUNDINGS

THE NIGHT

ONE midsummer night a farmer's boy living about ten miles from the city of Cincinnati was following a bridle path through a dense and dark forest. He had lost himself while searching for some missing cows, and near midnight was a long way from home, in a part of the country with which he was unfamiliar. But he was a stout-hearted lad, and knowing his general direction from his home, he plunged into the forest without hesitation, guided by the stars. Coming into the bridle path, and observing that it ran in the right direction, he followed it.

The night was clear, but in the woods it was exceedingly dark. It was more by the sense of touch than by that of sight that the lad kept the path. He could not, indeed, very easily go astray; the undergrowth on both sides was so thick as to be almost impenetrable. He had gone into the forest a mile or more when he was surprised to see a feeble gleam of light shining through the foliage skirting the path on his left. The sight of it startled him and set his heart beating audibly.

"The old Breede house is somewhere about here," he said to himself. "This must be the other end of the path which we reach it by from our side. Ugh! what should a light be doing there?"

Nevertheless, he pushed on. A moment later he had emerged from the forest into a small, open space, mostly upgrown to brambles. There were remnants of a rotting fence. A few yards from the trail, in the middle of the "clearing," was the house from which the light came, through an un-glazed window. The window had once contained glass, but that and its supporting frame had long ago yielded to missiles flung by hands of ven-turesome boys to attest alike their courage and their hostility to the super-natural; for the Breede house bore the evil reputation of being haunted. Possibly it was not, but even the hardiest sceptic could not deny that it was deserted—which in rural regions is much the same thing.

Looking at the mysterious dim light shining from the ruined window the boy remembered with apprehension that his own hand had assisted at the destruction. His penitence was of course poignant in proportion to its tardiness and inefficacy. He half expected to be set upon by all the unworldly and bodiless malevolences whom he had outraged by as-sisting to break alike their windows and their peace. Yet this stubborn lad, shaking in every limb, would not retreat. The blood in his veins was strong and rich with the iron of the frontiersman. He was but two removes from the generation that had subdued the Indian. He started to pass the house.

As he was going by he looked in at the blank window space and saw a strange and terrifying sight,—the figure of a man seated in the centre of the room, at a table upon which lay some loose sheets of paper. The elbows rested on the table, the hands supporting the head, which was un-covered. On each side the fingers were pushed into the hair. The face showed dead-yellow in the light of a single candle a little to one side. The flame illuminated that side of the face, the other was in deep shadow. The man's eyes were fixed upon the blank window space with a stare in which an older and cooler observer might have discerned some-thing of apprehension, but which seemed to the lad altogether soulless. He believed the man to be dead.

The situation was horrible, but not without its fascination. The boy stopped to note it all. He was weak, faint and trembling; he could feel the blood forsaking his face. Nevertheless, he set his teeth and resolutely advanced to the house. He had no conscious intention—it was the mere courage of terror. He thrust his white face forward into the illuminated opening. At that instant a strange, harsh cry, a shriek, broke upon the silence of the night—the note of a screech-owl. The man sprang to his feet, overturning the table and extinguishing the candle. The boy took to his heels.

THE DAY BEFORE

"Good-morning, Colston. I am in luck, it seems. You have often said that my commendation of your literary work was mere civility, and here you find me absorbed—actually merged—in your latest story in the *Messenger*. Nothing less shocking than your touch upon my shoulder would have roused me to consciousness."

"The proof is stronger than you seem to know," replied the man addressed: "so keen is your eagerness to read my story that you are willing to renounce selfish considerations and forego all the pleasure that you could get from it."

"I don't understand you," said the other, folding the newspaper that he held and putting it into his pocket. "You writers are a queer lot, anyhow. Come, tell me what I have done or omitted in this matter. In what way does the pleasure that I get, or might get, from your work depend on me?"

"In many ways. Let me ask you how you would enjoy your breakfast if you took it in this street car. Suppose the phonograph so perfected as to be able to give you an entire opera,—singing, orchestration, and all; do you think you would get much pleasure out of it if you turned it on at your office during business hours? Do you really care for a serenade by Schubert when you hear it fiddled by an untimely Italian on a morning ferryboat? Are you always cocked and primed for enjoyment? Do you keep every mood on tap, ready to any demand? Let me remind you, sir, that the story which you have done me the honor to begin as a means of becoming oblivious to the discomfort of this car is a ghost story!"

"Well?"

"Well! Has the reader no duties corresponding to his privileges? You have paid five cents for that newspaper. It is yours. You have the right to read it when and where you will. Much of what is in it is neither helped nor harmed by time and place and mood; some of it actually requires to be read at once—while it is fizzing. But my story is not of that character. It is not 'the very latest advices' from Ghostland. You are not expected to keep yourself *au courant* with what is going on in the realm of spooks. The stuff will keep until you have leisure to put yourself into the frame of mind appropriate to the sentiment of the piece—which I respectfully submit that you cannot do in a street car, even if you are the only passenger. The solitude is not of the right sort. An author has rights which the reader is bound to respect."

"For specific example?"

"The right to the reader's undivided attention. To deny him this is immoral. To make him share your attention with the rattle of a street car, the moving panorama of the crowds on the sidewalks, and the buildings beyond—with any of the thousands of distractions which make our customary environment—is to treat him with gross injustice. By God, it is infamous!"

The speaker had risen to his feet and was steadying himself by one of the straps hanging from the roof of the car. The other man looked up at him in sudden astonishment, wondering how so trivial a grievance could seem to justify so strong language. He saw that his friend's face was uncommonly pale and that his eyes glowed like living coals.

"You know what I mean," continued the writer, impetuously crowding his words—"you know what I mean, Marsh. My stuff in this morning's *Messenger* is plainly subheaded 'A Ghost Story.' That is ample notice to all. Every honorable reader will understand it as prescribing by implication the conditions under which the work is to be read."

The man addressed as Marsh winced a trifle, then asked with a smile: "What conditions? You know that I am only a plain business man who cannot be supposed to understand such things. How, when, where should I read your ghost story?"

"In solitude—at night—by the light of a candle. There are certain emotions which a writer can easily enough excite—such as compassion or merriment. I can move you to tears or laughter under almost any circumstances. But for my ghost story to be effective you must be made to feel fear—at least a strong sense of the supernatural—and that is a difficult matter. I have a right to expect that if you read me at all you will give me a chance; that you will make yourself accessible to the emotion that I try to inspire."

The car had now arrived at its terminus and stopped. The trip just completed was its first for the day and the conversation of the two early passengers had not been interrupted. The streets were yet silent and desolate; the house tops were just touched by the rising sun. As they stepped from the car and walked away together Marsh narrowly eyed his companion, who was reported, like most men of uncommon literary ability, to be addicted to various destructive vices. That is the revenge which dull minds take upon bright ones in resentment of their superiority. Mr. Colston was known as a man of genius. There are honest souls who believe that genius is a mode of excess. It was known that Colston did not drink liquor, but many said that he ate opium. Something in his appearance that morning—a certain wildness of the eyes, an unusual pallor, a thickness and rapidity of speech—were taken by Mr. Marsh to confirm the report. Nevertheless, he had not the self-denial to abandon a subject which he found interesting, however it might excite his friend.

"Do you mean to say," he began, "that if I take the trouble to observe your directions—place myself in the conditions that you demand: solitude, night and a tallow candle—you can with your ghostly work give me an uncomfortable sense of the supernatural, as you call it? Can you accelerate my pulse, make me start at sudden noises, send a nervous chill along my spine and cause my hair to rise?"

Colston turned suddenly and looked him squarely in the eyes as they walked. "You would not dare—you have not the courage," he said. He emphasized the words with a contemptuous gesture. "You are brave enough to read me in a street car, but—in a deserted house—alone—in the forest—at night! Bah! I have a manuscript in my pocket that would kill you."

Marsh was angry. He knew himself courageous, and the words stung him. "If you know such a place," he said, "take me there to-night and leave me your story and a candle. Call for me when I've had time enough to read it and I'll tell you the entire plot and—kick you out of the place."

That is how it occurred that the farmer's boy, looking in at an unglazed window of the Breede house, saw a man sitting in the light of a candle.

THE DAY AFTER

Late in the afternoon of the next day three men and a boy approached the Breede house from that point of the compass toward which the boy had fled the preceding night. The men were in high spirits; they talked very loudly and laughed. They made facetious and good-humored ironical remarks to the boy about his adventure, which evidently they did not believe in. The boy accepted their raillery with seriousness, making no reply. He had a sense of the fitness of things and knew that one who professes to have seen a dead man rise from his seat and blow out a candle is not a credible witness.

Arriving at the house and finding the door unlocked, the party of investigators entered without ceremony. Leading out of the passage into which this door opened was another on the right and one on the left. They entered the room on the left—the one which had the blank front window. Here was the dead body of a man.

It lay partly on one side, with the forearm beneath it, the cheek on the floor. The eyes were wide open; the stare was not an agreeable thing to encounter. The lower jaw had fallen; a little pool of saliva had collected beneath the mouth. An overthrown table, a partly burned candle, a chair and some paper with writing on it were all else that the room contained. The men looked at the body, touching the face in turn. The boy gravely stood at the head, assuming a look of ownership. It was the proudest moment of his life. One of the men said to him, "You're a good 'un"—a remark which was received by the two others with nods of acquiescence. It was Scepticism apologizing to Truth. Then one of the men took from the floor the sheet of manuscript and stepped to the window, for already the evening shadows were glooming the forest. The song of the whip-poor-will was heard in the distance and a monstrous beetle sped by the window on roaring wings and thundered away out of hearing. The man read:

THE MANUSCRIPT

"Before committing the act which, rightly or wrongly, I have resolved on and appearing before my Maker for judgment, I, James R. Colston, deem it my duty as a journalist to make a statement to the public. My name is, I believe, tolerably well known to the people as a writer of tragic tales, but the somberest imagination never conceived anything so tragic as my own life and history. Not in incident: my life has been destitute of adventure and action. But my mental career has been lurid with experiences such as kill and damn. I shall not recount them here—some of them are written and ready for publication elsewhere. The object of these lines is to explain to whomsoever may be interested that my death is voluntary—my own act. I shall die at twelve o'clock on the night of the 15th of July—a significant anniversary to me, for it was on that day, and at that hour, that my friend in time and eternity, Charles Breede, performed his vow to me by the same act which his fidelity to our pledge now entails upon me. He took his life in his little house in the Copeton woods. There was the customary verdict of 'temporary insanity.' Had I testified at that inquest—had I told all I knew, they would have called *me* mad!"

Here followed an evidently long passage which the man reading read to himself only. The rest he read aloud.

"I have still a week of life in which to arrange my worldly affairs and prepare for the great change. It is enough, for I have but few affairs and it is now four years since death became an imperative obligation.

"I shall bear this writing on my body; the finder will please hand it to the coroner.

"JAMES R. COLSTON.

"P. S.—Willard Marsh, on this the fatal fifteenth day of July I hand you this manuscript, to be opened and read under the conditions agreed upon, and at the place which I designated. I forego my intention to keep it on my body to explain the manner of my death, which is not important. It will serve to explain the manner of yours. I am to call for you during the night to receive assurance that you have read the manuscript. You know me well enough to expect me. But, my friend, it *will be after twelve o'clock*. May God have mercy on our souls!

"J. R. C."

Before the man who was reading this manuscript had finished, the candle had been picked up and lighted. When the reader had done, he quietly thrust the paper against the flame and despite the protestations of the others held it until it was burnt to ashes. The man who did this, and who afterward placidly endured a severe reprimand from the coroner, was a son-in-law of the late Charles Breede. At the inquest nothing could elicit an intelligent account of what the paper had contained.

FROM "THE TIMES"

"Yesterday the Commissioners of Lunacy committed to the asylum Mr. James R. Colston, a writer of some local reputation, connected with the *Messenger*. It will be remembered that on the evening of the 15th inst. Mr. Colston was given into custody by one of his fellow-lodgers in the Baine House, who had observed him acting very suspiciously, baring his throat and whetting a razor—occasionally trying its edge by actually cutting through the skin of his arm, etc. On being handed over to the police, the unfortunate man made a desperate resistance, and has ever since been so violent that it has been necessary to keep him in a strait-jacket. Most of our esteemed contemporary's other writers are still at large."

THE BOARDED WINDOW

IN 1830, only a few miles away from what is now the great city of Cincinnati, lay an immense and almost unbroken forest. The whole region was sparsely settled by people of the frontier—restless souls who no sooner had hewn fairly habitable homes out of the wilderness and attained to that degree of prosperity which to-day we should call indigence than impelled by some mysterious impulse of their nature they abandoned all and pushed farther westward, to encounter new perils and privations in the effort to regain the meagre comforts which they had voluntarily renounced. Many of them had already forsaken that region for the remoter settlements, but among those remaining was one who had been of those first arriving. He lived alone in a house of logs surrounded on all sides by the great forest, of whose gloom and silence he seemed a part, for no one had ever known him to smile nor speak a needless word. His simple wants were supplied by the sale or barter of skins of wild animals in the river town, for not a thing did he grow upon the land which, if needful, he might have claimed by right of undisturbed possession. There were evidences of "improvement"—a few acres of ground immediately about the house had once been cleared of its trees, the decayed stumps of which were half concealed by the new growth that had been suffered to repair the ravage wrought by the ax. Apparently the man's zeal for agriculture had burned with a failing flame, expiring in penitential ashes.

The little log house, with its chimney of sticks, its roof of warping clapboards weighted with traversing poles and its "chinking" of clay, had a single door and, directly opposite, a window. The latter, however, was boarded up—nobody could remember a time when it was not. And none knew why it was so closed; certainly not because of the occupant's dislike of light and air, for on those rare occasions when a hunter had passed that lonely spot the recluse had commonly been seen sunning himself on his doorstep if heaven had provided sunshine for his need. I fancy there are few persons living to-day who ever knew the secret of that window, but I am one, as you shall see.

The man's name was said to be Murlock. He was apparently seventy years old, actually about fifty. Something besides years had had a hand in his aging. His hair and long, full beard were white, his gray, lustreless eyes sunken, his face singularly seamed with wrinkles which appeared to belong to two intersecting systems. In figure he was tall and spare, with a stoop of the shoulders—a burden bearer. I never saw him; these particulars I learned from my grandfather, from whom also I got the man's story when I was a lad. He had known him when living near by in that early day.

One day Murlock was found in his cabin, dead. It was not a time and place for coroners and newspapers, and I suppose it was agreed that he had died from natural causes or I should have been told, and should remember. I know only that with what was probably a sense of the fitness of things the body was buried near the cabin, alongside the grave of his wife, who had preceded him by so many years that local tradition had retained hardly a hint of her existence. That closes the final chapter of this true story—excepting, indeed, the circumstances that many years afterward, in company with an equally intrepid spirit, I penetrated to the place and ventured near enough to the ruined cabin to throw a stone against it, and ran away to avoid the ghost which every well-informed boy thereabout knew haunted the spot. But there is an earlier chapter— that supplied by my grandfather.

When Murlock built his cabin and began laying sturdily about with his ax to hew out a farm—the rifle, meanwhile, his means of support— he was young, strong and full of hope. In that eastern country whence he came he had married, as was the fashion, a young woman in all ways worthy of his honest devotion, who shared the dangers and privations of his lot with a willing spirit and light heart. There is no known record of her name; of her charms of mind and person tradition is silent and the doubter is at liberty to entertain his doubt; but God forbid that I should share it! Of their affection and happiness there is abundant as- surance in every added day of the man's widowed life; for what but the magnetism of a blessed memory could have chained that venturesome spirit to a lot like that?

One day Murlock returned from gunning in a distant part of the forest to find his wife prostrate with fever, and delirious. There was no physician within miles, no neighbor; nor was she in a condition to be left, to summon help. So he set about the task of nursing her back to health, but at the end of the third day she fell into unconsciousness and so passed away, apparently, with never a gleam of returning reason.

From what we know of a nature like his we may venture to sketch in some of the details of the outline picture drawn by my grandfather. When convinced that she was dead, Murlock had sense enough to re- member that the dead must be prepared for burial. In performance of this sacred duty he blundered now and again, did certain things in- correctly, and others which he did correctly were done over and over. His occasional failures to accomplish some simple and ordinary act filled him with astonishment, like that of a drunken man who wonders at the suspension of familiar natural laws. He was surprised, too, that he did not weep—surprised and a little ashamed; surely it is unkind not to weep for the dead. "To-morrow," he said aloud, "I shall have to make the coffin and dig the grave; and then I shall miss her, when she is no longer in sight; but now—she is dead, of course, but it is all right—it *must* be all right, somehow. Things cannot be so bad as they seem."

He stood over the body in the fading light, adjusting the hair and put- ting the finishing touches to the simple toilet, doing all mechanically, with soulless care. And still through his consciousness ran an undersense of conviction that all was right—that he should have her again as before, and everything explained. He had had no experience in grief; his capacity had not been enlarged by use. His heart could not contain it all, nor his imagination rightly conceive it. He did not know he was so hard struck; *that* knowledge would come later, and never go. Grief is an artist of powers as various as the instruments upon which he plays his dirges for the dead, evoking from some the sharpest, shrillest notes, from others the low, grave chords that throb recurrent like the slow beating of a distant drum. Some natures it startles; some it stupefies. To one it comes like the stroke of an arrow, stinging all the sensibilities to a keener life; to another as the blow of a bludgeon, which in crushing benumbs. We may conceive Murlock to have been that way affected, for (and here we are upon surer ground than that of conjecture) no sooner had he finished his pious work than, sinking into a chair by the side of the table upon which the body lay, and noting how white the profile showed in the deepening gloom, he laid his arms upon the table's edge, and dropped his face into them, tearless yet and unutterably weary. At that moment came in through the open window a long, wailing sound like the cry of a lost child in the far deeps of the darkening wood! But the man did not move. Again, and nearer than before, sounded that unearthly cry upon his failing sense. Perhaps it was a wild beast; perhaps it was a dream. For Murlock was asleep.

Some hours later, as it afterward appeared, this unfaithful watcher awoke and lifting his head from his arms intently listened—he knew not why. There in the black darkness by the side of the dead, recalling all without a shock, he strained his eyes to see—he knew not what. His senses were all alert, his breath was suspended, his blood had stilled its tides as if to assist the silence. Who—what had waked him, and where was it?

Suddenly the table shook beneath his arms, and at the same moment he heard, or fancied that he heard, a light, soft step—another—sounds as of bare feet upon the floor!

He was terrified beyond the power to cry out or move. Perforce he waited—waited there in the darkness through seeming centuries of such dread as one may know, yet live to tell. He tried vainly to speak the dead woman's name, vainly to stretch forth his hand across the table to learn if she were there. His throat was powerless, his arms and hands were like lead. Then occurred something most frightful. Some heavy body seemed hurled against the table with an impetus that pushed it against his breast so sharply as nearly to overthrow him, and at the same instant he heard and felt the fall of something upon the floor with so violent a thump that the whole house was shaken by the impact. A scuffling ensued, and a confusion of sounds impossible to describe. Murlock had risen to his feet. Fear had by excess forfeited control of his faculties. He flung his hands upon the table. Nothing was there!

There is a point at which terror may turn to madness; and madness incites to action. With no definite intent, from no motive but the wayward impulse of a madman, Murlock sprang to the wall, with a little groping seized his loaded rifle, and without aim discharged it. By the flash which lit up the room with a vivid illumination, he saw an enormous panther dragging the dead woman toward the window, its teeth fixed in her throat! Then there were darkness blacker than before, and silence; and when he returned to consciousness the sun was high and the wood vocal with songs of birds.

The body lay near the window, where the beast had left it when frightened away by the flash and report of the rifle. The clothing was deranged, the long hair in disorder, the limbs lay anyhow. From the throat, dreadfully lacerated, had issued a pool of blood not yet entirely coagulated. The ribbon with which he had bound the wrists was broken; the hands were tightly clenched. Between the teeth was a fragment of the animal's ear.

A LADY FROM REDHORSE

CORONADO, JUNE 20.

I FIND myself more and more interested in him. It is not, I am sure, his—do you know any good noun corresponding to the adjective "handsome"? One does not like to say "beauty" when speaking of a man. He is beautiful enough, Heaven knows; I should not even care to trust you with him—faithfulest of all possible wives that you are—when he looks his best, as he always does. Nor do I think the fascination of his manner has much to do with it. You recollect that the charm of art inheres in that which is undefinable, and to you and me, my dear Irene, I fancy there is rather less of that in the branch of art under consideration than to girls in their first season. I fancy I know how my fine gentleman produces many of his effects and could perhaps give him a pointer on heightening them. Nevertheless, his manner is something truly delightful. I suppose what interests me chiefly is the man's brains. His conversation is the best I have ever heard and altogether unlike any one else's. He seems to know everything, as indeed he ought, for he has been everywhere, read everything, seen all there is to see—sometimes I think rather more than is good for him—and had acquaintance with the *queerest* people. And then his voice—Irene, when I hear it I actually feel as if I ought to have paid at the door, though of course it is my own door.

JULY 3.

I fear my remarks about Dr. Barritz must have been, being thoughtless, very silly, or you would not have written of him with such levity, not to say disrespect. Believe me, dearest, he has more dignity and seriousness (of the kind, I mean, which is not inconsistent with a manner sometimes playful and always charming) than any of the men that you and I ever met. And young Raynor—you knew Raynor at Monterey—tells me that the men all like him and that he is treated with something like deference everywhere. There is a mystery, too—something about his connection with the Blavatsky people in Northern India. Raynor either would not or could not tell me the particulars. I infer that Dr. Barritz is thought—don't you dare to laugh!—a magician. Could anything be finer than that? An ordinary mystery is not, of course, so good as a scandal, but when it relates to dark and dreadful practices—to the exercise of unearthly powers—could anything be more piquant? It explains, too, the singular influence the man has upon me. It is the undefinable in his art —black art. Seriously, dear, I quite tremble when he looks me full in the eyes with those unfathomable orbs of his, which I have already vainly attempted to describe to you. How dreadful if he has the power to make one fall in love! Do you know if the Blavatsky crowd have that power —outside of Sepoy?

JULY 16.

The strangest thing! Last evening while Auntie was attending one of the hotel hops (I hate them) Dr. Barritz called. It was scandalously late—I actually believe that he had talked with Auntie in the ballroom and learned from her that I was alone. I had been all the evening contriving how to worm out of him the truth about his connection with the Thugs in Sepoy, and all of that black business, but the moment he fixed his eyes on me (for I admitted him, I'm ashamed to say) I was helpless. I trembled, I blushed, I—O Irene, Irene, I love the man beyond expression and you know how it is yourself.

Fancy! I, an ugly duckling from Redhorse—daughter (they say) of old Calamity Jim—certainly his heiress, with no living relation but an absurd old aunt who spoils me a thousand and fifty ways—absolutely destitute of everything but a million dollars and a hope in Paris,—I daring to love a god like him! My dear, if I had you here I could tear your hair out with mortification.

I am convinced that he is aware of my feeling, for he stayed but a few moments, said nothing but what another man might have said half as well, and pretending that he had an engagement went away. I learned to-day (a little bird told me—the bell-bird) that he went straight to bed. How does that strike you as evidence of exemplary habits?

JULY 17.

That little wretch, Raynor, called yesterday and his babble set me almost wild. He never runs down—that is to say, when he exterminates a score of reputations, more or less, he does not pause between one reputation and the next. (By the way, he inquired about you, and his manifestations of interest in you had, I confess, a good deal of *vraisemblance*.) Mr. Raynor observes no game laws; like Death (which he would inflict if slander were fatal) he has all seasons for his own. But I like him, for we knew each other at Redhorse when we were young. He was known in those days as "Giggles," and I—O Irene, can you ever forgive me?—I was called "Gunny." God knows why; perhaps in allusion to the material of my pinafores; perhaps because the name is in alliteration with "Giggles," for Gig and I were inseparable playmates, and the miners may have thought it a delicate civility to recognize some kind of relationship between us.

Later, we took in a third—another of Adversity's brood, who, like Garrick between Tragedy and Comedy, had a chronic inability to adjudicate the rival claims of Frost and Famine. Between him and misery there was seldom anything more than a single suspender and the hope of a meal which would at the same time support life and make it insupportable. He literally picked up a precarious living for himself and an aged mother by "chloriding the dumps," that is to say, the miners permitted him to search the heaps of waste rock for such pieces of "pay ore" as had been overlooked; and these he sacked up and sold at the Syndicate Mill. He became a member of our firm—"Gunny, Giggles, and Dumps" thenceforth—through my favor; for I could not then, nor can I now, be indifferent to his courage and prowess in defending against Giggles the immemorial right of his sex to insult a strange and unprotected female—myself. After old Jim struck it in the Calamity and I began to wear shoes and go to school, and in emulation Giggles took to washing his face and became Jack Raynor, of Wells, Fargo & Co., and old Mrs. Barts was herself chlorided to her fathers, Dumps drifted over to San Juan Smith and turned stage driver, and was killed by road agents, and so forth.

Why do I tell you all this, dear? Because it is heavy on my heart. Because I walk the Valley of Humility. Because I am subduing myself to permanent consciousness of my unworthiness to unloose the latchet of Dr. Barritz's shoe. Because, oh dear, oh dear, there's a cousin of Dumps at this hotel! I haven't spoken to him. I never had much acquaintance with him,—but do you suppose he has recognized me? Do, please give me in your next your candid, sure-enough opinion about it, and say you don't think so. Do you suppose He knows about me already, and that that is why He left me last evening when He saw that I blushed and trembled like a fool under His eyes? You know I can't bribe *all* the newspapers, and I can't go back on anybody who was civil to Gunny at Redhorse—not if I'm pitched out of society into the sea. So the skeleton sometimes rattles behind the door. I never cared much before, as you know, but now—*now* it is not the same. Jack Raynor I am sure of—he will not tell Him. He seems, indeed, to hold Him in such respect as hardly to dare speak to Him at all, and I'm a good deal that way myself. Dear, dear! I wish I had something besides a million dollars! If Jack were three inches taller I'd marry him alive and go back to Redhorse and wear sackcloth again to the end of my miserable days.

JULY 25.

We had a perfectly splendid sunset last evening and I must tell you all about it. I ran away from Auntie and everybody and was walking alone on the beach. I expect you to believe, you infidel! that I had not looked out of my window on the seaward side of the hotel and seen Him walking alone on the beach. If you are not lost to every feeling of womanly delicacy you will accept my statement without question. I soon established myself under my sunshade and had for some time been gazing out dreamily over the sea, when he approached, walking close to the edge of the water—it was ebb tide. I assure you the wet sand actually brightened about his feet! As he approached me he lifted his hat, saying, "Miss Dement, may I sit with you?—or will you walk with me?"

The possibility that neither might be agreeable seems not to have occurred to him. Did you ever know such assurance? Assurance? My dear, it was gall, downright *gall!* Well, I didn't find it wormwood, and replied, with my untutored Redhorse heart in my throat, "I—I shall be pleased to do *anything.*" Could words have been more stupid? There are depths of fatuity in me, friend o' my soul, that are simply bottomless!

He extended his hand, smiling, and I delivered mine into it without a moment's hesitation, and when his fingers closed about it to assist me to my feet the consciousness that it trembled made me blush worse than the red west. I got up, however, and after a while, observing that he had not let go my hand I pulled on it a little, but unsuccessfully. He simply held on, saying nothing, but looking down into my face with some kind of smile—I didn't know—how could I?—whether it was affectionate, derisive, or what, for I did not look at him. How beautiful he was!—with the red fires of the sunset burning in the depths of his eyes. Do you know, dear, if the Thugs and Experts of the Blavatsky region have any special kind of eyes? Ah, you should have seen his superb attitude, the godlike inclination of his head as he stood over me after I had got upon my feet! It was a noble picture, but I soon destroyed it, for I began at once to sink again to the earth. There was only one thing for him to do, and he did it; he supported me with an arm about my waist.

"Miss Dement, are you ill?" he said.

It was not an exclamation; there was neither alarm nor solicitude in it. If he had added: "I suppose that is about what I am expected to say," he would hardly have expressed his sense of the situation more clearly. His manner filled me with shame and indignation, for I was suffering acutely. I wrenched my hand out of his, grasped the arm supporting me

and pushing myself free, fell plump into the sand and sat helpless. My
hat had fallen off in the struggle and my hair tumbled about my face
and shoulders in the most mortifying way.

"Go away from me," I cried, half choking. "O *please* go away, you—
you Thug! How dare you think *that* when my leg is asleep?"

I actually said those identical words! And then I broke down and
sobbed. Irene, I *blubbered!*

His manner altered in an instant—I could see that much through my
fingers and hair. He dropped on one knee beside me, parted the tangle
of hair and said in the tenderest way: "My poor girl, God knows I have
not intended to pain you. How should I?—I who love you—I who have
loved you for—for years and years!"

He had pulled my wet hands away from my face and was covering
them with kisses. My cheeks were like two coals, my whole face was
flaming and, I think, steaming. What could I do? I hid it on his shoulder
—there was no other place. And, O my dear friend, how my leg tingled
and thrilled, and how I wanted to kick!

We sat so for a long time. He had released one of my hands to pass his
arm about me again and I possessed myself of my handkerchief and was
drying my eyes and my nose. I would not look up until that was done;
he tried in vain to push me a little away and gaze into my face. Presently,
when all was right, and it had grown a bit dark, I lifted my head, looked
him straight in the eyes and smiled my best—my level best, dear.

"What do you mean," I said, "by 'years and years'?"

"Dearest," he replied, very gravely, very earnestly, "in the absence of
the sunken cheeks, the hollow eyes, the lank hair, the slouching gait,
the rags, dirt, and youth, can you not—will you not understand? Gunny,
I'm Dumps!"

In a moment I was upon my feet and he upon his. I seized him by the
lapels of his coat and peered into his handsome face in the deepening
darkness. I was breathless with excitement.

"And you are not dead?" I asked, hardly knowing what I said.

"Only dead in love, dear. I recovered from the road agent's bullet, but
this, I fear, is fatal."

"But about Jack—Mr. Raynor? Don't you know—"

"I am ashamed to say, darling, that it was through that unworthy
person's suggestion that I came here from Vienna."

Irene, they have roped in your affectionate friend,

MARY JANE DEMENT.

P. S.—The worst of it is that there is no mystery; that was the invention of Jack Raynor, to arouse my curiosity. James is not a Thug. He solemnly assures me that in all his wanderings he has never set foot in Sepoy.

THE EYES OF THE PANTHER

I
ONE DOES NOT ALWAYS MARRY WHEN INSANE

A MAN and a woman—nature had done the grouping—sat on a rustic seat, in the late afternoon. The man was middle-aged, slender, swarthy, with the expression of a poet and the complexion of a pirate—a man at whom one would look again. The woman was young, blonde, graceful, with something in her figure and movements suggesting the word "lithe." She was habited in a gray gown with odd brown markings in the texture. She may have been beautiful; one could not readily say, for her eyes denied attention to all else. They were gray-green, long and narrow, with an expression defying analysis. One could only know that they were disquieting. Cleopatra may have had such eyes.

The man and the woman talked.

"Yes," said the woman, "I love you, God knows! But marry you, no. I cannot, will not."

"Irene, you have said that many times, yet always have denied me a reason. I've a right to know, to understand, to feel and prove my fortitude if I have it. Give me a reason."

"For loving you?"

The woman was smiling through her tears and her pallor. That did not stir any sense of humor in the man.

"No; there is no reason for that. A reason for not marrying me. I've a right to know. I must know. I will know!"

He had risen and was standing before her with clenched hands, on his face a frown—it might have been called a scowl. He looked as if he might attempt to learn by strangling her. She smiled no more—merely sat looking up into his face with a fixed, set regard that was utterly without emotion or sentiment. Yet it had something in it that tamed his resentment and made him shiver.

"You are determined to have my reason?" she asked in a tone that was entirely mechanical—a tone that might have been her look made audible.

"If you please—if I'm not asking too much."

Apparently this lord of creation was yielding some part of his dominion over his co-creature.

"Very well, you shall know: I am insane."

The man started, then looked incredulous and was conscious that he ought to be amused. But, again, the sense of humor failed him in his need and despite his disbelief he was profoundly disturbed by that which he did not believe. Between our convictions and our feelings there is no good understanding.

"That is what the physicians would say," the woman continued—"if they knew. I might myself prefer to call it a case of 'possession.' Sit down and hear what I have to say."

The man silently resumed his seat beside her on the rustic bench by the wayside. Over-against them on the eastern side of the valley the hills were already sunset-flushed and the stillness all about was of that peculiar quality that foretells the twilight. Something of its mysterious and significant solemnity had imparted itself to the man's mood. In the spiritual, as in the material world, are signs and presages of night. Rarely meeting her look, and whenever he did so conscious of the indefinable dread with which, despite their feline beauty, her eyes always affected him, Jenner Brading listened in silence to the story told by Irene Marlowe. In deference to the reader's possible prejudice against the artless method of an unpractised historian the author ventures to substitute his own version for hers.

II

A ROOM MAY BE TOO NARROW FOR THREE, THOUGH ONE IS OUTSIDE

In a little log house containing a single room sparely and rudely furnished, crouching on the floor against one of the walls, was a woman, clasping to her breast a child. Outside, a dense unbroken forest extended for many miles in every direction. This was at night and the room was black dark: no human eye could have discerned the woman and the child. Yet they were observed, narrowly, vigilantly, with never even a momentary slackening of attention; and that is the pivotal fact upon which this narrative turns.

Charles Marlowe was of the class, now extinct in this country, of woodmen pioneers—men who found their most acceptable surroundings in sylvan solitudes that stretched along the eastern slope of the Mississippi Valley, from the Great Lakes to the Gulf of Mexico. For more than a hundred years these men pushed ever westward, generation after generation, with rifle and ax, reclaiming from Nature and her savage children here and there an isolated acreage for the plow, no sooner reclaimed than surrendered to their less venturesome but more thrifty successors. At last they burst through the edge of the forest into the open country and vanished as if they had fallen over a cliff. The woodman pioneer is no more; the pioneer of the plains—he whose easy task it was to subdue for occupancy two-thirds of the country in a single generation—is another and inferior creation. With Charles Marlowe in the wilderness, sharing the dangers, hardships and privations of that strange, unprofitable life, were his wife and child, to whom, in the manner of his class, in which the domestic virtues were a religion, he was passionately attached. The woman was still young enough to be comely, new enough to the awful isolation of her lot to be cheerful. By withholding the large capacity for happiness which the simple satisfactions of the forest life could not have filled, Heaven had dealt honorably with her. In her light household tasks, her child, her husband and her few foolish books, she found abundant provision for her needs.

One morning in midsummer Marlowe took down his rifle from the wooden hooks on the wall and signified his intention of getting game.

"We've meat enough," said the wife; "please don't go out to-day. I dreamed last night, O, such a dreadful thing! I cannot recollect it, but I'm almost sure that it will come to pass if you go out."

It is painful to confess that Marlowe received this solemn statement with less of gravity than was due to the mysterious nature of the calamity foreshadowed. In truth, he laughed.

"Try to remember," he said. "Maybe you dreamed that Baby had lost the power of speech."

The conjecture was obviously suggested by the fact that Baby, clinging to the fringe of his hunting-coat with all her ten pudgy thumbs was at that moment uttering her sense of the situation in a series of exultant goo-goos inspired by sight of her father's raccoon-skin cap.

The woman yielded: lacking the gift of humor she could not hold out against his kindly badinage. So, with a kiss for the mother and a kiss for the child, he left the house and closed the door upon his happiness forever.

At nightfall he had not returned. The woman prepared supper and waited. Then she put Baby to bed and sang softly to her until she slept. By this time the fire on the hearth, at which she had cooked supper, had burned out and the room was lighted by a single candle. This she afterward placed in the open window as a sign and welcome to the hunter if he should approach from that side. She had thoughtfully closed and barred the door against such wild animals as might prefer it to an open window—of the habits of beasts of prey in entering a house uninvited she was not advised, though with true female prevision she may have considered the possibility of their entrance by way of the chimney. As the night wore on she became not less anxious, but more drowsy, and at last rested her arms upon the bed by the child and her head upon the arms. The candle in the window burned down to the socket, sputtered and flared a moment and went out unobserved; for the woman slept and dreamed.

In her dreams she sat beside the cradle of a second child. The first one was dead. The father was dead. The home in the forest was lost and the dwelling in which she lived was unfamiliar. There were heavy oaken doors, always closed, and outside the windows, fastened into the thick stone walls, were iron bars, obviously (so she thought) a provision against Indians. All this she noted with an infinite self-pity, but without surprise—an emotion unknown in dreams. The child in the cradle was invisible under its coverlet which something impelled her to remove. She did so, disclosing the face of a wild animal! In the shock of this dreadful revelation the dreamer awoke, trembling in the darkness of her cabin in the wood.

As a sense of her actual surroundings came slowly back to her she felt for the child that was not a dream, and assured herself by its breathing that all was well with it; nor could she forbear to pass a hand lightly across its face. Then, moved by some impulse for which she probably could not have accounted, she rose and took the sleeping babe in her arms, holding it close against her breast. The head of the child's cot was against the wall to which the woman now turned her back as she stood. Lifting her eyes she saw two bright objects starring the darkness with a reddish-green glow. She took them to be two coals on the hearth, but with her returning sense of direction came the disquieting conscious- ness that they were not in that quarter of the room, moreover were too high, being nearly at the level of the eyes—of her own eyes. For these were the eyes of a panther.

The beast was at the open window directly opposite and not five paces away. Nothing but those terrible eyes was visible, but in the dreadful tumult of her feelings as the situation disclosed itself to her understand- ing she somehow knew that the animal was standing on its hinder feet, supporting itself with its paws on the window-ledge. That signified a malign interest—not the mere gratification of an indolent curiosity. The consciousness of the attitude was an added horror, accentuating the menace of those awful eyes, in whose steadfast fire her strength and courage were alike consumed. Under their silent questioning she shuddered and turned sick. Her knees failed her, and by degrees, in- stinctively striving to avoid a sudden movement that might bring the beast upon her, she sank to the floor, crouched against the wall and tried to shield the babe with her trembling body without withdrawing her gaze from the luminous orbs that were killing her. No thought of her husband came to her in her agony—no hope nor suggestion of rescue or escape. Her capacity for thought and feeling had narrowed to the dimen- sions of a single emotion—fear of the animal's spring, of the impact of its body, the buffeting of its great arms, the feel of its teeth in her throat, the mangling of her babe. Motionless now and in absolute silence, she awaited her doom, the moments growing to hours, to years, to ages; and still those devilish eyes maintained their watch.

Returning to his cabin late at night with a deer on his shoulders Charles Marlowe tried the door. It did not yield. He knocked; there was no answer. He laid down his deer and went round to the window. As he turned the angle of the building he fancied he heard a sound as of stealthy footfalls and a rustling in the undergrowth of the forest, but they were too slight for certainty, even to his practised ear. Approaching the window, and to his surprise finding it open, he threw his leg over the sill and entered. All was darkness and silence. He groped his way to the fire-place, struck a match and lit a candle. Then he looked about. Cowering on the floor against a wall was his wife, clasping his child. As he sprang toward her she rose and broke into laughter, long, loud, and mechanical, devoid of gladness and devoid of sense—the laughter that is not out of keeping with the clanking of a chain. Hardly knowing what he did he extended his arms. She laid the babe in them. It was dead—pressed to death in its mother's embrace.

III
THE THEORY OF THE DEFENSE

That is what occurred during a night in a forest, but not all of it did Irene Marlowe relate to Jenner Brading; not all of it was known to her. When she had concluded the sun was below the horizon and the long summer twilight had begun to deepen in the hollows of the land. For some moments Brading was silent, expecting the narrative to be carried forward to some definite connection with the conversation introducing it; but the narrator was as silent as he, her face averted, her hands clasping and unclasping themselves as they lay in her lap, with a singular suggestion of an activity independent of her will.

"It is a sad, a terrible story," said Brading at last, "but I do not understand. You call Charles Marlowe father; that I know. That he is old before his time, broken by some great sorrow, I have seen, or thought I saw. But, pardon me, you said that you—that you—"

"That I am insane," said the girl, without a movement of head or body.

"But, Irene, you say—please, dear, do not look away from me—you say that the child was dead, not demented."

"Yes, that one—I am the second. I was born three months after that night, my mother being mercifully permitted to lay down her life in giving me mine."

Brading was again silent; he was a trifle dazed and could not at once think of the right thing to say. Her face was still turned away. In his embarrassment he reached impulsively toward the hands that lay closing and unclosing in her lap, but something—he could not have said what—restrained him. He then remembered, vaguely, that he had never altogether cared to take her hand.

"Is it likely," she resumed, "that a person born under such circumstances is like others—is what you call sane?"

Brading did not reply; he was preoccupied with a new thought that was taking shape in his mind—what a scientist would have called an hypothesis; a detective, a theory. It might throw an added light, albeit a lurid one, upon such doubt of her sanity as her own assertion had not dispelled.

The country was still new and, outside the villages, sparsely populated. The professional hunter was still a familiar figure, and among his trophies were heads and pelts of the larger kinds of game. Tales variously credible of nocturnal meetings with savage animals in lonely roads were sometimes current, passed through the customary stages of growth and decay, and were forgotten. A recent addition to these popular apocrypha, originating, apparently, by spontaneous generation in several households, was of a panther which had frightened some of their members by looking in at windows by night. The yarn had caused its little ripple of excitement—had even attained to the distinction of a place in the local newspaper; but Brading had given it no attention. Its likeness to the story to which he had just listened now impressed him as perhaps more than accidental. Was it not possible that the one story had suggested the other—that finding congenial conditions in a morbid mind and a fertile fancy, it had grown to the tragic tale that he had heard?

Brading recalled certain circumstances of the girl's history and disposition, of which, with love's incuriosity, he had hitherto been heedless —such as her solitary life with her father, at whose house no one, apparently, was an acceptable visitor and her strange fear of the night, by which those who knew her best accounted for her never being seen after dark. Surely in such a mind imagination once kindled might burn with a lawless flame, penetrating and enveloping the entire structure. That she was mad, though the conviction gave him the acutest pain, he could no longer doubt; she had only mistaken an effect of her mental disorder for its cause, bringing into imaginary relation with her own personality the vagaries of the local myth-makers. With some vague intention of testing his new "theory," and no very definite notion of how to set about it he said, gravely, but with hesitation:

"Irene, dear, tell me—I beg you will not take offence, but tell me—"

"I have told you," she interrupted, speaking with a passionate earnestness that he had not known her to show—"I have already told you that we cannot marry; is anything else worth saying?"

Before he could stop her she had sprung from her seat and without another word or look was gliding away among the trees toward her father's house. Brading had risen to detain her; he stood watching her in silence until she had vanished in the gloom. Suddenly he started as if he had been shot; his face took on an expression of amazement and alarm: in one of the black shadows into which she had disappeared he had caught a quick, brief glimpse of shining eyes! For an instant he was dazed and irresolute; then he dashed into the wood after her, shouting: "Irene, Irene, look out! The panther! The panther!"

In a moment he had passed through the fringe of forest into open ground and saw the girl's gray skirt vanishing into her father's door. No panther was visible.

IV
AN APPEAL TO THE CONSCIENCE OF GOD

Jenner Brading, attorney-at-law, lived in a cottage at the edge of the town. Directly behind the dwelling was the forest. Being a bachelor, and therefore, by the Draconian moral code of the time and place denied the services of the only species of domestic servant known thereabout, the "hired girl," he boarded at the village hotel, where also was his office. The woodside cottage was merely a lodging maintained—at no great cost, to be sure—as an evidence of prosperity and respectability. It would hardly do for one to whom the local newspaper had pointed with pride as "the foremost jurist of his time" to be "homeless," albeit he may sometimes have suspected that the words "home" and "house" were not strictly synonymous. Indeed, his consciousness of the disparity and his will to harmonize it were matters of logical inference, for it was generally reported that soon after the cottage was built its owner had made a futile venture in the direction of marriage—had, in truth, gone so far as to be rejected by the beautiful but eccentric daughter of Old Man Marlowe, the recluse. This was publicly believed because he had told it himself and she had not—a reversal of the usual order of things which could hardly fail to carry conviction.

Brading's bedroom was at the rear of the house, with a single window facing the forest. One night he was awakened by a noise at that window; he could hardly have said what it was like. With a little thrill of the nerves he sat up in bed and laid hold of the revolver which, with a forethought most commendable in one addicted to the habit of sleeping on the ground floor with an open window, he had put under his pillow.

The room was in absolute darkness, but being unterrified he knew where to direct his eyes, and there he held them, awaiting in silence what further might occur. He could now dimly discern the aperture—a square of lighter black. Presently there appeared at its lower edge two gleaming eyes that burned with a malignant lustre inexpressibly terrible! Brading's heart gave a great jump, then seemed to stand still. A chill passed along his spine and through his hair; he felt the blood forsake his cheeks. He could not have cried out—not to save his life; but being a man of courage he would not, to save his life, have done so if he had been able. Some trepidation his coward body might feel, but his spirit was of sterner stuff. Slowly the shining eyes rose with a steady motion that seemed an approach, and slowly rose Brading's right hand, holding the pistol. He fired!

Blinded by the flash and stunned by the report, Brading nevertheless heard, or fancied that he heard, the wild, high scream of the panther, so human in sound, so devilish in suggestion. Leaping from the bed he hastily clothed himself and, pistol in hand, sprang from the door, meeting two or three men who came running up from the road. A brief explanation was followed by a cautious search of the house. The grass was wet with dew; beneath the window it had been trodden and partly leveled for a wide space, from which a devious trail, visible in the light of a lantern, led away into the bushes. One of the men stumbled and fell upon his hands, which as he rose and rubbed them together were slippery. On examination they were seen to be red with blood.

An encounter, unarmed, with a wounded panther was not agreeable to their taste; all but Brading turned back. He, with lantern and pistol, pushed courageously forward into the wood. Passing through a difficult undergrowth he came into a small opening, and there his courage had its reward, for there he found the body of his victim. But it was no panther. What it was is told, even to this day, upon a weather-worn headstone in the village churchyard, and for many years was attested daily at the graveside by the bent figure and sorrow-seamed face of Old Man Marlowe, to whose soul, and to the soul of his strange, unhappy child, peace. Peace and reparation.

THE DEVIL'S DICTIONARY

PREFACE

The Devil's Dictionary was begun in a weekly paper in 1881, and was continued in a desultory way and at long intervals until 1906. In that year a large part of it was published in covers with the title *The Cynic's Word Book,* a name which the author had not the power to reject nor the happiness to approve. To quote the publishers of the present work:

"This more reverent title had previously been forced upon him by the religious scruples of the last newspaper in which a part of the work had appeared, with the natural consequence that when it came out in covers the country already had been flooded by its imitators with a score of 'cynic' books—*The Cynic's This, The Cynic's That,* and *The Cynic's t'Other.* Most of these books were merely stupid, though some of them added the distinction of silliness. Among them, they brought the word 'cynic' into disfavor so deep that any book bearing it was discredited in advance of publication."

Meantime, too, some of the enterprising humorists of the country had helped themselves to such parts of the work as served their needs, and many of its definitions, anecdotes, phrases and so forth, had become more or less current in popular speech. This explanation is made, not with any pride of priority in trifles, but in simple denial of possible charges of plagiarism, which is no trifle. In merely resuming his own the author hopes to be held guiltless by those to whom the work is addressed —enlightened souls who prefer dry wines to sweet, sense to sentiment, wit to humor and clean English to slang.

A conspicuous, and it is hoped not unpleasing, feature of the book is its abundant illustrative quotations from eminent poets, chief of whom is that learned and ingenious cleric, Father Gassalasca Jape, S. J., whose lines bear his initials. To Father Jape's kindly encouragement and assistance the author of the prose text is greatly indebted.

A. B.

A

ABASEMENT, *n*. A decent and customary mental attitude in the presence of wealth or power. Peculiarly appropriate in an employee when addressing an employer.

ABDICATION, *n*. An act whereby a sovereign attests his sense of the high temperature of the throne.

> Poor Isabella's dead, whose abdication
> Set all tongues wagging in the Spanish nation.
> For that performance 'twere unfair to scold her:
> She wisely left a throne too hot to hold her.
> To History she'll be no royal riddle—
> Merely a plain parched pea that jumped the griddle.
>   *G. J.*

ABDOMEN, *n*. The temple of the god Stomach, in whose worship, with sacrificial rights, all true men engage. From women this ancient faith commands but a stammering assent. They sometimes minister at the altar in a half-hearted and ineffective way, but true reverence for the one deity that men really adore they know not. If woman had a free hand in the world's marketing the race would become graminivorous.

ABILITY, *n*. The natural equipment to accomplish some small part of the meaner ambitions distinguishing able men from dead ones. In the last analysis ability is commonly found to consist mainly in a high degree of solemnity. Perhaps, however, this impressive quality is rightly appraised; it is no easy task to be solemn.

ABNORMAL, *adj*. Not conforming to standard. In matters of thought and conduct, to be independent is to be abnormal, to be abnormal is to be detested. Wherefore the lexicographer adviseth a striving toward a straiter resemblance to the Average Man than he hath to himself. Whoso attaineth thereto shall have peace, the prospect of death and the hope of Hell.

ABORIGINES, *n.* Persons of little worth found cumbering the soil of a
newly discovered country. They soon cease to cumber; they fertilize.

ABRACADABRA.

By *Abracadabra* we signify
  An infinite number of things.
'Tis the answer to What? and How? and Why?
And Whence? and Whither?—a word whereby
  The Truth (with the comfort it brings)
Is open to all who grope in night,
Crying for Wisdom's holy light.

Whether the word is a verb or a noun
  Is knowledge beyond my reach.
I only know that 'tis handed down
    From sage to sage,
    From age to age—
  An immortal part of speech!

Of an ancient man the tale is told
That he lived to be ten centuries old,
  In a cave on a mountain side.
  (True, he finally died.)
The fame of his wisdom filled the land,
For his head was bald, and you'll understand
  His beard was long and white
  And his eyes uncommonly bright.

Philosophers gathered from far and near
To sit at his feet and hear and hear,
    Though he never was heard
    To utter a word
  But "*Abracadabra, abracadab,*
    Abracada, abracad,
  Abraca, abrac, abra, ab!"
    'Twas all he had,
'Twas all they wanted to hear, and each
Made copious notes of the mystical speech,
    Which they published next—
    A trickle of text
In a meadow of commentary.
  Mighty big books were these,
  In number, as leaves of trees;
In learning, remarkable—very!

> He's dead,
> As I said,
> And the books of the sages have perished,
> But his wisdom is sacredly cherished.
> In *Abracadabra* it solemnly rings,
> Like an ancient bell that forever swings.
> O, I love to hear
> That word make clear
> Humanity's General Sense of Things.
>
> *Jamrach Holobom.*

ABRIDGE, *v. t.* To shorten.

When in the course of human events it becomes necessary for a people to abridge their king, a decent respect for the opinions of mankind requires that they should declare the causes which impel them to the separation.

> *Oliver Cromwell.*

ABRUPT, *adj.* Sudden, without ceremony, like the arrival of a cannon-shot and the departure of the soldier whose interests are most affected by it. Dr. Samuel Johnson beautifully said of another author's ideas that they were "concatenated without abruption."

ABSCOND, *v. i.* To "move in a mysterious way," commonly with the property of another.

> Spring beckons! All things to the call respond;
> The trees are leaving and cashiers abscond.
>
> *Phela Orm.*

ABSENT, *adj.* Peculiarly exposed to the tooth of detraction; vilified; hopelessly in the wrong; superseded in the consideration and affection of another.

> To men a man is but a mind. Who cares
> What face he carries or what form he wears?
> But woman's body is the woman. O,
> Stay thou, my sweetheart, and do never go,
> But heed the warning words the sage hath said:
> A woman absent is a woman dead.
>
> *Jogo Tyree.*

ABSENTEE, *n.* A person with an income who has had the forethought to remove himself from the sphere of exaction.

ABSOLUTE, *adj.* Independent, irresponsible. An absolute monarchy is one in which the sovereign does as he pleases so long as he pleases the assassins. Not many absolute monarchies are left, most of them having been replaced by limited monarchies, where the sovereign's power for evil (and for good) is greatly curtailed, and by republics, which are governed by chance.

ABSTAINER, *n.* A weak person who yields to the temptation of denying himself a pleasure. A total abstainer is one who abstains from everything but abstention, and especially from inactivity in the affairs of others.

> Said a man to a crapulent youth: "I thought
> You a total abstainer, my son."
> "So I am, so I am," said the scapegrace caught—
> "But not, sir, a bigoted one."
>
> *G. J.*

ABSURDITY, *n.* A statement or belief manifestly inconsistent with one's own opinion.

ACADEME, *n.* An ancient school where morality and philosophy were taught.

ACADEMY, *n.* (from academe). A modern school where football is taught.

ACCIDENT, *n.* An inevitable occurrence due to the action of immutable natural laws.

ACCOMPLICE, *n.* One associated with another in a crime, having guilty knowledge and complicity, as an attorney who defends a criminal, knowing him guilty. This view of the attorney's position in the matter has not hitherto commanded the assent of attorneys, no one having offered them a fee for assenting.

ACCORD, *n.* Harmony.

ACCORDION, *n.* An instrument in harmony with the sentiments of an assassin.

ACCOUNTABILITY, *n.* The mother of caution.

> "My accountability, bear in mind,"
> Said the Grand Vizier: "Yes, yes,"
> Said the Shah: "I do—'tis the only kind
> Of ability you possess."
>
> *Joram Tate.*

ACCUSE, *v. t.* To affirm another's guilt or unworth; most commonly as a justification of ourselves for having wronged him.

ACEPHALOUS, *adj.* In the surprising condition of the Crusader who absently pulled at his forelock some hours after a Saracen scimitar had, unconsciously to him, passed through his neck, as related by de Joinville.

ACHIEVEMENT, *n.* The death of endeavor and the birth of disgust.

ACKNOWLEDGE, *v. t.* To confess. Acknowledgment of one another's faults is the highest duty imposed by our love of truth.

ACQUAINTANCE, *n.* A person whom we know well enough to borrow from, but not well enough to lend to. A degree of friendship called slight when its object is poor or obscure, and intimate when he is rich or famous.

ACTUALLY, *adv.* Perhaps; possibly.

ADAGE, *n.* Boned wisdom for weak teeth.

ADAMANT, *n.* A mineral frequently found beneath a corset. Soluble in solicitate of gold.

ADDER, *n.* A species of snake. So called from its habit of adding funeral outlays to the other expenses of living.

ADHERENT, *n.* A follower who has not yet obtained all that he expects to get.

ADMINISTRATION, *n.* An ingenious abstraction in politics, designed to receive the kicks and cuffs due to the premier or president. A man of straw, proof against bad-egging and dead-catting.

ADMIRAL, *n.* That part of a war-ship which does the talking while the figure-head does the thinking.

ADMIRATION, *n.* Our polite recognition of another's resemblance to ourselves.

ADMONITION, *n.* Gentle reproof, as with a meat-axe. Friendly warning.
> Consigned, by way of admonition,
> His soul forever to perdition.
> *Judibras.*

ADORE, *v. t.* To venerate expectantly.

ADVICE, *n.* The smallest current coin.
> "The man was in such deep distress,"
> Said Tom, "that I could do no less
> Than give him good advice." Said Jim:
> "If less could have been done for him
> I know you well enough, my son,
> To know that's what you would have done."
> *Jebel Jocordy.*

AFFIANCED, *pp.* Fitted with an ankle-ring for the ball-and-chain.

AFFLICTION, *n.* An acclimatizing process preparing the soul for another and bitter world.

AGE, *n.* That period of life in which we compound for the vices that we still cherish by reviling those that we have no longer the enterprise to commit.

AGITATOR, *n.* A statesman who shakes the fruit trees of his neighbors—to dislodge the worms.

AIM, *n.* The task we set our wishes to.

"Cheer up! Have you no aim in life?"
    She tenderly inquired.
"An aim? Well, no, I haven't, wife;
    The fact is—I have fired."

G. J.

AIR, *n.* A nutritious substance supplied by a bountiful Providence for the fattening of the poor.

ALDERMAN, *n.* An ingenious criminal who covers his secret thieving with a pretence of open marauding.

ALIEN, *n.* An American sovereign in his probationary state.

ALLAH, *n.* The Mahometan Supreme Being, as distinguished from the Christian, Jewish, and so forth.

    Allah's good laws I faithfully have kept,
    And ever for the sins of man have wept;
      And sometimes kneeling in the temple I
    Have reverently crossed my hands and slept.

Junker Barlow.

ALLEGIANCE, *n.*

    This thing Allegiance, as I suppose,
    Is a ring fitted in the subject's nose,
    Whereby that organ is kept rightly pointed
    To smell the sweetness of the Lord's anointed.

G. J.

ALLIANCE, *n.* In international politics, the union of two thieves who have their hands so deeply inserted in each other's pocket that they cannot separately plunder a third.

ALLIGATOR, *n.* The crocodile of America, superior in every detail to the crocodile of the effete monarchies of the Old World. Herodotus says the Indus is, with one exception, the only river that produces crocodiles, but they appear to have gone West and grown up with the other rivers. From the notches on his back the alligator is called a sawrian.

ALONE, *adj.* In bad company.

> In contact, lo! the flint and steel,
> By spark and flame, the thought reveal
> That he the metal, she the stone,
> Had cherished secretly alone.
> *Booley Fito.*

ALTAR, *n.* The place whereon the priest formerly raveled out the small intestine of the sacrificial victim for purposes of divination and cooked its flesh for the gods. The word is now seldom used, except with reference to the sacrifice of their liberty and peace by a male and a female fool.

> They stood before the altar and supplied
> The fire themselves in which their fat was fried.
> In vain the sacrifice!—no god will claim
> An offering burnt with an unholy flame.
> *M. P. Nopput.*

AMBIDEXTROUS, *adj.* Able to pick with equal skill a right-hand pocket or a left.

AMBITION, *n.* An overmastering desire to be vilified by enemies while living and made ridiculous by friends when dead.

AMNESTY, *n.* The state's magnanimity to those offenders whom it would be too expensive to punish.

ANOINT, *v. t.* To grease a king or other great functionary already sufficiently slippery.

> As sovereigns are anointed by the priesthood,
> So pigs to lead the populace are greased good.
> *Judibras.*

ANTIPATHY, *n.* The sentiment inspired by one's friend's friend.

APHORISM, *n.* Predigested wisdom.

> The flabby wine-skin of his brain
> Yields to some pathologic strain,
> And voids from its unstored abysm
> The driblet of an aphorism.
> *"The Mad Philosopher,"* 1697.

APOLOGIZE, *v. i.* To lay the foundation for a future offence.

APOSTATE, *n.* A leech who, having penetrated the shell of a turtle only to find that the creature has long been dead, deems it expedient to form a new attachment to a fresh turtle.

APOTHECARY, *n.* The physician's accomplice, undertaker's benefactor and grave worm's provider.

> When Jove sent blessings to all men that are,
> And Mercury conveyed them in a jar,
> That friend of tricksters introduced by stealth
> Disease for the apothecary's health,
> Whose gratitude impelled him to proclaim:
> "My deadliest drug shall bear my patron's name!"
> *G. J.*

APPEAL, *v. t.* In law, to put the dice into the box for another throw.

APPLAUSE, *n.* The echo of a platitude.

APRIL FOOL, *n.* The March fool with another month added to his folly.

ARCHBISHOP, *n.* An ecclesiastical dignitary one point holier than a bishop.

> If I were a jolly archbishop,
> On Fridays I'd eat all the fish up—
> Salmon and flounders and smelts;
> On other days everything else.
> *Jodo, Rem.*

ARCHITECT, *n.* One who drafts a plan of your house, and plans a draft of your money.

ARDOR, *n.* The quality that distinguishes love without knowledge.

ARENA, *n.* In politics, an imaginary rat-pit in which the statesman wrestles with his record.

ARISTOCRACY, *n.* Government by the best men. (In this sense the word is obsolete; so is that kind of government.) Fellows that wear downy hats and clean shirts—guilty of education and suspected of bank accounts.

ARMOR, *n.* The kind of clothing worn by a man whose tailor is a blacksmith.

ARRAYED, *pp.* Drawn up and given an orderly disposition, as a rioter hanged to a lamppost.

ARREST, *v. t.* Formally to detain one accused of unusualness.

God made the world in six days and was arrested on the seventh.—
The Unauthorized Version.

ARSENIC, *n.* A kind of cosmetic greatly affected by the ladies, whom it greatly affects in turn.

> "Eat arsenic? Yes, all you get,"
> Consenting, he did speak up;
> " 'Tis better you should eat it, pet,
> Than put it in my teacup."
> *Joel Huck.*

ART, *n.* This word has no definition. Its origin is related as follows by the ingenious Father Gassalasca Jape, S. J.

> One day a wag—what would the wretch be at?—
> Shifted a letter of the cipher RAT,
> And said it was a god's name! Straight arose
> Fantastic priests and postulants (with shows,
> And mysteries, and mummeries, and hymns,
> And disputations dire that lamed their limbs)
> To serve his temple and maintain the fires,
> Expound the law, manipulate the wires.
> Amazed, the populace the rites attend,
> Believe whate'er they cannot comprehend,
> And, inly edified to learn that two
> Half-hairs joined so and so (as Art can do)
> Have sweeter values and a grace more fit
> Than Nature's hairs that never have been split,
> Bring cates and wines for sacrificial feasts,
> And sell their garments to support the priests.

ARTLESSNESS, *n.* A certain engaging quality to which women attain by long study and severe practice upon the admiring male, who is pleased to fancy it resembles the candid simplicity of his young.

ASPERSE, *v. t.* Maliciously to ascribe to another vicious actions which one has not had the temptation and opportunity to commit.

ASS, *n.* A public singer with a good voice but no ear. In Virginia City, Nevada, he is called the Washoe Canary, in Dakota, the Senator, and everywhere the Donkey. The animal is widely and variously celebrated in the literature, art and religion of every age and country; no other so engages and fires the human imagination as this noble vertebrate. Indeed, it is doubted by some (Ramasilus, *lib. II., De Clem.,* and C. Stantatus, *De Temperamente*) if it is not a god; and as such we know it was worshiped by the Etruscans, and, if we may believe Macrobious, by the Cupasians also. Of the only two animals admitted into the Mahometan Paradise along with the souls of men, the ass that carried Balaam is one, the dog of the Seven Sleepers the other. This is no small distinction. From what has been written about this beast might be compiled a library of great splendor and magnitude, rivaling that of the Shakespearean cult, and that which clusters about the Bible. It may be said, generally, that all literature is more or less Asinine.

> "Hail, holy Ass!" the quiring angels sing;
> "Priest of Unreason, and of Discords King!
> Great co-Creator, let Thy glory shine:
> God made all else; the Mule, the Mule is thine!"
> *G. J.*

AUCTIONEER, *n.* The man who proclaims with a hammer that he has picked a pocket with his tongue.

AUSTRALIA, *n.* A country lying in the South Sea, whose industrial and commercial development has been unspeakably retarded by an unfortunate dispute among geographers as to whether it is a continent or an island.

AVERNUS, *n.* The lake by which the ancients entered the infernal regions. The fact that access to the infernal regions was obtained by a lake is believed by the learned Marcus Ansello Scrutator to have suggested the Christian rite of baptism by immersion. This, however, has been shown by Lactantius to be an error.

> *Facilis descensus Averni,*
>> The poet remarks; and the sense
>> Of it is that when down-hill I turn I
>> Will get more of punches than pence.
>>
>> *Jehal Dai Lupe.*

B

BAAL, *n.* An old deity formerly much worshiped under various names. As Baal he was popular with the Phœnicians; as Belus or Bel he had the honor to be served by the priest Berosus, who wrote the famous account of the Deluge; as Babel he had a tower partly erected to his glory on the Plain of Shinar. From Babel comes our English word "babble." Under whatever name worshiped, Baal is the Sun-god. As Beelzebub he is the god of flies, which are begotten of the sun's rays on stagnant water. In Physicia Baal is still worshiped as Bolus, and as Belly he is adored and served with abundant sacrifice by the priests of Guttledom.

BABE OR BABY, *n.* A misshapen creature of no particular age, sex, or condition, chiefly remarkable for the violence of the sympathies and antipathies it excites in others, itself without sentiment or emotion. There have been famous babes; for example, little Moses, from whose adventure in the bulrushes the Egyptian hierophants of seven centuries before doubtless derived their idle tale of the child Osiris being preserved on a floating lotus leaf.

> Ere babes were invented
> The girls were contented.
> Now man is tormented
> Until to buy babes he has squandered

His money. And so I have pondered
  This thing, and thought may be
    'T were better that Baby
The First had been eagled or condored.
Ro Amil.

BACCHUS, *n.* A convenient deity invented by the ancients as an excuse for getting drunk.

  Is public worship, then, a sin,
    That for devotions paid to Bacchus
  The lictors dare to run us in,
    And resolutely thump and whack us?
Jorace.

BACK, *n.* That part of your friend which it is your privilege to contemplate in your adversity.

BACKBITE, *v. t.* To speak of a man as you find him when he can't find you.

BAIT, *n.* A preparation that renders the hook more palatable. The best kind is beauty.

BAPTISM, *n.* A sacred rite of such efficacy that he who finds himself in heaven without having undergone it will be unhappy forever. It is performed with water in two ways—by immersion, or plunging, and by aspersion, or sprinkling.

  But whether the plan of immersion
  Is better than simple aspersion
    Let those immersed
    And those aspersed
  Decide by the Authorized Version,
  And by matching their agues tertian.
G. J.

BAROMETER, *n.* An ingenious instrument which indicates what kind of weather we are having.

BARRACK, *n.* A house in which soldiers enjoy a portion of that of which it is their business to deprive others.

BASILISK, *n.* The cockatrice. A sort of serpent hatched from the egg of a cock. The basilisk had a bad eye, and its glance was fatal. Many infidels deny this creature's existence, but Semprello Aurator saw and handled one that had been blinded by lightning as a punishment for having fatally gazed on a lady of rank whom Jupiter loved. Juno afterward restored the reptile's sight and hid it in a cave. Nothing is so well attested by the ancients as the existence of the basilisk, but the cocks have stopped laying.

BASTINADO, *n.* The act of walking on wood without exertion.

BATH, *n.* A kind of mystic ceremony substituted for religious worship, with what spiritual efficacy has not been determined.

> The man who taketh a steam bath
> He loseth all the skin he hath,
> And, for he's boiled a brilliant red,
> Thinketh to cleanliness he's wed,
> Forgetting that his lungs he's soiling
> With dirty vapors of the boiling.
> *Richard Gwow.*

BATTLE, *n.* A method of untying with the teeth a political knot that would not yield to the tongue.

BEARD, *n.* The hair that is commonly cut off by those who justly execrate the absurd Chinese custom of shaving the head.

BEAUTY, *n.* The power by which a woman charms a lover and terrifies a husband.

BEFRIEND, *v. t.* To make an ingrate.

BEG, *v.* To ask for something with an earnestness proportioned to the belief that it will not be given.

> Who is that, father?
> A mendicant, child,
> Haggard, morose, and unaffable—wild!
> See how he glares through the bars of his cell!
> With Citizen Mendicant all is not well.

Why did they put him there, father?

> Because
Obeying his belly he struck at the laws.

His belly?

> Oh, well, he was starving, my boy—
A state in which, doubtless, there's little of joy.
No bite had he eaten for days, and his cry
Was "Bread!" ever "Bread!"

> What's the matter with pie?

With little to wear, he had nothing to sell;
To beg was unlawful—improper as well.

Why didn't he work?

> He would even have done that,
But men said: "Get out!" and the State remarked: "Scat!"
I mention these incidents merely to show
That the vengeance he took was uncommonly low.
Revenge, at the best, is the act of a Siou,
But for trifles—

> Pray what did bad Mendicant do?

Stole two loaves of bread to replenish his lack
And tuck out the belly that clung to his back.

Is that *all*, father dear?

> There is little to tell:
They sent him to jail, and they'll send him to—well,
The company's better than here we can boast,
And there's—

> Bread for the needy, dear father?

> Um—toast.
> *Atka Mip.*

BEGGAR, *n*. One who has relied on the assistance of his friends.

BEHAVIOR, *n*. Conduct, as determined, not by principle, but by breeding.

The word seems to be somewhat loosely used in Dr. Jamrach Holobom's translation of the following lines in the *Dies Iræ*:

> Recordare, Jesu pie,
> Quod sum causa tuæ viæ.
> Ne me perdas illa die.

> Pray remember, sacred Savior,
> Whose the thoughtless hand that gave your
> Death-blow. Pardon such behavior.

BELLADONNA, *n.* In Italian a beautiful lady; in English a deadly poison. A striking example of the essential identity of the two tongues.

BENEDICTINES, *n.* An order of monks otherwise known as black friars.
> She thought it a crow, but it turned out to be
> A monk of St. Benedict croaking a text.
> "Here's one of an order of cooks," said she—
> "Black friars in this world, fried black in the next."
> *"The Devil on Earth"* (*London,* 1712).

BENEFACTOR, *n.* One who makes heavy purchases of ingratitude, without, however, materially affecting the price, which is still within the means of all.

BERENICE'S HAIR, *n.* A constellation (*Coma Berenices*) named in honor of one who sacrificed her hair to save her husband.
> Her locks an ancient lady gave
> Her loving husband's life to save;
> And men—they honored so the dame—
> Upon some stars bestowed her name.

> But to our modern married fair,
> Who'd give their lords to save their hair,
> No stellar recognition's given.
> There are not stars enough in heaven.
>
> *G. J.*

BIGAMY, *n.* A mistake in taste for which the wisdom of the future will adjudge a punishment called trigamy.

BIGOT, *n.* One who is obstinately and zealously attached to an opinion that you do not entertain.

BILLINGSGATE, *n.* The invective of an opponent.

BIRTH, *n.* The first and direst of all disasters. As to the nature of it there appears to be no uniformity. Castor and Pollux were born from the egg. Pallas came out of a skull. Galatea was once a block of stone. Peresilis, who wrote in the tenth century, avers that he grew up out of the ground where a priest had spilled holy water. It is known that Arimaxus was derived from a hole in the earth, made by a stroke of lightning. Leucomedon was the son of a cavern in Mount Ætna, and I have myself seen a man come out of a wine cellar.

BLACKGUARD, *n.* A man whose qualities, prepared for display like a box of berries in a markct—the fine ones on top—have been opened on the wrong side. An inverted gentleman.

BLANK-VERSE, *n.* Unrhymed iambic pentameters—the most difficult kind of English verse to write acceptably; a kind, therefore, much affected by those who cannot acceptably write any kind.

BODY-SNATCHER, *n.* A robber of grave-worms. One who supplies the young physicians with that which the old physicians have supplied the undertaker. The hyena.

> "One night," a doctor said, "last fall,
> I and my comrades, four in all,
>   When visiting a graveyard stood
>   Within the shadow of a wall.
>
> "While waiting for the moon to sink
> We saw a wild hyena slink
>   About a new-made grave, and then
>   Begin to excavate its brink!
>
> "Shocked by the horrid act, we made
> A sally from our ambuscade,
>   And, falling on the unholy beast,
>   Dispatched him with a pick and spade."
>   *Bettel K. Jhones.*

BONDSMAN, *n.* A fool who, having property of his own, undertakes to become responsible for that entrusted by another to a third.

Philippe of Orleans wishing to appoint one of his favorites, a dissolute nobleman, to a high office, asked him what security he would be able to give. "I need no bondsmen," he replied, "for I can give you my word of honor." "And pray what may be the value of that?" inquired the amused Regent. "Monsieur, it is worth its weight in gold."

BORE, *n.* A person who talks when you wish him to listen.

BOTANY, *n.* The science of vegetables—those that are not good to eat, as well as those that are. It deals largely with their flowers, which are commonly badly designed, inartistic in color, and ill-smelling.

BOTTLE-NOSED, *adj.* Having a nose created in the image of its maker.

BOUNDARY, *n.* In political geography, an imaginary line between two nations, separating the imaginary rights of one from the imaginary rights of the other.

BOUNTY, *n.* The liberality of one who has much, in permitting one who has nothing to get all that he can.

A single swallow, it is said, devours ten millions of insects every year. The supplying of these insects I take to be a signal instance of the Creator's bounty in providing for the lives of His Creatures.—*Henry Ward Beecher.*

BRAHMA, *n.* He who created the Hindoos, who are preserved by Vishnu and destroyed by Siva—a rather neater division of labor than is found among the deities of some other nations. The Abracadabranese, for example, are created by Sin, maintained by Theft and destroyed by Folly. The priests of Brahma, like those of the Abracadabranese, are holy and learned men who are never naughty.

> O Brahma, thou rare old Divinity,
> First Person of the Hindoo Trinity,
> You sit there so calm and securely,
> With feet folded up so demurely—
> You're the First Person Singular, surely.
> > *Polydore Smith.*

BRAIN, *n.* An apparatus with which we think that we think. That which distinguishes the man who is content to *be* something from the man who wishes to *do* something. A man of great wealth, or one who has been pitchforked into high station, has commonly such a headful of brain that his neighbors cannot keep their hats on. In our civilization, and under our republican form of government, brain is so highly honored that it is rewarded by exemption from the cares of office.

BRANDY, *n.* A cordial composed of one part thunder-and-lightning, one part remorse, two parts bloody murder, one part death-hell-and-the-grave and four parts clarified Satan. Dose, a headful all the time. Brandy is said by Dr. Johnson to be the drink of heroes. Only a hero will venture to drink it.

BRIDE, *n.* A woman with a fine prospect of happiness behind her.

BRUTE, *n.* See HUSBAND.

C

CAABA, *n.* A large stone presented by the archangel Gabriel to the patriarch Abraham, and preserved at Mecca. The patriarch had perhaps asked the archangel for bread.

CABBAGE, *n.* A familiar kitchen-garden vegetable about as large and wise as a man's head.

The cabbage is so called from Cabagius, a prince who on ascending the throne issued a decree appointing a High Council of Empire consisting of the members of his predecessor's Ministry and the cabbages in the royal garden. When any of his Majesty's measures of state policy miscarried conspicuously it was gravely announced that several members of the High Council had been beheaded, and his murmuring subjects were appeased.

CALAMITY, *n.* A more than commonly plain and unmistakable reminder that the affairs of this life are not of our own ordering. Calamities are of two kinds: misfortune to ourselves, and good fortune to others.

CALLOUS, *adj.* Gifted with great fortitude to bear the evils afflicting another.

When Zeno was told that one of his enemies was no more he was observed to be deeply moved. "What!" said one of his disciples, "you weep at the death of an enemy?" "Ah, 'tis true," replied the great Stoic; "but you should see me smile at the death of a friend."

CALUMNUS, *n.* A graduate of the School for Scandal.

CAMEL, *n.* A quadruped (the *Splaypes humpidorsus*) of great value to the show business. There are two kinds of camels—the camel proper and the camel improper. It is the latter that is always exhibited.

CANNIBAL, *n.* A gastronome of the old school who preserves the simple tastes and adheres to the natural diet of the pre-pork period.

CANNON, *n.* An instrument employed in the rectification of national boundaries.

CANONICALS, *n.* The motley worn by Jesters of the Court of Heaven.

CAPITAL, *n.* The seat of misgovernment. That which provides the fire, the pot, the dinner, the table and the knife and fork for the anarchist; the part of the repast that himself supplies is the disgrace before meat. *Capital Punishment,* a penalty regarding the justice and expediency of which many worthy persons—including all the assassins—entertain grave misgivings.

CARMELITE, *n.* A mendicant friar of the order of Mount Carmel.

> As Death was a-riding out one day,
> Across Mount Carmel he took his way,
>   Where he met a mendicant monk,
>   Some three or four quarters drunk,
> With a holy leer and a pious grin,
> Ragged and fat and as saucy as sin,
>   Who held out his hands and cried:

"Give, give in Charity's name, I pray.
Give in the name of the Church. O give,
Give that her holy sons may live!"
  And Death replied,
  Smiling long and wide:
"I'll give, holy father, I'll give thee—a ride."

With a rattle and bang
Of his bones, he sprang
From his famous Pale Horse, with his spear;
  By the neck and the foot
  Seized the fellow, and put
Him astride with his face to the rear.

The Monarch laughed loud with a sound that fell
Like clods on the coffin's sounding shell:
"Ho, ho! A beggar on horseback, they say,
  Will ride to the devil!"—and *thump*
  Fell the flat of his dart on the rump
Of the charger, which galloped away.

Faster and faster and faster it flew,
Till the rocks and the flocks and the trees that grew
By the road were dim and blended and blue
  To the wild, wide eyes
  Of the rider—in size
Resembling a couple of blackberry pies.
Death laughed again, as a tomb might laugh
  At a burial service spoiled,
  And the mourners' intentions foiled
  By the body erecting
  Its head and objecting
To further proceedings in its behalf.

Many a year and many a day
Have passed since these events away.
The monk has long been a dusty corse,
And Death has never recovered his horse.
  For the friar got hold of its tail,
  And steered it within the pale
Of the monastery gray,
Where the beast was stabled and fed
With barley and oil and bread
Till fatter it grew than the fattest friar,
And so in due course was appointed Prior.

                                    G. J.

CARNIVOROUS, *adj.* Addicted to the cruelty of devouring the timorous vegetarian, his heirs and assigns.

CARTESIAN, *adj.* Relating to Descartes, a famous philosopher, author of the celebrated dictum, *Cogito ergo sum*—whereby he was pleased to suppose he demonstrated the reality of human existence. The dictum might be improved, however, thus: *Cogito cogito ergo cogito sum*—"I think that I think, therefore I think that I am"; as close an approach to certainty as any philosopher has yet made.

CAT, *n.* A soft, indestructible automaton provided by nature to be kicked when things go wrong in the domestic circle.

> This is a dog,
>   This is a cat,
> This is a frog,
>   This is a rat.
> Run, dog, mew, cat,
> Jump, frog, gnaw, rat.
> *Elevenson.*

CAVILER, *n.* A critic of our own work.

CEMETERY, *n.* An isolated suburban spot where mourners match lies, poets write at a target and stone-cutters spell for a wager. The inscriptions following will serve to illustrate the success attained in these Olympian games:

His virtues were so conspicuous that his enemies, unable to overlook them, denied them, and his friends, to whose loose lives they were a rebuke, represented them as vices. They are here commemorated by his family, who shared them.

> In the earth we here prepare a
> Place to lay our little Clara.
>   *—Thomas M. and Mary Frazer.*
> P. S.—Gabriel will raise her.

CENTAUR, *n.* One of a race of persons who lived before the division of labor had been carried to such a pitch of differentiation, and who followed the primitive economic maxim, "Every man his own horse." The best of the lot was Chiron, who to the wisdom and virtues of the horse added the fleetness of man. The scripture story of the head of

John the Baptist on a charger shows that pagan myths have somewhat sophisticated sacred history.

CERBERUS, *n.* The watch-dog of Hades, whose duty it was to guard the entrance—against whom or what does not clearly appear; everybody, sooner or later, had to go there, and nobody wanted to carry off the entrance. Cerberus is known to have had three heads, and some of the poets have credited him with as many as a hundred. Professor Graybill, whose clerky erudition and profound knowledge of Greek give his opinion great weight, has averaged all the estimates, and makes the number twenty-seven—a judgment that would be entirely conclusive if Professor Graybill had known (*a*) something about dogs, and (*b*) something about arithmetic.

CHILDHOOD, *n.* The period of human life intermediate between the idiocy of infancy and the folly of youth—two removes from the sin of manhood and three from the remorse of age.

CHRISTIAN, *n.* One who believes that the New Testament is a divinely inspired book admirably suited to the spiritual needs of his neighbor. One who follows the teachings of Christ in so far as they are not inconsistent with a life of sin.

> I dreamed I stood upon a hill, and, lo!
> The godly multitudes walked to and fro
> Beneath, in Sabbath garments fitly clad,
> With pious mien, appropriately sad,
> While all the church bells made a solemn din—
> A fire-alarm to those who lived in sin.
> Then saw I gazing thoughtfully below,
> With tranquil face, upon that holy show
> A tall, spare figure in a robe of white,
> Whose eyes diffused a melancholy light.
> "God keep you, stranger," I exclaimed. "You are
> No doubt (your habit shows it) from afar;
> And yet I entertain the hope that you,
> Like these good people, are a Christian too."
> He raised his eyes and with a look so stern
> It made me with a thousand blushes burn
> Replied—his manner with disdain was spiced:
> "What! I a Christian? No, indeed! I'm Christ."
> G. J.

CIRCUS, *n.* A place where horses, ponies and elephants are permitted to see men, women and children acting the fool.

CLAIRVOYANT, *n.* A person, commonly a woman, who has the power of seeing that which is invisible to her patron—namely, that he is a blockhead.

CLARIONET, *n.* An instrument of torture operated by a person with cotton in his ears. There are two instruments that are worse than a clarionet—two clarionets.

CLERGYMAN, *n.* A man who undertakes the management of our spiritual affairs as a method of bettering his temporal ones.

CLIO, *n.* One of the nine Muses. Clio's function was to preside over history —which she did with great dignity, many of the prominent citizens of Athens occupying seats on the platform, the meetings being addressed by Messrs. Xenophon, Herodotus and other popular speakers.

CLOCK, *n.* A machine of great moral value to man, allaying his concern for the future by reminding him what a lot of time remains to him.

> A busy man complained one day:
> "I get no time!" "What's that you say?"
> Cried out his friend, a lazy quiz;
> "You have, sir, all the time there is.
> There's plenty, too, and don't you doubt it—
> We're never for an hour without it."
> *Purzil Crofe.*

CLOSE-FISTED, *adj.* Unduly desirous of keeping that which many meritorious persons wish to obtain.

> "Close-fisted Scotchman!" Johnson cried
>   To thrifty J. Macpherson;
> "See me—I'm ready to divide
>   With any worthy person."
> Said Jamie: "That is very true—
>   The boast requires no backing;
> And all are worthy, sir, to you,
>   Who have what you are lacking."
> *Anita M. Bobe.*

CŒNOBITE, *n.* A man who piously shuts himself up to meditate upon the sin of wickedness; and to keep it fresh in his mind joins a brotherhood of awful examples.

> O Cœnobite, O Cœnobite,
>   Monastical gregarian,
> You differ from the anchorite,
>   That solitudinarian:
> With vollied prayers you wound Old Nick;
> With dropping shots he makes him sick.
>   *Quincy Giles.*

COMFORT, *n.* A state of mind produced by contemplation of a neighbor's uneasiness.

COMMENDATION, *n.* The tribute that we pay to achievements that resemble, but do not equal, our own.

COMMERCE, *n.* A kind of transaction in which A plunders from B the goods of C, and for compensation B picks the pocket of D of money belonging to E.

COMMONWEALTH, *n.* An administrative entity operated by an incalculable multitude of political parasites, logically active but fortuitously efficient.

> This commonwealth's capitol's corridors view,
> So thronged with a hungry and indolent crew
> Of clerks, pages, porters and all attachés
> Whom rascals appoint and the populace pays
> That a cat cannot slip through the thicket of shins
> Nor hear its own shriek for the noise of their chins.
> On clerks and on pages, and porters, and all,
> Misfortune attend and disaster befall!
> May life be to them a succession of hurts;
> May fleas by the bushel inhabit their shirts;
> May aches and diseases encamp in their bones,
> Their lungs full of tubercles, bladders of stones;
> May microbes, bacilli, their tissues infest,
> And tapeworms securely their bowels digest;
> May corn-cobs be snared without hope in their hair,
> And frequent impalement their pleasure impair.
> Disturbed be their dreams by the awful discourse

Of audible sofas sepulchrally hoarse,
By chairs acrobatic and wavering floors—
The mattress that kicks and the pillow that snores!
Sons of cupidity, cradled in sin!
Your criminal ranks may the death angel thin,
Avenging the friend whom I couldn't work in.

K. Q.

COMPROMISE, *n.* Such an adjustment of conflicting interests as gives each adversary the satisfaction of thinking he has got what he ought not to have, and is deprived of nothing except what was justly his due.

COMPULSION, *n.* The eloquence of power.

CONDOLE, *v. i.* To show that bereavement is a smaller evil than sympathy.

CONFIDANT, CONFIDANTE, *n.* One entrusted by A with the secrets of B, confided by *him* to C.

CONGRATULATION, *n.* The civility of envy.

CONGRESS, *n.* A body of men who meet to repeal laws.

CONNOISSEUR, *n.* A specialist who knows everything about something and nothing about anything else.
An old wine-bibber having been smashed in a railway collision, some wine was poured upon his lips to revive him. "Pauillac, 1873," he murmured and died.

CONSERVATIVE, *n.* A statesman who is enamored of existing evils, as
. distinguished from the Liberal, who wishes to replace them with others.

CONSOLATION, *n.* The knowledge that a better man is more unfortunate than yourself.

CONSUL, *n.* In American politics, a person who having failed to secure an office from the people is given one by the Administration on condition that he leave the country.

CONSULT, *v. t.* To seek another's approval of a course already decided on.

CONTEMPT, *n.* The feeling of a prudent man for an enemy who is too formidable safely to be opposed.

CONTROVERSY, *n.* A battle in which spittle or ink replaces the injurious cannon-ball and the inconsiderate bayonet.

> In controversy with the facile tongue—
> That bloodless warfare of the old and young—
> So seek your adversary to engage
> That on himself he shall exhaust his rage,
> And, like a snake that's fastened to the ground,
> With his own fangs inflict the fatal wound.
> You ask me how this miracle is done?
> Adopt his own opinions, one by one,
> And taunt him to refute them; in his wrath
> He'll sweep them pitilessly from his path.
> Advance them gently all you wish to prove,
> Each proposition prefaced with, "As you've
> So well remarked," or, "As you wisely say,
> And I cannot dispute," or, "By the way,
> This view of it which, better far expressed,
> Runs through your argument." Then leave the rest
> To him, secure that he'll perform his trust
> And prove your views intelligent and just.
>   *Conmore Apel Brune.*

CONVENT, *n.* A place of retirement for women who wish for leisure to meditate upon the vice of idleness.

CONVERSATION, *n.* A fair for the display of the minor mental commodities, each exhibitor being too intent upon the arrangement of his own wares to observe those of his neighbor.

CORONATION, *n.* The ceremony of investing a sovereign with the outward and visible signs of his divine right to be blown skyhigh with a dynamite bomb.

CORPORAL, *n.* A man who occupies the lowest rung of the military ladder.

> Fiercely the battle raged and, sad to tell,
> Our corporal heroically fell!

Fame from her height looked down upon the brawl
And said: "He hadn't very far to fall."
Giacomo Smith.

CORPORATION, *n.* An ingenious device for obtaining individual profit without individual responsibility.

CORSAIR, *n.* A politician of the seas.

COURT FOOL, *n.* The plaintiff.

COWARD, *n.* One who in a perilous emergency thinks with his legs.

CRAFT, *n.* A fool's substitute for brains.

CRAYFISH, *n.* A small crustacean very much resembling the lobster, but less indigestible.
     In this small fish I take it that human wisdom is admirably figured and symbolized; for whereas the crayfish doth move only backward, and can have only retrospection, seeing naught but the perils already passed, so the wisdom of man doth not enable him to avoid the follies that beset his course, but only to apprehend their nature afterward.—*Sir James Merivale.*

CREDITOR, *n.* One of a tribe of savages dwelling beyond the Financial Straits and dreaded for their desolating incursions.

CREMONA, *n.* A high-priced violin made in Connecticut.

CRITIC, *n.* A person who boasts himself hard to please because nobody tries to please him.

There is a land of pure delight,
     Beyond the Jordan's flood,
Where saints, apparelled all in white,
     Fling back the critic's mud.

And as he legs it through the skies,
     His pelt a sable hue,
He sorrows sore to recognize
     The missiles that he threw.
Orrin Goof.

CROSS, *n.* An ancient religious symbol erroneously supposed to owe its significance to the most solemn event in the history of Christianity, but really antedating it by thousands of years. By many it has been believed to be identical with the *crux ansata* of the ancient phallic worship, but it has been traced even beyond all that we know of that, to the rites of primitive peoples. We have to-day the White Cross as a symbol of chastity, and the Red Cross as a badge of benevolent neutrality in war. Having in mind the former, the reverend Father Gassalasca Jape smites the lyre to the effect following:

"Be good, be good!" the sisterhood
Cry out in holy chorus,
And, to dissuade from sin, parade
Their various charms before us.

But why, O why, has ne'er an eye
Seen her of winsome manner
And youthful grace and pretty face
Flaunting the White Cross banner?

Now where's the need of speech and screed
To better our behaving?
A simpler plan for saving man
(But, first, is he worth saving?)

Is, dears, when he declines to flee
From bad thoughts that beset him,
Ignores the Law as 't were a straw,
And wants to sin—don't let him.

CUI BONO? (Latin) What good would that do *me*?

CUNNING, *n.* The faculty that distinguishes a weak animal or person from a strong one. It brings its possessor much mental satisfaction and great material adversity. An Italian proverb says: "The furrier gets the skins of more foxes than asses."

CUPID, *n.* The so-called god of love. This bastard creation of a barbarous fancy was no doubt inflicted upon mythology for the sins of its deities. Of all unbeautiful and inappropriate conceptions this is the most reasonless and offensive. The notion of symbolizing sexual love by a semisexless babe, and comparing the pains of passion to the wounds of an arrow—of introducing this pudgy homunculus into art grossly to materialize the subtle spirit and suggestion of the work—this is eminently worthy of the age that, giving it birth, laid it on the doorstep of posterity.

CURIOSITY, *n.* An objectionable quality of the female mind. The desire to know whether or not a woman is cursed with curiosity is one of the most active and insatiable passions of the masculine soul.

CURSE, *v. t.* Energetically to belabor with a verbal slap-stick. This is an operation which in literature, particularly in the drama, is commonly fatal to the victim. Nevertheless, the liability to a cursing is a risk that cuts but a small figure in fixing the rates of life insurance.

CYNIC, *n.* A blackguard whose faulty vision sees things as they are, not as they ought to be. Hence the custom among the Scythians of plucking out a cynic's eyes to improve his vision.

D

DAMN, *v.* A word formerly much used by the Paphlagonians, the meaning of which is lost. By the learned Dr. Dolabelly Gak it is believed to have been a term of satisfaction, implying the highest possible degree of mental tranquillity. Professor Groke, on the contrary, thinks it expressed an emotion of tumultuous delight, because it so frequently occurs in combination with the word *jod* or *god,* meaning "joy." It would be with great diffidence that I should advance an opinion conflicting with that of either of these formidable authorities.

DANCE, *v. i.* To leap about to the sound of tittering music, preferably with arms about your neighbor's wife or daughter. There are many kinds of dances, but all those requiring the participation of the two sexes have two characteristics in common: they are conspicuously innocent, and warmly loved by the vicious.

DANGER, *n.*

> A savage beast which, when it sleeps,
> Man girds at and despises,
> But takes himself away by leaps
> And bounds when it arises.
> > *Ambat Delaso.*

DARING, *n.* One of the most conspicuous qualities of a man in security.

DATARY, *n.* A high ecclesiastic official of the Roman Catholic Church, whose important function is to brand the Pope's bulls with the words *Datum Romæ.* He enjoys a princely revenue and the friendship of God.

DAWN, *n.* The time when men of reason go to bed. Certain old men prefer to rise at about that time, taking a cold bath and a long walk with an empty stomach, and otherwise mortifying the flesh. They then point with pride to these practices as the cause of their sturdy health and ripe years; the truth being that they are hearty and old, not because of their habits, but in spite of them. The reason we find only robust persons doing this thing is that it has killed all the others who have tried it.

DAY, *n.* A period of twenty-four hours, mostly misspent. This period is divided into two parts, the day proper and the night, or day improper —the former devoted to sins of business, the latter consecrated to the other sort. These two kinds of social activity overlap.

DEAD, *adj.*

> Done with the work of breathing; done
> With all the world; the mad race run
> Through to the end; the golden goal
> Attained and found to be a hole!
> > *Squatol Johnes.*

DEBAUCHEE, *n.* One who has so earnestly pursued pleasure that he has had the misfortune to overtake it.

DEBT, *n.* An ingenious substitute for the chain and whip of the slave-driver.

> As, pent in an aquarium, the troutlet
> Swims round and round his tank to find an outlet,
> Pressing his nose against the glass that holds him,
> Nor ever sees the prison that enfolds him;
> So the poor debtor, seeing naught around him,
> Yet feels the narrow limits that impound him,
> Grieves at his debt and studies to evade it,
> And finds at last he might as well have paid it.
>
> *Barlow S. Vode.*

DECALOGUE, *n.* A series of commandments, ten in number—just enough to permit an intelligent selection for observance, but not enough to embarrass the choice. Following is the revised edition of the Decalogue, calculated for this meridian.

> Thou shalt no God but me adore:
> 'Twere too expensive to have more.
>
> No images nor idols make
> For Robert Ingersoll to break.
>
> Take not God's name in vain; select
> A time when it will have effect.
>
> Work not on Sabbath days at all,
> But go to see the teams play ball.
>
> Honor thy parents. That creates
> For life insurance lower rates.
>
> Kill not, abet not those who kill;
> Thou shalt not pay thy butcher's bill.
>
> Kiss not thy neighbor's wife, unless
> Thine own thy neighbor doth caress.
>
> Don't steal; thou'lt never thus compete
> Successfully in business. Cheat.
>
> Bear not false witness—that is low—
> But "hear 'tis rumored so and so."
>
> Covet thou naught that thou hast not
> By hook or crook, or somehow, got.
>
> *G. J.*

DECIDE, *v. i.* To succumb to the preponderance of one set of influences over another set.

> A leaf was riven from a tree,
> "I mean to fall to earth," said he.
>
> The west wind, rising, made him veer.
> "Eastward," said he, "I now shall steer."
>
> The east wind rose with greater force.
> Said he: " 'Twere wise to change my course."
>
> With equal power they contend.
> He said: "My judgment I suspend."
>
> Down died the winds; the leaf, elate,
> Cried: "I've decided to fall straight."
>
> "First thoughts are best?" That's not the moral;
> Just choose your own and we'll not quarrel.
>
> Howe'er your choice may chance to fall,
> You'll have no hand in it at all.
>
> *G. J.*

DEFAME, *v. t.* To lie about another. To tell the truth about another.

DEFENCELESS, *adj.* Unable to attack.

DEGENERATE, *adj.* Less conspicuously admirable than one's ancestors. The contemporaries of Homer were striking examples of degeneracy; it required ten of them to raise a rock or a riot that one of the heroes of the Trojan war could have raised with ease. Homer never tires of sneering at "men who live in these degenerate days," which is perhaps why they suffered him to beg his bread—a marked instance of returning good for evil, by the way, for if they had forbidden him he would certainly have starved.

DEGRADATION, *n.* One of the stages of moral and social progress from private station to political preferment.

DEINOTHERIUM, *n.* An extinct pachyderm that flourished when the Pterodactyl was in fashion. The latter was a native of Ireland, its name being pronounced Terry Dactyl or Peter O'Dactyl, as the man pronouncing it may chance to have heard it spoken or seen it printed.

DEJEUNER, *n*. The breakfast of an American who has been in Paris. Variously pronounced.

DELEGATION, *n*. In American politics, an article of merchandise that comes in sets.

DELIBERATION, *n*. The act of examining one's bread to determine which side it is buttered on.

DELUGE, *n*. A notable first experiment in baptism which washed away the sins (and sinners) of the world.

DELUSION, *n*. The father of a most respectable family, comprising Enthusiasm, Affection, Self-denial, Faith, Hope, Charity and many other goodly sons and daughters.

> All hail, Delusion! Were it not for thee
> The world turned topsy-turvy we should see;
> For Vice, respectable with cleanly fancies,
> Would fly abandoned Virtue's gross advances.
> *Mumfrey Mappel.*

DENTIST, *n*. A prestidigitator who, putting metal into your mouth, pulls coins out of your pocket.

DEPENDENT, *adj*. Reliant upon another's generosity for the support which you are not in a position to exact from his fears.

DEPUTY, *n*. A male relative of an office-holder, or of his bondsman. The deputy is commonly a beautiful young man, with a red necktie and an intricate system of cobwebs extending from his nose to his desk. When accidentally struck by the janitor's broom, he gives off a cloud of dust.

> "Chief Deputy," the Master cried,
> "To-day the books are to be tried
> By experts and accountants who
> Have been commissioned to go through

Our office here, to see if we
Have stolen injudiciously.
Please have the proper entries made,
The proper balances displayed,
Conforming to the whole amount
Of cash on hand—which they will count.
I've long admired your punctual way—
Here at the break and close of day,
Confronting in your chair the crowd
Of business men, whose voices loud
And gestures violent you quell
By some mysterious, calm spell—
Some magic lurking in your look
That brings the noisiest to book
And spreads a holy and profound
Tranquillity o'er all around.
So orderly all's done that they
Who came to draw remain to pay.
But now the time demands, at last,
That you employ your genius vast
In energies more active. Rise
And shake the lightnings from your eyes;
Inspire your underlings, and fling
Your spirit into everything!"
The Master's hand here dealt a whack
Upon the Deputy's bent back,
When straightway to the floor there fell
A shrunken globe, a rattling shell,
A blackened, withered, eyeless head!
The man had been a twelvemonth dead.

Jamrach Holobom.

DESTINY, *n.* A tyrant's authority for crime and a fool's excuse for failure.

DIAGNOSIS, *n.* A physician's forecast of disease by the patient's pulse and purse.

DIAPHRAGM, *n.* A muscular partition separating disorders of the chest from disorders of the bowels.

DIARY, *n.* A daily record of that part of one's life, which he can relate to himself without blushing.

> Hearst kept a diary wherein were writ
> All that he had of wisdom and of wit.
> So the Recording Angel, when Hearst died,
> Erased all entries of his own and cried:
> "I'll judge you by your diary." Said Hearst:
> "Thank you; 'twill show you I am Saint the First"—
> Straightway producing, jubilant and proud,
> That record from a pocket in his shroud.
> The Angel slowly turned the pages o'er,
> Each stupid line of which he knew before,
> Glooming and gleaming as by turns he hit
> On shallow sentiment and stolen wit;
> Then gravely closed the book and gave it back.
> "My friend, you've wandered from your proper track:
> You'd never be content this side the tomb—
> For big ideas Heaven has little room,
> And Hell's no latitude for making mirth,"
> He said, and kicked the fellow back to earth.
>   *"The Mad Philosopher."*

DICTATOR, *n.* The chief of a nation that prefers the pestilence of despotism to the plague of anarchy.

DICTIONARY, *n.* A malevolent literary device for cramping the growth of a language and making it hard and inelastic. This dictionary, however, is a most useful work.

DIE, *n.* The singular of "dice." We seldom hear the word, because there is a prohibitory proverb, "Never say die." At long intervals, however, some one says: "The die is cast," which is not true, for it is cut. The word is found in an immortal couplet by that eminent poet and domestic economist, Senator Depew:

> A cube of cheese no larger than a die
> May bait the trap to catch a nibbling mie.

DIGESTION, *n.* The conversion of victuals into virtues. When the process is imperfect, vices are evolved instead—a circumstance from which that wicked writer, Dr. Jeremiah Blenn, infers that the ladies are the greater sufferers from dyspepsia.

DIPLOMACY, *n.* The patriotic art of lying for one's country.

DISABUSE, *v. t.* To present your neighbor with another and better error than the one which he has deemed it advantageous to embrace.

DISCRIMINATE, *v. i.* To note the particulars in which one person or thing is, if possible, more objectionable than another.

DISCUSSION, *n.* A method of confirming others in their errors.

DISOBEDIENCE, *n.* The silver lining to the cloud of servitude.

DISOBEY, *v. t.* To celebrate with an appropriate ceremony the maturity of a command.

> His right to govern me is clear as day,
> My duty manifest to disobey;
> And if that fit observance e'er I shun
> May I and duty be alike undone.
> > *Israfel Brown.*

DISSEMBLE, *v. i.* To put a clean shirt upon the character.
> Let us dissemble.—*Adam.*

DISTANCE, *n.* The only thing that the rich are willing for the poor to call theirs, and keep.

DISTRESS, *n.* A disease incurred by exposure to the prosperity of a friend.

DIVINATION, *n.* The art of nosing out the occult. Divination is of as many kinds as there are fruit-bearing varieties of the flowering dunce and the early fool.

DOG, *n.* A kind of additional or subsidiary Deity designed to catch the overflow and surplus of the world's worship. This Divine Being in some of his smaller and silkier incarnations takes, in the affection of Woman, the place to which there is no human male aspirant. The Dog is a survival—an anachronism. He toils not, neither does he spin, yet Solomon in all his glory never lay upon a door-mat all day long, sun-soaked and fly-fed and fat, while his master worked for the means wherewith to purchase an idle wag of the Solomonic tail, seasoned with a look of tolerant recognition.

DRAGOON, *n.* A soldier who combines dash and steadiness in so equal measure that he makes his advances on foot and his retreats on horseback.

DRAMATIST, *n.* One who adapts plays from the French.

DRUIDS, *n.* Priests and ministers of an ancient Celtic religion which did not disdain to employ the humble allurement of human sacrifice. Very little is now known about the Druids and their faith. Pliny says their religion, originating in Britain, spread eastward as far as Persia. Cæsar says those who desired to study its mysteries went to Britain. Cæsar himself went to Britain, but does not appear to have obtained any high preferment in the Druidical Church, although his talent for human sacrifice was considerable.

Druids performed their religious rites in groves, and knew nothing of church mortgages and the season-ticket system of pew rents. They were, in short, heathens and—as they were once complacently catalogued by a distinguished prelate of the Church of England—Dissenters.

DUEL, *n.* A formal ceremony preliminary to the reconciliation of two enemies. Great skill is necessary to its satisfactory observance; if awkwardly performed the most unexpected and deplorable consequences sometimes ensue. A long time ago a man lost his life in a duel.

> That dueling's a gentlemanly vice
> I hold; and wish that it had been my lot
> To live my life out in some favored spot—
> Some country where it is considered nice
> To split a rival like a fish, or slice
> A husband like a spud, or with a shot
> Bring down a debtor doubled in a knot
> And ready to be put upon the ice.
> Some miscreants there are, whom I do long
> To shoot, or stab, or some such way reclaim
> The scurvy rogues to better lives and manners,
> I seem to see them now—a mighty throng.
> It looks as if to challenge *me* they came,
> Jauntily marching with brass bands and banners!
> > *Xamba Q. Dar.*

DULLARD, *n.* A member of the reigning dynasty in letters and life. The Dullards came in with Adam, and being both numerous and sturdy have overrun the habitable world. The secret of their power is their insensibility to blows; tickle them with a bludgeon and they laugh with a platitude. The Dullards came originally from Bœotia, whence they were driven by stress of starvation, their dulness having blighted the crops. For some centuries they infested Philistia, and many of them are called Philistines to this day. In the turbulent times of the Crusades they withdrew thence and gradually overspread all Europe, occupying most of the high places in politics, art, literature, science and theology. Since a detachment of Dullards came over with the Pilgrims in the *Mayflower* and made a favorable report of the country, their increase by birth, immigration, and conversion has been rapid and steady. According to the most trustworthy statistics the number of adult Dullards in the United States is but little short of thirty millions, including the statisticians. The intellectual centre of the race is somewhere about Peoria, Illinois, but the New England Dullard is the most shockingly moral.

DUTY, *n.* That which sternly impels us in the direction of profit, along the line of desire.

> Sir Lavender Portwine, in favor at court,
> Was wroth at his master, who'd kissed Lady Port.
> His anger provoked him to take the king's head,
> But duty prevailed, and he took the king's bread, Instead.
>   *G. J.*

E

EAT, *v. i.* To perform successively (and successfully) the functions of mastication, humectation, and deglutition.

"I was in the drawing-room, enjoying my dinner," said Brillat-Savarin, beginning an anecdote. "What!" interrupted Rochebriant;

"eating dinner in a drawing-room?" "I must beg you to observe, monsieur," explained the great gastronome, "that I did not say I was eating my dinner, but enjoying it. I had dined an hour before."

EAVESDROP, *v. i.* Secretly to overhear a catalogue of the crimes and vices of another or yourself.

> A lady with one of her ears applied
> To an open keyhole heard, inside,
> Two female gossips in converse free—
> The subject engaging them was she.
> "I think," said one, "and my husband thinks
> That she's a prying, inquisitive minx!"
> As soon as no more of it she could hear
> The lady, indignant, removed her ear.
> "I will not stay," she said, with a pout,
> "To hear my character lied about!"
> > *Gopete Sherany.*

ECCENTRICITY, *n.* A method of distinction so cheap that fools employ it to accentuate their incapacity.

ECONOMY, *n.* Purchasing the barrel of whiskey that you do not need for the price of the cow that you cannot afford.

EDIBLE, *adj.* Good to eat, and wholesome to digest, as a worm to a toad, a toad to a snake, a snake to a pig, a pig to a man, and a man to a worm.

EDITOR, *n.* A person who combines the judicial functions of Minos, Rhadamanthus and Æacus, but is placable with an obolus; a severely virtuous censor, but so charitable withal that he tolerates the virtues of others and the vices of himself; who flings about him the splintering lightning and sturdy thunders of admonition till he resembles a bunch of firecrackers petulantly uttering its mind at the tail of a dog; then straightway murmurs a mild, melodious lay, soft as the cooing of a donkey intoning its prayer to the evening star. Master of mysteries and lord of law, high-pinnacled upon the throne of thought, his face suffused with the dim splendors of the Transfiguration, his legs intertwisted and his tongue a-cheek, the editor spills his will along the paper and cuts it off in lengths to suit. And at intervals from behind the veil of the temple is heard the voice of the foreman demanding three inches of wit and six lines of religious meditation, or bidding him turn off the wisdom and whack up some pathos.

> O, the Lord of Law on the Throne of Thought.
> A gilded impostor is he.
> Of shreds and patches his robes are wrought,
> His crown is brass,
> Himself is an ass,
> And his power is fiddle-dee-dee.
> Prankily, crankily prating of naught,
> Silly old quilly old Monarch of Thought.
> Public opinion's camp-follower he,
> Thundering, blundering, plundering free.
> Affected,
> Ungracious,
> Suspected,
> Mendacious,
> Respected contemporaree!

J. H. Bumbleshook.

EDUCATION, *n.* That which discloses to the wise and disguises from the foolish their lack of understanding.

EFFECT, *n.* The second of two phenomena which always occur together in the same order. The first, called a Cause, is said to generate the other—which is no more sensible than it would be for one who has never seen a dog except in pursuit of a rabbit to declare the rabbit the cause of the dog.

EGOTIST, *n.* A person of low taste, more interested in himself than in me.

> Megaceph, chosen to serve the State
> In the halls of legislative debate,
> One day with all his credentials came
> To the capitol's door and announced his name.
> The doorkeeper looked, with a comical twist
> Of the face, at the eminent egotist,
> And said: "Go away, for we settle here
> All manner of questions, knotty and queer,
> And we cannot have, when the speaker demands
> To be told how every member stands,
> A man who to all things under the sky
> Assents by eternally voting 'I'."

EJECTION, *n*. An approved remedy for the disease of garrulity. It is also much used in cases of extreme poverty.

ELECTOR, *n*. One who enjoys the sacred privilege of voting for the man of another man's choice.

ELECTRICITY, *n*. The power that causes all natural phenomena not known to be caused by something else. It is the same thing as lightning, and its famous attempt to strike Dr. Franklin is one of the most picturesque incidents in that great and good man's career. The memory of Dr. Franklin is justly held in great reverence, particularly in France, where a waxen effigy of him was recently on exhibition, bearing the following touching account of his life and services to science:

> "Monsieur Franqulin, inventor of electricity. This illustrious savant, after having made several voyages around the world, died on the Sandwich Islands and was devoured by savages, of whom not a single fragment was ever recovered."

Electricity seems destined to play a most important part in the arts and industries. The question of its economical application to some purposes is still unsettled, but experiment has already proved that it will propel a street car better than a gas jet and give more light than a horse.

ELEGY, *n*. A composition in verse, in which, without employing any of the methods of humor, the writer aims to produce in the reader's mind the dampest kind of dejection. The most famous English example begins somewhat like this:

> The cur foretells the knell of parting day;
> The loafing herd winds slowly o'er the lea;
> The wise man homeward plods; I only stay
> To fiddle-faddle in a minor key.

ELOQUENCE, *n*. The art of orally persuading fools that white is the color that it appears to be. It includes the gift of making any color appear white.

ELYSIUM, *n*. An imaginary delightful country which the ancients foolishly believed to be inhabited by the spirits of the good. This ridiculous and mischievous fable was swept off the face of the earth by the early Christians—may their souls be happy in Heaven!

EMANCIPATION, *n.* A bondman's change from the tyranny of another to the despotism of himself.

> He was a slave: at word he went and came;
> His iron collar cut him to the bone.
> Then Liberty erased his owner's name,
> Tightened the rivets and inscribed his own.
> *G. J.*

EMBALM, *v. t.* To cheat vegetation by locking up the gases upon which it feeds. By embalming their dead and thereby deranging the natural balance between animal and vegetable life, the Egyptians made their once fertile and populous country barren and incapable of supporting more than a meagre crew. The modern metallic burial casket is a step in the same direction, and many a dead man who ought now to be ornamenting his neighbor's lawn as a tree, or enriching his table as a bunch of radishes, is doomed to a long inutility. We shall get him after awhile if we are spared, but in the meantime the violet and rose are languishing for a nibble at his *glutœus maximus.*

EMOTION, *n.* A prostrating disease caused by a determination of the heart to the head. It is sometimes accompanied by a copious discharge of hydrated chloride of sodium from the eyes.

ENCOMIAST, *n.* A special (but not particular) kind of liar.

END, *n.* The position farthest removed on either hand from the Interlocutor.

> The man was perishing apace
> Who played the tambourine:
> The seal of death was on his face—
> 'Twas pallid, for 'twas clean.

> "This is the end," the sick man said
> In faint and failing tones.
> A moment later he was dead,
> And Tambourine was Bones.
> *Tinley Roquot.*

ENOUGH, *pro*. All there is in the world if you like it.

> Enough is as good as a feast—for that matter
> Enougher's as good as a feast and the platter.
>> *Arbely C. Strunk*.

ENTERTAINMENT, *n*. Any kind of amusement whose inroads stop short of death by dejection.

ENTHUSIASM, *n*. A distemper of youth, curable by small doses of repentance in connection with outward applications of experience. Byron, who recovered long enough to call it "entuzy-muzy," had a relapse which carried him off—to Missolonghi.

ENVELOPE, *n*. The coffin of a document; the scabbard of a bill; the husk of a remittance; the bed-gown of a love-letter.

ENVY, *n*. Emulation adapted to the meanest capacity.

EPAULET, *n*. An ornamented badge, serving to distinguish a military officer from the enemy—that is to say, from the officer of lower rank to whom his death would give promotion.

EPICURE, *n*. An opponent of Epicurus, an abstemious philosopher who, holding that pleasure should be the chief aim of man, wasted no time in gratification of the senses.

EPIGRAM, *n*. A short, sharp saying in prose or verse, frequently characterized by acidity or acerbity and sometimes by wisdom. Following are some of the more notable epigrams of the learned and ingenious Dr. Jamrach Holobom:

> We know better the needs of ourselves than of others. To serve oneself is economy of administration.

> In each human heart are a tiger, a pig, an ass and a nightingale. Diversity of character is due to their unequal activity.

> There are three sexes; males, females and girls.

> Beauty in women and distinction in men are alike in this: they seem to the unthinking a kind of credibility.

Women in love are less ashamed than men. They have less to be ashamed of.

While your friend holds you affectionately by both your hands you are safe, for you can watch both his.

EPITAPH, *n.* An inscription on a tomb, showing that virtues acquired by death have a retroactive effect. Following is a touching example:

> Here lie the bones of Parson Platt,
> Wise, pious, humble and all that,
> Who showed us life as all should live it;
> Let that be said—and God forgive it!

ERUDITION, *n.* Dust shaken out of a book into an empty skull.

> So wide his erudition's mighty span,
> He knew Creation's origin and plan
> And only came by accident to grief—
> He thought, poor man, 'twas right to be a thief.
> *Romach Pute.*

ESOTERIC, *adj.* Very particularly abstruse and consummately occult. The ancient philosophies were of two kinds,—*exoteric,* those that the philosophers themselves could partly understand, and *esoteric,* those that nobody could understand. It is the latter that have most profoundly affected modern thought and found greatest acceptance in our time.

ETHNOLOGY, *n.* The science that treats of the various tribes of Man, as robbers, thieves, swindlers, dunces, lunatics, idiots and ethnologists.

EUCHARIST, *n.* A sacred feast of the religious sect of Theophagi.

A dispute once unhappily arose among the members of this sect as to what it was that they ate. In this controversy some five hundred thousand have already been slain, and the question is still unsettled.

EULOGY, *n.* Praise of a person who has either the advantages of wealth and power, or the consideration to be dead.

EVANGELIST, *n.* A bearer of good tidings, particularly (in a religious sense) such as assure us of our own salvation and the damnation of our neighbors.

EVERLASTING, *adj.* Lasting forever. It is with no small diffidence that I venture to offer this brief and elementary definition, for I am not unaware of the existence of a bulky volume by a sometime Bishop of Worcester, entitled, *A Partial Definition of the Word "Everlasting," as Used in the Authorized Version of the Holy Scriptures.* His book was once esteemed of great authority in the Anglican Church, and is still, I understand, studied with pleasure to the mind and profit to the soul.

EXCEPTION, *n.* A thing which takes the liberty to differ from other things of its class, as an honest man, a truthful woman, etc. "The exception proves the rule" is an expression constantly upon the lips of the ignorant, who parrot it from one another with never a thought of its absurdity. In the Latin, *"Exceptio probat regulam"* means that the exception *tests* the rule, puts it to the proof, not *confirms* it. The malefactor who drew the meaning from this excellent dictum and substituted a contrary one of his own exerted an evil power which appears to be immortal.

EXCESS, *n.* In morals, an indulgence that enforces by appropriate penalties the law of moderation.

> Hail, high Excess—especially in wine.
>   To thee in worship do I bend the knee
>   Who preach abstemiousness unto me—
> My skull thy pulpit, as my paunch thy shrine.
> Precept on precept, aye, and line on line,
>   Could ne'er persuade so sweetly to agree
>   With reason as thy touch, exact and free,
> Upon my forehead and along my spine.
> At thy command eschewing pleasure's cup,
>   With the hot grape I warm no more my wit;
>   When on thy stool of penitence I sit
> I'm quite converted, for I can't get up.
> Ungrateful he who afterward would falter
> To make new sacrifices at thine altar!

EXCOMMUNICATION, *n.*

> This "excommunication" is a word
> In speech ecclesiastical oft heard,
> And means the damning, with bell, book and candle,

Some sinner whose opinions are a scandal—
A rite permitting Satan to enslave him
Forever, and forbidding Christ to save him.
                                    Gat Huckle.

EXECUTIVE, *n.* An officer of the Government, whose duty it is to enforce the wishes of the legislative power until such time as the judicial department shall be pleased to pronounce them invalid and of no effect. Following is an extract from an old book entitled, *The Lunarian Astonished*—Pfeiffer & Co., Boston, 1803:

LUNARIAN: Then when your Congress has passed a law it goes directly to the Supreme Court in order that it may at once be known whether it is constitutional?

TERRESTRIAN: O no; it does not require the approval of the Supreme Court until having perhaps been enforced for many years somebody objects to its operation against himself—I mean his client. The President, if he approves it, begins to execute it at once.

LUNARIAN: Ah, the executive power is a part of the legislative. Do your policemen also have to approve the local ordinances that they enforce?

TERRESTRIAN: Not yet—at least not in their character of constables. Generally speaking, though, all laws require the approval of those whom they are intended to restrain.

LUNARIAN: I see. The death warrant is not valid until signed by the murderer.

TERRESTRIAN: My friend, you put it too strongly; we are not so consistent.

LUNARIAN: But this system of maintaining an expensive judicial machinery to pass upon the validity of laws only after they have long been executed, and then only when brought before the court by some private person—does it not cause great confusion?

TERRESTRIAN: It does.

LUNARIAN: Why then should not your laws, previously to being executed, be validated, not by the signature of your President, but by that of the Chief Justice of the Supreme Court?

TERRESTRIAN: There is no precedent for any such course.

LUNARIAN: Precedent. What is that?

TERRESTRIAN: It has been defined by five hundred lawyers in three volumes each. So how can any one know?

EXHORT, *v. t.* In religious affairs, to put the conscience of another upon the spit and roast it to a nut-brown discomfort.

EXILE, *n.* One who serves his country by residing abroad, yet is not an ambassador.

An English sea-captain being asked if he had read "The Exile of Erin," replied: "No, sir, but I should like to anchor on it." Years afterwards, when he had been hanged as a pirate after a career of unparalleled atrocities, the following memorandum was found in the ship's log that he had kept at the time of his reply:

Aug. 3d, 1842. Made a joke on the ex-Isle of Erin. Coldly received. War with the whole world!

EXISTENCE, *n.*

> A transient, horrible, fantastic dream,
> Wherein is nothing yet all things do seem:
> From which we're wakened by a friendly nudge
> Of our bedfellow Death, and cry: "O fudge!"

EXPERIENCE, *n.* The wisdom that enables us to recognize as an undesirable old acquaintance the folly that we have already embraced.

> To one who, journeying through night and fog,
> Is mired neck-deep in an unwholesome bog,
> Experience, like the rising of the dawn,
> Reveals the path that he should not have gone.
> *Joel Frad Bink.*

EXPOSTULATION, *n.* One of the many methods by which fools prefer to lose their friends.

EXTINCTION, *n.* The raw material out of which theology created the future state.

F

FAIRY, *n.* A creature, variously fashioned and endowed, that formerly inhabited the meadows and forests. It was nocturnal in its habits, and somewhat addicted to dancing and the theft of children. The fairies are now believed by naturalists to be extinct, though a clergyman of the Church of England saw three near Colchester as lately as 1855, while passing through a park after dining with the lord of the manor. The sight greatly staggered him, and he was so affected that his account of it was incoherent. In the year 1807 a troop of fairies visited a wood near Aix and carried off the daughter of a peasant, who had been seen to enter it with a bundle of clothing. The son of a wealthy *bourgeois* disappeared about the same time, but afterward returned. He had seen the abduction and been in pursuit of the fairies. Justinian Gaux, a writer of the fourteenth century, avers that so great is the fairies' power of transformation that he saw one change itself into two opposing armies and fight a battle with great slaughter, and that the next day, after it had resumed its original shape and gone away, there were seven hundred bodies of the slain which the villagers had to bury. He does not say if any of the wounded recovered. In the time of Henry III, of England, a law was made which prescribed the death penalty for "Kyllynge, wowndynge, or mamynge" a fairy, and it was universally respected.

FAITH, *n.* Belief without evidence in what is told by one who speaks without knowledge, of things without parallel.

FAMOUS, *adj.* Conspicuously miserable.

> Done to a turn on the iron, behold
> Him who to be famous aspired.
> Content? Well, his grill has a plating of gold,
> And his twistings are greatly admired.
> *Hassan Brubuddy.*

FASHION, *n.* A despot whom the wise ridicule and obey.

> A king there was who lost an eye
> In some excess of passion;
> And straight his courtiers all did try
> To follow the new fashion.
>
> Each dropped one eyelid when before
> The throne he ventured, thinking
> 'Twould please the king. That monarch swore
> He'd slay them all for winking.

What should they do? They were not hot
  To hazard such disaster;
They dared not close an eye—dared not
  See better than their master.

Seeing them lacrymose and glum,
  A leech consoled the weepers:
He spread small rags with liquid gum
  And covered half their peepers.

The court all wore the stuff, the flame
  Of royal anger dying.
That's how court-plaster got its name
  Unless I'm greatly lying.

                         Naramy Oof.

FEAST, *n*. A festival. A religious celebration usually signalized by gluttony and drunkenness, frequently in honor of some holy person distinguished for abstemiousness. In the Roman Catholic Church feasts are "movable" and "immovable," but the celebrants are uniformly immovable until they are full. In the earliest development these entertainments took the form of feasts for the dead; such were held by the Greeks, under the name of *Nemeseia,* by the Aztecs and Peruvians, as in modern times they are popular with the Chinese; though it is believed that the ancient dead, like the modern, were light eaters. Among the many feasts of the Romans was the *Novemdiale,* which was held, according to Livy, whenever stones fell from heaven.

FELON, *n*. A person of greater enterprise than discretion, who in embracing an opportunity has formed an unfortunate attachment.

FEMALE, *n*. One of the opposing, or unfair, sex.
      The Maker, at Creation's birth,
      With living things had stocked the earth.
      From elephants to bats and snails,
      They all were good, for all were males.
      But when the Devil came and saw
      He said: "By Thine eternal law
      Of growth, maturity, decay,
      These all must quickly pass away
      And leave untenanted the earth
      Unless Thou dost establish birth"—

Then tucked his head beneath his wing
To laugh—he had no sleeve—the thing
With deviltry did so accord,
That he'd suggested to the Lord.
The Master pondered this advice,
Then shook and threw the fateful dice
Wherewith all matters here below
Are ordered, and observed the throw;
Then bent His head in awful state,
Confirming the decree of Fate.
From every part of earth anew
The conscious dust consenting flew,
While rivers from their courses rolled
To make it plastic for the mould.
Enough collected (but no more,
For niggard Nature hoards her store)
He kneaded it to flexile clay,
While Nick unseen threw some away.
And then the various forms He cast,
Gross organs first and finer last;
No one at once evolved, but all
By even touches grew and small
Degrees advanced, till, shade by shade,
To match all living things He'd made
Females, complete in all their parts
Except (His clay gave out) the hearts.
"No matter," Satan cried; "with speed
I'll fetch the very hearts they need"—
So flew away and soon brought back
The number needed, in a sack.
That night earth rang with sounds of strife—
Ten million males had each a wife;
That night sweet Peace her pinions spread
O'er Hell—ten million devils dead!

G. J.

FIB, *n.* A lie that has not cut its teeth. An habitual liar's nearest approach
to truth: the perigee of his eccentric orbit.

When David said: "All men are liars," Dave,
Himself a liar, fibbed like any thief.
Perhaps he thought to weaken disbelief
By proof that even himself was not a slave
To Truth; though I suspect the aged knave
Had been of all her servitors the chief

>   Had he but known a fig's reluctant leaf
>   Is more than e'er she wore on land or wave.
>   No, David served not Naked Truth when he
>   Struck that sledge-hammer blow at all his race;
>   Nor did he hit the nail upon the head:
>   For reason shows that it could never be,
>   And the facts contradict him to his face.
>   Men are not liars all, for some are dead.
>   *Bartle Quinker.*

FICKLENESS, *n.* The iterated satiety of an enterprising affection.

FIDDLE, *n.* An instrument to tickle human ears by friction of a horse's tail on the entrails of a cat.

>   To Rome said Nero: "If to smoke you turn
>   I shall not cease to fiddle while you burn."
>   To Nero Rome replied: "Pray do your worst,
>   'Tis my excuse that you were fiddling first."
>   *Orm Pludge.*

FIDELITY, *n.* A virtue peculiar to those who are about to be betrayed.

FINANCE, *n.* The art or science of managing revenues and resources for the best advantage of the manager. The pronunciation of this word with the i long and the accent on the first syllable is one of America's most precious discoveries and possessions.

FLAG, *n.* A colored rag borne above troops and hoisted on forts and ships. It appears to serve the same purpose as certain signs that one sees on vacant lots in London—"Rubbish may be shot here."

FLESH, *n.* The Second Person of the secular Trinity.

FLOP, *v.* Suddenly to change one's opinions and go over to another party. The most notable flop on record was that of Saul of Tarsus, who has been severely criticised as a turn-coat by some of our partisan journals.

FLY-SPECK, *n.* The prototype of punctuation. It is observed by Garvinus that the systems of punctuation in use by the various literary nations depended originally upon the social habits and general diet of the flies infesting the several countries. These creatures, which have always been distinguished for a neighborly and companionable familiarity with authors, liberally or niggardly embellish the manuscripts in process of growth under the pen, according to their bodily habit, bringing out the sense of the work by a species of interpretation superior to, and independent of, the writer's powers. The "old masters" of literature—that is to say, the early writers whose work is so esteemed by later scribes and critics in the same language—never punctuated at all, but worked right along free-handed, without that abruption of the thought which comes from the use of points. (We observe the same thing in children to-day, whose usage in this particular is a striking and beautiful instance of the law that the infancy of individuals reproduces the methods and stages of development characterizing the infancy of races.) In the work of these primitive scribes all the punctuation is found, by the modern investigator with his optical instruments and chemical tests, to have been inserted by the writers' ingenious and serviceable collaborator, the common house-fly—*Musca maledicta*. In transcribing these ancient MSS, for the purpose of either making the work their own or preserving what they naturally regard as divine revelations, later writers reverently and accurately copy whatever marks they find upon the papyrus or parchment, to the unspeakable enhancement of the lucidity of the thought and value of the work. Writers contemporary with the copyists naturally avail themselves of the obvious advantages of these marks in their own work, and with such assistance as the flies of their own household may be willing to grant, frequently rival and sometimes surpass the older compositions, in respect at least of punctuation, which is no small glory. Fully to understand the important services that flies perform to literature it is only necessary to lay a page of some popular novelist alongside a saucer of cream-and-molasses in a sunny room and observe "how the wit brightens and the style refines" in accurate proportion to the duration of exposure.

FOLLY, *n.* That "gift and faculty divine" whose creative and controlling energy inspires Man's mind, guides his actions and adorns his life.

> Folly! although Erasmus praised thee once
> In a thick volume, and all authors known,
> If not thy glory yet thy power have shown,

Deign to take homage from thy son who hunts
Through all thy maze his brothers, fool and dunce,
 To mend their lives and to sustain his own,
 However feebly be his arrows thrown,

Howe'er each hide the flying weapons blunts.
All-Father Folly! be it mine to raise,
 With lusty lung, here on this western strand
 With all thine offspring thronged from every land,
Thyself inspiring me, the song of praise.
And if too weak, I'll hire, to help me bawl,
Dick Watson Gilder, gravest of us all.
       Aramis Loto Frope.

FOOL, *n.* A person who pervades the domain of intellectual speculation and diffuses himself through the channels of moral activity. He is omnific, omniform, omnipercipient, omniscient, omnipotent. He it was who invented letters, printing, the railroad, the steamboat, the telegraph, the platitude and the circle of the sciences. He created patriotism and taught the nations war—founded theology, philosophy, law, medicine and Chicago. He established monarchical and republican government. He is from everlasting to everlasting—such as creation's dawn beheld he fooleth now. In the morning of time he sang upon primitive hills, and in the noonday of existence headed the procession of being. His grandmotherly hand has warmly tucked-in the set sun of civilization, and in the twilight he prepares Man's evening meal of milk-and-morality and turns down the covers of the universal grave. And after the rest of us shall have retired for the night of eternal oblivion he will sit up to write a history of human civilization.

FORCE, *n.*

   "Force is but might," the teacher said—
    "That definition's just."
   The boy said naught but thought instead,
   Remembering his pounded head:
    "Force is not might but must!"

FOREFINGER, *n.* The finger commonly used in pointing out two malefactors.

FOREORDINATION, *n.* This looks like an easy word to define, but when I consider that pious and learned theologians have spent long lives in explaining it, and written libraries to explain their explanations; when I remember that nations have been divided and bloody battles caused by the difference between foreordination and predestination, and that millions of treasure have been expended in the effort to prove and disprove its compatibility with freedom of the will and the efficacy of prayer, praise, and a religious life,—recalling these awful facts in the history of the word, I stand appalled before the mighty problem of its signification, abase my spiritual eyes, fearing to contemplate its portentous magnitude, reverently uncover and humbly refer it to His Eminence Cardinal Gibbons and His Grace Bishop Potter.

FORGETFULNESS, *n.* A gift of God bestowed upon debtors in compensation for their destitution of conscience.

FORK, *n.* An instrument used chiefly for the purpose of putting dead animals into the mouth. Formerly the knife was employed for this purpose, and by many worthy persons is still thought to have many advantages over the other tool, which, however, they do not altogether reject, but use to assist in charging the knife. The immunity of these persons from swift and awful death is one of the most striking proofs of God's mercy to those that hate Him.

FORMA PAUPERIS (Latin). In the character of a poor person—a method by which a litigant without money for lawyers is considerately permitted to lose his case.

> When Adam long ago in Cupid's awful court
> (For Cupid ruled ere Adam was invented)
> Sued for Eve's favor, says an ancient law report,
> He stood and pleaded unhabilimented.
>
> "You sue *in forma pauperis,* I see," Eve cried;
> "Actions can't here be that way prosecuted."
> So all poor Adam's motions coldly were denied:
> He went away—as he had come—nonsuited.
> *G. J.*

FRANKALMOIGNE, *n.* The tenure by which a religious corporation holds lands on condition of praying for the soul of the donor. In mediæval times many of the wealthiest fraternities obtained their estates in this simple and cheap manner, and once when Henry VIII of England sent an officer to confiscate certain vast possessions which a fraternity of monks held by frankalmoigne, "What!" said the Prior, "would your master stay our benefactor's soul in Purgatory?" "Ay," said the officer, coldly, "an ye will not pray him thence for naught he must e'en roast." "But look you, my son," persisted the good man, "this act hath rank as robbery of God!" "Nay, nay, good father, my master the king doth but deliver Him from the manifold temptations of too great wealth."

FREEBOOTER, *n.* A conqueror in a small way of business, whose annexations lack the sanctifying merit of magnitude.

FREEDOM, *n.* Exemption from the stress of authority in a beggarly half dozen of restraint's infinite multitude of methods. A political condition that every nation supposes itself to enjoy in virtual monopoly. Liberty. The distinction between freedom and liberty is not accurately known; naturalists have never been able to find a living specimen of either.

> Freedom, as every schoolboy knows,
>   Once shrieked as Kosciusko fell;
> On every wind, indeed, that blows
>   I hear her yell.
>
> She screams whenever monarchs meet,
>   And parliaments as well,
> To bind the chains about her feet
>   And toll her knell.
>
> And when the sovereign people cast
>   The votes they cannot spell,
> Upon the pestilential blast,
>   Her clamors swell.
>
> For all to whom the power's given
>   To sway or to compel,
> Among themselves apportion Heaven
>   And give her Hell.
>   *Blary O'Gary.*

FREEMASONS, *n.* An order with secret rites, grotesque ceremonies and fantastic costumes, which, originating in the reign of Charles II, among working artisans of London, has been joined successively by the dead of past centuries in unbroken retrogression until now it embraces all the generations of man on the hither side of Adam and is drumming up distinguished recruits among the pre-Creational inhabitants of Chaos and the Formless Void. The order was founded at different times by Charlemagne, Julius Cæsar, Cyrus, Solomon, Zoroaster, Confucius, Thothmes, and Buddha. Its emblems and symbols have been found in the Catacombs of Paris and Rome, on the stones of the Parthenon and the Chinese Great Wall, among the temples of Karnak and Palmyra and in the Egyptian Pyramids—always by a Freemason.

FRIENDLESS, *adj.* Having no favors to bestow. Destitute of fortune. Addicted to utterance of truth and common sense.

FRIENDSHIP, *n.* A ship big enough to carry two in fair weather, but only one in foul.

> The sea was calm and the sky was blue;
> Merrily, merrily sailed we two.
> (High barometer maketh glad.)
> On the tipsy ship, with a dreadful shout,
> The tempest descended and we fell out.
> (O the walking is nasty bad!)
> *Armit Huff Bettle.*

FROG, *n.* A reptile with edible legs. The first mention of frogs in profane literature is in Homer's narrative of the war between them and the mice. Skeptical persons have doubted Homer's authorship of the work, but the learned, ingenious and industrious Dr. Schliemann has set the question forever at rest by uncovering the bones of the slain frogs. One of the forms of moral suasion by which Pharaoh was besought to favor the Israelites was a plague of frogs, but Pharaoh, who liked them *fricasées,* remarked, with truly oriental stoicism, that he could stand it as long as the frogs and the Jews could; so the programme was changed. The frog is a diligent songster, having a good voice but no ear. The libretto of his favorite opera, as written by Aristophanes, is brief, simple and effective—"brekekex-koäx"; the music is apparently by that eminent composer, Richard Wagner. Horses have a frog in each hoof—a thoughtful provision of nature, enabling them to shine in a hurdle race.

FRYING-PAN, *n.* One part of the penal apparatus employed in that punitive institution, a woman's kitchen. The frying-pan was invented by Calvin, and by him used in cooking span-long infants that had died without baptism; and observing one day the horrible torment of a tramp who had incautiously pulled a fried babe from the waste-dump and devoured it, it occurred to the great divine to rob death of its terrors by introducing the frying-pan into every household in Geneva. Thence it spread to all corners of the world, and has been of invaluable assistance in the propagation of his sombre faith. The following lines (said to be from the pen of his Grace Bishop Potter) seem to imply that the usefulness of this utensil is not limited to this world; but as the consequences of its employment in this life reach over into the life to come, so also itself may be found on the other side, rewarding its devotees:

> Old Nick was summoned to the skies.
>   Said Peter: "Your intentions
> Are good, but you lack enterprise
>   Concerning new inventions.
>
> "Now, broiling is an ancient plan
>   Of torment, but I hear it
> Reported that the frying-pan
>   Sears best the wicked spirit.
>
> "Go get one—fill it up with fat—
>   Fry sinners brown and good in't."
> "I know a trick worth two o' that,"
>   Said Nick—"I'll cook their food in't."

FUNERAL, *n.* A pageant whereby we attest our respect for the dead by enriching the undertaker, and strengthen our grief by an expenditure that deepens our groans and doubles our tears.

> The savage dies—they sacrifice a horse
> To bear to happy hunting-grounds the corse.
> Our friends expire—we make the money fly
> In hope their souls will chase it to the sky.
>   *Jex Wopley.*

FUTURE, *n.* That period of time in which our affairs prosper, our friends are true and our happiness is assured.

G

GALLOWS, *n.* A stage for the performance of miracle plays, in which the leading actor is translated to heaven. In this country the gallows is chiefly remarkable for the number of persons who escape it.

> Whether on the gallows high
> Or where blood flows the reddest,
> The noblest place for man to die—
> Is where he died the deadest.
>   *Old Play.*

GARGOYLE, *n.* A rain-spout projecting from the eaves of mediæval buildings, commonly fashioned into a grotesque caricature of some personal enemy of the architect or owner of the building. This was especially the case in churches and ecclesiastical structures generally, in which the gargoyles presented a perfect rogues' gallery of local heretics and controversialists. Sometimes when a new dean and chapter were installed the old gargoyles were removed and others substituted having a closer relation to the private animosities of the new incumbents.

GARTER, *n.* An elastic band intended to keep a woman from coming out of her stockings and desolating the country.

GENEROUS, *adj.* Originally this word meant noble by birth and was rightly applied to a great multitude of persons. It now means noble by nature and is taking a bit of a rest.

GENEALOGY, *n.* An account of one's descent from an ancestor who did not particularly care to trace his own.

GENTEEL, *adj.* Refined, after the fashion of a gent.

> Observe with care, my son, the distinction I reveal:
> A gentleman is gentle and a gent genteel.
> Heed not the definitions your "Unabridged" presents,
> For dictionary makers are generally gents.
>
> **G. J.**

GEOGRAPHER, *n.* A chap who can tell you offhand the difference between the outside of the world and the inside.

> Habeam, geographer of wide renown,
> Native of Abu-Keber's ancient town,
> In passing thence along the river Zam
> To the adjacent village of Xelam,
> Bewildered by the multitude of roads,
> Got lost, lived long on migratory toads,
> Then from exposure miserably died,
> And grateful travelers bewailed their guide.
>
> *Henry Haukhorn.*

GEOLOGY, *n.* The science of the earth's crust—to which, doubtless, will be added that of its interior whenever a man shall come up garrulous out of a well. The geological formations of the globe already noted are catalogued thus: The Primary, or lower one, consists of rocks, bones of mired mules, gas-pipes, miners' tools, antique statues minus the nose, Spanish doubloons and ancestors. The Secondary is largely made up of red worms and moles. The Tertiary comprises railway tracks, patent pavements, grass, snakes, mouldy boots, beer bottles, tomato cans, intoxicated citizens, garbage, anarchists, snap-dogs and fools.

GHOST, *n.* The outward and visible sign of an inward fear.

> He saw a ghost.
> It occupied—that dismal thing!—
> The path that he was following.
> Before he'd time to stop and fly,
> An earthquake trifled with the eye
> That saw a ghost.
> He fell as fall the early good;
> Unmoved that awful vision stood.
> The stars that danced before his ken
> He wildly brushed away, and then
> He saw a post.
>
> *Jared Macphester.*

Accounting for the uncommon behavior of ghosts, Heine mentions somebody's ingenious theory to the effect that they are as much afraid of us as we of them. Not quite, if I may judge from such tables of comparative speed as I am able to compile from memories of my own experience.

There is one insuperable obstacle to a belief in ghosts. A ghost never comes naked: he appears either in a winding-sheet or "in his habit as he lived." To believe in him, then, is to believe that not only have the dead the power to make themselves visible after there is nothing left of them, but that the same power inheres in textile fabrics. Supposing the products of the loom to have this ability, what object would they have in exercising it? And why does not the apparition of a suit of clothes sometimes walk abroad without a ghost in it? These be riddles of significance. They reach away down and get a convulsive grasp on the very tap-root of this flourishing faith.

GHOUL, *n.* A demon addicted to the reprehensible habit of devouring the dead. The existence of ghouls has been disputed by that class of controversialists who are more concerned to deprive the world of comforting beliefs than to give it anything good in their place. In 1640 Father Secchi saw one in a cemetery near Florence and frightened it away with the sign of the cross. He describes it as gifted with many heads and an uncommon allowance of limbs, and he saw it in more than one place at a time. The good man was coming away from dinner at the time and explains that if he had not been "heavy with eating" he would have seized the demon at all hazards. Atholston relates that a ghoul was caught by some sturdy peasants in a churchyard at Sudbury and ducked in a horsepond. (He appears to think that so distinguished a criminal should have been ducked in a tank of rosewater.) The water turned at once to blood "and so contynues unto ys daye." The pond has since been bled with a ditch. As late as the beginning of the fourteenth century a ghoul was cornered in the crypt of the cathedral at Amiens and the whole population surrounded the place. Twenty armed men with a priest at their head, bearing a crucifix, entered and captured the ghoul, which, thinking to escape by the stratagem, had transformed itself to the semblance of a well known citizen, but was nevertheless hanged, drawn and quartered in the midst of hideous popular orgies. The citizen whose shape the demon had assumed was so affected by the sinister occurrence that he never again showed himself in Amiens and his fate remains a mystery.

GLUTTON, *n.* A person who escapes the evils of moderation by committing dyspepsia.

GNOME, *n.* In North-European mythology, a dwarfish imp inhabiting the interior parts of the earth and having special custody of mineral treasures. Bjorsen, who died in 1765, says gnomes were common enough in the southern parts of Sweden in his boyhood, and he frequently saw them scampering on the hills in the evening twilight. Ludwig Binkerhoof saw three as recently as 1792, in the Black Forest, and Sneddeker avers that in 1803 they drove a party of miners out of a Silesian mine. Basing our computations upon data supplied by these statements, we find that the gnomes were probably extinct as early as 1764.

GNOSTICS, *n.* A sect of philosophers who tried to engineer a fusion between the early Christians and the Platonists. The former would not go into the caucus and the combination failed, greatly to the chagrin of the fusion managers.

GNU, *n.* An animal of South Africa, which in its domesticated state resembles a horse, a buffalo and a stag. In its wild condition it is something like a thunderbolt, an earthquake and a cyclone.

> A hunter from Kew caught a distant view
>   Of a peacefully meditative gnu,
> And he said: "I'll pursue, and my hands imbrue
>   In its blood at a closer interview."
> But that beast did ensue and the hunter it threw
>   O'er the top of a palm that adjacent grew;
> And he said as he flew: "It is well I withdrew
>   Ere, losing my temper, I wickedly slew
>   That really meritorious gnu."
>   *Jarn Leffer.*

GOOD, *adj.* Sensible, madam, to the worth of this present writer. Alive, sir, to the advantages of letting him alone.

GOOSE, *n.* A bird that supplies quills for writing. These, by some occult process of nature, are penetrated and suffused with various degrees of the bird's intellectual energies and emotional character, so that when inked and drawn mechanically across paper by a person called an "author," there results a very fair and accurate transcript of the fowl's thought and feeling. The difference in geese, as discovered by this ingenious method, is considerable: many are found to have only trivial and insignificant powers, but some are seen to be very great geese indeed.

GORGON, *n.*

> The Gorgon was a maiden bold
> Who turned to stone the Greeks of old
> That looked upon her awful brow.
> We dig them out of ruins now,
> And swear that workmanship so bad
> Proves all the ancient sculptors mad.

GOUT, *n.* A physician's name for the rheumatism of a rich patient.

GRACES, *n.* Three beautiful goddesses, Aglaia, Thalia and Euphrosyne, who attended upon Venus, serving without salary. They were at no expense for board and clothing, for they ate nothing to speak of and dressed according to the weather, wearing whatever breeze happened to be blowing.

GRAMMAR, *n.* A system of pitfalls thoughtfully prepared for the feet of the self-made man, along the path by which he advances to distinction.

GRAPE, *n.*

> Hail noble fruit!—by Homer sung,
>   Anacreon and Khayyam;
> Thy praise is ever on the tongue
>   Of better men than I am.
>
> The lyre my hand has never swept,
>   The song I cannot offer:
> My humbler service pray accept—
>   I'll help to kill the scoffer.

> The water-drinkers and the cranks
>   Who load their skins with liquor—
> I'll gladly bare their belly-tanks
>   And tap them with my sticker.
>
> Fill up, fill up, for wisdom cools
>   When e'er we let the wine rest.
> Here's death to Prohibition's fools,
>   And every kind of vine-pest!
>   *Jamrach Holobom.*

GRAVE, *n.* A place in which the dead are laid to await the coming of the medical student.

> Beside a lonely grave I stood—
>   With brambles 'twas encumbered;
> The winds were moaning in the wood,
>   Unheard by him who slumbered.
>
> A rustic standing near, I said:
>   "He cannot hear it blowing!"
> " 'Course not," said he: "the feller's dead—
>   He can't hear nowt that's going."
>
> "Too true," I said; "alas, too true—
>   No sound his sense can quicken!"
> "Well, mister, wot is that to you?—
>   The deadster ain't a-kickin'."
>
> I knelt and prayed: "O Father, smile
>   On him, and mercy show him!"
> That countryman looked on the while,
>   And said: "Ye didn't know him."
>   *Pobeter Dunk.*

GRAVITATION, *n.* The tendency of all bodies to approach one another with a strength proportioned to the quantity of matter they contain—the quantity of matter they contain being ascertained by the strength of their tendency to approach one another. This is a lovely and edifying illustration of how science, having made A the proof of B, makes B the proof of A.

GREAT, *adj.*

> "I'm great," the Lion said—"I reign
> The monarch of the wood and plain!"
>
> The Elephant replied: "I'm great—
> No quadruped can match my weight!"
>
> "I'm great—no animal has half
> So long a neck!" said the Giraffe.
>
> "I'm great," the Kangaroo said—"see
> My femoral muscularity!"
>
> The 'Possum said: "I'm great—behold,
> My tail is lithe and bald and cold!"
>
> An Oyster fried was understood
> To say: "I'm great because I'm good!"
>
> Each reckons greatness to consist
> In that in which he heads the list,
>
> And Vierick thinks he tops his class
> Because he is the greatest ass.
> > *Arion Spurl Doke.*

GUILLOTINE, *n.* A machine which makes a Frenchman shrug his shoulders with good reason.

In his great work on *Divergent Lines of Racial Evolution,* the learned Professor Brayfugle argues from the prevalence of this gesture —the shrug—among Frenchmen, that they are descended from turtles and it is simply a survival of the habit of retracting the head inside the shell. It is with reluctance that I differ with so eminent an authority, but in my judgment (as more elaborately set forth and enforced in my work entitled *Hereditary Emotions*—lib. II, c. XI) the shrug is a poor foundation upon which to build so important a theory, for previously to the Revolution the gesture was unknown. I have not a doubt that it is directly referable to the terror inspired by the guillotine during the period of that instrument's activity.

GUNPOWDER, *n.* An agency employed by civilized nations for the settlement of disputes which might become troublesome if left unadjusted. By most writers the invention of gunpowder is ascribed to the Chinese, but not upon very convincing evidence. Milton says it was invented by the devil to dispel angels with, and this opinion seems to derive some support from the scarcity of angels. Moreover, it has the hearty concurrence of the Hon. James Wilson, Secretary of Agriculture.

Secretary Wilson became interested in gunpowder through an event that occurred on the Government experimental farm in the District of Columbia. One day, several years ago, a rogue imperfectly reverent of the Secretary's profound attainments and personal character presented him with a sack of gunpowder, representing it as the seed of the *Flashawful flabbergastor,* a Patagonian cereal of great commercial value, admirably adapted to this climate. The good Secretary was instructed to spill it along in a furrow and afterward inhume it with soil. This he at once proceeded to do, and had made a continuous line of it all the way across a ten-acre field, when he was made to look backward by a shout from the generous donor, who at once dropped a lighted match into the furrow at the starting-point. Contact with the earth had somewhat dampened the powder, but the startled functionary saw himself pursued by a tall moving pillar of fire and smoke in fierce evolution. He stood for a moment paralyzed and speechless, then he recollected an engagement and, dropping all, absented himself thence with such surprising celerity that to the eyes of spectators along the route selected he appeared like a long, dim streak prolonging itself with inconceivable rapidity through seven villages, and audibly refusing to be comforted. "Great Scott! what is that?" cried a surveyor's chainman, shading his eyes and gazing at the fading line of agriculturist which bisected his visible horizon. "That," said the surveyor, carelessly glancing at the phenomenon and again centering his attention upon his instrument, "is the Meridian of Washington."

H

HABEAS CORPUS. A writ by which a man may be taken out of jail when confined for the wrong crime.

HABIT, *n*. A shackle for the free.

HADES, *n*. The lower world; the residence of departed spirits; the place where the dead live.

Among the ancients the idea of Hades was not synonymous with our Hell, many of the most respectable men of antiquity residing there in a very comfortable kind of way. Indeed, the Elysian Fields themselves were a part of Hades, though they have since been removed to Paris. When the Jacobean version of the New Testament was in process of evolution the pious and learned men engaged in the work insisted by a majority vote on translating the Greek word "Ἀιδης" as "Hell"; but a conscientious minority member secretly possessed himself of the record and struck out the objectionable word wherever he could find it. At the next meeting, the Bishop of Salisbury, looking over the work, suddenly sprang to his feet and said with considerable excitement: "Gentlemen, somebody has been razing 'Hell' here!" Years afterward the good prelate's death was made sweet by the reflection that he had been the means (under Providence) of making an important, serviceable and immortal addition to the phraseology of the English tongue.

HAG, *n*. An elderly lady whom you do not happen to like; sometimes called, also, a hen, or cat. Old witches, sorceresses, etc., were called hags from the belief that their heads were surrounded by a kind of baleful lumination or nimbus—hag being the popular name of that peculiar electrical light sometimes observed in the hair. At one time hag was not a word of reproach: Drayton speaks of a "beautiful hag, all smiles," much as Shakespeare said, "sweet wench." It would not now be proper to call your sweetheart a hag—that compliment is reserved for the use of her grandchildren.

HALF, *n.* One of two equal parts into which a thing may be divided, or considered as divided. In the fourteenth century a heated discussion arose among theologians and philosophers as to whether Omniscience could part an object into three halves; and the pious Father Aldrovinus publicly prayed in the cathedral at Rouen that God would demonstrate the affirmative of the proposition in some signal and unmistakable way, and particularly (if it should please Him) upon the body of that hardy blasphemer, Manutius Procinus, who maintained the negative. Procinus, however, was spared to die of the bite of a viper.

HALO, *n.* Properly, a luminous ring encircling an astronomical body, but not infrequently confounded with "aureola," or "nimbus," a somewhat similar phenomenon worn as a head-dress by divinities and saints. The halo is a purely optical illusion, produced by moisture in the air, in the manner of a rainbow; but the aureola is conferred as a sign of superior sanctity, in the same way as a bishop's mitre, or the Pope's tiara. In the painting of the Nativity, by Szedgkin, a pious artist of Pesth, not only do the Virgin and the Child wear the nimbus, but an ass nibbling hay from the sacred manger is similarly decorated and, to his lasting honor be it said, appears to bear his unaccustomed dignity with a truly saintly grace.

HAND, *n.* A singular instrument worn at the end of the human arm and commonly thrust into somebody's pocket.

HANDKERCHIEF, *n.* A small square of silk or linen, used in various ignoble offices about the face and especially serviceable at funerals to conceal the lack of tears. The handkerchief is of recent invention; our ancestors knew nothing of it and intrusted its duties to the sleeve. Shakespeare's introducing it into the play of "Othello" is an anachronism: Desdemona dried her nose with her skirt, as Dr. Mary Walker and other reformers have done with their coat-tails in our own day—an evidence that revolutions sometimes go backward.

HANGMAN, *n.* An officer of the law charged with duties of the highest dignity and utmost gravity, and held in hereditary disesteem by a populace having a criminal ancestry. In some of the American States his functions are now performed by an electrician, as in New Jersey, where executions by electricity have recently been ordered—the first instance known to this lexicographer of anybody questioning the expediency of hanging Jerseymen.

HAPPINESS, *n.* An agreeable sensation arising from contemplating the misery of another.

HARANGUE, *n.* A speech by an opponent, who is known as an harangue-outang.

HARBOR, *n.* A place where ships taking shelter from storms are exposed to the fury of the customs.

HARMONISTS, *n.* A sect of Protestants, now extinct, who came from Europe in the beginning of the last century and were distinguished for the bitterness of their internal controversies and dissensions.

HASH, *x.* There is no definition for this word—nobody knows what hash is.

HATCHET, *n.* A young axe, known among Indians as a Thomashawk.
> "O bury the hatchet, irascible Red,
> For peace is a blessing," the White Man said.
> The Savage concurred, and that weapon interred,
> With imposing rites, in the White Man's head.
> > *John Lukkus.*

HATRED, *n.* A sentiment appropriate to the occasion of another's superiority.

HEAD-MONEY, *n.* A capitation tax, or poll-tax.
> In ancient times there lived a king
> Whose tax-collectors could not wring
> From all his subjects gold enough
> To make the royal way less rough.

For pleasure's highway, like the dames
Whose premises adjoin it, claims
Perpetual repairing. So
The tax-collectors in a row
Appeared before the throne to pray
Their master to devise some way
To swell the revenue. "So great,"
Said they, "are the demands of state
A tithe of all that we collect
Will scarcely meet them. Pray reflect:
How, if one-tenth we must resign,
Can we exist on t'other nine?"
The monarch asked them in reply:
"Has it occurred to you to try
The advantage of economy?"
"It has," the spokesman said: "we sold
All of our gay garrotes of gold;
With plated-ware we now compress
The necks of those whom we assess.
Plain iron forceps we employ
To mitigate the miser's joy
Who hoards, with greed that never tires,
That which your Majesty requires."
Deep lines of thought were seen to plow
Their way across the royal brow.
"Your state is desperate, no question;
Pray favor me with a suggestion."
"O King of Men," the spokesman said,
"If you'll impose upon each head
A tax, the augmented revenue
We'll cheerfully divide with you."
As flashes of the sun illume
The parted storm-cloud's sullen gloom,
The king smiled grimly. "I decree
That it be so—and, not to be
In generosity outdone,
Declare you, each and every one,
Exempted from the operation
Of this new law of capitation.
But lest the people censure me
Because they're bound and you are free,
'Twere well some clever scheme were laid
By you this poll-tax to evade.
I'll leave you now while you confer

With my most trusted minister."
The monarch from the throne-room walked
And straightway in among them stalked
A silent man, with brow concealed,
Bare-armed—his gleaming axe revealed!

G. J.

HEARSE, *n.* Death's baby-carriage.

HEART, *n.* An automatic, muscular blood-pump. Figuratively, this useful organ is said to be the seat of emotions and sentiments—a very pretty fancy which, however, is nothing but a survival of a once universal belief. It is now known that the sentiments and emotions reside in the stomach, being evolved from food by chemical action of the gastric fluid. The exact process by which a beefsteak becomes a feeling— tender or not, according to the age of the animal from which it was cut; the successive stages of elaboration through which a caviar sandwich is transmuted to a quaint fancy and reappears as a pungent epigram; the marvelous functional methods of converting a hard-boiled egg into religious contrition, or a cream-puff into a sigh of sensibility— these things have been patiently ascertained by M. Pasteur, and by him expounded with convincing lucidity. (See, also, my monograph, *The Essential Identity of the Spiritual Affections and Certain Intestinal Gases Freed in Digestion*—4to, 687 pp.) In a scientific work entitled, I believe, *Delectatio Demonorum* (John Camden Hotton, London, 1873) this view of the sentiments receives a striking illustration; and for further light consult Professor Dam's famous treatise on *Love as a Product of Alimentary Maceration*.

HEAT, *n.*

Heat, says Professor Tyndall, is a mode
   Of motion, but I know not how he's proving
His point; but this I know—hot words bestowed
   With skill will set the human fist a-moving,
And where it stops the stars burn free and wild.
Crede expertum—I have seen them, child.

Gorton Swope.

HEATHEN, *n.* A benighted creature who has the folly to worship some-

thing that he can see and feel. According to Professor Howison, of the
California State University, Hebrews are heathens.

> "The Hebrews are heathens!" says Howison. He's
> A Christian philosopher. I'm
> A scurril agnostical chap, if you please,
> Addicted too much to the crime
> Of religious discussion in rhyme.
>
> Though Hebrew and Howison cannot agree
> On a *modus vivendi*—not they!—
> Yet Heaven has had the designing of me,
> And I haven't been reared in a way
> To joy in the thick of the fray.
>
> For this of my creed is the soul and the gist,
> And the truth of it I aver:
> Who differs from me in his faith is an 'ist,
> An 'ite, an 'ic, or an 'er—
> And I'm down upon him or her!
>
> Let Howison urge with perfunctory chin
> Toleration—that's all very well,
> But a roast is "nuts" to his nostril thin,
> And he's running—I know by the smell—
> A secret and personal Hell!
>
> *Bissell Gip.*

HEAVEN, *n.* A place where the wicked cease from troubling you with
talk of their personal affairs, and the good listen with attention while
you expound your own.

HELPMATE, *n.* A wife, or bitter half.

> "Now, why is yer wife called a helpmate, Pat?"
> Says the priest. "Since the time o' yer wooin'
> She's niver assisted in what ye were at—
> For it's naught ye are ever doin'."
>
> "That's true of yer Riverence," Patrick replies,
> And no sign of contrition evinces;
> "But, bedad, it's a fact which the word implies,
> For she helps to mate the expinses!"
>
> *Marley Wottel.*

HEMP, *n.* A plant from whose fibrous bark is made an article of neckwear which is frequently put on after public speaking in the open air and prevents the wearer from taking cold.

HERMIT, *n.* A person whose vices and follies are not sociable.

HERS, *pron.* His.

HIBERNATE, *v. i.* To pass the winter season in domestic seclusion. There have been many singular popular notions about the hibernation of various animals. Many believe that the bear hibernates during the whole winter and subsists by mechanically sucking its paws. It is admitted that it comes out of its retirement in the spring so lean that it has to try twice before it can cast a shadow. Three or four centuries ago, in England, no fact was better attested than that swallows passed the winter months in the mud at the bottoms of the brooks, clinging together in globular masses. They have apparently been compelled to give up the custom on account of the foulness of the brooks. Sotus Escobius discovered in Central Asia a whole nation of people who hibernate. By some investigators, the fasting of Lent is supposed to have been originally a modified form of hibernation, to which the Church gave a religious significance; but this view was strenuously opposed by that eminent authority, Bishop Kip, who did not wish any honors denied to the memory of the Founder of his family.

HIPPOGRIFF, *n.* An animal (now extinct) which was half horse and half griffin. The griffin was itself a compound creature, half lion and half eagle. The hippogriff was actually, therefore, only one-quarter eagle, which is two dollars and fifty cents in gold. The study of zoology is full of surprises.

HISTORIAN, *n.* A broad-gauge gossip.

HISTORY, *n.* An account mostly false, of events mostly unimportant, which are brought about by rulers mostly knaves, and soldiers mostly fools.

> Of Roman history, great Niebuhr's shown
> 'Tis nine-tenths lying. Faith, I wish 'twere known,

Ere we accept great Niebuhr as a guide,
Wherein he blundered and how much he lied.
                                        Salder Bupp.

HOG, *n.* A bird remarkable for the catholicity of its appetite and serving
to illustrate that of ours. Among the Mahometans and Jews, the hog
is not in favor as an article of diet, but is respected for the delicacy of
its habits, the beauty of its plumage and the melody of its voice. It is
chiefly as a songster that the fowl is esteemed; a cage of him in full
chorus has been known to draw tears from two persons at once. The
scientific name of this dicky-bird is *Porcus Rockefelleri.* Mr. Rockefeller did not discover the hog, but it is considered his by right of
resemblance.

HOMŒOPATHIST, *n.* The humorist of the medical profession.

HOMŒOPATHY, *n.* A school of medicine midway between Allopathy and
Christian Science. To the last both the others are distinctly inferior,
for Christian Science will cure imaginary diseases, and they can not.

HOMICIDE, *n.* The slaying of one human being by another. There are
four kinds of homicide: felonious, excusable, justifiable and praiseworthy, but it makes no great difference to the person slain whether
he fell by one kind or another—the classification is for advantage of
the lawyers.

HOMILETICS, *n.* The science of adapting sermons to the spiritual needs,
capacities and conditions of the congregation.

So skilled the parson was in homiletics
That all his moral purges and emetics
To medicine the spirit were compounded
With a most just discrimination founded
Upon a rigorous examination
Of tongue and pulse and heart and respiration.
Then, having diagnosed each one's condition,.
His scriptural specifics this physician
Administered—his pills so efficacious
And pukes of disposition so vivacious
That souls afflicted with ten kinds of Adam
Were convalescent ere they knew they had 'em.

But Slander's tongue—itself all coated—uttered
Her bilious mind and scandalously muttered
That in the case of patients having money
The pills were sugar and the pukes were honey.
                                   Biography of Bishop Potter.

HONORABLE, *adj.* Afflicted with an impediment in one's reach. In legislative bodies it is customary to mention all members as honorable; as, "the honorable gentleman is a scurvy cur."

HOPE, *n.* Desire and expectation rolled into one.
                Delicious Hope! when naught to man is left—
                Of fortune destitute, of friends bereft;
                When even his dog deserts him, and his goat
                With tranquil disaffection chews his coat
                While yet it hangs upon his back; then thou,
                The star far-flaming on thine angel brow,
                Descendest, radiant, from the skies to hint
                The promise of a clerkship in the Mint.
                                   Fogarty Weffing.

HOSPITALITY, *n.* The virtue which induces us to feed and lodge certain persons who are not in need of food and lodging.

HOSTILITY, *n.* A peculiarly sharp and specially applied sense of the earth's overpopulation. Hostility is classed as active and passive; as (respectively) the feeling of a woman for her female friends, and that which she entertains for all the rest of her sex.

HOURI, *n.* A comely female inhabiting the Mohammedan Paradise to make things cheery for the good Mussulman, whose belief in her existence marks a noble discontent with his earthly spouse, whom he denies a soul. By that good lady the Houris are said to be held in deficient esteem.

HOUSE, *n.* A hollow edifice erected for the habitation of man, rat, mouse, beetle, cockroach, fly, mosquito, flea, bacillus and microbe. *House of Correction,* a place of reward for political and personal service, and for the detention of offenders and appropriations. *House of God,* a building with a steeple and a mortgage on it. *House-dog,* a pestilent beast kept on domestic premises to insult persons passing by and appal the hardy visitor. *House-maid,* a youngerly person of the opposing sex employed to be variously disagreeable and ingeniously unclean in the station in which it has pleased God to place her.

HOUSELESS, *adj.* Having paid all taxes on household goods.

HOVEL, *n.* The fruit of a flower called the Palace.

> Twaddle had a hovel,
>   Twiddle had a palace;
> Twaddle said: "I'll grovel
>   Or he'll think I bear him malice"—
> A sentiment as novel
>   As a castor on a chalice.
>
> Down upon the middle
>   Of his legs fell Twaddle
> And astonished Mr. Twiddle,
>   Who began to lift his noddle,
> Feed upon the fiddle-
>   Faddle flummery, unswaddle
> A new-born self-sufficiency and think himself a model.
>   *G. J.*

HUMANITY, *n.* The human race, collectively, exclusive of the anthropoid poets.

HUMORIST, *n.* A plague that would have softened down the hoar austerity of Pharaoh's heart and persuaded him to dismiss Israel with his best wishes, cat-quick.

> Lo! the poor humorist, whose tortured mind
> Sees jokes in crowds, though still to gloom inclined—
> Whose simple appetite, untaught to stray,
> His brains, renewed by night, consumes by day.
> He thinks, admitted to an equal sty,
> A graceful hog would bear his company.
>   *Alexander Poke.*

HURRICANE, *n.* An atmospheric demonstration once very common but now generally abandoned for the tornado and cyclone. The hurricane is still in popular use in the West Indies and is preferred by certain old-fashioned sea-captains. It is also used in the construction of the upper decks of steamboats, but generally speaking, the hurricane's usefulness has outlasted it.

HURRY, *n*. The dispatch of bunglers.

HUSBAND, *n*. One who, having dined, is charged with the care of the plate.

HYBRID, *n*. A pooled issue.

HYDRA, *n*. A kind of animal that the ancients catalogued under many heads.

HYENA, *n*. A beast held in reverence by some oriental nations from its habit of frequenting at night the burial-places of the dead. But the medical student does that.

HYPOCHONDRIASIS, *n*. Depression of one's own spirits.

> Some heaps of trash upon a vacant lot
> Where long the village rubbish had been shot
> Displayed a sign among the stuff and stumps—
> "Hypochondriasis." It meant The Dumps.
> *Bogul S. Purvy.*

HYPOCRITE, *n*. One who, professing virtues that he does not respect, secures the advantage of seeming to be what he despises.

I

I is the first letter of the alphabet, the first word of the language, the first thought of the mind, the first object of affection. In grammar it is a pronoun of the first person and singular number. Its plural is said to be *We,* but how there can be more than one myself is doubtless clearer to the grammarians than it is to the author of this incomparable dictionary. Conception of two myselves is difficult, but fine. The frank yet graceful use of "I" distinguishes a good writer from a bad; the latter carries it with the manner of a thief trying to cloak his loot.

ICHOR, *n.* A fluid that serves the gods and goddesses in place of blood.

> Fair Venus, speared by Diomed,
> Restrained the raging chief and said:
> "Behold, rash mortal, whom you've bled—
> Your soul's stained white with ichorshed!"
>
> *Mary Doke.*

ICONOCLAST, *n.* A breaker of idols, the worshipers whereof are imperfectly gratified by the performance, and most strenuously protest that he unbuildeth but doth not reëdify, that he pulleth down but pileth not up. For the poor things would have other idols in place of those he thwacketh upon the mazzard and dispelleth. But the iconoclast saith: "Ye shall have none at all, for ye need them not; and if the rebuilder fooleth round hereabout, behold I will depress the head of him and sit thereon till he squawk it."

IDIOT, *n.* A member of a large and powerful tribe whose influence in human affairs has always been dominant and controlling. The Idiot's activity is not confined to any special field of thought or action, but "pervades and regulates the whole." He has the last word in everything; his decision is unappealable. He sets the fashions of opinion and taste, dictates the limitations of speech and circumscribes conduct with a dead-line.

IDLENESS, *n.* A model farm where the devil experiments with seeds of new sins and promotes the growth of staple vices.

IGNORAMUS, *n.* A person unacquainted with certain kinds of knowledge familiar to yourself, and having certain other kinds that you know nothing about.

> Dumble was an ignoramus,
> Mumble was for learning famous.
> Mumble said one day to Dumble:
> "Ignorance should be more humble.

Not a spark have you of knowledge
That was got in any college."
Dumble said to Mumble: "Truly
You're self-satisfied unduly.
Of things in college I'm denied
A knowledge—you of all beside."
                                        Borelli.

ILLUMINATI, *n.* A sect of Spanish heretics of the latter part of the sixteenth century; so called because they were light weights—*cunctationes il-luminati.*

ILLUSTRIOUS, *adj.* Suitably placed for the shafts of malice, envy and detraction.

IMAGINATION, *n.* A warehouse of facts, with poet and liar in joint ownership.

IMBECILITY, *n.* A kind of divine inspiration, or sacred fire affecting censorious critics of this dictionary.

IMMIGRANT, *n.* An unenlightened person who thinks one country better than another.

IMMODEST, *adj.* Having a strong sense of one's own merit, coupled with a feeble conception of worth in others.

There was once a man in Ispahan
    Ever and ever so long ago,
And he had a head, the phrenologists said,
    That fitted him for a show.

For his modesty's bump was so large a lump
    (Nature, they said, had taken a freak)
That its summit stood far above the wood
    Of his hair, like a mountain peak.

So modest a man in all Ispahan,
    Over and over again they swore—
So humble and meek, you would vainly seek;
    None ever was found before.

Meantime the hump of that awful bump
Into the heavens contrived to get
To so great a height that they called the wight
The man with a minaret.

There wasn't a man in all Ispahan
   Prouder, or louder in praise of his chump:
With a tireless tongue and a brazen lung
   He bragged of that beautiful bump

Till the Shah in a rage sent a trusty page
   Bearing a sack and a bow-string too,
And that gentle child explained as he smiled:
   "A little present for you."

The saddest man in all Ispahan,
   Sniffed at the gift, yet accepted the same.
"If I'd lived," said he, "my humility
   Had given me deathless fame!"
                              Sukker Uffro.

IMMORAL, *adj.* Inexpedient. Whatever in the long run and with regard to the greater number of instances men find to be generally inexpedient comes to be considered wrong, wicked, immoral. If man's notions of right and wrong have any other basis than this of expediency; if they originated, or could have originated, in any other way; if actions have in themselves a moral character apart from, and nowise dependent on, their consequences—then all philosophy is a lie and reason a disorder of the mind.

IMMORTALITY, *n.*

A toy which people cry for,
And on their knees apply for,
Dispute, contend and lie for,
      And if allowed
      Would be right proud
Eternally to die for.
                              G. J.

IMPALE, *v. t.* In popular usage to pierce with any weapon which remains fixed in the wound. This, however, is inaccurate; to impale is, properly, to put to death by thrusting an upright sharp stake into the body, the victim being left in a sitting posture. This was a common mode of punishment among many of the nations of antiquity, and is still in high favor in China and other parts of Asia. Down to the beginning of the fifteenth century it was widely employed in "churching" heretics and schismatics. Wolecraft calls it the "stoole of repentynge," and among the common people it was jocularly known as "riding the one legged horse." Ludwig Salzmann informs us that in Thibet impalement is considered the most appropriate punishment for crimes against religion; and although in China it is sometimes awarded for secular offences, it is most frequently adjudged in cases of sacrilege. To the person in actual experience of impalement it must be a matter of minor importance by what kind of civil or religious dissent he was made acquainted with its discomforts; but doubtless he would feel a certain satisfaction if able to contemplate himself in the character of a weathercock on the spire of the True Church.

IMPARTIAL, *adj.* Unable to perceive any promise of personal advantage from espousing either side of a controversy or adopting either of two conflicting opinions.

IMPENITENCE, *n.* A state of mind intermediate in point of time between sin and punishment.

IMPIETY, *n.* Your irreverence toward my deity.

IMPOSITION, *n.* The act of blessing or consecrating by the laying on of hands—a ceremony common to many ecclesiastical systems, but performed with the frankest sincerity by the sect known as Thieves.

> "Lo! by the laying on of hands,"
> Say parson, priest and dervise,
> "We consecrate your cash and lands
> To ecclesiastic service.
> No doubt you'll swear till all is blue
> At such an imposition. Do."
> *Pollo Doncas.*

IMPOSTOR, *n.* A rival aspirant to public honors.

IMPROBABILITY, *n.*

> His tale he told with a solemn face
> And a tender, melancholy grace.
>   Improbable 'twas, no doubt,
>   When you came to think it out,
>   But the fascinated crowd
>   Their deep surprise avowed
> And all with a single voice averred
> 'Twas the most amazing thing they'd heard—
> All save one who spake never a word,
>   But sat as mum
>   As if deaf and dumb,
> Serene, indifferent and unstirred.
>   Then all the others turned to him
>   And scrutinized him limb from limb—
>   Scanned him alive;
>   But he seemed to thrive
>   And tranquiler grow each minute,
>   As if there were nothing in it.
> "What! what!" cried one, "are you not amazed
> At what our friend has told?" He raised
> Soberly then his eyes and gazed
>   In a natural way
>   And proceeded to say,
> As he crossed his feet on the mantel-shelf:
> "O no—not at all; I'm a liar myself."

IMPROVIDENCE, *n.* Provision for the needs of to-day from the revenues of to-morrow.

IMPUNITY, *n.* Wealth.

INADMISSIBLE, *adj.* Not competent to be considered. Said of certain kinds of testimony which juries are supposed to be unfit to be entrusted with, and which judges, therefore, rule out, even of proceedings before themselves alone. Hearsay evidence is inadmissible because the person quoted was unsworn and is not before the court for examination; yet most momentous actions, military, political, commercial and of every other kind, are daily undertaken on hearsay evidence. There is no religion in the world that has any other basis than hearsay evidence. Revelation is hearsay evidence; that the Scriptures are the word of God we have only the testimony of men long dead whose identity is not clearly established and who are not known to have been sworn in any sense. Under the rules of evidence as they now exist in this country, no single assertion in the Bible has in its support any evidence admissible in a court of law. It cannot be proved that the battle of Blenheim ever was fought, that there was such a person as Julius Cæsar, such an empire as Assyria.

But as records of courts of justice are admissible, it can easily be proved that powerful and malevolent magicians once existed and were a scourge to mankind. The evidence (including confession) upon which certain women were convicted of witchcraft and executed was without a flaw; it is still unimpeachable. The judges' decisions based on it were sound in logic and in law. Nothing in any existing court was ever more thoroughly proved than the charges of witchcraft and sorcery for which so many suffered death. If there were no witches, human testimony and human reason are alike destitute of value.

INAUSPICIOUSLY, *adv.* In an unpromising manner, the auspices being unfavorable. Among the Romans it was customary before undertaking any important action or enterprise to obtain from the augurs, or state prophets, some hint of its probable outcome; and one of their favorite and most trustworthy modes of divination consisted in observing the flight of birds—the omens thence derived being called *auspices.* Newspaper reporters and certain miscreant lexicographers have decided that the word—always in the plural—shall mean "patronage" or "management"; as, "The festivities were under the auspices of the Ancient and Honorable Order of Body-Snatchers"; or, "The hilarities were auspicated by the Knights of Hunger."

> A Roman slave appeared one day
> Before the Augur. "Tell me, pray,
> If—" here the Augur, smiling, made
> A checking gesture and displayed
> His open palm, which plainly itched,
> For visibly its surface twitched.
> A *denarius* (the Latin nickel)
> Successfully allayed the tickle,
> And then the slave proceeded: "Please
> Inform me whether Fate decrees
> Success or failure in what I

To-night (if it be dark) shall try.
Its nature? Never mind—I think
'Tis writ on this"—and with a wink
Which darkened half the earth, he drew
Another denarius to view,
Its shining face attentive scanned,
Then slipped it into the good man's hand,
Who with great gravity said: "Wait
While I retire to question Fate."
That holy person then withdrew
His sacred clay and, passing through
The temple's rearward gate, cried "Shoo!"
Waving his robe of office. Straight
Each sacred peacock and its mate
(Maintained for Juno's favor) fled
With clamor from the trees o'erhead,
Where they were perching for the night.
The temple's roof received their flight,
For thither they would always go,
When danger threatened them below.
Back to the slave the Augur went:
"My son, forecasting the event
By flight of birds, I must confess
The auspices deny success."
That slave retired, a sadder man,
Abandoning his secret plan—
Which was (as well the crafty seer
Had from the first divined) to clear
The wall and fraudulently seize
On Juno's poultry in the trees.

                                                    G. J.

INCOME, *n.* The natural and rational gauge and measure of respectability,
the commonly accepted standards being artificial, arbitrary and fal-
lacious; for, as "Sir Sycophas Chrysolater" in the play has justly remarked, "the true use and function of property (in whatsoever it consisteth—coins, or land, or houses, or merchant-stuff, or anything which
may be named as holden of right to one's own subservience) as also
of honors, titles, preferments and place, and all favor and acquaintance
of persons of quality or ableness, are but to get money. Hence it followeth that all things are truly to be rated as of worth in measure of
their serviceableness to that end; and their possessors should take rank

in agreement thereto, neither the lord of an unproducing manor, howsoever broad and ancient, nor he who bears an unremunerate dignity, nor yet the pauper favorite of a king, being esteemed of level excellency with him whose riches are of daily accretion; and hardly should they whose wealth is barren claim and rightly take more honor than the poor and unworthy."

INCOMPATIBILITY, *n*. In matrimony a similarity of tastes, particularly the taste for domination. Incompatibility may, however, consist of a meek-eyed matron living just around the corner. It has even been known to wear a moustache.

INCOMPOSSIBLE, *adj.* Unable to exist if something else exists. Two things are incompossible when the world of being has scope enough for one of them, but not enough for both—as Walt Whitman's poetry and God's mercy to man. Incompossibility, it will be seen, is only incompatibility let loose. Instead of such low language as "Go heel yourself —I mean to kill you on sight," the words, "Sir, we are incompossible," would convey an equally significant intimation and in stately courtesy are altogether superior.

INCUBUS, *n*. One of a race of highly improper demons who, though probably not wholly extinct, may be said to have seen their best nights. For a complete account of *incubi* and *succubi,* including *incubæ,* and *succubæ,* see the *Liber Demonorum* of Protassus (Paris, 1328), which contains much curious information that would be out of place in a dictionary intended as a text-book for the public schools.

    Victor Hugo relates that in the Channel Islands Satan himself— tempted more than elsewhere by the beauty of the women, doubtless —sometimes plays at *incubus,* greatly to the inconvenience and alarm of the good dames who wish to be loyal to their marriage vows, generally speaking. A certain lady applied to the parish priest to learn how they might, in the dark, distinguish the hardy intruder from their husbands. The holy man said they must feel his brow for horns; but Hugo is ungallant enough to hint a doubt of the efficacy of the test.

INCUMBENT, *n*. A person of the liveliest interest to the outcumbents.

INDECISION, *n*. The chief element of success; "for whereas," saith Sir Thomas Brewbold, "there is but one way to do nothing and divers ways to do something, whereof, to a surety, only one is the right way, it followeth that he who from indecision standeth still hath not so many chances of going astray as he who pusheth forwards"—a most clear and satisfactory exposition of the matter.

"Your prompt decision to attack," said General Grant on a certain occasion to General Gordon Granger, "was admirable; you had but five minutes to make up your mind in."

"Yes, sir," answered the victorious subordinate, "it is a great thing to know exactly what to do in an emergency. When in doubt whether to attack or retreat I never hesitate a moment—I toss up a copper."

"Do you mean to say that's what you did this time?"

"Yes, General; but for Heaven's sake don't reprimand me: I disobeyed the coin."

INDIFFERENT, *adj*. Imperfectly sensible to distinctions among things.
> "You tiresome man!" cried Indolentio's wife,
> "You've grown indifferent to all in life."
> "Indifferent?" he drawled with a slow smile;
> "I would be, dear, but it is not worth while."
> *Apuleius M. Gokul.*

INDIGESTION, *n*. A disease which the patient and his friends frequently mistake for deep religious conviction and concern for the salvation of mankind. As the simple Red Man of the western wild put it, with, it must be confessed, a certain force: "Plenty well, no pray; big bellyache, heap God."

INDISCRETION, *n*. The guilt of woman.

INEXPEDIENT, *adj*. Not calculated to advance one's interests.

INFANCY, *n*. The period of our lives when, according to Wordsworth, "Heaven lies about us." The world begins lying about us pretty soon afterward.

INFERIÆ, *n*. (Latin.) Among the Greeks and Romans, sacrifices for propitiation of the *Dii Manes,* or souls of dead heroes; for the pious ancients could not invent enough gods to satisfy their spiritual needs, and had to have a number of makeshift deities, or, as a sailor might say, jury-gods, which they made out of the most unpromising materials. It was while sacrificing a bullock to the spirit of Agamemnon that Laiaides, a priest of Aulis, was favored with an audience of that illustrious warrior's shade, who prophetically recounted to him the birth of Christ and the triumph of Christianity, giving him also a rapid but tolerably complete review of events down to the reign of Saint Louis. The narrative ended abruptly at that point, owing to the inconsiderate crowing of a cock, which compelled the ghosted King of Men to scamper back to Hades. There is a fine mediæval flavor to this story, and as it has not been traced back further than Père Brateille, a pious but obscure writer at the court of Saint Louis, we shall probably not err on the side of presumption in considering it apocryphal, though Monsignor Capel's judgment of the matter might be different; and to that I bow—wow.

INFIDEL, *n.* In New York, one who does not believe in the Christian religion; in Constantinople, one who does. (See GIAOUR.) A kind of scoundrel imperfectly reverent of, and niggardly contributory to, divines, ecclesiastics, popes, parsons, canons, monks, mollahs, voodoos, presbyters, hierophants, prelates, obeah-men, abbés, nuns, missionaries, exhorters, deacons, friars, hadjis, high-priests, muezzins, brahmins, medicine-men, confessors, eminences, elders, primates, prebendaries, pilgrims, prophets, imaums, beneficiaries, clerks, vicars-choral, arch-bishops, bishops, abbots, priors, preachers, padres, abbotesses, caloyers, palmers, curates, patriarchs, bonezs, santons, beadsmen, canonesses, residentiaries, diocesans, deans, subdeans, rural deans, abdals, charm-sellers, archdeacons, hierarchs, class-leaders, incumbents, capitulars, sheiks, talapoins, postulants, scribes, gooroos, precentors, beadles, fakeers, sextons, reverences, revivalists, cenobites, perpetual curates, chaplains, mudjoes, readers, novices, vicars, pastors, rabbis, ulemas, lamas, sacristans, vergers, dervises, lectors, church wardens, cardinals, prioresses, suffragans, acolytes, rectors, curés, and pumpums.

INFLUENCE, *n.* In politics, a visionary *quo* given in exchange for a substantial *quid.*

INFRALAPSARIAN, *n*. One who ventures to believe that Adam need not have sinned unless he had a mind to—in opposition to the Supralapsarians, who hold that that luckless person's fall was decreed from the beginning. Infralapsarians are sometimes called Sublapsarians without material effect upon the importance and lucidity of their views about Adam.

> Two theologues once, as they wended their way
> To chapel, engaged in colloquial fray—
> An earnest logomachy, bitter as gall,
> Concerning poor Adam and what made him fall.
> " 'Twas Predestination," cried one—"for the Lord
> Decreed he should fall of his own accord."
> "Not so—'twas Free Will," the other maintained,
> "Which led him to choose what the Lord had ordained."
> So fierce and so fiery grew the debate
> That nothing but bloodshed their dudgeon could sate;
> So off flew their cassocks and caps to the ground
> And, moved by the spirit, their hands went round.
> Ere either had proved his theology right
> By winning, or even beginning, the fight,
> A gray old professor of Latin came by,
> A staff in his hand and a scowl in his eye,
> And learning the cause of their quarrel (for still
> As they clumsily sparred they disputed with skill
> Of foreordinational freedom of will)
> Cried: "Sirrahs! this reasonless warfare compose:
> Atwixt ye's no difference worthy of blows.
> The sects ye belong to—I'm ready to swear
> Ye wrongly interpret the names that they bear.
> *You*—Infralapsarian son of a clown!—
> Should only contend that Adam slipped down;
> While *you*—you Supralapsarian pup!—
> Should nothing aver but that Adam slipped up."
> It's all the same whether up or down
> You slip on a peel of banana brown.
> Even Adam analyzed not his blunder,
> But thought he had slipped on a peal of thunder!
>   *G. J.*

INGRATE, *n*. One who receives a benefit from another, or is otherwise an object of charity.

> "All men are ingrates," sneered the cynic. "Nay,"
>   The good philanthropist replied;

"I did great service to a man one day
Who never since has cursed me to repay,
  Nor vilified."

"Ho!" cried the cynic, "lead me to him straight—
  With veneration I am overcome,
And fain would have his blessing." "Sad your fate—
He cannot bless you, for I grieve to state
  The man is dumb."

Ariel Selp.

INJURY, *n.* An offense next in degree of enormity to a slight.

INJUSTICE, *n.* A burden which of all those that we load upon others and carry ourselves is lightest in the hands and heaviest upon the back.

INK, *n.* A villainous compound of tanno-gallate of iron, gum-arabic and water, chiefly used to facilitate the infection of idiocy and promote intellectual crime. The properties of ink are peculiar and contradictory: it may be used to make reputations and unmake them; to blacken them and to make them white; but it is most generally and acceptably employed as a mortar to bind together the stones in an edifice of fame, and as a whitewash to conceal afterward the rascal quality of the material. There are men called journalists who have established ink baths which some persons pay money to get into, others to get out of. Not infrequently it occurs that a person who has paid to get in pays twice as much to get out.

INNATE, *adj.* Natural, inherent—as innate ideas, that is to say, ideas that we are born with, having had them previously imparted to us. The doctrine of innate ideas is one of the most admirable faiths of philosophy, being itself an innate idea and therefore inaccessible to disproof, though Locke foolishly supposed himself to have given it "a black eye." Among innate ideas may be mentioned the belief in one's ability to conduct a newspaper, in the greatness of one's country, in the superiority of one's civilization, in the importance of one's personal affairs and in the interesting nature of one's diseases.

IN'ARDS, *n.* The stomach, heart, soul and other bowels. Many eminent investigators do not class the soul as an in'ard, but that acute observer and renowned authority, Dr. Gunsaulus, is persuaded that the mysterious organ known as the spleen is nothing less than our immortal part. To the contrary, Professor Garrett P. Servis holds that man's soul is that prolongation of his spinal marrow which forms the pith of his no tail; and for demonstration of his faith points confidently to the fact that tailed animals have no souls. Concerning these two theories, it is best to suspend judgment by believing both.

INSCRIPTION, *n.* Something written on another thing. Inscriptions are of many kinds, but mostly memorial, intended to commemorate the fame of some illustrious person and hand down to distant ages the record of his services and virtues. To this class of inscriptions belongs the name of John Smith, penciled on the Washington monument. Following are examples of memorial inscriptions on tombstones: (See EPITAPH.)

> "In the sky my soul is found,
> And my body in the ground.
> By and by my body'll rise
> To my spirit in the skies,
> Soaring up to Heaven's gate.
> 1878."

"Sacred to the memory of Jeremiah Tree. Cut down May 9th, 1862, aged 27 yrs. 4 mos. and 12 ds. Indigenous."

> "Affliction sore long time she boar,
> Phisicians was in vain,
> Till Deth released the dear deceased
> And left her a remain.
> Gone to join Ananias in the regions of bliss."

> "The clay that rests beneath this stone
> As Silas Wood was widely known.
> Now, lying here, I ask what good
> It was to me to be S. Wood.
> O Man, let not ambition trouble you,
> Is the advice of Silas W."

"Richard Haymon, of Heaven. Fell to Earth Jan. 20, 1807, and had the dust brushed off him Oct. 3, 1874."

INSECTIVORA, *n.*

> "See," cries the chorus of admiring preachers,
> "How Providence provides for all His creatures!"
> "His care," the gnat said, "even the insects follows:
> For us He has provided wrens and swallows."
>
> Sempen Railey.

INSURANCE, *n.* An ingenious modern game of chance in which the player is permitted to enjoy the comfortable conviction that he is beating the man who keeps the table.

INSURANCE AGENT: My dear sir, that is a fine house—pray let me insure it.

HOUSE OWNER: With pleasure. Please make the annual premium so low that by the time when, according to the tables of your actuary, it will probably be destroyed by fire I will have paid you considerably less than the face of the policy.

INSURANCE AGENT: O dear, no—we could not afford to do that. We must fix the premium so that you will have paid more.

HOUSE OWNER: How, then, can *I* afford *that?*

INSURANCE AGENT: Why, your house may burn down at any time. There was Smith's house, for example, which—

HOUSE OWNER: Spare me—there were Brown's house, on the contrary, and Jones's house, and Robinson's house, which—

INSURANCE AGENT: Spare *me!*

HOUSE OWNER: Let us understand each other. You want me to pay you money on the supposition that something will occur previously to the time set by yourself for its occurrence. In other words, you expect me to bet that my house will not last so long as you say that it will probably last.

INSURANCE AGENT: But if your house burns without insurance it will be a total loss.

HOUSE OWNER: Beg your pardon—by your own actuary's tables I shall probably have saved, when it burns, all the premiums I would otherwise have paid to you—amounting to more than the face of the policy they would have bought. But suppose it to burn, uninsured, before the time upon which your figures are based. If I could not afford that, how could you if it were insured?

INSURANCE AGENT: O, we should make ourselves whole from our luckier ventures with other clients. Virtually, they pay your loss.

HOUSE OWNER: And virtually, then, don't I help to pay their losses? Are not their houses as likely as mine to burn before they have paid you as much as you must pay them? The case stands this way: you expect to take more money from your clients than you pay to them, do you not?

INSURANCE AGENT: Certainly; if we did not—

HOUSE OWNER: I would not trust you with my money. Very well, then. If it is *certain*, with reference to the whole body of your clients, that they lose money on you it is *probable*, with reference to any one of them, that *he* will. It is these individual probabilities that make the aggregate certainty.

INSURANCE AGENT: I will not deny it—but look at the figures in this pamph—

HOUSE OWNER: Heaven forbid!

INSURANCE AGENT: You spoke of saving the premiums which you would otherwise pay to me. Will you not be more likely to squander them? We offer you an incentive to thrift.

HOUSE OWNER: The willingness of A to take care of B's money is not peculiar to insurance, but as a charitable institution you command esteem. Deign to accept its expression from a Deserving Object.

INSURRECTION, *n.* An unsuccessful revolution. Disaffection's failure to substitute misrule for bad government.

INTENTION, *n.* The mind's sense of the prevalence of one set of influences over another set; an effect whose cause is the imminence, immediate or remote, of the performance of an involuntary act.

INTERPRETER, *n.* One who enables two persons of different languages to understand each other by repeating to each what it would have been to the interpreter's advantage for the other to have said.

INTERREGNUM, *n.* The period during which a monarchical country is governed by a warm spot on the cushion of the throne. The experiment of letting the spot grow cold has commonly been attended by most unhappy results from the zeal of many worthy persons to make it warm again.

INTIMACY, *n.* A relation into which fools are providentially drawn for their mutual destruction.

> Two Seidlitz powders, one in blue
> And one in white, together drew,
> And having each a pleasant sense

Of t'other powder's excellence,
Forsook their jackets for the snug
Enjoyment of a common mug.
So close their intimacy grew
One paper would have held the two.
To confidences straight they fell,
Less anxious each to hear than tell;
Then each remorsefully confessed
To all the virtues he possessed,
Acknowledging he had them in
So high degree it was a sin.
The more they said, the more they felt
Their spirits with emotion melt,
Till tears of sentiment expressed
Their feelings. Then they effervesced!
So Nature executes her feats
Of wrath on friends and sympathetes
The good old rule who won't apply,
That you are you and I am I.

INTRODUCTION, *n.* A social ceremony invented by the devil for the gratification of his servants and the plaguing of his enemies. The introduction attains its most malevolent development in this country, being, indeed, closely related to our political system. Every American being the equal of every other American, it follows that everybody has the right to know everybody else, which implies the right to introduce without request or permission. The Declaration of Independence should have read thus:

"We hold these truths to be self-evident: that all men are created equal; that they are endowed by their Creator with certain inalienable rights; that among these are life, and the right to make that of another miserable by thrusting upon him an incalculable quantity of acquaintances; liberty, particularly the liberty to introduce persons to one another without first ascertaining if they are not already acquainted as enemies; and the pursuit of another's happiness with a running pack of strangers."

INVENTOR, *n.* A person who makes an ingenious arrangement of wheels, levers and springs, and believes it civilization.

IRRELIGION, *n.* The principal one of the great faiths of the world.

ITCH, *n.* The patriotism of a Scotchman.

J is a consonant in English, but some nations use it as a vowel—than which nothing could be more absurd. Its original form, which has been but slightly modified, was that of the tail of a subdued dog, and it was not a letter but a character, standing for a Latin verb, *jacere,* "to throw," because when a stone is thrown at a dog the dog's tail assumes that shape. This is the origin of the letter, as expounded by the renowned Dr. Jocolpus Bumer, of the University of Belgrade, who established his conclusions on the subject in a work of three quarto volumes and committed suicide on being reminded that the j in the Roman alphabet had originally no curl.

JEALOUS, *adj.* Unduly concerned about the preservation of that which can be lost only if not worth keeping.

JESTER, *n.* An officer formerly attached to a king's household, whose business it was to amuse the court by ludicrous actions and utterances, the absurdity being attested by his motley costume. The king himself being attired with dignity, it took the world some centuries to discover that his own conduct and decrees were sufficiently ridiculous for the amusement not only of his court but of all mankind. The jester was commonly called a fool, but the poets and romancers have ever delighted to represent him as a singularly wise and witty person. In the circus of to-day the melancholy ghost of the court fool effects the dejection of humbler audiences with the same jests wherewith in life he gloomed the marble hall, panged the patrician sense of humor and tapped the tank of royal tears.

> The widow-queen of Portugal
>   Had an audacious jester
> Who entered the confessional
>   Disguised, and there confessed her.

> "Father," she said, "thine ear bend down—
>   My sins are more than scarlet:

> I love my fool—blaspheming clown,
>   And common, base-born varlet."
>
> "Daughter," the mimic priest replied,
>   "That sin, indeed, is awful:
> The church's pardon is denied
>   To love that is unlawful.
>
> "But since thy stubborn heart will be
>   For him forever pleading,
> Thou'dst better make him, by decree,
>   A man of birth and breeding."
>
> She made the fool a duke, in hope
>   With Heaven's taboo to palter;
> Then told a priest, who told the Pope,
>   Who damned her from the altar!
>   *Barel Dort.*

JEW'S-HARP, *n.* An unmusical instrument, played by holding it fast with the teeth and trying to brush it away with the finger.

JOSS-STICKS, *n.* Small sticks burned by the Chinese in their pagan tomfoolery, in imitation of certain sacred rites of our holy religion.

JUSTICE, *n.* A commodity which in a more or less adulterated condition the State sells to the citizen as a reward for his allegiance, taxes and personal service.

K

K is a consonant that we get from the Greeks, but it can be traced away back beyond them to the Cerathians, a small commercial nation inhabiting the peninsula of Smero. In their tongue it was called *Klatch,* which means "destroyed." The form of the letter was originally precisely that of our H, but the erudite Dr. Snedeker explains that it was altered to its present shape to commemorate the destruction of the great temple of Jarute by an earthquake, *circa* 730 B. C. This building was famous for the two lofty columns of its portico, one of which was broken in half by the catastrophe, the other remaining intact. As the earlier form of the letter is supposed to have been suggested by these pillars, so, it is thought by the great antiquary, its later was adopted as a simple and natural—not to say touching—means of keeping the calamity ever in the national memory. It is not known if the name of the letter was altered as an additional mnemonic, or if the name was always *Klatch* and the destruction one of nature's puns. As each theory seems probable enough, I see no objection to believing both—and Dr. Snedeker arrayed himself on that side of the question.

KEEP, *v. t.*

> He willed away his whole estate,
>   And then in death he fell asleep,
> Murmuring: "Well, at any rate,
>   My name unblemished I shall keep."
> But when upon the tomb 'twas wrought
> Whose was it?—for the dead keep naught.
>   *Durang Gophel Arn.*

KILL, *v. t.* To create a vacancy without nominating a successor.

KILT, *n.* A costume sometimes worn by Scotchmen in America and Americans in Scotland.

KINDNESS, *n.* A brief preface to ten volumes of exaction.

KING, *n.* A male person commonly known in America as a "crowned head," although he never wears a crown and has usually no head to speak of.

> A king, in times long, long gone by,
>   Said to his lazy jester:
> "If I were you and you were I
> My moments merrily would fly—
>   No care nor grief to pester."

> "The reason, Sire, that you would thrive,"
>   The fool said—"if you'll hear it—
> Is that of all the fools alive
> Who own you for their sovereign, I've
>   The most forgiving spirit."
>   *Oogum Bem.*

KING'S EVIL, *n.* A malady that was formerly cured by the touch of the sovereign, but has now to be treated by the physicians. Thus "the most pious Edward" of England used to lay his royal hand upon his ailing subjects and make them whole—

>   a crowd of wretched souls
> That stay his cure: their malady convinces
> The great essay of art; but at his touch,
> Such sanctity hath Heaven given his hand,
> They presently amend,

as the "Doctor" in *Macbeth* hath it. This useful property of the royal hand could, it appears, be transmitted along with other crown properties; for according to "Malcolm,"

>   'tis spoken,
> To the succeeding royalty he leaves
> The healing benediction.

But the gift somewhere dropped out of the line of succession: the later sovereigns of England have not been tactful healers, and the disease once honored with the name "king's evil" now bears the humbler one of "scrofula," from *scrofa,* a sow. The date and author of the following epigram are known only to the author of this dictionary, but it is old enough to show that the jest about Scotland's national disorder is not a thing of yesterday.

> Yᵉ Kynge his evill in me laye,
> Wh. he of Scottlande charmed awaye.
> He layde his hand on mine and sayd:
> "Be gone!" Yᵉ ill no longer stayd.
> But O yᵉ wofull plyght in wh.
> I'm now y-pight: I have yᵉ itche!

The superstition that maladies can be cured by royal taction is dead, but like many a departed conviction it has left a monument of custom to keep its memory green. The practice of forming in line and shaking the President's hand had no other origin, and when that great dignitary bestows his healing salutation on

> strangely visited people,
> All swoln and ulcerous, pitiful to the eye,
> The mere despair of surgery,

he and his patients are handing along an extinguished torch which once was kindled at the altar-fire of a faith long held by all classes of men. It is a beautiful and edifying "survival"—one which brings the sainted past close home to our "business and bosoms."

KISS, *n.* A word invented by the poets as a rhyme for "bliss." It is supposed to signify, in a general way, some kind of rite or ceremony appertaining to a good understanding; but the manner of its performance is unknown to this lexicographer.

KLEPTOMANIAC, *n.* A rich thief.

KNIGHT, *n.*

> Once a warrior gentle of birth,
> Then a person of civic worth,
> Now a fellow to move our mirth.
> Warrior, person, and fellow—no more:
> We must knight our dogs to get any lower.
> Brave Knights Kennelers then shall be,
> Noble Knights of the Golden Flea,
> Knights of the Order of St. Steboy,
> Knights of St. Gorge and Sir Knights Jawy.
> God speed the day when this knighting fad
> Shall go to the dogs and the dogs go mad.

KORAN, *n.* A book which the Mohammedans foolishly believe to have been written by divine inspiration, but which Christians know to be a wicked imposture, contradictory to the Holy Scriptures.

L

LABOR, *n.* One of the processes by which A acquires property for B.

LAND, *n.* A part of the earth's surface, considered as property. The theory that land is property subject to private ownership and control is the foundation of modern society, and is eminently worthy of the superstructure. Carried to its logical conclusion, it means that some have the right to prevent others from living; for the right to own implies the right exclusively to occupy; and in fact laws of trespass are enacted wherever property in land is recognized. It follows that if the whole area of *terra firma* is owned by A, B and C, there will be no place for D, E, F and G to be born, or, born as trespassers, to exist.

> A life on the ocean wave,
>   A home on the rolling deep,
> For the spark that nature gave
>   I have there the right to keep.
>
> They give me the cat-o'-nine
>   Whenever I go ashore.
> Then ho! for the flashing brine—
>   I'm a natural commodore!
>   *Dodle.*

LANGUAGE, *n.* The music with which we charm the serpents guarding another's treasure.

LAOCOÖN, *n.* A famous piece of antique sculpture representing a priest of that name and his two sons in the folds of two enormous serpents. The skill and diligence with which the old man and lads support the serpents and keep them up to their work have been justly regarded as one of the noblest artistic illustrations of the mastery of human intelligence over brute inertia.

LAP, *n.* One of the most important organs of the female system—an admirable provision of nature for the repose of infancy, but chiefly useful in rural festivities to support plates of cold chicken and heads of adult males. The male of our species has a rudimentary lap, imperfectly developed and in no way contributing to the animal's substantial welfare.

LAST, *n.* A shoemaker's implement, named by a frowning Providence as opportunity to the maker of puns.

> Ah, punster, would my lot were cast,
>   Where the cobbler is unknown,
> So that I might forget his last
>   And hear your own.
>   *Gargo Repsky.*

LAUGHTER, *n.* An interior convulsion, producing a distortion of the features and accompanied by inarticulate noises. It is infectious and, though intermittent, incurable. Liability to attacks of laughter is one of the characteristics distinguishing man from the animals—these being not only inaccessible to the provocation of his example, but impregnable to the microbes having original jurisdiction in bestowal of the disease. Whether laughter could be imparted to animals by inoculation from the human patient is a question that has not been answered by experimentation. Dr. Meir Witchell holds that the infectious character of laughter is due to instantaneous fermentation of *sputa* diffused in a spray. From this peculiarity he names the disorder *Convulsio spargens.*

LAUREATE, *adj.* Crowned with leaves of the laurel. In England the Poet Laureate is an officer of the sovereign's court, acting as dancing skeleton at every royal feast and singing-mute at every royal funeral. Of all incumbents of that high office, Robert Southey had the most notable knack at drugging the Samson of public joy and cutting his hair to the quick; and he had an artistic color-sense which enabled him so to blacken a public grief as to give it the aspect of a national crime.

LAUREL, *n.* The *laurus,* a vegetable dedicated to Apollo, and formerly defoliated to wreathe the brows of victors and such poets as had influence at court. (*Vide Supra.*)

LAW, *n*.

> Once Law was sitting on the bench,
>   And Mercy knelt a-weeping.
> "Clear out!" he cried, "disordered wench!
>   Nor come before me creeping.
> Upon your knees if you appear,
> 'Tis plain you have no standing here."
> Then Justice came. His Honor cried:
>   "*Your* status?—devil seize you!"
> "*Amica curiae*," she replied—
>   "Friend of the court, so please you."
> "Begone!" he shouted—"there's the door—
> I never saw your face before!"
>
> G. J.

LAWFUL, *adj*. Compatible with the will of a judge having jurisdiction.

LAWYER, *n*. One skilled in circumvention of the law.

LAZINESS, *n*. Unwarranted repose of manner in a person of low degree.

LEAD, *n*. A heavy blue-gray metal much used in giving stability to light lovers—particularly to those who love not wisely but other men's wives. Lead is also of great service as a counterpoise to an argument of such weight that it turns the scale of debate the wrong way. An interesting fact in the chemistry of international controversy is that at the point of contact of two patriotisms lead is precipitated in great quantities.

> Hail, holy Lead!—of human feuds the great
>   And universal arbiter; endowed
>   With penetration to pierce any cloud
> Fogging the field of controversial hate,
> And with a swift, inevitable, straight,
>   Searching precision find the unavowed
>   But vital point. Thy judgment, when allowed
> By the chirurgeon, settles the debate.
> O useful metal!—were it not for thee
>   We'd grapple one another's ears alway:
> But when we hear thee buzzing like a bee
>   We, like old Muhlenberg, "care not to stay."
> And when the quick have run away like pullets
> Jack Satan smelts the dead to make new bullets.

LEARNING, *n.* The kind of ignorance distinguishing the studious.

LECTURER, *n.* One with his hand in your pocket, his tongue in your ear and his faith in your patience.

LEGACY, *n.* A gift from one who is legging it out of this vale of tears.

LEONINE, *adj.* Unlike a menagerie lion. Leonine verses are those in which a word in the middle of a line rhymes with a word at the end, as in this famous passage from Bella Peeler Silcox:

> The electric light invades the dunnest deep of Hades.
> Cries Pluto, 'twixt his snores: "O tempora! O mores!"

It should be explained that Mrs. Silcox does not undertake to teach the pronunciation of the Greek and Latin tongues. Leonine verses are so called in honor of a poet named Leo, whom prosodists appear to find a pleasure in believing to have been the first to discover that a rhyming couplet could be run into a single line.

LETTUCE, *n.* An herb of the genus *Lactuca,* "Wherewith," says that pious gastronome, Hengist Pelly, "God has been pleased to reward the good and punish the wicked. For by his inner light the righteous man has discerned a manner of compounding for it a dressing to the appetency whereof a multitude of gustible condiments conspire, being reconciled and ameliorated with profusion of oil, the entire comestible making glad the heart of the godly and causing his face to shine. But the person of spiritual unworth is successfully tempted of the Adversary to eat of lettuce with destitution of oil, mustard, egg, salt and garlic, and with a rascal bath of vinegar polluted with sugar. Wherefore the person of spiritual unworth suffers an intestinal pang of strange complexity and raises the song."

LEVIATHAN, *n.* An enormous aquatic animal mentioned by Job. Some suppose it to have been the whale, but that distinguished ichthyologer, Dr. Jordan, of Stanford University, maintains with considerable heat that it was a species of gigantic Tadpole, (*Thaddeus Polandensis*) or Polliwig—*Maria pseudo-hirsuta.* For an exhaustive description and history of the Tadpole consult the famous monograph of Jane Porter, *Thaddeus of Warsaw.*

LEXICOGRAPHER, *n.* A pestilent fellow who, under the pretense of record-
ing some particular stage in the development of a language, does what
he can to arrest its growth, stiffen its flexibility and mechanize its
methods. For your lexicographer, having written his dictionary, comes
to be considered "as one having authority," whereas his function is
only to make a record, not to give a law. The natural servility of the
human understanding having invested him with judicial power, sur-
renders its right of reason and submits itself to a chronicle as if it
were a statute. Let the dictionary (for example) mark a good word
as "obsolete" or "obsolescent" and few men thereafter venture to use
it, whatever their need of it and however desirable its restoration to
favor—whereby the process of impoverishment is accelerated and
speech decays. On the contrary, the bold and discerning writer who,
recognizing the truth that language must grow by innovation if it
grow at all, makes new words and uses the old in an unfamiliar sense,
has no following and is tartly reminded that "it isn't in the dictionary"
—although down to the time of the first lexicographer (Heaven forgive him!) no author ever had used a word that *was* in the dictionary.
In the golden prime and high noon of English speech; when from the
lips of the great Elizabethans fell words that made their own meaning
and carried it in their very sound; when a Shakspeare and a Bacon
were possible, and the language now rapidly perishing at one end and
slowly renewed at the other was in vigorous growth and hardy
preservation—sweeter than honey and stronger than a lion—the lexicographer was a person unknown, the dictionary a creation which his
Creator had not created him to create.

> God said: "Let Spirit perish into Form,"
> And lexicographers arose, a swarm!
> Thought fled and left her clothing, which they took,
> And catalogued each garment in a book.
> Now, from her leafy covert when she cries:
> "Give me my clothes and I'll return," they rise
> And scan the list, and say without compassion:
> "Excuse us—they are mostly out of fashion."
>
> *Sigismund Smith.*

LIAR, *n.* A lawyer with a roving commission.

LIBERTY, *n.* One of Imagination's most precious possessions.

The rising People, hot and out of breath,
Roared round the palace: "Liberty or death!"
"If death will do," the King said, "let me reign;
You'll have, I'm sure, no reason to complain."
Martha Braymance.

LICKSPITTLE, *n*. A useful functionary, not infrequently found editing a newspaper. In his character of editor he is closely allied to the blackmailer by the tie of occasional identity; for in truth the lickspittle is only the blackmailer under another aspect, though the latter is frequently found as an independent species. Lickspittling is more detestable than blackmailing, precisely as the business of a confidence man is more detestable than that of a highway robber; and the parallel maintains itself throughout, for whereas few robbers will cheat, every sneak will plunder if he dare.

LIFE, *n*. A spiritual pickle preserving the body from decay. We live in daily apprehension of its loss; yet when lost it is not missed. The question, "Is life worth living?" has been much discussed; particularly by those who think it is not, many of whom have written at great length in support of their view and by careful observance of the laws of health enjoyed for long terms of years the honors of successful controversy.

"Life's not worth living, and that's the truth,"
Carelessly caroled the golden youth.
In manhood still he maintained that view
And held it more strongly the older he grew.
When kicked by a jackass at eighty-three,
"Go fetch me a surgeon at once!" cried he.
Han Soper.

LIGHTHOUSE, *n*. A tall building on the seashore in which the government maintains a lamp and the friend of a politician.

LIMB, *n*. The branch of a tree or the leg of an American woman.

'Twas a pair of boots that the lady bought,
And the salesman laced them tight
To a very remarkable height—
Higher, indeed, than I think he ought—
Higher than *can* be right.

For the Bible declares—but never mind:
  It is hardly fit
To censure freely and fault to find
With others for sins that I'm not inclined
  Myself to commit.
Each has his weakness, and though my own
  Is freedom from every sin,
  It still were unfair to pitch in,
Discharging the first censorious stone.
Besides, the truth compels me to say,
The boots in question were *made* that way.
As he drew the lace she made a grimace,
  And blushingly said to him:
"This boot, I'm sure, is too high to endure,
It hurts my—hurts my—limb."
The salesman smiled in a manner mild,
Like an artless, undesigning child;
Then, checking himself, to his face he gave
A look as sorrowful as the grave,
  Though he didn't care two figs
  For her pains and throes,
  As he stroked her toes,
Remarking with speech and manner just
Befitting his calling: "Madam, I trust
  That it doesn't hurt your twigs."
                    B. Percival Dike.

LINEN, *n.* "A kind of cloth the making of which, when made of hemp, entails a great waste of hemp."—*Calcraft the Hangman.*

LITIGANT, *n.* A person about to give up his skin for the hope of retaining his bones.

LITIGATION, *n.* A machine which you go into as a pig and come out of as a sausage.

LIVER, *n.* A large red organ thoughtfully provided by nature to be bilious with. The sentiments and emotions which every literary anatomist now knows to haunt the heart were anciently believed to infest the liver; and even Gascoygne, speaking of the emotional side of human nature, calls it "our hepaticall parte." It was at one time considered the seat of life; hence its name—liver, the thing we live with. The liver is heaven's best gift to the goose; without it that bird would be unable to supply us with the Strasbourg *pâté.*

LL.D. Letters indicating the degree *Legumptionorum Doctor,* one learned in laws, gifted with legal gumption. Some suspicion is cast upon this derivation by the fact that the title was formerly *£ £.d.,* and conferred only upon gentlemen distinguished for their wealth. At the date of this writing Columbia University is considering the expediency of making another degree for clergymen, in place of the old D.D.— *Damnator Diaboli.* The new honor will be known as *Sanctorum Custus,* and written *$$c.* The name of the Rev. John Satan has been suggested as a suitable recipient by a lover of consistency, who points out that Professor Harry Thurston Peck has long enjoyed the advantage of a degree.

LOCK-AND-KEY, *n.* The distinguishing device of civilization and enlightenment.

LODGER, *n.* A less popular name for the Second Person of that delectable newspaper Trinity, the Roomer, the Bedder and the Mealer.

LOGIC, *n.* The art of thinking and reasoning in strict accordance with the limitations and incapacities of the human misunderstanding. The basic of logic is the syllogism, consisting of a major and a minor premise and a conclusion—thus:

Major Premise: Sixty men can do a piece of work sixty times as quickly as one man.

Minor Premise: One man can dig a posthole in sixty seconds; therefore—

Conclusion: Sixty men can dig a posthole in one second.

This may be called the syllogism arithmetical, in which, by combining logic and mathematics, we obtain a double certainty and are twice blessed.

LOGOMACHY, *n.* A war in which the weapons are words and the wounds punctures in the swim-bladder of self-esteem—a kind of contest in which, the vanquished being unconscious of defeat, the victor is denied the reward of success.

> 'Tis said by divers of the scholar-men
> That poor Salmasius died of Milton's pen.
> Alas! we cannot know if this is true,
> For reading Milton's wit we perish too.

LONGANIMITY, *n.* The disposition to endure injury with meek forbearance while maturing a plan of revenge.

LONGEVITY, *n.* Uncommon extension of the fear of death.

LOOKING-GLASS, *n.* A vitreous plane upon which to display a fleeting show for man's disillusion given.

The King of Manchuria had a magic looking-glass, whereon whoso looked saw, not his own image, but only that of the king. A certain courtier who had long enjoyed the king's favor and was thereby enriched beyond any other subject of the realm, said to the king: "Give me, I pray, thy wonderful mirror, so that when absent out of thine august presence I may yet do homage before thy visible shadow, prostrating myself night and morning in the glory of thy benign countenance, as which nothing has so divine splendor, O Noonday Sun of the Universe!"

Pleased with the speech, the king commanded that the mirror be conveyed to the courtier's palace; but after, having gone thither without apprisal, he found it in an apartment where was naught but idle lumber. And the mirror was dimmed with dust and overlaced with cobwebs. This so angered him that he fisted it hard, shattering the glass, and was sorely hurt. Enraged all the more by this mischance, he commanded that the ungrateful courtier be thrown into prison, and that the glass be repaired and taken back to his own palace; and this was done. But when the king looked again on the mirror he saw not his image as before, but only the figure of a crowned ass, having a bloody bandage on one of its hinder hooves—as the artificers and all who had looked upon it had before discerned but feared to report. Taught wisdom and charity, the king restored his courtier to liberty, had the mirror set into the back of the throne and reigned many years with justice and humility; and one day when he fell asleep in death while on the throne, the whole court saw in the mirror the luminous figure of an angel, which remains to this day.

LOQUACITY, *n.* A disorder which renders the sufferer unable to curb his tongue when you wish to talk.

LORD, *n.* In American society, an English tourist above the state of a costermonger, as, Lord 'Aberdasher, Lord Hartisan and so forth. The traveling Briton of lesser degree is addressed as "Sir," as, Sir 'Arry Donkiboi, of 'Amstead 'Eath. The word "Lord" is sometimes used, also, as a title of the Supreme Being; but this is thought to be rather flattery than true reverence.

> Miss Sallie Ann Splurge, of her own accord,
> Wedded a wandering English lord—
> Wedded and took him to dwell with her "paw,"
> A parent who throve by the practice of Draw.
> Lord Cadde I don't hesitate here to declare
> Unworthy the father-in-legal care
> Of that elderly sport, notwithstanding the truth
> That Cadde had renounced all the follies of youth;
> For, sad to relate, he'd arrived at the stage
> Of existence that's marked by the vices of age.
> Among them, cupidity caused him to urge
> Repeated demands on the pocket of Splurge,
> Till, wrecked in his fortune, that gentleman saw
> Inadequate aid in the practice of Draw,
> And took, as a means of augmenting his pelf,
> To the business of being a lord himself.
> His neat-fitting garments he wilfully shed
> And sacked himself strangely in checks instead;
> Denuded his chin, but retained at each ear
> A whisker that looked like a blasted career.
> He painted his neck an incarnadine hue
> Each morning and varnished it all that he knew.
> The moony monocular set in his eye
> Appeared to be scanning the Sweet Bye-and-Bye.
> His head was enroofed with a billycock hat,
> And his low-necked shoes were aduncous and flat.
> In speech he eschewed his American ways,
> Denying his nose to the use of his A's
> And dulling their edge till the delicate sense
> Of a babe at their temper could take no offence.
> His H's—'twas most inexpressibly sweet,
> The patter they made as they fell at his feet!
> Re-outfitted thus, Mr. Splurge without fear
> Began as Lord Splurge his recouping career.

Alas, the Divinity shaping his end
Entertained other views and decided to send
His lordship in horror, despair and dismay
From the land of the nobleman's natural prey.
For, smit with his Old World ways, Lady Cadde
Fell—suffering Cæsar!—in love with her dad!

G. J.

LORE, *n.* Learning—particularly that sort which is not derived from a regular course of instruction but comes of the reading of occult books, or by nature. This latter is commonly designated as folk-lore and embraces popularly myths and superstitions. In Baring-Gould's *Curious Myths of the Middle Ages* the reader will find many of these traced backward, through various peoples on converging lines, toward a common origin in remote antiquity. Among these are the fables of "Teddy the Giant Killer," "The Sleeping John Sharp Williams," "Little Red Riding Hood and the Sugar Trust," "Beauty and the Brisbane," "The Seven Aldermen of Ephesus," "Rip Van Fairbanks," and so forth. The fable which Goethe so affectingly relates under the title of "The Erl-King" was known two thousand years ago in Greece as "The Demos and the Infant Industry." One of the most general and ancient of these myths is that Arabian tale of "Ali Baba and the Forty Rockefellers."

LOSS, *n.* Privation of that which we had, or had not. Thus, in the latter sense, it is said of a defeated candidate that he "lost his election"; and of that eminent man, the poet Gilder, that he has "lost his mind." It is in the former and more legitimate sense, that the word is used in the famous epitaph:

Here Huntington's ashes long have lain
Whose loss is our own eternal gain,
For while he exercised all his powers
Whatever he gained, the loss was ours.

LOVE, *n.* A temporary insanity curable by marriage or by removal of the patient from the influences under which he incurred the disorder. This disease, like *caries* and many other ailments, is prevalent only among civilized races living under artificial conditions; barbarous nations breathing pure air and eating simple food enjoy immunity from its ravages. It is sometimes fatal, but more frequently to the physicians than to the patient.

LOW-BRED, *adj.* "Raised" instead of brought up.

LUMINARY, *n.* One who throws light upon a subject; as an editor by not writing about it.

LUNARIAN, *n.* An inhabitant of the moon, as distinguished from Lunatic, one whom the moon inhabits. The Lunarians have been described by Lucian, Locke and other observers, but without much agreement. For example, Bragellos avers their anatomical identity with Man, but Professor Newcomb says they are more like the hill tribes of Vermont.

LYRE, *n.* An ancient instrument of torture. The word is now used in a figurative sense to denote the poetic faculty, as in the following fiery lines of our great poet, Ella Wheeler Wilcox:

> I sit astride Parnassus with my lyre,
> And pick with care the disobedient wire.
> The stupid shepherd lolling on his crook
> With deaf attention scarcely deigns to look.
> I bide my time, and it shall come at length,
> When, with a Titan's energy and strength,
> I'll grab a fistful of the strings, and O,
> The world shall suffer when I let them go!
> *Farquharson Harris.*

M

MACE, *n.* A staff of office signifying authority. Its form, that of a heavy club, indicates its original purpose and use in dissuading from dissent.

MACHINATION, *n.* The method employed by one's opponents in baffling one's open and honorable efforts to do the right thing.

So plain the advantages of machination
It constitutes a moral obligation,
And honest wolves who think upon't with loathing
Feel bound to don the sheep's deceptive clothing.
So prospers still the diplomatic art,
And Satan bows, with hand upon his heart.
                                          R. S. K.

MACROBIAN, *n.* One forgotten of the gods and living to a great age. History is abundantly supplied with examples, from Methuselah to Old Parr, but some notable instances of longevity are less well known. A Calabrian peasant named Coloni, born in 1753, lived so long that he had what he considered a glimpse of the dawn of universal peace. Scanavius relates that he knew an archbishop who was so old that he could remember a time when he did not deserve hanging. In 1566 a linen draper of Bristol, England, declared that he had lived five hundred years, and that in all that time he had never told a lie. There are instances of longevity (*macrobiosis*) in our own country. Senator Chauncey Depew is old enough to know better. The editor of *The American,* a newspaper in New York City, has a memory that goes back to the time when he was a rascal, but not to the fact. The President of the United States was born so long ago that many of the friends of his youth have risen to high political and military preferment without the assistance of personal merit. The verses following were written by a macrobian:

When I was young the world was fair
    And amiable and sunny.
A brightness was in all the air,
    In all the waters, honey.
The jokes were fine and funny,
The statesmen honest in their views,
    And in their lives, as well,
And when you heard a bit of news
    'Twas true enough to tell.
Men were not ranting, shouting, reeking,
Nor women "generally speaking."

The Summer then was long indeed:
    It lasted one whole season!
The sparkling Winter gave no heed
    When ordered by Unreason

To bring the early peas on.
Now, where the dickens is the sense
   In calling that a year
Which does no more than just commence
   Before the end is near?
When I was young the year extended
From month to month until it ended.

I know not why the world has changed
   To something dark and dreary,
And everything is now arranged
   To make a fellow weary.
   The Weather Man—I fear he
Has much to do with it, for, sure,
   The air is not the same:
It chokes you when it is impure,
   When pure it makes you lame.
With windows closed you are asthmatic;
Open, neuralgic or sciatic.

Well, I suppose this new régime
   Of dun degeneration
Seems eviler than it would seem
   To a better observation,
   And has for compensation
Some blessings in a deep disguise
   Which mortal sight has failed
To pierce, although to angels' eyes
   They're visibly unveiled.
If Age is such a boon, good land!
He's costumed by a master hand!
                    Venable Strigg.

MAD, *adj.* Affected with a high degree of intellectual independence; not
conforming to standards of thought, speech and action derived by the
conformants from study of themselves; at odds with the majority; in
short, unusual. It is noteworthy that persons are pronounced mad by
officials destitute of evidence that themselves are sane. For illustration,
this present (and illustrious) lexicographer is no firmer in the faith
of his own sanity than is any inmate of any madhouse in the land;
yet for aught he knows to the contrary, instead of the lofty occupation that seems to him to be engaging his powers he may really be
beating his hands against the window bars of an asylum and declar-

ing himself Noah Webster, to the innocent delight of many thought-less spectators.

MAGDALENE, *n.* An inhabitant of Magdala. Popularly, a woman found out. This definition of the word has the authority of ignorance, Mary of Magdala being another person than the penitent woman mentioned by St. Luke. It has also the official sanction of the governments of Great Britain and the United States. In England the word is pro-nounced Maudlin, whence maudlin, adjective, unpleasantly senti-mental. With their Maudlin for Magdalene, and their Bedlam for Bethlehem, the English may justly boast themselves the greatest of revisers.

MAGIC, *n.* An art of converting superstition into coin. There are other arts serving the same high purpose, but the discreet lexicographer does not name them.

MAGNET, *n.* Something acted upon by magnetism.

MAGNETISM, *n.* Something acting upon a magnet.

The two definitions immediately foregoing are condensed from the works of one thousand eminent scientists, who have illuminated the subject with a great white light, to the inexpressible advancement of human knowledge.

MAGNIFICENT, *adj.* Having a grandeur or splendor superior to that to which the spectator is accustomed, as the ears of an ass, to a rabbit, or the glory of a glowworm, to a maggot.

MAGNITUDE, *n.* Size. Magnitude being purely relative, nothing is large and nothing small. If everything in the universe were increased in bulk one thousand diameters nothing would be any larger than it was before, but if one thing remained unchanged all the others would be larger than they had been. To an understanding familiar with the relativity of magnitude and distance the spaces and masses of the astronomer would be no more impressive than those of the micro-scopist. For anything we know to the contrary, the visible universe may be a small part of an atom, with its component ions, floating in the life-fluid (luminiferous ether) of some animal. Possibly the wee creatures peopling the corpuscles of our own blood are overcome with the proper emotion when contemplating the unthinkable distance from one of these to another.

MAGPIE, *n.* A bird whose thievish disposition suggested to some one that it might be taught to talk.

MAIDEN, *n.* A young person of the unfair sex addicted to clewless conduct and views that madden to crime. The genus has a wide geographical distribution, being found wherever sought and deplored wherever found. The maiden is not altogether unpleasing to the eye, nor (without her piano and her views) insupportable to the ear, though in respect to comeliness distinctly inferior to the rainbow, and, with regard to the part of her that is audible, beaten out of the field by the canary—which, also, is more portable.

>   A lovelorn maiden she sat and sang—
>   This quaint, sweet song sang she:
>   "It's O for a youth with a football bang
>   And a muscle fair to see!
>   The Captain he
>   Of a team to be!
>   On the gridiron he shall shine,
>   A monarch by right divine,
>   And never to roast on it—me!"
>   *Opoline Jones.*

MAJESTY, *n.* The state and title of a king. Regarded with a just contempt by the Most Eminent Grand Masters, Grand Chancellors, Great Incohonees and Imperial Potentates of the ancient and honorable orders of republican America.

MALE, *n.* A member of the unconsidered, or negligible sex. The male of the human race is commonly known (to the female) as Mere Man. The genus has two varieties: good providers and bad providers.

MALEFACTOR, *n.* The chief factor in the progress of the human race.

MALTHUSIAN, *adj.* Pertaining to Malthus and his doctrines. Malthus believed in artificially limiting population, but found that it could not be done by talking. One of the most practical exponents of the Malthusian idea was Herod of Judea, though all the famous soldiers have been of the same way of thinking.

MAMMALIA, *n. pl.* A family of vertebrate animals whose females in a state of nature suckle their young, but when civilized and enlightened put them out to nurse, or use the bottle.

MAMMON, *n.* The god of the world's leading religion. His chief temple is in the holy city of New York.

> He swore that all other religions were gammon,
> And wore out his knees in the worship of Mammon.
> *Jared Oopf.*

MAN, *n.* An animal so lost in rapturous contemplation of what he thinks he is as to overlook what he indubitably ought to be. His chief occupation is extermination of other animals and his own species, which, however, multiplies with such insistent rapidity as to infest the whole habitable earth and Canada.

> When the world was young and Man was new,
>   And everything was pleasant,
> Distinctions Nature never drew
>   'Mongst king and priest and peasant.
>   We're not that way at present,
> Save here in this Republic, where
>   We have that old régime,
> For all are kings, however bare
>   Their backs, howe'er extreme
> Their hunger. And, indeed, each has a voice
> To accept the tyrant of his party's choice.
>
> A citizen who would not vote,
>   And, therefore, was detested,
> Was one day with a tarry coat
>   (With feathers backed and breasted)
>   By patriots invested.
> "It is your duty," cried the crowd,
>   "Your ballot true to cast
> For the man o' your choice." He humbly bowed,
>   And explained his wicked past:

"That's what I very gladly would have done,
Dear patriots, but he has never run."
Apperton Duke.

MANES, *n.* The immortal parts of dead Greeks and Romans. They were in a state of dull discomfort until the bodies from which they had exhaled were buried and burned; and they seem not to have been particularly happy afterward.

MANICHEISM, *n.* The ancient Persian doctrine of an incessant warfare between Good and Evil. When Good gave up the fight the Persians joined the victorious Opposition.

MANNA, *n.* A food miraculously given to the Israelites in the wilderness. When it was no longer supplied to them they settled down and tilled the soil, fertilizing it, as a rule, with the bodies of the original occupants.

MARRIAGE, *n.* The state or condition of a community consisting of a master, a mistress and two slaves, making in all, two.

MARTYR, *n.* One who moves along the line of least reluctance to a desired death.

MATERIAL, *adj.* Having an actual existence, as distinguished from an imaginary one. Important.

> Material things I know, or feel, or see;
> All else is immaterial to me.
> *Jamarach Holobom.*

MAUSOLEUM, *n.* The final and funniest folly of the rich.

MAYONNAISE, *n.* One of the sauces which serve the French in place of a state religion.

ME, *pro.* The objectionable case of I. The personal pronoun in English has three cases, the dominative, the objectionable and the oppressive. Each is all three.

MEANDER, *n.* To proceed sinuously and aimlessly. The word is the ancient name of a river about one hundred and fifty miles south of Troy, which turned and twisted in the effort to get out of hearing when the Greeks and Trojans boasted of their prowess.

MEDAL, *n.* A small metal disk given as a reward for virtues, attainments or services more or less authentic.

It is related of Bismark, who had been awarded a medal for gallantly rescuing a drowning person, that, being asked the meaning of the medal, he replied: "I save lives sometimes." And sometimes he didn't.

MEDICINE, *n.* A stone flung down the Bowery to kill a dog in Broadway.

MEEKNESS, *n.* Uncommon patience in planning a revenge that is worth while.

> M is for Moses,
>   Who slew the Egyptian.
> As sweet as a rose is
> The meekness of Moses.
> No monument shows his
>   Post-mortem inscription,
> But M is for Moses,
>   Who slew the Egyptian.
> *The Biographical Alphabet.*

MEERSCHAUM, *n.* (Literally, seafoam, and by many erroneously supposed to be made of it.) A fine white clay, which for convenience in coloring it brown is made into tobacco pipes and smoked by the workmen engaged in that industry. The purpose of coloring it has not been disclosed by the manufacturers.

> There was a youth (you've heard before,
>   This woful tale, may be),
> Who bought a meerschaum pipe and swore
>   That color it would he!
>
> He shut himself from the world away,
>   Nor any soul he saw.
> He smoked by night, he smoked by day,
>   As hard as he could draw.

His dog died moaning in the wrath
　Of winds that blew aloof;
The weeds were in the gravel path,
　The owl was on the roof.

"He's gone afar, he'll come no more,"
　The neighbors sadly say.
And so they batter in the door
　To take his goods away.

Dead, pipe in mouth, the youngster lay,
　Nut-brown in face and limb.
"That pipe's a lovely white," they say,
　"But it has colored him!"

The moral there's small need to sing—
　'Tis plain as day to you:
Don't play your game on any thing
　That is a gamester too.

　　　　　　　　　　Martin Bulstrode.

MENDACIOUS, *adj.* Addicted to rhetoric.

MERCHANT, *n.* One engaged in a commercial pursuit. A commercial pursuit is one in which the thing pursued is a dollar.

MERCY, *n.* An attribute beloved of detected offenders.

MESMERISM, *n.* Hypnotism before it wore good clothes, kept a carriage and asked Incredulity to dinner.

METROPOLIS, *n.* A stronghold of provincialism.

MILLENNIUM, *n.* The period of a thousand years when the lid is to be screwed down, with all reformers on the under side.

MIND, *n.* A mysterious form of matter secreted by the brain. Its chief activity consists in the endeavor to ascertain its own nature, the futility of the attempt being due to the fact that it has nothing but itself to know itself with. From the Latin *mens,* a fact unknown to that honest shoe-seller, who, observing that his learned competitor over the way had displayed the motto *"Mens conscia recti,"* emblazoned his own shop front with the words "Men's, women's and children's conscia recti."

MINE, *adj.* Belonging to me if I can hold or seize it.

MINISTER, *n.* An agent of a higher power with a lower responsibility. In diplomacy an officer sent into a foreign country as the visible embodiment of his sovereign's hostility. His principal qualification is a degree of plausible inveracity next below that of an ambassador.

MINOR, *adj.* Less objectionable.

MIRACLE, *n.* An act or event out of the order of nature and unaccountable, as beating a normal hand of four kings and an ace with four aces and a king.

MISCREANT, *n.* A person of the highest degree of unworth. Etymologically, the word means unbeliever, and its present signification may be regarded as theology's noblest contribution to the development of our language.

MISDEMEANOR, *n.* An infraction of the law having less dignity than a felony and constituting no claim to admittance into the best criminal society.

> By misdemeanors he essayed to climb
> Into the aristocracy of crime.
> O, woe was him!—with manner chill and grand
> "Captains of industry" refused his hand,
> "Kings of finance" denied him recognition
> And "railway magnates" jeered his low condition.
> He robbed a bank to make himself respected.
> They still rebuffed him, for he was detected.
> *S. V. Hanipur.*

MISERICORDE, *n.* A dagger which in mediæval warfare was used by the foot soldier to remind an unhorsed knight that he was mortal.

MISFORTUNE, *n.* The kind of fortune that never misses.

MISS, *n.* A title with which we brand unmarried women to indicate that they are in the market. Miss, Missis (Mrs.) and Mister (Mr.) are the three most distinctly disagreeable words in the language, in sound and sense. Two are corruptions of Mistress, the other of Master. In the general abolition of social titles in this our country they miraculously escaped to plague us. If we must have them let us be consistent and give one to the unmarried man. I venture to suggest Mush, abbreviated to Mh.

MOLECULE, *n.* The ultimate, indivisible unit of matter. It is distinguished from the corpuscle, also the ultimate, indivisible unit of matter, by a closer resemblance to the atom, also the ultimate, indivisible unit of matter. Three great scientific theories of the structure of the universe are the molecular, the corpuscular and the atomic. A fourth affirms, with Haeckel, the condensation or precipitation of matter from ether —whose existence is proved by the condensation or precipitation. The present trend of scientific thought is toward the theory of ions. The ion differs from the molecule, the corpuscle and the atom in that it is an ion. A fifth theory is held by idiots, but it is doubtful if they know any more about the matter than the others.

MONAD, *n.* The ultimate, indivisible unit of matter. (See *Molecule.*) According to Leibnitz, as nearly as he seems willing to be understood, the monad has body without bulk, and mind without manifestation— Leibnitz knows him by the innate power of considering. He has founded upon him a theory of the universe, which the creature bears without resentment, for the monad is a gentleman. Small as he is, the monad contains all the powers and possibilities needful to his evolution into a German philosopher of the first class—altogether a very capable little fellow. He is not to be confounded with the microbe, or bacillus; by its inability to discern him, a good microscope shows him to be of an entirely distinct species.

MONARCH, *n.* A person engaged in reigning. Formerly the monarch ruled, as the derivation of the word attests, and as many subjects have had occasion to learn. In Russia and the Orient the monarch has still a considerable influence in public affairs and in the disposition of the human head, but in western Europe political administration is mostly entrusted to his ministers, he being somewhat preoccupied with reflections relating to the status of his own head.

MONARCHICAL GOVERNMENT, *n*. Government.

MONDAY, *n*. In Christian countries, the day after the baseball game.

MONEY, *n*. A blessing that is of no advantage to us excepting when we part with it. An evidence of culture and a passport to polite society. Supportable property.

MONKEY, *n*. An arboreal animal which makes itself at home in genealogical trees.

MONOSYLLABIC, *adj*. Composed of words of one syllable, for literary babes who never tire of testifying their delight in the vapid compound by appropriate googoogling. The words are commonly Saxon—that is to say, words of a barbarous people destitute of ideas and incapable of any but the most elementary sentiments and emotions.

> The man who writes in Saxon
> Is the man to use an ax on.
> *Judibras.*

MONSIGNOR, *n*. A high ecclesiastical title, of which the Founder of our religion overlooked the advantages.

MONUMENT, *n*. A structure intended to commemorate something which either needs no commemoration or cannot be commemorated.

> The bones of Agamemnon are a show,
> And ruined is his royal monument,

but Agamemnon's fame suffers no diminution in consequence. The monument custom has its *reductiones ad absurdum* in monuments "to the unknown dead"—that is to say, monuments to perpetuate the memory of those who have left no memory.

MORAL, *adj*. Conforming to a local and mutable standard of right. Having the quality of general expediency.

It is sayd there be a raunge of mountaynes in the Easte, on one syde of the which certayn conducts are immorall, yet on the other syde there are holden in good esteeme; wherebye the mountayneer is much conveenyenced, for it is given to him to goe downe eyther way and act as it shall suite his moode, withouten offence.—*Gooke's Meditations.*

MORE, *adj.* The comparative degree of too much.

MOUSE, *n.* An animal which strews its path with fainting women. As in Rome Christians were thrown to the lions, so centuries earlier in Otumwee, the most ancient and famous city of the world, female heretics were thrown to the mice. Jakak-Zotp, the historian, the only Otumwump whose writings have descended to us, says that these martyrs met their death with little dignity and much exertion. He even attempts to exculpate the mice (such is the malice of bigotry) by declaring that the unfortunate women perished, some from exhaustion, some of broken necks from falling over their own feet, and some from lack of restoratives. The mice, he avers, enjoyed the pleasures of the chase with composure. But if "Roman history is nine-tenths lying," we can hardly expect a smaller proportion of that rhetorical figure in the annals of a people capable of so incredible cruelty to lovely woman; for a hard heart has a false tongue.

MOUSQUETAIRE, *n.* A long glove covering a part of the arm. Worn in New Jersey. But "mousquetaire" is a mighty poor way to spell muskeeter.

MOUTH, *n.* In man, the gateway to the soul; in woman, the outlet of the heart.

MUGWUMP, *n.* In politics one afflicted with self-respect and addicted to the vice of independence. A term of contempt.

MULTITUDE, *n.* A crowd; the source of political wisdom and virtue. In a republic, the object of the statesman's adoration. "In a multitude of counsellors there is wisdom," saith the proverb. If many men of equal individual wisdom are wiser than any one of them, it must be that they acquire the excess of wisdom by the mere act of getting together. Whence comes it? Obviously from nowhere—as well say that a range of mountains is higher than the single mountains composing it. A multitude is as wise as its wisest member if it obey him; if not, it is no wiser than its most foolish.

MUMMY, *n.* An ancient Egyptian, formerly in universal use among modern civilized nations as medicine, and now engaged in supplying art with an excellent pigment. He is handy, too, in museums in gratifying the vulgar curiosity that serves to distinguish man from the lower animals.

> By means of the Mummy, mankind, it is said,
> Attests to the gods its respect for the dead.
> We plunder his tomb, be he sinner or saint,
> Distil him for physic and grind him for paint,
> Exhibit for money his poor, shrunken frame,
> And with levity flock to the scene of the shame.
> O, tell me, ye gods, for the use of my rhyme:
> For respecting the dead what's the limit of time?
> *Scopas Brune.*

MUSTANG, *n.* An indocile horse of the western plains. In English society, . the American wife of an English nobleman.

MYRMIDON, *n.* A follower of Achilles—particularly when he didn't lead.

MYTHOLOGY, *n.* The body of a primitive people's beliefs concerning its origin, early history, heroes, deities and so forth, as distinguished from the true accounts which it invents later.

N

NECTAR, *n.* A drink served at banquets of the Olympian deities. The secret of its preparation is lost, but the modern Kentuckians believe that they come pretty near to a knowledge of its chief ingredient.

Juno drank a cup of nectar,
But the draught did not affect her.
Juno drank a cup of rye—
Then she bade herself good-bye.

J. G.

NEIGHBOR, *n.* One whom we are commanded to love as ourselves, and who does all he knows how to make us disobedient.

NEPOTISM, *n.* Appointing your grandmother to office for the good of the party.

NEWTONIAN, *adj.* Pertaining to a philosophy of the universe, invented by Newton, who discovered that an apple will fall to the ground, but was unable to say why. His successors and disciples have advanced so far as to be able to say when.

NIHILIST, *n.* A Russian who denies the existence of anything but Tolstoi. The leader of the school is Tolstoi.

NIRVANA, *n.* In the Buddhist religion, a state of pleasurable annihilation awarded to the wise, particularly to those wise enough to understand it.

NOBLEMAN, *n.* Nature's provision for wealthy American maids ambitious to incur social distinction and suffer high life.

NOISE, *n.* A stench in the ear. Undomesticated music. The chief product and authenticating sign of civilization.

NOMINATE, *v.* To designate for the heaviest political assessment. To put forward a suitable person to incur the mudgobbing and deadcatting of the opposition.

NOMINEE, *n.* A modest gentleman shrinking from the distinction of private life and diligently seeking the honorable obscurity of public office.

NON-COMBATANT, *n.* A dead Quaker.

NONSENSE, *n.* The objections that are urged against this excellent dictionary.

NOSE, *n.* The extreme outpost of the face. From the circumstance that great conquerors have great noses, Getius, whose writings antedate the age of humor, calls the nose the organ of quell. It has been observed that one's nose is never so happy as when thrust into the affairs of another, from which some physiologists have drawn the inference that the nose is devoid of the sense of smell.

> There's a man with a Nose,
> And wherever he goes
> The people run from him and shout:
> "No cotton have we
> For our ears if so be
> He blow that interminous snout!"

> So the lawyers applied
> For injunction. "Denied,"
> Said the Judge: "the defendant prefixion,
> Whate'er it portend,
> Appears to transcend
> The bounds of this court's jurisdiction."
> *Arpad Singiny.*

NOTORIETY, *n.* The fame of one's competitor for public honors. The kind of renown most accessible and acceptable to mediocrity. A Jacob's-ladder leading to the vaudeville stage, with angels ascending and descending.

NOUMENON, *n.* That which exists, as distinguished from that which merely seems to exist, the latter being a phenomenon. The noumenon is a bit difficult to locate; it can be apprehended only by a process of reasoning—which is a phenomenon. Nevertheless, the discovery and exposition of noumena offer a rich field for what Lewes calls "the endless variety and excitement of philosophic thought." Hurrah (therefore) for the noumenon!

NOVEL, *n.* A short story padded. A species of composition bearing the same relation to literature that the panorama bears to art. As it is too long to be read at a sitting the impressions made by its successive parts are successively effaced, as in the panorama. Unity, totality of effect, is impossible; for besides the few pages last read all that is carried in mind is the mere plot of what has gone before. To the romance the novel is what photography is to painting. Its distinguishing principle, probability, corresponds to the literal actuality of the photograph and puts it distinctly into the category of reporting; whereas the free wing of the romancer enables him to mount to such altitudes of imagination as he may be fitted to attain; and the first three essentials of the literary art are imagination, imagination and imagination. The art of writing novels, such as it was, is long dead everywhere except in Russia, where it is new. Peace to its ashes—some of which have a large sale.

NOVEMBER, *n.* The eleventh twelfth of a weariness.

O

OATH, *n.* In law, a solemn appeal to the Deity, made binding upon the conscience by a penalty for perjury.

OBLIVION, *n.* The state or condition in which the wicked cease from struggling and the dreary are at rest. Fame's eternal dumping ground. Cold storage for high hopes. A place where ambitious authors meet their works without pride and their betters without envy. A dormitory without an alarm clock.

OBSERVATORY, *n.* A place where astronomers conjecture away the guesses of their predecessors.

OBSESSED, *pp.* Vexed by an evil spirit, like the Gadarene swine and other critics. Obsession was once more common than it is now. Arasthus tells of a peasant who was occupied by a different devil for every day in the week, and on Sundays by two. They were frequently seen, always walking in his shadow, when he had one, but were finally driven away by the village notary, a holy man; but they took the peasant with them, for he vanished utterly. A devil thrown out of a woman by the Archbishop of Rheims ran through the streets, pursued by a hundred persons, until the open country was reached, where by a leap higher than a church spire he escaped into a bird. A chaplain in Cromwell's army exorcised a soldier's obsessing devil by throwing the soldier into the water, when the devil came to the surface. The soldier, unfortunately, did not.

OBSOLETE, *adj.* No longer used by the timid. Said chiefly of words. A word which some lexicographer has marked obsolete is ever thereafter an object of dread and loathing to the fool writer, but if it is a good word and has no exact modern equivalent equally good, it is good enough for the good writer. Indeed, a writer's attitude toward "obsolete" words is as true a measure of his literary ability as anything except the character of his work. A dictionary of obsolete and obsolescent words would not only be singularly rich in strong and sweet parts of speech; it would add large possessions to the vocabulary of every competent writer who might not happen to be a competent reader.

OBSTINATE, *adj.* Inaccessible to the truth as it is manifest in the splendor and stress of our advocacy.

The popular type and exponent of obstinacy is the mule, a most intelligent animal.

OCCASIONAL, *adj.* Afflicting us with greater or less frequency. That, however, is not the sense in which the word is used in the phrase "occasional verses," which are verses written for an "occasion," such as an anniversary, a celebration or other event. True, they afflict us a little worse than other sorts of verse, but their name has no reference to irregular recurrence.

OCCIDENT, *n.* The part of the world lying west (or east) of the Orient. It is largely inhabited by Christians, a powerful sub-tribe of the Hypocrites, whose principal industries are murder and cheating, which they are pleased to call "war" and "commerce." These, also, are the principal industries of the Orient.

OCEAN, *n.* A body of water occupying about two-thirds of a world made for man—who has no gills.

OFFENSIVE, *adj.* Generating disagreeable emotions or sensations, as the advance of an army against its enemy.

"Were the enemy's tactics offensive?" the king asked. "I should say so!" replied the unsuccessful general. "The blackguard wouldn't come out of his works!"

OLD, *adj.* In that stage of usefulness which is not inconsistent with general inefficiency, as an *old man.* Discredited by lapse of time and offensive to the popular taste, as an *old* book.

"Old books? The devil take them!" Goby said.
"Fresh every day must be my books and bread."
Nature herself approves the Goby rule
And gives us every moment a fresh fool.

Harley Shum.

OLEAGINOUS, *adj.* Oily, smooth, sleek.

Disraeli once described the manner of Bishop Wilberforce as "unctuous, oleaginous, saponaceous." And the good prelate was ever afterward known as Soapy Sam. For every man there is something in the vocabulary that would stick to him like a second skin. His enemies have only to find it.

OLYMPIAN, *adj.* Relating to a mountain in Thessaly, once inhabited by gods, now a repository of yellowing newspapers, beer bottles and mutilated sardine cans, attesting the presence of the tourist and his appetite.

His name the smirking tourist scrawls
Upon Minerva's temple walls,
Where thundered once Olympian Zeus,
And marks his appetite's abuse.

Averil Joop.

OMEN, *n.* A sign that something will happen if nothing happens.

ONCE, *adv.* Enough.

OPERA, *n.* A play representing life in another world, whose inhabitants have no speech but song, no motions but gestures and no postures but attitudes. All acting is simulation, and the word *simulation* is from *simia,* an ape; but in opera the actor takes for his model *Simia audibilis* (or *Pithecanthropos stentor*)—the ape that howls.

> The actor apes a man—at least in shape;
> The opera performer apes an ape.

OPIATE, *n.* An unlocked door in the prison of Identity. It leads into the jail yard.

OPPORTUNITY, *n.* A favorable occasion for grasping a disappointment.

OPPOSE, *v.* To assist with obstructions and objections.

> How lonely he who thinks to vex
> With badinage the Solemn Sex!
> Of levity, Mere Man, beware;
> None but the Grave deserve the Unfair.
> > *Percy P. Orminder.*

OPPOSITION, *n.* In politics the party that prevents the Government from running amuck by hamstringing it.

The King of Ghargaroo, who had been abroad to study the science of government, appointed one hundred of his fattest subjects as members of a parliament to make laws for the collection of revenue. Forty of these he named the Party of Opposition and had his Prime Minister carefully instruct them in their duty of opposing every royal measure. Nevertheless, the first one that was submitted passed unanimously. Greatly displeased, the King vetoed it, informing the Opposition that if they did that again they would pay for their obstinacy with their heads. The entire forty promptly disemboweled themselves.

"What shall we do now?" the King asked. "Liberal institutions cannot be maintained without a party of Opposition."

"Splendor of the universe," replied the Prime Minister, "it is true these dogs of darkness have no longer their credentials, but all is not lost. Leave the matter to this worm of the dust."

So the Minister had the bodies of his Majesty's Opposition embalmed and stuffed with straw, put back into the seats of power and nailed there. Forty votes were recorded against every bill and the nation prospered. But one day a bill imposing a tax on warts was defeated—the members of the Government party had not been nailed to their seats! This so enraged the King that the Prime Minister was put to death, the parliament was dissolved with a battery of artillery, and government of the people, by the people, for the people perished from Ghargaroo.

OPTIMISM, *n.* The doctrine, or belief, that everything is beautiful, including what is ugly, everything good, especially the bad, and everything right that is wrong. It is held with greatest tenacity by those most accustomed to the mischance of falling into adversity, and is most acceptably expounded with the grin that apes a smile. Being a blind faith, it is inaccessible to the light of disproof—an intellectual disorder, yielding to no treatment but death. It is hereditary, but fortunately not contagious.

OPTIMIST, *n.* A proponent of the doctrine that black is white.

A pessimist applied to God for relief.

"Ah, you wish me to restore your hope and cheerfulness," said God.

"No," replied the petitioner, "I wish you to create something that would justify them."

"The world is all created," said God, "but you have overlooked something—the mortality of the optimist."

ORATORY, *n.* A conspiracy between speech and action to cheat the understanding. A tyranny tempered by stenography.

ORPHAN, *n.* A living person whom death has deprived of the power of filial ingratitude—a privation appealing with a particular eloquence to all that is sympathetic in human nature. When young the orphan is commonly sent to an asylum, where by careful cultivation of its rudimentary sense of locality it is taught to know its place. It is then instructed in the arts of dependence and servitude and eventually turned loose to prey upon the world as a bootblack or scullery maid.

ORTHODOX, *n.* An ox wearing the popular religious yoke.

ORTHOGRAPHY, *n.* The science of spelling by the eye instead of the ear. Advocated with more heat than light by the outmates of every asylum for the insane. They have had to concede a few things since the time of Chaucer, but are none the less hot in defence of those to be conceded hereafter.

> A spelling reformer indicted
> For fudge was before the court cicted.
> The judge said: "Enough—
> His candle we'll snough,
> And his sepulchre shall not be whicted."

OSTRICH, *n.* A large bird to which (for its sins, doubtless) nature has denied that hinder toe in which so many pious naturalists have seen a conspicuous evidence of design. The absence of a good working pair of wings is no defect, for, as has been ingeniously pointed out, the ostrich does not fly.

OTHERWISE, *adv.* No better.

OUTCOME, *n.* A particular type of disappointment. By the kind of intelligence that sees in an exception a proof of the rule the wisdom of an act is judged by the outcome, the result. This is immortal nonsense; the wisdom of an act is to be judged by the light that the doer had when he performed it.

OUTDO, *v. t.* To make an enemy.

OUT-OF-DOORS, *n.* That part of one's environment upon which no government has been able to collect taxes. Chiefly useful to inspire poets.

> I climbed to the top of a mountain one day
>   To see the sun setting in glory,
> And I thought, as I looked at his vanishing ray,
>   Of a perfectly splendid story.

> 'Twas about an old man and the ass he bestrode
>   Till the strength of the beast was o'ertested;
> Then the man would carry him miles on the road
>   Till Neddy was pretty well rested.

> The moon rising solemnly over the crest
>   Of the hills to the east of my station

Displayed her broad disk to the darkening west
  Like a visible new creation.

And I thought of a joke (and I laughed till I cried)
  Of an idle young woman who tarried
About a church-door for a look at the bride,
  Although 'twas herself that was married.

To poets all Nature is pregnant with grand
  Ideas—with thought and emotion.
I pity the dunces who don't understand
  The speech of earth, heaven and ocean.

                                        Stromboli Smith.

OVATION, *n.* In ancient Rome, a definite, formal pageant in honor of one who had been disserviceable to the enemies of the nation. A lesser "triumph." In modern English the word is improperly used to signify any loose and spontaneous expression of popular homage to the hero of the hour and place.

"I had an ovation!" the actor man said,
    But I thought it uncommonly queer,
That people and critics by him had been led
    By the ear.

The Latin lexicon makes his absurd
    Assertion as plain as a peg;
In "ovum" we find the true root of the word.
    It means egg.

                                        Dudley Spink.

OVEREAT, *v.* To dine.

Hail, Gastronome, Apostle of Excess,
Well skilled to overeat without distress!
Thy great invention, the unfatal feast,
Shows Man's superiority to Beast.

                                        John Boop.

OVERWORK, *n.* A dangerous disorder affecting high public functionaries who want to go fishing.

OWE, *v.* To have (and to hold) a debt. The word formerly signified not indebtedness, but possession; it meant "own," and in the minds of debtors there is still a good deal of confusion between assets and liabilities.

OYSTER, *n.* A slimy, gobby shellfish which civilization gives men the hardihood to eat without removing its entrails! The shells are sometimes given to the poor.

P

PAIN, *n.* An uncomfortable frame of mind that may have a physical basis in something that is being done to the body, or may be purely mental, caused by the good fortune of another.

PAINTING, *n.* The art of protecting flat surfaces from the weather and exposing them to the critic.

Formerly, painting and sculpture were combined in the same work: the ancients painted their statues. The only present alliance between the two arts is that the modern painter chisels his patrons.

PALACE, *n.* A fine and costly residence, particularly that of a great official. The residence of a high dignitary of the Christian Church is called a palace; that of the Founder of his religion was known as a field, or wayside. There is progress.

PALM, *n.* A species of tree having several varieties, of which the familiar "itching palm" (*Palma hominis*) is most widely distributed and sedulously cultivated. This noble vegetable exudes a kind of invisible gum, which may be detected by applying to the bark a piece of gold or silver. The metal will adhere with remarkable tenacity. The fruit of the itching palm is so bitter and unsatisfying that a considerable percentage of it is sometimes given away in what are known as "benefactions."

PALMISTRY, *n.* The 947th method (according to Mimbleshaw's classification) of obtaining money by false pretences. It consists in "reading character" in the wrinkles made by closing the hand. The pretence is not altogether false; character can really be read very accurately in this way, for the wrinkles in every hand submitted plainly spell the word "dupe." The imposture consists in not reading it aloud.

PANDEMONIUM, *n*. Literally, the Place of All the Demons. Most of them have escaped into politics and finance, and the place is now used as a lecture hall by the Audible Reformer. When disturbed by his voice the ancient echoes clamor appropriate responses most gratifying to his pride of distinction.

PANTALOONS, *n*. A nether habiliment of the adult civilized male. The garment is tubular and unprovided with hinges at the points of flexion. Supposed to have been invented by a humorist. Called "trousers" by the enlightened and "pants" by the unworthy.

PANTHEISM, *n*. The doctrine that everything is God, in contradistinction to the doctrine that God is everything.

PANTOMIME, *n*. A play in which the story is told without violence to the language. The least disagreeable form of dramatic action.

PARDON, *v*. To remit a penalty and restore to a life of crime. To add to the lure of crime the temptation of ingratitude.

PASSPORT, *n*. A document treacherously inflicted upon a citizen going abroad, exposing him as an alien and pointing him out for special reprobation and outrage.

PAST, *n*. That part of Eternity with some small fraction of which we have a slight and regrettable acquaintance. A moving line called the Present parts it from an imaginary period known as the Future. These two grand divisions of Eternity, of which the one is continually effacing the other, are entirely unlike. The one is dark with sorrow and disappointment, the other bright with prosperity and joy. The Past is the region of sobs, the Future is the realm of song. In the one crouches Memory, clad in sackcloth and ashes, mumbling penitential prayer; in the sunshine of the other Hope flies with a free wing, beckoning to temples of success and bowers of ease. Yet the Past is the Future of yesterday, the Future is the Past of to-morrow. They are one—the knowledge and the dream.

PASTIME, *n.* A device for promoting dejection. Gentle exercise for intellectual debility.

PATIENCE, *n.* A minor form of despair, disguised as a virtue.

PATRIOT, *n.* One to whom the interests of a part seem superior to those of the whole. The dupe of statesmen and the tool of conquerors.

PATRIOTISM, *n.* Combustible rubbish ready to the torch of any one ambitious to illuminate his name.

In Dr. Johnson's famous dictionary patriotism is defined as the last resort of a scoundrel. With all due respect to an enlightened but inferior lexicographer I beg to submit that it is the first.

PEACE, *n.* In international affairs, a period of cheating between two periods of fighting.

> O, what's the loud uproar assailing
>   Mine ears without cease?
> 'Tis the voice of the hopeful, all-hailing
>   The horrors of peace.
>
> Ah, Peace Universal; they woo it—
>   Would marry it, too.
> If only they knew how to do it
>   'Twere easy to do.
>
> They're working by night and by day
>   On their problem, like moles.
> Have mercy, O Heaven, I pray,
>   On their meddlesome souls!
>   *Ro Amil.*

PEDESTRIAN, *n.* The variable (and audible) part of the roadway for an automobile.

PEDIGREE, *n.* The known part of the route from an arboreal ancestor with a swim bladder to an urban descendant with a cigarette.

PENITENT, *adj.* Undergoing or awaiting punishment.

PERFECTION, *n.* An imaginary state or quality distinguished from the actual by an element known as excellence; an attribute of the critic.

The editor of an English magazine having received a letter pointing out the erroneous nature of his views and style, and signed "Perfection," promptly wrote at the foot of the letter: "I don't agree with you," and mailed it to Matthew Arnold.

PERIPATETIC, *adj.* Walking about. Relating to the philosophy of Aristotle, who, while expounding it, moved from place to place in order to avoid his pupil's objections. A needless precaution—they knew no more of the matter than he.

PERORATION, *n.* The explosion of an oratorical rocket. It dazzles, but to an observer having the wrong kind of nose its most conspicuous peculiarity is the smell of the several kinds of powder used in preparing it.

PERSEVERANCE, *n.* A lowly virtue whereby mediocrity achieves an inglorious success.

> "Persevere, persevere!" cry the homilists all,
> Themselves, day and night, persevering to bawl.
> "Remember the fable of tortoise and hare—
> The one at the goal while the other is—where?"
> Why, back there in Dreamland, renewing his lease
> Of life, all his muscles preserving the peace,
> The goal and the rival forgotten alike,
> And the long fatigue of the needless hike.
> His spirit a-squat in the grass and the dew
> Of the dogless Land beyond the Stew,
> He sleeps, like a saint in a holy place,
> A winner of all that is good in a race.
>
> *Sukker Uffro.*

PESSIMISM, *n.* A philosophy forced upon the convictions of the observer by the disheartening prevalence of the optimist with his scarecrow hope and his unsightly smile.

PHILANTHROPIST, *n.* A rich (and usually bald) old gentleman who has trained himself to grin while his conscience is picking his pocket.

PHILISTINE, *n.* One whose mind is the creature of its environment, following the fashion in thought, feeling and sentiment. He is sometimes learned, frequently prosperous, commonly clean and always solemn.

PHILOSOPHY, *n.* A route of many roads leading from nowhere to nothing.

PHONOGRAPH, *n.* An irritating toy that restores life to dead noises.

PHOTOGRAPH, *n.* A picture painted by the sun without instruction in art. It is a little better than the work of an Apache, but not quite so good as that of a Cheyenne.

PHRENOLOGY, *n.* The science of picking the pocket through the scalp. It consists in locating and exploiting the organ that one is a dupe with.

PHYSICIAN, *n.* One upon whom we set our hopes when ill and our dogs when well.

PHYSIOGNOMY, *n.* The art of determining the character of another by the resemblances and differences between his face and our own, which is the standard of excellence.

> "There is no art," says Shakespeare, foolish man,
> "To read the mind's construction in the face."
> The physiognomists his portrait scan,
> And say: "How little wisdom here we trace!
> He knew his face disclosed his mind and heart,
> So, in his own defence, denied our art."
> *Lavatar Shunk.*

PIANO, *n.* A parlor utensil for subduing the impenitent visitor. It is operated by depressing the keys of the machine and the spirits of the audience.

PICTURE, *n.* A representation in two dimensions of something wearisome in three.

> "Behold great Daubert's picture here on view—
> Taken from Life." If that description's true,
> Grant, heavenly Powers, that I be taken, too.
> *Jali Hane.*

PIE, *n.* An advance agent of the reaper whose name is Indigestion.

> Cold pie was highly esteemed by the remains.—*The Rev. Dr. Mucker, in a Funeral Sermon Over a British Nobleman.*

> Cold pie is a detestable
> American comestible.
> That's why I'm done—or undone—
> So far from that dear London.
> —*From the Headstone of a British Nobleman, in Kalamazoo.*

PIETY, *n.* Reverence for the Supreme Being, based upon His supposed resemblance to man.

> The pig is taught by sermons and epistles
> To think the God of Swine has snout and bristles.
> *Judibras.*

PIG, *n.* An animal (*Porcus omnivorus*) closely allied to the human race by the splendor and vivacity of its appetite, which, however, is inferior in scope, for it sticks at pig.

PIGMY, *n.* One of a tribe of very small men found by ancient travelers in many parts of the world, but by modern in Central Africa only. The Pigmies are so called to distinguish them from the bulkier Caucasians—who are Hogmies.

PILGRIM, *n.* A traveler that is taken seriously. A Pilgrim Father was one who, leaving Europe in 1620 because not permitted to sing psalms through his nose, followed it to Massachusetts, where he could personate God according to the dictates of his conscience.

PILLORY, *n.* A mechanical device for inflicting personal distinction—prototype of the modern newspaper conducted by persons of austere virtues and blameless lives.

PIRACY, *n.* Commerce without its folly-swaddles, just as God made it.

PITIFUL, *adj.* The state of an enemy or opponent after an imaginary encounter with oneself.

PITY, *n.* A failing sense of exemption, inspired by contrast.

PLAGIARISM, *n.* A literary coincidence compounded of a discreditable priority and an honorable subsequence.

PLAGIARIZE, *v.* To take the thought or style of another writer whom one has never, never read.

PLAGUE, *n.* In ancient times a general punishment of the innocent for admonition of their ruler, as in the familiar instance of Pharaoh the Immune. The plague as we of to-day have the happiness to know it is merely Nature's fortuitous manifestation of her purposeless objectionableness.

PLAN, *v. t.* To bother about the best method of accomplishing an accidental result.

PLATITUDE, *n.* The fundamental element and special glory of popular literature. A thought that snores in words that smoke. The wisdom of a million fools in the diction of a dullard. A fossil sentiment in artificial rock. A moral without the fable. All that is mortal of a departed truth. A demi-tasse of milk-and-morality. The Pope's-nose of a featherless peacock. A jelly-fish withering on the shore of the sea of thought. The cackle surviving the egg. A desiccated epigram.

PLATONIC, *adj.* Pertaining to the philosophy of Socrates. Platonic Love is a fool's name for the affection between a disability and a frost.

PLAUDITS, *n.* Coins with which the populace pays those who tickle and devour it.

PLEASE, *v.* To lay the foundation for a superstructure of imposition.

PLEASURE, *n.* The least hateful form of dejection.

PLEBEIAN, *n.* An ancient Roman who in the blood of his country stained nothing but his hands. Distinguished from the Patrician, who was a saturated solution.

PLEBISCITE, *n.* A popular vote to ascertain the will of the sovereign.

PLENIPOTENTIARY, *adj.* Having full power. A Minister Plenipotentiary is a diplomatist possessing absolute authority on condition that he never exert it.

PLEONASM, *n.* An army of words escorting a corporal of thought.

PLOW, *n.* An implement that cries aloud for hands accustomed to the pen.

PLUNDER, *v.* To take the property of another without observing the decent and customary reticences of theft. To effect a change of ownership with the candid concomitance of a brass band. To wrest the wealth of A from B and leave C lamenting a vanished opportunity.

POCKET, *n.* The cradle of motive and the grave of conscience. In woman this organ is lacking; so she acts without motive, and her conscience, denied burial, remains ever alive, confessing the sins of others.

POETRY, *n.* A form of expression peculiar to the Land beyond the Magazines.

POKER, *n.* A game said to be played with cards for some purpose to this lexicographer unknown.

POLICE, *n.* An armed force for protection and participation.

POLITENESS, *n.* The most acceptable hypocrisy.

POLITICS, *n.* A strife of interests masquerading as a contest of principles. The conduct of public affairs for private advantage.

POLITICIAN, *n.* An eel in the fundamental mud upon which the super-structure of organized society is reared. When he wriggles he mistakes the agitation of his tail for the trembling of the edifice. As compared with the statesman, he suffers the disadvantage of being alive.

POLYGAMY, *n.* A house of atonement, or expiatory chapel, fitted with several stools of repentance, as distinguished from monogamy, which has but one.

POPULIST, *n.* A fossil patriot of the early agricultural period, found in the old red soapstone underlying Kansas; characterized by an uncommon spread of ear, which some naturalists contend gave him the power of flight, though Professors Morse and Whitney, pursuing independent lines of thought, have ingeniously pointed out that had he possessed it he would have gone elsewhere. In the picturesque speech of his period, some fragments of which have come down to us, he was known as "The Matter with Kansas."

PORTABLE, *adj.* Exposed to a mutable ownership through vicissitudes of possession.

> His light estate, if neither he did make it
> Nor yet its former guardian forsake it,
> Is portable improperty, I take it.
> *Worgum Slupsky.*

PORTUGUESE, *n. pl.* A species of geese indigenous to Portugal. They are mostly without feathers and imperfectly edible, even when stuffed with garlic.

POSITIVE, *adj.* Mistaken at the top of one's voice.

POSITIVISM, *n.* A philosophy that denies our knowledge of the Real and affirms our ignorance of the Apparent. Its longest exponent is Comte, its broadest Mill and its thickest Spencer.

POSTERITY, *n.* An appellate court which reverses the judgment of a popular author's contemporaries, the appellant being his obscure competitor.

POTABLE, *n.* Suitable for drinking. Water is said to be potable; indeed, some declare it our natural beverage, although even they find it palatable only when suffering from the recurrent disorder known as thirst, for which it is a medicine. Upon nothing has so great and diligent ingenuity been brought to bear in all ages and in all countries, except the most uncivilized, as upon the invention of substitutes for water. To hold that this general aversion to that liquid has no basis in the preservative instinct of the race is to be unscientific—and without science we are as the snakes and toads.

POVERTY, *n.* A file provided for the teeth of the rats of reform. The number of plans for its abolition equals that of the reformers who suffer from it, plus that of the philosophers who know nothing about it. Its victims are distinguished by possession of all the virtues and by their faith in leaders seeking to conduct them into a prosperity where they believe these to be unknown.

PRAY, *v.* To ask that the laws of the universe be annulled in behalf of a single petitioner confessedly unworthy.

PRE-ADAMITE, *n.* One of an experimental and apparently unsatisfactory race that antedated Creation and lived under conditions not easily conceived. Melsius believed them to have inhabited "the Void" and to have been something intermediate between fishes and birds. Little is known of them beyond the fact that they supplied Cain with a wife and theologians with a controversy.

PRECEDENT, *n.* In Law, a previous decision, rule or practice which, in the absence of a definite statute, has whatever force and authority a Judge may choose to give it, thereby greatly simplifying his task of doing as he pleases. As there are precedents for everything, he has only to ignore those that make against his interest and accentuate those in the line of his desire. Invention of the precedent elevates the trial-at-law from the low estate of a fortuitous ordeal to the noble attitude of a dirigible arbitrament.

PRECIPITATE, *adj.* Anteprandial.
> Precipitate in all, this sinner
> Took action first, and then his dinner.
> *Judibras.*

PREDESTINATION, *n.* The doctrine that all things occur according to programme. This doctrine should not be confused with that of foreordination, which means that all things are programmed, but does not affirm their occurrence, that being only an implication from other doctrines by which this is entailed. The difference is great enough to have deluged Christendom with ink, to say nothing of the gore. With the distinction of the two doctrines kept well in mind, and a reverent belief in both, one may hope to escape perdition if spared.

PREDICAMENT, *n.* The wage of consistency.

PREDILECTION, *n.* The preparatory stage of disillusion.

PRE-EXISTENCE, *n.* An unnoted factor in creation.

PREFERENCE, *n.* A sentiment, or frame of mind, induced by the erroneous belief that one thing is better than another.

An ancient philosopher, expounding his conviction that life is no better than death, was asked by a disciple why, then, he did not die. "Because," he replied, "death is no better than life."

It is longer.

PREHISTORIC, *adj.* Belonging to an early period and a museum. Antedating the art and practice of perpetuating falsehood.

> He lived in a period prehistoric,
> When all was absurd and phantasmagoric.
> Born later, when Clio, celestial recorder,
> Set down great events in succession and order,
> He surely had seen nothing droll or fortuitous
> In anything here but the lies that she threw at us.
>   *Orpheus Bowen.*

PREJUDICE, *n.* A vagrant opinion without visible means of support.

PRELATE, *n.* A church officer having a superior degree of holiness and a fat preferment. One of Heaven's aristocracy. A gentleman of God.

PREROGATIVE, *n.* A sovereign's right to do wrong.

PRESBYTERIAN, *n.* One who holds the conviction that the governing authorities of the Church should be called presbyters.

PRESCRIPTION, *n*. A physician's guess at what will best prolong the situation with least harm to the patient.

PRESENT, *n*. That part of eternity dividing the domain of disappointment from the realm of hope.

PRESENTABLE, *adj*. Hideously appareled after the manner of the time and place.

In Boorioboola-Gha a man is presentable on occasions of ceremony if he have his abdomen painted a bright blue and wear a cow's tail; in New York he may, if it please him, omit the paint, but after sunset he must wear two tails made of the wool of a sheep and dyed black.

PRESIDE, *v*. To guide the action of a deliberative body to a desirable result. In Journalese, to perform upon a musical instrument; as, "He presided at the piccolo."

    The Headliner, holding the copy in hand,
      Read with a solemn face:
    "The music was very uncommonly grand—
      The best that was ever provided,
      For our townsman Brown presided
    At the organ with skill and grace."
    The Headliner discontinued to read,
      And, spreading the paper down
    On the desk, he dashed in at the top of the screed:
    "Great playing by President Brown."
                  Orpheus Bowen.

PRESIDENCY, *n*. The greased pig in the field game of American politics.

PRESIDENT, *n*. The leading figure in a small group of men of whom—and of whom only—it is positively known that immense numbers of their countrymen did not want any of them for President.

    If that's an honor surely 'tis a greater
    To have been a simple and undamned spectator.
    Behold in me a man of mark and note
    Whom no elector e'er denied a vote!—
    An undiscredited, unhooted gent
    Who might, for all we know, be President
    By acclamation. Cheer, ye varlets, cheer—

I'm passing with a wide and open ear!
Jonathan Fomry.

PREVARICATOR, *n.* A liar in the caterpillar state.

PRICE, *n.* Value, plus a reasonable sum for the wear and tear of conscience in demanding it.

PRIMATE, *n.* The head of a church, especially a State church supported by involuntary contributions. The Primate of England is the Archbishop of Canterbury, an amiable old gentleman, who occupies Lambeth Palace when living and Westminster Abbey when dead. He is commonly dead.

PRISON, *n.* A place of punishments and rewards. The poet assures us that—
        "Stone walls do not a prison make,"
but a combination of the stone wall, the political parasite and the moral instructor is no garden of sweets.

PRIVATE, *n.* A military gentleman with a field-marshal's baton in his knapsack and an impediment in his hope.

PROBOSCIS, *n.* The rudimentary organ of an elephant which serves him in place of the knife-and-fork that Evolution has as yet denied him. For purposes of humor it is popularly called a trunk.
    Asked how he knew that an elephant was going on a journey, the illustrious Jo. Miller cast a reproachful look upon his tormentor, and answered, absently: "When it is ajar," and threw himself from a high promontory into the sea. Thus perished in his pride the most famous humorist of antiquity, leaving to mankind a heritage of woe! No successor worthy of the title has appeared, though Mr. Edward Bok, of *The Ladies' Home Journal,* is much respected for the purity and sweetness of his personal character.

PROJECTILE, *n.* The final arbiter in international disputes. Formerly these disputes were settled by physical contact of the disputants, with such simple arguments as the rudimentary logic of the times could supply

—the sword, the spear, and so forth. With the growth of prudence in military affairs the projectile came more and more into favor, and is now held in high esteem by the most courageous. Its capital defect is that it requires personal attendance at the point of propulsion.

PROOF, *n.* Evidence having a shade more of plausibility than of unlikelihood. The testimony of two credible witnesses as opposed to that of only one.

PROOF-READER, *n.* A malefactor who atones for making your writing nonsense by permitting the compositor to make it unintelligible.

PROPERTY, *n.* Any material thing, having no particular value, that may be held by A against the cupidity of B. Whatever gratifies the passion for possession in one and disappoints it in all others. The object of man's brief rapacity and long indifference.

PROPHECY, *n.* The art and practice of selling one's credibility for future delivery.

PROSPECT, *n.* An outlook, usually forbidding. An expectation, usually forbidden.

> Blow, blow, ye spicy breezes—
> O'er Ceylon blow your breath,
> Where every prospect pleases,
> Save only that of death.
> *Bishop Sheber.*

PROVIDENTIAL, *adj.* Unexpectedly and conspicuously beneficial to the person so describing it.

PRUDE, *n.* A bawd hiding behind the back of her demeanor.

PUBLISH, *v.* In literary affairs, to become the fundamental element in a cone of critics.

PUSH, *n.* One of the two things mainly conducive to success, especially in politics. The other is Pull.

PYRRHONISM, *n.* An ancient philosophy, named for its inventor. It consisted of an absolute disbelief in everything but Pyrrhonism. Its modern professors have added that.

Q

QUEEN, *n.* A woman by whom the realm is ruled when there is a king, and through whom it is ruled when there is not.

QUILL, *n.* An implement of torture yielded by a goose and commonly wielded by an ass. This use of the quill is now obsolete, but its modern equivalent, the steel pen, is wielded by the same everlasting Presence.

QUIVER, *n.* A portable sheath in which the ancient statesman and the aboriginal lawyer carried their lighter arguments.

> He extracted from his quiver,
> Did this controversial Roman,
> An argument well fitted
> To the question as submitted,
> Then addressed it to the liver,
> Of the unpersuaded foeman.
> *Oglum P. Boomp.*

QUIXOTIC, *adj.* Absurdly chivalric, like Don Quixote. An insight into the beauty and excellence of this incomparable adjective is unhappily denied to him who has the misfortune to know that the gentleman's name is pronounced Ke-ho-tay.

> When ignorance from out our lives can banish
> Philology, 'tis folly to know Spanish.
> *Juan Smith.*

QUORUM, *n.* A sufficient number of members of a deliberative body to have their own way and their own way of having it. In the United

States Senate a quorum consists of the chairman of the Committee on Finance and a messenger from the White House; in the House of Representatives, of the Speaker and the devil.

QUOTATION, *n.* The act of repeating erroneously the words of another. The words erroneously repeated.

> Intent on making his quotation truer,
> He sought the page infallible of Brewer,
> Then made a solemn vow that he would be
> Condemned eternally. Ah, me, ah, me!
>
> *Stumpo Gaker.*

QUOTIENT, *n.* A number showing how many times a sum of money belonging to one person is contained in the pocket of another—usually about as many times as it can be got there.

R

RABBLE, *n.* In a republic, those who exercise a supreme authority tempered by fraudulent elections. The rabble is like the sacred Simurgh, of Arabian fable—omnipotent on condition that it do nothing. (The word is Aristocratese, but has no exact equivalent in our tongue, but means, as nearly as may be, "soaring swine.")

RACK, *n.* An argumentative implement formerly much used in persuading devotees of a false faith to embrace the living truth. As a call to the unconverted the rack never had any particular efficacy, and is now held in light popular esteem.

RANK, *n.* Relative elevation in the scale of human worth.

> He held at court a rank so high
> That other noblemen asked why.

"Because," 'twas answered, "others lack
His skill to scratch the royal back."
Aramis Jukes.

RANSOM, *n.* The purchase of that which neither belongs to the seller, nor can belong to the buyer. The most unprofitable of investments.

RAPACITY, *n.* Providence without industry. The thrift of power.

RAREBIT, *n.* A Welsh rabbit, in the speech of the humorless, who point out that it is not a rabbit. To whom it may be solemnly explained that the comestible known as toad-in-a-hole is really not a toad, and that *riz-de-veau à la financière* is not the smile of a calf prepared after the recipe of a she banker.

RASCAL, *n.* A fool considered under another aspect.

RASCALITY, *n.* Stupidity militant. The activity of a clouded intellect.

RASH, *adj.* Insensible to the value of our advice.
"Now lay your bet with mine, nor let
These gamblers take your cash."
"Nay, this child makes no bet." "Great snakes!
How can you be so rash?"
Bootle P. Gish.

RATIONAL, *adj.* Devoid of all delusions save those of observation, experience and reflection.

RATTLESNAKE, *n.* Our prostrate brother, *Homo ventrambulans.*

REACH, *n.* The radius of action of the human hand. The area within which it is possible (and customary) to gratify directly the propensity to provide.
This is a truth, as old as the hills,
That life and experience teach:
The poor man suffers that keenest of ills,
An impediment in his reach.
G. J.

READING, *n.* The general body of what one reads. In our country it consists, as a rule, of Indiana novels, short stories in "dialect" and humor in slang.

> We know by one's reading
> His learning and breeding;
> By what draws his laughter
> We know his Hereafter.
> Read nothing, laugh never—
> The Sphinx was less clever!
>
> *Jupiter Muke.*

RADICALISM, *n.* The conservatism of to-morrow injected into the affairs of to-day.

RADIUM, *n.* A mineral that gives off heat and stimulates the organ that a scientist is a fool with.

RAILROAD, *n.* The chief of many mechanical devices enabling us to get away from where we are to where we are no better off. For this purpose the railroad is held in highest favor by the optimist, for it permits him to make the transit with great expedition.

RAMSHACKLE, *adj.* Pertaining to a certain order of architecture, otherwise known as the Normal American. Most of the public buildings of the United States are of the Ramshackle order, though some of our earlier architects preferred the Ironic. Recent additions to the White House in Washington are Theo-Doric, the ecclesiastic order of the Dorians. They are exceedingly fine and cost one hundred dollars a brick.

REALISM, *n.* The art of depicting nature as it is seen by toads. The charm suffusing a landscape painted by a mole, or a story written by a measuring-worm.

REALITY, *n.* The dream of a mad philosopher. That which would remain in the cupel if one should assay a phantom. The nucleus of a vacuum.

REALLY, *adv.* Apparently.

REAR, *n.* In American military matters, that exposed part of the army that is nearest to Congress.

REASON, *v. i.* To weigh probabilities in the scales of desire.

REASON, *n.* Propensitate of prejudice.

REASONABLE, *adj.* Accessible to the infection of our own opinions. Hospitable to persuasion, dissuasion and evasion.

REBEL, *n.* A proponent of a new misrule who has failed to establish it.

RECOLLECT, *v.* To recall with additions something not previously known.

RECONCILIATION, *n.* A suspension of hostilities. An armed truce for the purpose of digging up the dead.

RECONSIDER, *v.* To seek a justification for a decision already made.

RECOUNT, *n.* In American politics, another throw of the dice, accorded to the player against whom they are loaded.

RECREATION, *n.* A particular kind of dejection to relieve a general fatigue.

RECRUIT, *n.* A person distinguishable from a civilian by his uniform and from a soldier by his gait.
> Fresh from the farm or factory or street,
> His marching, in pursuit or in retreat,
> Were an impressive martial spectacle
> Except for two impediments—his feet.
> *Thompson Johnson.*

RECTOR, *n.* In the Church of England, the Third Person of the parochial Trinity, the Curate and the Vicar being the other two.

REDEMPTION, *n.* Deliverance of sinners from the penalty of their sin, through their murder of the deity against whom they sinned. The doctrine of Redemption is the fundamental mystery of our holy religion, and whoso believeth in it shall not perish, but have everlasting life in which to try to understand it.

> We must awake Man's spirit from its sin,
>   And take some special measure for redeeming it;
> Though hard indeed the task to get it in
>   Among the angels any way but teaming it,
>   Or purify it otherwise than steaming it.
> I'm awkward at Redemption—a beginner:
> My method is to crucify the sinner.
>   *Golgo Brone.*

REDRESS, *n.* Reparation without satisfaction.

Among the Anglo-Saxons a subject conceiving himself wronged by the king was permitted, on proving his injury, to beat a brazen image of the royal offender with a switch that was afterward applied to his own naked back. The latter rite was performed by the public hangman, and it assured moderation in the plaintiff's choice of a switch.

RED-SKIN, *n.* A North American Indian, whose skin is not red—at least not on the outside.

REDUNDANT, *adj.* Superfluous; needless; *de trop.*

> The Sultan said: "There's evidence abundant
> To prove this unbelieving dog redundant."
> To whom the Grand Vizier, with mien impressive,
> Replied: "His head, at least, appears excessive."
>   *Habeeb Suleiman.*

Mr. Debs is a redundant citizen.—*Theodore Roosevelt.*

REFERENDUM, *n.* A law for submission of proposed legislation to a popular vote to learn the nonsensus of public opinion.

REFLECTION, *n.* An action of the mind whereby we obtain a clearer view of our relation to the things of yesterday and are able to avoid the perils that we shall not again encounter.

REFORM, *n.* A thing that mostly satisfies reformers opposed to reformation.

REFUGE, *n.* Anything assuring protection to one in peril. Moses and Joshua provided six cities of refuge—Bezer, Golan, Ramoth, Kadesh, Schekem and Hebron—to which one who had taken life inadvertently could flee when hunted by relatives of the deceased. This admirable expedient supplied him with wholesome exercise and enabled them to enjoy the pleasures of the chase; whereby the soul of the dead man was appropriately honored by obervances akin to the funeral games of early Greece.

REFUSAL, *n*. Denial of something desired; as an elderly maiden's hand in marriage, to a rich and handsome suitor; a valuable franchise to a rich corporation, by an alderman; absolution to an impenitent king, by a priest, and so forth. Refusals are graded in a descending scale of finality thus: the refusal absolute, the refusal conditional, the refusal tentative and the refusal feminine. The last is called by some casuists the refusal assentive.

REGALIA, *n*. Distinguishing insignia, jewels and costume of such ancient and honorable orders as Knights of Adam; Visionaries of Delectable Bosh; the Ancient Order of Modern Troglodytes; the League of Holy Humbug; the Golden Phalanx of Phalangers; the Genteel Society of Expurgated Hoodlums; the Mystic Alliance of Gorgeous Regalians; Knights and Ladies of the Yellow Dog; the Oriental Order of Sons of the West; the Blatherhood of Insufferable Stuff; Warriors of the Long Bow; Guardians of the Great Horn Spoon; the Band of Brutes; the Impenitent Order of Wife-Beaters; the Sublime Legion of Flamboyant Conspicuants; Worshipers at the Electroplated Shrine; Shining Inaccessibles; Fee-Faw-Fummers of the Inimitable Grip; Jannissaries of the Broad-Blown Peacock; Plumed Increscencies of the Magic Temple; the Grand Cabal of Able-Bodied Sedentarians; Associated Deities of the Butter Trade; the Garden of Galoots; the Affectionate Fraternity of Men Similarly Warted; the Flashing Astonishers; Ladies of Horror; Coöperative Association for Breaking into the Spotlight; Dukes of Eden; Disciples Militant of the Hidden Faith; Knights-Champions of the Domestic Dog; the Holy Gregarians; the Resolute Optimists; the Ancient Sodality of Inhospitable Hogs; Associated Sovereigns of Mendacity; Dukes-Guardian of the Mystic Cess-Pool; the Society for Prevention of Prevalence; Kings of Drink; Polite Federation of Gents-Consequential; the Mysterious Order of the Undecipherable Scroll; Uniformed Rank of Lousy Cats; Monarchs of

Worth and Hunger; Sons of the South Star; Prelates of the Tub-and-Sword.

RELIGION, *n.* A daughter of Hope and Fear, explaining to Ignorance the nature of the Unknowable.

"What is your religion my son?" inquired the Archbishop of Rheims.

"Pardon, monseigneur," replied Rochebriant; "I am ashamed of it."

"Then why do you not become an atheist?"

"Impossible! I should be ashamed of atheism."

"In that case, monsieur, you should join the Protestants."

RELIQUARY, *n.* A receptacle for such sacred objects as pieces of the true cross, short-ribs of saints, the ears of Balaam's ass, the lung of the cock that called Peter to repentance and so forth. Reliquaries are commonly of metal, and provided with a lock to prevent the contents from coming out and performing miracles at unseasonable times. A feather from the wing of the Angel of the Annunciation once escaped during a sermon in Saint Peter's and so tickled the noses of the congregation that they woke and sneezed with great vehemence three times each. It is related in the "Gesta Sanctorum" that a sacristan in the Canterbury cathedral surprised the head of Saint Dennis in the library. Reprimanded by its stern custodian, it explained that it was seeking a body of doctrine. This unseemly levity so enraged the diocesan that the offender was publicly anathematized, thrown into the Stour and replaced by another head of Saint Dennis, brought from Rome.

RENOWN, *n.* A degree of distinction between notoriety and fame—a little more supportable than the one and a little more intolerable than the other. Sometimes it is conferred by an unfriendly and inconsiderate hand.

> I touched the harp in every key,
>   But found no heeding ear;
> And then Ithuriel touched me
>   With a revealing spear.
> Not all my genius, great as 'tis,
>   Could urge me out of night.
> I felt the faint appulse of his,
>   And leapt into the light!
>   *W. J. Candleton.*

REPARATION, *n.* Satisfaction that is made for a wrong and deducted from the satisfaction felt in committing it.

REPARTEE, *n.* Prudent insult in retort. Practiced by gentlemen with a constitutional aversion to violence, but a strong disposition to offend. In a war of words, the tactics of the North American Indian.

REPENTANCE, *n.* The faithful attendant and follower of Punishment. It is usually manifest in a degree of reformation that is not inconsistent with continuity of sin.

> Desirous to avoid the pains of Hell,
> You will repent and join the Church, Parnell?
> How needless!—Nick will keep you off the coals
> And add you to the woes of other souls.
> *Jomater Abemy.*

REPLICA, *n.* A reproduction of a work of art, by the artist that made the original. It is so called to distinguish it from a "copy," which is made by another artist. When the two are made with equal skill the replica is the more valuable, for it is supposed to be more beautiful than it looks.

REPORTER, *n.* A writer who guesses his way to the truth and dispels it with a tempest of words.

> "More dear than all my bosom knows, O thou
> Whose 'lips are sealed' and will not disavow!"
> So sang the blithe reporter-man as grew
> Beneath his hand the leg-long "interview."
> *Barson Maith.*

REPOSE, *v. i.* To cease from troubling.

REPRESENTATIVE, *n.* In national politics, a member of the Lower House in this world, and without discernible hope of promotion in the next.

REPROBATION, *n.* In theology, the state of a luckless mortal prenatally damned. The doctrine of reprobation was taught by Calvin, whose joy in it was somewhat marred by the sad sincerity of his conviction that although some are foredoomed to perdition, others are predestined to salvation.

REPUBLIC, *n.* A nation in which, the thing governing and the thing governed being the same, there is only a permitted authority to enforce an optional obedience. In a republic the foundation of public order is the ever lessening habit of submission inherited from ancestors who, being truly governed, submitted because they had to. There are as many kinds of republics as there are gradations between the despotism whence they came and the anarchy whither they lead.

REQUIEM, *n.* A mass for the dead which the minor poets assure us the winds sing o'er the graves of their favorites. Sometimes, by way of providing a varied entertainment, they sing a dirge.

RESIDENT, *adj.* Unable to leave.

RESIGN, *v. t.* To renounce an honor for an advantage. To renounce an advantage for a greater advantage.

> 'Twas rumored Leonard Wood had signed
> A true renunciation
> Of title, rank and every kind
> Of military station—
> Each honorable station.
>
> By his example fired—inclined
> To noble emulation,
> The country humbly was resigned
> To Leonard's resignation—
> His Christian resignation.
> *Politian Greame.*

RESOLUTE, *adj.* Obstinate in a course that we approve.

RESPECTABILITY, *n.* The offspring of a *liaison* between a bald head and a bank account.

RESPIRATOR, *n.* An apparatus fitted over the nose and mouth of an inhabitant of London, whereby to filter the visible universe in its passage to the lungs.

RESPITE, *n.* A suspension of hostilities against a sentenced assassin, to enable the Executive to determine whether the murder may not have been done by the prosecuting attorney. Any break in the continuity of a disagreeable expectation.

> Altgeld upon his incandescent bed
> Lay, an attendant demon at his head.
>
> "O cruel cook, pray grant me some relief—
> Some respite from the roast, however brief.
>
> "Remember how on earth I pardoned all
> Your friends in Illinois when held in thrall."
>
> "Unhappy soul! for that alone you squirm
> O'er fire unquenched, a never-dying worm.
>
> "Yet, for I pity your uneasy state,
> Your doom I'll mollify and pains abate.
>
> "Naught, for a season, shall your comfort mar,
> Not even the memory of who you are."
>
> Throughout eternal space dread silence fell;
> Heaven trembled as Compassion entered Hell.
>
> "As long, sweet demon, let my respite be
> As, governing down here, I'd respite thee."
>
> "As long, poor soul, as any of the pack
> You thrust from jail consumed in getting back."
>
> A genial chill affected Altgeld's hide
> While they were turning him on t'other side.
>   *Joel Spate Woop.*

RESPLENDENT, *adj.* Like a simple American citizen beduking himself in his lodge, or affirming his consequence in the Scheme of Things as an elemental unit of a parade.

The Knights of Dominion were so resplendent in their velvet-and-gold that their masters would hardly have known them.—*"Chronicles of the Classes."*

RESPOND, *v. i.* To make answer, or disclose otherwise a consciousness of having inspired an interest in what Herbert Spencer calls "external coexistences," as Satan "squat like a toad" at the ear of Eve, responded to the touch of the angel's spear. To respond in damages is to contribute to the maintenance of the plaintiff's attorney and, incidentally, to the gratification of the plaintiff.

RESPONSIBILITY, *n.* A detachable burden easily shifted to the shoulders of God, Fate, Fortune, Luck or one's neighbor. In the days of astrology it was customary to unload it upon a star.

> Alas, things ain't what we should see
> If Eve had let that apple be;
> And many a feller which had ought
> To set with monarchses of thought,
> Or play some rosy little game
> With battle-chaps on fields of fame,
> Is downed by his unlucky star,
> And hollers: "Peanuts!—here you are!"
> *"The Sturdy Beggar."*

RESTITUTION, *n.* The founding or endowing of universities and public libraries by gift or bequest.

RESTITUTOR, *n.* Benefactor; philanthropist.

RETALIATION, *n.* The natural rock upon which is reared the Temple of Law.

RETRIBUTION, *n.* A rain of fire-and-brimstone that falls alike upon the just and such of the unjust as have not procured shelter by evicting them.

In the lines following, addressed to an Emperor in exile by Father Gassalasca Jape, the reverend poet appears to hint his sense of the imprudence of turning about to face Retribution when it is taking exercise:

> What, what! Dom Pedro, you desire to go
> Back to Brazil to end your days in quiet?
> Why, what assurance have you 'twould be so?
> 'Tis not so long since you were in a riot,
> And your dear subjects showed a will to fly at
> Your throat and shake you like a rat. You know
> That empires are ungrateful; are you certain
> Republics are less handy to get hurt in?

REVEILLE, *n.* A signal to sleeping soldiers to dream of battlefields no more, but get up and have their blue noses counted. In the American army it is ingeniously called "rev-e-lee," and to that pronunciation our countrymen have pledged their lives, their misfortunes and their sacred dishonor.

REVELATION, *n.* A famous book in which St. John the Divine concealed all that he knew. The revealing is done by the commentators, who know nothing.

REVERENCE, *n.* The spiritual attitude of a man to a god and a dog to a man.

REVIEW, *v. t.*

To set your wisdom (holding not a doubt of it,
    Although in truth there's neither bone nor skin to it)
At work upon a book, and so read out of it
    The qualities that you have first read into it.

REVOLUTION, *n.* In politics, an abrupt change in the form of misgovernment. Specifically, in American history, the substitution of the rule of an Administration for that of a Ministry, whereby the welfare and happiness of the people were advanced a full half-inch. Revolutions are usually accompanied by a considerable effusion of blood, but are accounted worth it—this appraisement being made by beneficiaries whose blood had not the mischance to be shed. The French revolution is of incalculable value to the Socialist of to-day; when he pulls the string actuating its bones its gestures are inexpressibly terrifying to gory tyrants suspected of fomenting law and order.

RHADOMANCER, *n.* One who uses a divining-rod in prospecting for precious metals in the pocket of a fool.

RIBALDRY, *n.* Censorious language by another concerning oneself.

RIBROASTER, *n.* Censorious language by oneself concerning another. The word is of classical refinement, and is even said to have been used in a fable by Georgius Coadjutor, one of the most fastidious writers of the fifteenth century—commonly, indeed, regarded as the founder of the Fastidiotic School.

RICE-WATER, *n.* A mystic beverage secretly used by our most popular novelists and poets to regulate the imagination and narcotize the conscience. It is said to be rich in both obtundite and lethargine, and is brewed in a midnight fog by a fat witch of the Dismal Swamp.

RICH, *adj.* Holding in trust and subject to an accounting the property of the indolent, the incompetent, the unthrifty, the envious and the luckless. That is the view that prevails in the underworld, where the Brotherhood of Man finds its most logical development and candid advocacy. To denizens of the midworld the word means good and wise.

RICHES, *n.*

A gift from Heaven signifying, "This is my beloved son, in whom I am well pleased."—*John D. Rockefeller.*

The reward of toil and virtue.—*J. P. Morgan.*

The savings of many in the hands of one.—*Eugene Debs.*

To these excellent definitions the inspired lexicographer feels that he can add nothing of value.

RIDICULE, *n.* Words designed to show that the person of whom they are uttered is devoid of the dignity of character distinguishing him who utters them. It may be graphic, mimetic or merely rident. Shaftesbury is quoted as having pronounced it the test of truth—a ridiculous assertion, for many a solemn fallacy has undergone centuries of ridicule with no abatement of its popular acceptance. What, for example, has been more valorously derided than the doctrine of Infant Respectability?

RIGHT, *n.* Legitimate authority to be, to do or to have; as the right to be a king, the right to do one's neighbor, the right to have measles, and the like. The first of these rights was once universally believed to be derived directly from the will of God; and this is still sometimes affirmed *in partibus infidelium* outside the enlightened realms of Democracy; as the well known lines of Sir Abednego Bink, following:

By what right, then, do royal rulers rule?
Whose is the sanction of their state and pow'r?
He surely were as stubborn as a mule
Who, God unwilling, could maintain an hour
His uninvited session on the throne, or air
His pride securely in the Presidential chair.

Whatever is is so by Right Divine;
Whate'er occurs, God wills it so. Good land!
It were a wondrous thing if His design

A fool could baffle or a rogue withstand!
If so, then God, I say (intending no offence)
Is guilty of contributory negligence.

RIGHTEOUSNESS, *n*. A sturdy virtue that was once found among the Pantidoodles inhabiting the lower part of the peninsula of Oque. Some feeble attempts were made by returned missionaries to introduce it into several European countries, but it appears to have been imperfectly expounded. An example of this faulty exposition is found in the only extant sermon of the pious Bishop Rowley, a characteristic passage from which is here given:

"Now righteousness consisteth not merely in a holy state of mind, nor yet in performance of religious rites and obedience to the letter of the law. It is not enough that one be pious and just: one must see to it that others also are in the same state; and to this end compulsion is a proper means. Forasmuch as my injustice may work ill to another, so by his injustice may evil be wrought upon still another, the which it is as manifestly my duty to estop as to forestall mine own tort. Wherefore if I would be righteous I am bound to restrain my neighbor, by force if needful, in all those injurious enterprises from which, through a better disposition and by the help of Heaven, I do myself refrain."

RIME, *n*. Agreeing sounds in the terminals of verse, mostly bad. The verses themselves, as distinguished from prose, mostly dull. Usually (and wickedly) spelled "rhyme."

RIMER, *n*. A poet regarded with indifference or disesteem.
    The rimer quenches his unheeded fires,
    The sound surceases and the sense expires.
    Then the domestic dog, to east and west,
    Expounds the passions burning in his breast.
    The rising moon o'er that enchanted land
    Pauses to hear and yearns to understand.
                    Mowbray Myles.

RIOT, *n*. A popular entertainment given to the military by innocent bystanders.

R. I. P. A careless abbreviation of *requiescat in pace,* attesting an indolent goodwill to the dead. According to the learned Dr. Drigge, however, the letters originally meant nothing more than *reductus in pulvis.*

RITE, *n.* A religious or semi-religious ceremony fixed by law, precept or custom, with the essential oil of sincerity carefully squeezed out of it.

RITUALISM, *n.* A Dutch Garden of God where He may walk in rectilinear freedom, keeping off the grass.

ROAD, *n.* A strip of land along which one may pass from where it is too tiresome to be to where it is futile to go.

> All roads, howsoe'er they diverge, lead to Rome,
> Whence, thank the good Lord, at least one leads back home.
> *Borey the Bald.*

ROBBER, *n.* A candid man of affairs.

It is related of Voltaire that one night he and some traveling companions lodged at a wayside inn. The surroundings were suggestive, and after supper they agreed to tell robber stories in turn. When Voltaire's turn came he said: "Once there was a Farmer-General of the Revenues." Saying nothing more, he was encouraged to continue. "That," he said, "is the story."

ROMANCE, *n.* Fiction that owes no allegiance to the God of Things as They Are. In the novel the writer's thought is tethered to probability, as a domestic horse to the hitching-post, but in romance it ranges at will over the entire region of the imagination—free, lawless, immune to bit and rein. Your novelist is a poor creature, as Carlyle might say—a mere reporter. He may invent his characters and plot, but he must not imagine anything taking place that might not occur, albeit his entire narrative is candidly a lie. Why he imposes this hard condition on himself, and "drags at each remove a lengthening chain" of his own forging he can explain in ten thick volumes without illuminating by so much as a candle's ray the black profound of his own ignorance of the matter. There are great novels, for great writers have "laid waste their powers" to write them, but it remains true that far and away the most fascinating fiction that we have is "The Thousand and One Nights."

ROPE, *n.* An obsolescent appliance for reminding assassins that they too are mortal. It is put about the neck and remains in place one's whole life long. It has been largely superseded by a more complex electrical device worn upon another part of the person; and this is rapidly giving place to an apparatus known as the preachment.

ROSTRUM, *n*. In Latin, the beak of a bird or the prow of a ship. In America, a place from which a candidate for office energetically expounds the wisdom, virtue and power of the rabble.

ROUNDHEAD, *n*. A member of the Parliamentarian party in the English civil war—so called from his habit of wearing his hair short, whereas his enemy, the Cavalier, wore his long. There were other points of difference between them, but the fashion in hair was the fundamental cause of quarrel. The Cavaliers were royalists because the king, an indolent fellow, found it more convenient to let his hair grow than to wash his neck. This the Roundheads, who were mostly barbers and soap-boilers, deemed an injury to trade, and the royal neck was therefore the object of their particular indignation. Descendants of the belligerents now wear their hair all alike, but the fires of animosity enkindled in that ancient strife smoulder to this day beneath the snows of British civility.

RUBBISH, *n*. Worthless matter, such as the religions, philosophies, literatures, arts and sciences of the tribes infesting the regions lying due south from Boreaplas.

RUIN, *v*. To destroy. Specifically, to destroy a maid's belief in the virtue of maids.

RUM, *n*. Generically, fiery liquors that produce madness in total abstainers.

RUMOR, *n*. A favorite weapon of the assassins of character.

> Sharp, irresistible by mail or shield,
>   By guard unparried as by flight unstayed,
> O serviceable Rumor, let me wield
>   Against my enemy no other blade.
> His be the terror of a foe unseen,
>   His the inutile hand upon the hilt,
> And mine the deadly tongue, long, slender, keen,

Hinting a rumor of some ancient guilt.
So shall I slay the wretch without a blow,
Spare me to celebrate his overthrow,
And nurse my valor for another foe.
                                        Joel Buxter.

S

SABBATH, *n.* A weekly festival having its origin in the fact that God made the world in six days and was arrested on the seventh. Among the Jews observance of the day was enforced by a Commandment of which this is the Christian version: "Remember the seventh day to make thy neighbor keep it wholly." To the Creator it seemed fit and expedient that the Sabbath should be the last day of the week, but the Early Fathers of the Church held other views. So great is the sanctity of the day that even where the Lord holds a doubtful and precarious jurisdiction over those who go down to (and down into) the sea it is reverently recognized, as is manifest in the following deep-water version of the Fourth Commandment:

Six days shalt thou labor and do all thou art able,
And on the seventh holystone the deck and scrape the cable.

Decks are no longer holystoned, but the cable still supplies the captain with opportunity to attest a pious respect for the divine ordinance.

SACERDOTALIST, *n.* One who holds the belief that a clergyman is a priest. Denial of this momentous doctrine is the hardiest challenge that is now flung into the teeth of the Episcolopian church by the Neo-Dictionarians.

SACRAMENT, *n.* A solemn religious ceremony to which several degrees of authority and significance are attached. Rome has seven sacraments, but the Protestant churches, being less prosperous, feel that they can afford only two, and these of inferior sanctity. Some of the smaller sects have no sacraments at all—for which mean economy they will indubitably be damned.

SACRED, *adj.* Dedicated to some religious purpose; having a divine character; inspiring solemn thoughts or emotions; as, the Dalai Lama of Thibet; the Moogum of M'bwango; the temple of Apes in Ceylon; the Cow in India; the Crocodile, the Cat and the Onion of ancient Egypt; the Mufti of Moosh; the hair of the dog that bit Noah, etc.

> All things are either sacred or profane.
> The former to ecclesiasts bring gain;
> The latter to the devil appertain.
> *Dumbo Omohundro.*

SAFETY-CLUTCH, *n.* A mechanical device acting automatically to prevent the fall of an elevator, or cage, in case of an accident to the hoisting apparatus.

> Once I seen a human ruin
> In a elevator-well,
> And his members was bestrewin'
> All the place where he had fell.
>
> And I says, apostrophisin'
> That uncommon woful wreck:
> "Your position's so surprisin'
> That I tremble for your neck!"
>
> Then that ruin, smilin' sadly
> And impressive, up and spoke:
> "Well, I wouldn't tremble badly,
> For it's been a fortnight broke."
>
> Then, for further comprehension
> Of his attitude, he begs
> I will focus my attention
> On his various arms and legs—
>
> How they all are contumacious;
> Where they each, respective, lie;
> How one trotter proves ungracious,
> T'other one an *alibi.*
>
> These particulars is mentioned
> For to show his dismal state,
> Which I wasn't first intentioned
> To specifical relate.

None is worser to be dreaded
   That I ever have heard tell
Than the gent's who there was spreaded
   In that elevator-well.

Now this tale is allegoric—
   It is figurative all,
For the well is metaphoric
   And the feller didn't fall.

I opine it isn't moral
   For a writer-man to cheat,
And despise to wear a laurel
   As was gotten by deceit.

For 'tis Politics intended
   By the elevator, mind,
It will boost a person splendid
   If his talent is the kind.

Col. Bryan had the talent
   (For the busted man is him)
And it shot him up right gallant
   Till his head begun to swim.

Then the rope it broke above him
   And he painful come to earth
Where there's nobody to love him
   For his detrimented worth.

Though he's livin' none would know him,
   Or at leastwise not as such.
Moral of this woful poem:
   Frequent oil your safety-clutch.

                    Porfer Poog.

SAINT, *n.* A dead sinner revised and edited.

   The Duchess of Orleans relates that the irreverent old calumniator, Marshal Villeroi, who in his youth had known St. Francis de Sales, said, on hearing him called saint: "I am delighted to hear that Monsieur de Sales is a saint. He was fond of saying indelicate things, and used to cheat at cards. In other respects he was a perfect gentleman, though a fool."

SALACITY, *n.* A certain literary quality frequently observed in popular novels, especially in those written by women and young girls, who give it another name and think that in introducing it they are occupying a neglected field of letters and reaping an overlooked harvest. If they have the misfortune to live long enough they are tormented with a desire to burn their sheaves.

SALAMANDER, *n.* Originally a reptile inhabiting fire; later, an anthropomorphous immortal, but still a pyrophile. Salamanders are now believed to be extinct, the last one of which we have an account having been seen in Carcassonne by the Abbe Belloc, who exorcised it with a bucket of holy water.

SARCOPHAGUS, *n.* Among the Greeks a coffin which being made of a certain kind of carnivorous stone, had the peculiar property of devouring the body placed in it. The sarcophagus known to modern obsequiographers is commonly a product of the carpenter's art.

SATAN, *n.* One of the Creator's lamentable mistakes, repented in sashcloth and axes. Being instated as an archangel, Satan made himself multifariously objectionable and was finally expelled from Heaven. Halfway in his descent he paused, bent his head in thought a moment and at last went back. "There is one favor that I should like to ask," said he.

"Name it."

"Man, I understand, is about to be created. He will need laws."

"What, wretch! you his appointed adversary, charged from the dawn of eternity with hatred of his soul—you ask for the right to make his laws?"

"Pardon; what I have to ask is that he be permitted to make them himself."

It was so ordered.

SATIETY, *n.* The feeling that one has for the plate after he has eaten its contents, madam.

SATIRE, *n.* An obsolete kind of literary composition in which the vices and follies of the author's enemies were expounded with imperfect tenderness. In this country satire never had more than a sickly and uncertain existence, for the soul of it is wit, wherein we are dolefully deficient, the humor that we mistake for it, like all humor, being tolerant and sympathetic. Moreover, although Americans are "endowed by their Creator" with abundant vice and folly, it is not generally known that these are reprehensible qualities, wherefore the satirist is popularly regarded as a sour-spirited knave, and his every victim's outcry for codefendants evokes a national assent.

> Hail Satire! be thy praises ever sung
> In the dead language of a mummy's tongue,
> For thou thyself art dead, and damned as well—
> Thy spirit (usefully employed) in Hell.
> Had it been such as consecrates the Bible
> Thou hadst not perished by the law of libel.
>
> *Barney Stims.*

SATYR, *n.* One of the few characters of the Grecian mythology accorded recognition in the Hebrew. (Leviticus, xvii, 7.) The satyr was at first a member of the dissolute community acknowledging a loose allegiance to Dionysius, but underwent many transformations and improvements. Not infrequently he is confounded with the faun, a later and decenter creation of the Romans, who was less like a man and more like a goat.

SAUCE, *n.* The one infallible sign of civilization and enlightenment. A people with no sauces has one thousand vices; a people with one sauce has only nine hundred and ninety-nine. For every sauce invented and accepted a vice is renounced and forgiven.

SAW, *n.* A trite popular saying, or proverb. (Figurative and colloquial.) So called because it makes its way into a wooden head. Following are examples of old saws fitted with new teeth.

> A penny saved is a penny to squander.
> A man is known by the company that he organizes.
> A bad workman quarrels with the man who calls him that.
> A bird in the hand is worth what it will bring.
> Better late than before anybody has invited you.
> Example is better than following it.
> Half a loaf is better than a whole one if there is much else.
> Think twice before you speak to a friend in need.
> What is worth doing is worth the trouble of asking somebody to do it.
> Least said is soonest disavowed.

He laughs best who laughs least.
Speak of the Devil and he will hear about it.
Of two evils choose to be the least.
Strike while your employer has a big contract.
Where there's a will there's a won't.

SCARABÆUS, *n.* The sacred beetle of the ancient Egyptians, allied to our familiar "tumble-bug." It was supposed to symbolize immortality, the fact that God knew why giving it its peculiar sanctity. Its habit of incubating its eggs in a ball of ordure may also have commended it to the favor of the priesthood, and may some day assure it an equal reverence among ourselves. True, the American beetle is an inferior beetle, but the American priest is an inferior priest.

SCARABEE, *n.* The same as scarabæus.

> He fell by his own hand
> > Beneath the great oak tree.
> He'd traveled in a foreign land.
> He tried to make her understand
> The dance that's called the Saraband,
> > But he called it Scarabee.
> He had called it so through an afternoon,
> > And she, the light of his harem if so might be,
> > Had smiled and said naught. O the body was fair to see,
> All frosted there in the shine o' the moon—
> > Dead for a Scarabee
> And a recollection that came too late.
> > O Fate!
> > They buried him where he lay,
> > He sleeps awaiting the Day,
> > > In state,
> And two Possible Puns, moon-eyed and wan,
> Gloom over the grave and then move on.
> > Dead for a Scarabee!
> > > *Fernando Tapple.*

SCARIFICATION, *n.* A form of penance practised by the mediæval pious. The rite was performed, sometimes with a knife, sometimes with a hot iron, but always, says Arsenius Asceticus, acceptably if the penitent spared himself no pain nor harmless disfigurement. Scarification, with other crude penances, has now been superseded by benefaction.

The founding of a library or endowment of a university is said to yield to the penitent a sharper and more lasting pain than is conferred by the knife or iron, and is therefore a surer means of grace. There are, however, two grave objections to it as a penitential method: the good that it does and the taint of justice.

SCEPTER, *n.* A king's staff of office, the sign and symbol of his authority. It was originally a mace with which the sovereign admonished his jester and vetoed ministerial measures by breaking the bones of their proponents.

SCIMETAR, *n.* A curved sword of exceeding keenness, in the conduct of which certain Orientals attain a surprising proficiency, as the incident here related will serve to show. The account is translated from the Japanese of Shusi Itama, a famous writer of the thirteenth century.

When the great Gichi-Kuktai was Mikado he condemned to decapitation Jijiji Ri, a high officer of the Court. Soon after the hour appointed for performance of the rite what was his Majesty's surprise to see calmly approaching the throne the man who should have been at that time ten minutes dead!

"Seventeen hundred impossible dragons!" shouted the enraged monarch. "Did I not sentence you to stand in the market-place and have your head struck off by the public executioner at three o'clock? And is it not now 3:10?"

"Son of a thousand illustrious deities," answered the condemned minister, "all that you say is so true that the truth is a lie in comparison. But your heavenly Majesty's sunny and vitalizing wishes have been pestilently disregarded. With joy I ran and placed my unworthy body in the market-place. The executioner appeared with his bare scimetar, ostentatiously whirled it in air, and then, tapping me lightly upon the neck, strode away, pelted by the populace, with whom I was ever a favorite. I am come to pray for justice upon his own dishonorable and treasonous head."

"To what regiment of executioners does the black-boweled caitiff belong?" asked the Mikado.

"To the gallant Ninety-eight Hundred and Thirty-seventh—I know the man. His name is Sakko-Samshi."

"Let him be brought before me," said the Mikado to an attendant, and a half-hour later the culprit stood in the Presence.

"Thou bastard son of a three-legged hunchback without thumbs!" roared the sovereign—"why didst thou but lightly tap the neck that it should have been thy pleasure to sever?"

"Lord of Cranes and Cherry Blooms," replied the executioner, unmoved, "command him to blow his nose with his fingers."

Being commanded, Jijiji Ri lay hold of his nose and trumpeted like an elephant, all expecting to see the severed head flung violently from him. Nothing occurred: the performance prospered peacefully to the close, without incident.

All eyes were now turned on the executioner, who had grown as white as the snows on the summit of Fujiama. His legs trembled and his breath came in gasps of terror.

"Several kinds of spike-tailed brass lions!" he cried; "I am a ruined and disgraced swordsman! I struck the villain feebly because in flourishing the scimetar I had accidentally passed it through my own neck! Father of the Moon, I resign my office."

So saying, he grasped his top-knot, lifted off his head, and advancing to the throne laid it humbly at the Mikado's feet.

SCRAP-BOOK, *n.* A book that is commonly edited by a fool. Many persons of some small distinction compile scrap-books containing whatever they happen to read about themselves or employ others to collect. One of these egotists was addressed in the lines following, by Agamemnon Melancthon Peters:

> Dear Frank, that scrap-book where you boast
>   You keep a record true
> Of every kind of peppered roast
>   That's made of you;
>
> Wherein you paste the printed gibes
>   That revel round your name,
> Thinking the laughter of the scribes
>   Attests your fame;
>
> Where all the pictures you arrange
>   That comic pencils trace—
> Your funny figure and your strange
>   Semitic face—
>
> Pray lend it me. Wit I have not,
>   Nor art, but there I'll list
> The daily drubbings you'd have got
>   Had God a fist.

SCRIBBLER, *n.* A professional writer whose views are antagonistic to one's own.

SCRIPTURES, *n.* The sacred books of our holy religion, as distinguished from the false and profane writings on which all other faiths are based.

SEAL, *n.* A mark impressed upon certain kinds of documents to attest their authenticity and authority. Sometimes it is stamped upon wax, and attached to the paper, sometimes into the paper itself. Sealing, in this sense, is a survival of an ancient custom of inscribing important papers with cabalistic words or signs to give them a magical efficacy independent of the authority that they represent. In the British museum are preserved many ancient papers, mostly of a sacerdotal character, validated by necromantic pentagrams and other devices, frequently initial letters of words to conjure with; and in many instances these are attached in the same way that seals are appended now. As nearly every reasonless and apparently meaningless custom, rite or observance of modern times had origin in some remote utility, it is pleasing to note an example of ancient nonsense evolving in the process of ages into something really useful. Our word "sincere" is derived from *sine cero,* without wax, but the learned are not in agreement as to whether this refers to the absence of the cabalistic signs, or to that of the wax with which letters were formerly closed from public scrutiny. Either view of the matter will serve one in immediate need of an hypothesis. The initials L. S., commonly appended to signatures of legal documents, mean *locum sigillis,* the place of the seal, although the seal is no longer used—an admirable example of conservatism distinguishing Man from the beasts that perish. The words *locum sigillis* are humbly suggested as a suitable motto for the Pribyloff Islands whenever they shall take their place as a sovereign State of the American Union.

SEINE, *n.* A kind of net for effecting an involuntary change of environment. For fish it is made strong and coarse, but women are more easily taken with a singularly delicate fabric weighted with small, cut stones.

> The devil casting a seine of lace,
>   (With precious stones 'twas weighted)
> Drew it into the landing place
>   And its contents calculated.
>
> All souls of women were in that sack—
>   A draft miraculous, precious!

> But ere he could throw it across his back
> They'd all escaped through the meshes.
> *Baruch de Loppis.*

SELF-ESTEEM, *n.* An erroneous appraisement.

SELF-EVIDENT, *adj.* Evident to one's self and to nobody else.

SELFISH, *adj.* Devoid of consideration for the selfishness of others.

SENATE, *n.* A body of elderly gentlemen charged with high duties and misdemeanors.

SERIAL, *n.* A literary work, usually a story that is not true, creeping through several issues of a newspaper or magazine. Frequently appended to each instalment is a "synopsis of preceding chapters" for those who have not read them, but a direr need is a synopsis of succeeding chapters for those who do not intend to read *them*. A synopsis of the entire work would be still better.

The late James F. Bowman was writing a serial tale for a weekly paper in collaboration with a genius whose name has not come down to us. They wrote, not jointly but alternately, Bowman supplying the instalment for one week, his friend for the next, and so on, world without end, they hoped. Unfortunately they quarreled, and one Monday morning when Bowman read the paper to prepare himself for his task, he found his work cut out for him in a way to surprise and pain him. His collaborator had embarked every character of the narrative on a ship and sunk them all in the deepest part of the Atlantic.

SEVERALTY, *n.* Separateness, as, lands in severalty, *i. e.,* lands held individually, not in joint ownership. Certain tribes of Indians are believed now to be sufficiently civilized to have in severalty the lands that they have hitherto held as tribal organizations, and could not sell to the Whites for waxen beads and potato whiskey.

> Lo! the poor Indian whose unsuited mind
> Saw death before, hell and the grave behind;
> Whom thrifty settlers ne'er besought to stay—
> His small belongings their appointed prey;
> Whom Dispossession, with alluring wile,

Persuaded elsewhere every little while!
His fire unquenched and his undying worm
By "land in severalty" (charming term!)
Are cooled and killed, respectively, at last,
And he to his new holding anchored fast!

SHERIFF, *n.* In America the chief executive officer of a county, whose most characteristic duties, in some of the Western and Southern States, are catching and hanging of rogues.

John Elmer Pettibone Cajee
(I write of him with little glee)
Was just as bad as he could be.

'Twas frequently remarked: "I swon!
The sun has never looked upon
So bad a man as Neighbor John."

A sinner through and through, he had
This added fault: it made him mad
To know another man was bad.

In such a case he thought it right
To rise at any hour of night
And quench that wicked person's light.

Despite the town's entreaties, he
Would hale him to the nearest tree
And leave him swinging wide and free.

Or sometimes, if the humor came,
A luckless wight's reluctant frame
Was given to the cheerful flame.

While it was turning nice and brown,
All unconcerned John met the frown
Of that austere and righteous town.

"How sad," his neighbors said, "that he
So scornful of the law should be—
An anar c, h, i, s, t."

(That is the way that they preferred
To utter the abhorrent word,
So strong the aversion that it stirred.)

"Resolved," they said, continuing,
"That Badman John must cease this thing
Of having his unlawful fling.

"Now, by these sacred relics"—here
Each man had out a souvenir
Got at a lynching yesteryear—

"By these we swear he shall forsake
His ways, nor cause our hearts to ache
By sins of rope and torch and stake.

"We'll tie his red right hand until
He'll have small freedom to fulfil
The mandates of his lawless will."

So, in convention then and there,
They named him Sheriff. The affair
Was opened, it is said, with prayer.
J. Milton Sloluck.

SIREN, *n.* One of several musical prodigies famous for a vain attempt to dissuade Odysseus from a life on the ocean wave. Figuratively, any lady of splendid promise, dissembled purpose and disappointing performance.

SLANG, *n.* The grunt of the human hog (*Pignoramus intolerabilis*) with an audible memory. The speech of one who utters with his tongue what he thinks with his ear, and feels the pride of a creator in accomplishing the feat of a parrot. A means (under Providence) of setting up as a wit without a capital of sense.

SMITHAREEN, *n.* A fragment, a decomponent part, a remain. The word is used variously, but in the following verses on a noted female reformer who opposed bicycle-riding by women because it "led them to the devil" it is seen at its best:

The wheels go round without a sound—
    The maidens hold high revel;
In sinful mood, insanely gay,
True spinsters spin adown the way
    From duty to the devil!
They laugh, they sing, and—ting-a-ling!
    Their bells go all the morning;
Their lanterns bright bestar the night
    Pedestrians a-warning.
With lifted hands Miss Charlotte stands,
    Good-Lording and O-mying,

Her rheumatism forgotten quite,
　　Her fat with anger frying.
She blocks the path that leads to wrath,
　　Jack Satan's power defying.
The wheels go round without a sound
　　The lights burn red and blue and green.
What's this that's found upon the ground?
　　Poor Charlotte Smith's a smithareen!
　　　　　　　　　John William Yope.

SOPHISTRY, *n*. The controversial method of an opponent, distinguished from one's own by superior insincerity and fooling. This method is that of the later Sophists, a Grecian sect of philosophers who began by teaching wisdom, prudence, science, art and, in brief, whatever men ought to know, but lost themselves in a maze of quibbles and a fog of words.

His bad opponent's "facts" he sweeps away,
And drags his sophistry to light of day;
Then swears they're pushed to madness who resort
To falsehood of so desperate a sort.
Not so; like sods upon a dead man's breast,
He lies most lightly who the least is pressed.
　　　　　　　　　Polydore Smith.

SORCERY, *n*. The ancient prototype and forerunner of political influence. It was, however, deemed less respectable and sometimes was punished by torture and death. Augustine Nicholas relates that a poor peasant who had been accused of sorcery was put to the torture to compel a confession. After enduring a few gentle agonies the suffering simpleton admitted his guilt, but naively asked his tormentors if it were not possible to be a sorcerer without knowing it.

SOUL, *n*. A spiritual entity concerning which there hath been brave disputation. Plato held that those souls which in a previous state of existence (antedating Athens) had obtained the clearest glimpses of eternal truth entered into the bodies of persons who became philosophers. Plato was himself a philosopher. The souls that had least contemplated divine truth animated the bodies of usurpers and despots. Dionysius I, who had threatened to decapitate the broad-browed philosopher, was a usurper and despot. Plato, doubtless, was not the first to construct a system of philosophy that could be quoted against his enemies; certainly he was not the last.

"Concerning the nature of the soul," saith the renowned author of *Diversiones Sanctorum,* "there hath been hardly more argument than that of its place in the body. Mine own belief is that the soul hath her seat in the abdomen—in which faith we may discern and interpret a truth hitherto unintelligible, namely that the glutton is of all men most devout. He is said in the Scripture to 'make a god of his belly'— why, then, should he not be pious, having ever his Deity with him to freshen his faith? Who so well as he can know the might and majesty that he shrines? Truly and soberly, the soul and the stomach are one Divine Entity; and such was the belief of Promasius, who nevertheless erred in denying it immortality. He had observed that its visible and material substance failed and decayed with the rest of the body after death, but of its immaterial essence he knew nothing. This is what we call the Appetite, and it survives the wreck and reek of mortality, to be rewarded or punished in another world, according to what it hath demanded in the flesh. The Appetite whose coarse clamoring was for the unwholesome viands of the general market and the public refectory shall be cast into eternal famine, whilst that which firmly though civilly insisted on ortolans, caviare, terrapin, anchovies, *pâtès de foie gras* and all such Christian comestibles shall flesh its spiritual tooth in the souls of them forever and ever, and wreak its divine thirst upon the immortal parts of the rarest and richest wines ever quaffed here below. Such is my religious faith, though I grieve to confess that neither His Holiness the Pope nor His Grace the Archbishop of Canterbury (whom I equally and profoundly revere) will assent to its dissemination."

SPOOKER, *n.* A writer whose imagination concerns itself with supernatural phenomena, especially the doings of spooks. One of the most illustrious spookers of our time is Mr. William D. Howells, who introduces a well-credentialed reader to as respectable and mannerly a company of spooks as one could wish to meet. To the terror that invests the chairman of a district school board, the Howells ghost adds something of the mystery enveloping a farmer from another township.

STORY, *n.* A narrative, commonly untrue. The truth of the stories here following has, however, not been successfully impeached.

One evening Mr. Rudolph Block, of New York, found himself seated at dinner alongside Mr. Percival Pollard, the distinguished critic.

"Mr. Pollard," said he, "my book, *The Biography of a Dead Cow,* is published anonymously, but you can hardly be ignorant of its authorship. Yet in reviewing it you speak of it as the work of the Idiot of the Century. Do you think that fair criticism?"

"I am very sorry, sir," replied the critic, amiably, "but it did not occur to me that you really might not wish the public to know who wrote it."

Mr. W. C. Morrow, who used to live in San Jose, California, was addicted to writing ghost stories which made the reader feel as if a stream of lizards, fresh from the ice, were streaking it up his back and hiding in his hair. San Jose was at that time believed to be haunted by the visible spirit of a noted bandit named Vasquez, who had been hanged there. The town was not very well lighted, and it is putting it mildly to say that San Jose was reluctant to be out o' nights. One particularly dark night two gentlemen were abroad in the loneliest spot within the city limits, talking loudly to keep up their courage, when they came upon Mr. J. J. Owen, a well-known journalist.

"Why, Owen," said one, "what brings you here on such a night as this? You told me that this is one of Vasquez' favorite haunts! And you are a believer. Aren't you afraid to be out?"

"My dear fellow," the journalist replied with a drear autumnal cadence in his speech, like the moan of a leaf-laden wind, "I am afraid to be in. I have one of Will Morrow's stories in my pocket and I don't dare to go where there is light enough to read it."

Rear-Admiral Schley and Representative Charles F. Joy were standing near the Peace Monument, in Washington, discussing the question, Is success a failure? Mr. Joy suddenly broke off in the middle of an eloquent sentence, exclaiming: "Hello! I've heard that band before. Santlemann's, I think."

"I don't hear any band," said Schley.

"Come to think, I don't either," said Joy; "but I see General Miles coming down the avenue, and that pageant always affects me in the same way as a brass band. One has to scrutinize one's impressions pretty closely, or one will mistake their origin."

While the Admiral was digesting this hasty meal of philosophy General Miles passed in review, a spectacle of impressive dignity. When the tail of the seeming procession had passed and the two observers had recovered from the transient blindness caused by its effulgence—

"He seems to be enjoying himself," said the Admiral.

"There is nothing," assented Joy, thoughtfully, "that he enjoys one-half so well."

The illustrious statesman, Champ Clark, once lived about a mile from the village of Jebigue, in Missouri. One day he rode into town on a favorite mule, and, hitching the beast on the sunny side of a street, in front of a saloon, he went inside in his character of teetotaler, to apprise the barkeeper that wine is a mocker. It was a dreadfully hot day. Pretty soon a neighbor came in and seeing Clark, said:

"Champ, it is not right to leave that mule out there in the sun. He'll roast, sure!—he was smoking as I passed him."

"O, he's all right," said Clark, lightly; "he's an inveterate smoker."

The neighbor took a lemonade, but shook his head and repeated that it was not right.

He was a conspirator. There had been a fire the night before: a stable just around the corner had burned and a number of horses had put on their immortality, among them a young colt, which was roasted to a rich nut-brown. Some of the boys had turned Mr. Clark's mule loose and substituted the mortal part of the colt. Presently another man entered the saloon.

"For mercy's sake!" he said, taking it with sugar, "do remove that mule, barkeeper: it smells."

"Yes," interposed Clark, "that animal has the best nose in Missouri. But if he doesn't mind, you shouldn't."

In the course of human events Mr. Clark went out, and there, apparently, lay the incinerated and shrunken remains of his charger. The boys did not have any fun out of Mr. Clark, who looked at the body and, with the non-committal expression to which he owes so much of his political preferment, went away. But walking home late that night he saw his mule standing silent and solemn by the wayside in the misty moonlight. Mentioning the name of Helen Blazes with uncommon emphasis, Mr. Clark took the back track as hard as ever he could hook it, and passed the night in town.

General H. H. Wotherspoon, president of the Army War College, has a pet rib-nosed baboon, an animal of uncommon intelligence but imperfectly beautiful. Returning to his apartment one evening, the General was surprised and pained to find Adam (for so the creature is named, the general being a Darwinian) sitting up for him and wearing its master's best uniform coat, epaulettes and all.

"You confounded remote ancestor!" thundered the great strategist, "what do you mean by being out of bed after taps?—and with my coat on!"

Adam rose and with a reproachful look got down on all fours in the manner of his kind and, scuffling across the room to a table, returned with a visiting-card: General Barry had called and, judging by an empty champagne bottle and several cigar-stumps, had been hospitably entertained while waiting. The general apologized to his faithful progenitor and retired. The next day he met General Barry, who said:

"Spoon, old man, when leaving you last evening I forgot to ask you about those excellent cigars. Where do you get them?"

General Wotherspoon did not deign to reply, but walked away.

"Pardon me, please," said Barry, moving after him; "I was joking of course. Why, I knew it was not you before I had been in the room fifteen minutes."

SUCCESS, *n.* The one unpardonable sin against one's fellows. In literature, and particularly in poetry, the elements of success are exceedingly simple, and are admirably set forth in the following lines by the reverend Father Gassilasca Jape, entitled, for some mysterious reason, "John A. Joyce."

> The bard who would prosper must carry a book,
>   Do his thinking in prose and wear
> A crimson cravat, a far-away look
>   And a head of hexameter hair.
> Be thin in your thought and your body'll be fat;
> If you wear your hair long you needn't your hat.

SUFFRAGE, *n.* Expression of opinion by means of a ballot. The right of suffrage (which is held to be both a privilege and a duty) means, as commonly interpreted, the right to vote for the man of another man's choice, and is highly prized. Refusal to do so has the bad name of "incivism." The incivilian, however, cannot be properly arraigned for his crime, for there is no legitimate accuser. If the accuser is himself guilty he has no standing in the court of opinion; if not, he profits by the crime, for A's abstention from voting gives greater weight to the vote of B. By female suffrage is meant the right of a woman to vote as some man tells her to. It is based on female responsibility, which is somewhat limited. The woman most eager to jump out of her petticoat to assert her rights is first to jump back into it when threatened with a switching for misusing them.

SYCOPHANT, *n.* One who approaches Greatness on his belly so that he may not be commanded to turn and be kicked. He is sometimes an editor.

> As the lean leech, its victim found, is pleased
> To fix itself upon a part diseased
> Till, its black hide distended with bad blood,
> It drops to die of surfeit in the mud,
> So the base sycophant with joy descries
> His neighbor's weak spot and his mouth applies,
> Gorges and prospers like the leech, although,
> Unlike that reptile, he will not let go.
> Gelasma, if it paid you to devote
> Your talent to the service of a goat,
> Showing by forceful logic that its beard
> Is more than Aaron's fit to be revered;
> If to the task of honoring its smell
> Profit had prompted you, and love as well,
> The world would benefit at last by you
> And wealthy malefactors weep anew—
> Your favor for a moment's space denied
> And to the nobler object turned aside.
> Is't not enough that thrifty millionaires
> Who loot in freight and spoliate in fares,
> Or, cursed with consciences that bid them fly
> To safer villainies of darker dye,
> Forswearing robbery and fain, instead,
> To steal (they call it "cornering") our bread
> May see you groveling their boots to lick
> And begging for the favor of a kick?

> Still must you follow to the bitter end
> Your sycophantic disposition's trend,
> And in your eagerness to please the rich
> Hunt hungry sinners to their final ditch?
> In Morgan's praise you smite the sounding wire,
> And sing hosannas to great Havemeyer!
> What's Satan done that him you should eschew?
> He too is reeking rich—deducting *you*.

SYLLOGISM, *n*. A logical formula consisting of a major and a minor assumption and an inconsequent. (See LOGIC.)

SYLPH, *n*. An immaterial but visible being that inhabited the air when the air was an element and before it was fatally polluted by factory smoke, sewer gas and similar products of civilization. Sylphs were allied to gnomes, nymphs and salamanders, which dwelt, respectively, in earth, water and fire, all now insalubrious. Sylphs, like fowls of the air, were male and female, to no purpose, apparently, for if they had progeny they must have nested in inaccessible places, none of the chicks having ever been seen.

SYMBOL, *n*. Something that is supposed to typify or stand for something else. Many symbols are mere "survivals"—things which having no longer any utility continue to exist because we have inherited the tendency to make them; as funereal urns carved on memorial monuments. They were once real urns holding the ashes of the dead. We cannot stop making them, but we can give them a name that conceals our helplessness.

SYMBOLIC, *adj*. Pertaining to symbols and the use and interpretation of symbols.

> They say 'tis conscience feels compunction;
> I hold that that's the stomach's function,
> For of the sinner I have noted
> That when he's sinned he's somewhat bloated,
> Or ill some other ghastly fashion
> Within that bowel of compassion.
> True, I believe the only sinner
> Is he that eats a shabby dinner.
> You know how Adam with good reason,

For eating apples out of season,
Was "cursed." But that is all symbolic:
The truth is, Adam had the colic.
                                        G. J.

T

T, the twentieth letter of the English alphabet, was by the Greeks absurdly called *tau*. In the alphabet whence ours comes it had the form of the rude corkscrew of the period, and when it stood alone (which was more than the Phœnicians could always do) signified *Tallegal,* translated by the learned Dr. Brownrigg, "tanglefoot."

TABLE D'HÔTE, *n.* A caterer's thrifty concession to the universal passion for irresponsibility.

Old Paunchinello, freshly wed,
    Took Madame P. to table,
And there deliriously fed
    As fast as he was able.

"I dote upon good grub," he cried,
    Intent upon its throatage.
"Ah, yes," said the neglected bride,
    "You're in your *table d'hôtage.*"
                                Associated Poets.

TAIL, *n.* The part of an animal's spine that had transcended its natural limitations to set up an independent existence in a world of its own. Excepting in his fœtal state, Man is without a tail, a privation of which he attests an hereditary and uneasy consciousness by the coat-skirt of the male and the train of the female, and by a marked tendency to ornament that part of his attire where the tail should be, and indubitably once was. This tendency is most observable in the female of the species, in whom the ancestral sense is strong and persistent. The tailed men described by Lord Monboddo are now generally regarded as a product of an imagination unusually susceptible to influences generated in the golden age of our pithecan past.

TAKE, *v. t.* To acquire, frequently by force but preferably by stealth.

TALK, *v. t.* To commit an indiscretion without temptation, from an impulse without purpose.

TARIFF, *n.* A scale of taxes on imports, designed to protect the domestic producer against the greed of his consumer.

> The Enemy of Human Souls
> Sat grieving at the cost of coals;
> For Hell had been annexed of late,
> And was a sovereign Southern State.
>
> "It were no more than right," said he,
> "That I should get my fuel free.
> The duty, neither just nor wise,
> Compels me to economize—
> Whereby my broilers, every one,
> Are execrably underdone.
> What would they have?—although I yearn
> To do them nicely to a turn,
> I can't afford an honest heat.
> This tariff makes even devils cheat!
> I'm ruined, and my humble trade
> All rascals may at will invade:
> Beneath my nose the public press
> Outdoes me in sulphureousness;
> The bar ingeniously applies
> To my undoing my own lies;
> My medicines the doctors use
> (Albeit vainly) to refuse
> To me my fair and rightful prey
> And keep their own in shape to pay;
> The preachers by example teach
> What, scorning to perform, I preach;
> And statesmen, aping me, all make
> More promises than they can break.
> Against such competition I
> Lift up a disregarded cry.
> Since all ignore my just complaint,
> By Hokey-Pokey! I'll turn saint!"

> Now, the Republicans, who all
> Are saints, began at once to bawl
> Against *his* competition; so
> There was a devil of a go!
> They locked horns with him, tête-à-tête
> In acrimonious debate,
> Till Democrats, forlorn and lone,
> Had hopes of coming by their own.
> That evil to avert, in haste
> The two belligerents embraced;
> But since 'twere wicked to relax
> A title of the Sacred Tax,
> 'Twas finally agreed to grant
> The bold Insurgent-protestant
> A bounty on each soul that fell
> Into his ineffectual Hell.
>
> *Edam Smith.*

TECHNICALITY, *n.* In an English court a man named Home was tried for slander in having accused a neighbor of murder. His exact words were: "Sir Thomas Holt hath taken a cleaver and stricken his cook upon the head, so that one side of the head fell upon one shoulder and the other side upon the other shoulder." The defendant was acquitted by instruction of the court, the learned judges holding that the words did not charge murder, for they did not affirm the death of the cook, that being only an inference.

TEDIUM, *n.* Ennui, the state or condition of one that is bored. Many fanciful derivations of the word have been affirmed, but so high an authority as Father Jape says that it comes from a very obvious source— the first words of the ancient Latin hymn *Te Deum Laudamus*. In this apparently natural derivation there is something that saddens.

TEETOTALER, *n.* One who abstains from strong drink, sometimes totally, sometimes tolerably totally.

TELEPHONE, *n.* An invention of the devil which abrogates some of the advantages of making a disagreeable person keep his distance.

TELESCOPE, *n.* A device having a relation to the eye similar to that of the telephone to the ear, enabling distant objects to plague us with a multitude of needless details. Luckily it is unprovided with a bell summoning us to the sacrifice.

TENACITY, *n.* A certain quality of the human hand in its relation to the coin of the realm. It attains its highest development in the hand of authority and is considered a serviceable equipment for a career in politics. The following illustrative lines were written of a Californian gentleman in high political preferment, who has passed to his accounting:

> Of such tenacity his grip
> That nothing from his hand can slip.
> Well-buttered eels you may o'erwhelm
> In tubs of liquid slippery-elm
> In vain—from his detaining pinch
> They cannot struggle half an inch!
> 'Tis lucky that he so is planned
> That breath he draws not with his hand,
> For if he did, so great his greed
> He'd draw his last with eager speed.
> Nay, that were well, you say. Not so
> He'd draw but never let it go!

THEOSOPHY, *n.* An ancient faith having all the certitude of religion and all the mystery of science. The modern Theosophist holds, with the Buddhists, that we live an incalculable number of times on this earth, in as many several bodies, because one life is not long enough for our complete spiritual development; that is, a single lifetime does not suffice for us to become as wise and good as we choose to wish to become. To be absolutely wise and good—that is perfection; and the Theosophist is so keen-sighted as to have observed that everything desirous of improvement eventually attains perfection. Less competent observers are disposed to except cats, which seem neither wiser nor better than they were last year. The greatest and fattest of recent Theosophists was the late Madame Blavatsky, who had no cat.

TIGHTS, *n.* An habiliment of the stage designed to reinforce the general acclamation of the press agent with a particular publicity. Public attention was once somewhat diverted from this garment to Miss Lillian

Russell's refusal to wear it, and many were the conjectures as to her motive, the guess of Miss Pauline Hall showing a high order of ingenuity and sustained reflection. It was Miss Hall's belief that nature had not endowed Miss Russell with beautiful legs. This theory was impossible of acceptance by the male understanding, but the conception of a faulty female leg was of so prodigious originality as to rank among the most brilliant feats of philosophical speculation! It is strange that in all the controversy regarding Miss Russell's aversion to tights no one seems to have thought to ascribe it to what was known among the ancients as "modesty." The nature of that sentiment is now imperfectly understood, and possibly incapable of exposition with the vocabulary that remains to us. The study of lost arts has, however, been recently revived and some of the arts themselves recovered. This is an epoch of *renaissances,* and there is ground for hope that the primitive "blush" may be dragged from its hiding-place amongst the tombs of antiquity and hissed on to the stage.

TOMB, *n.* The House of Indifference. Tombs are now by common consent invested with a certain sanctity, but when they have been long tenanted it is considered no sin to break them open and rifle them, the famous Egyptologist, Dr. Huggyns, explaining that a tomb may be innocently "glened" as soon as its occupant is done "smellynge," the soul being then all exhaled. This reasonable view is now generally accepted by archæologists, whereby the noble science of Curiosity has been greatly dignified.

TOPE, *v.* To tipple, booze, swill, soak, guzzle, lush, bib, or swig. In the individual, toping is regarded with disesteem, but toping nations are in the forefront of civilization and power. When pitted against the hard-drinking Christians the abstemious Mahometans go down like grass before the scythe. In India one hundred thousand beef-eating and brandy-and-soda guzzling Britons hold in subjection two hundred and fifty million vegetarian abstainers of the same Aryan race. With what an easy grace the whisky-loving American pushed the temperate Spaniard out of his possessions! From the time when the Berserkers ravaged all the coasts of western Europe and lay drunk in every conquered port it has been the same way: everywhere the nations that drink too much are observed to fight rather well and not too righteously. Wherefore the estimable old ladies who abolished the canteen from the American army may justly boast of having materially augmented the nation's military power.

TORTOISE, *n.* A creature thoughtfully created to supply occasion for the following lines by the illustrious Ambat Delaso:

TO MY PET TORTOISE

My friend, you are not graceful—not at all;
Your gait's between a stagger and a sprawl.

Nor are you beautiful: your head's a snake's
To look at, and I do not doubt it aches.

As to your feet, they'd make an angel weep.
'Tis true you take them in whene'er you sleep.

No, you're not pretty, but you have, I own,
A certain firmness—mostly you're backbone.

Firmness and strength (you have a giant's thews)
Are virtues that the great know how to use—

I wish that they did not; yet, on the whole,
You lack—excuse my mentioning it—Soul.

So, to be candid, unreserved and true,
I'd rather you were I than I were you.

Perhaps, however, in a time to be,
When Man's extinct, a better world may see

Your progeny in power and control,
Due to the genesis and growth of Soul.

So I salute you as a reptile grand
Predestined to regenerate the land.

Father of Possibilities, O deign
To accept the homage of a dying reign!

In the far region of the unforeknown
I dream a tortoise upon every throne.

I see an Emperor his head withdraw
Into his carapace for fear of Law;

A King who carries something else than fat,
Howe'er acceptably he carries that;

A President not strenuously bent
On punishment of audible dissent—

Who never shot (it were a vain attack)
An armed or unarmed tortoise in the back;

Subjects and citizens that feel no need
To make the March of Mind a wild stampede;

All progress slow, contemplative, sedate,
And "Take your time" the word, in Church and State.

O Tortoise, 'tis a happy, happy dream,
My glorious testudinous régime!

I wish in Eden you'd brought this about
By slouching in and chasing Adam out.

TREE, *n.* A tall vegetable intended by nature to serve as a penal apparatus, though through a miscarriage of justice most trees bear only a negligible fruit, or none at all. When naturally fruited, the tree is a beneficent agency of civilization and an important factor in public morals. In the stern West and the sensitive South its fruit (white and black respectively) though not eaten, is agreeable to the public taste and, though not exported, profitable to the general welfare. That the legitimate relation of the tree to justice was no discovery of Judge Lynch (who, indeed, conceded it no primacy over the lamp-post and the bridge-girder) is made plain by the following passage from Morryster, who antedated him by two centuries:

While in y^t londe I was carryed to see ye Ghogo tree, whereof I had hearde moch talk; but sayynge y^t I saw naught remarkabyll in it, ye hed manne of ye villayge where it grewe made answer as followeth:

"Y^e tree is not nowe in fruite, but in his seasonne you shall see dependynge fr. his braunches all soch as have affroynted ye King his Majesty."

And I was furder tolde y^t ye worde "Ghogo" sygnifyeth in y^r tong ye same as "rapscal" in our owne.—*Trauvells in ye Easte.*

TRIAL, *n.* A formal inquiry designed to prove and put upon record the blameless characters of judges, advocates and jurors. In order to effect this purpose it is necessary to supply a contrast in the person of one who is called the defendant, the prisoner, or the accused. If the contrast is made sufficiently clear this person is made to undergo such an affliction as will give the virtuous gentlemen a comfortable sense of their immunity, added to that of their worth. In our day the accused is usually a human being, or a socialist, but in mediæval times, animals, fishes, reptiles and insects were brought to trial. A beast that had taken human life, or practiced sorcery, was duly arrested, tried and, if condemned, put to death by the public executioner. Insects ravaging grain fields, orchards or vineyards were cited to appeal by counsel before a civil tribunal, and after testimony, argument and condemnation, if they continued *in contumaciam* the matter was taken to a high ecclesiastical court, where they were solemnly excommunicated and anathematized. In a street of Toledo, some pigs that had wickedly run between the viceroy's legs, upsetting him, were arrested on a warrant, tried and punished. In Naples an ass was condemned to be burned at the stake, but the sentence appears not to have been executed. D'Addosio relates from the court records many trials of pigs, bulls, horses, cocks, dogs, goats, etc., greatly, it is believed, to the betterment of their conduct and morals. In 1451 a suit was brought against the leeches infesting some ponds about Berne, and the Bishop of Lausanne, instructed by the faculty of Heidelberg University, directed that some of "the aquatic worms" be brought before the local magistracy. This was done and the leeches, both present and absent, were ordered to leave the places that they had infested within three days on pain of incurring "the malediction of God." In the voluminous records of this *cause célèbre* nothing is found to show whether the offenders braved the punishment, or departed forthwith out of that inhospitable jurisdiction.

TRICHINOSIS, *n.* The pig's reply to proponents of porcophagy.

Moses Mendelssohn having fallen ill sent for a Christian physician, who at once diagnosed the philosopher's disorder as trichinosis, but tactfully gave it another name. "You need an immediate change of diet," he said; "you must eat six ounces of pork every other day."

"Pork?" shrieked the patient—"pork? Nothing shall induce me to touch it!"

"Do you mean that?" the doctor gravely asked.

"I swear it!"

"Good!—then I will undertake to cure you."

TRINITY, *n.* In the multiplex theism of certain Christian churches, three entirely distinct deities consistent with only one. Subordinate deities of the polytheistic faith, such as devils and angels, are not dowered with the power of combination, and must urge individually their claims to adoration and propitiation. The Trinity is one of the most sublime mysteries of our holy religion. In rejecting it because it is incomprehensible, Unitarians betray their inadequate sense of theological fundamentals. In religion we believe only what we do not understand, except in the instance of an intelligible doctrine that contradicts an incomprehensible one. In that case we believe the former as a part of the latter.

TROGLODYTE, *n.* Specifically, a cave-dweller of the paleolithic period, after the Tree and before the Flat. A famous community of troglodytes dwelt with David in the Cave of Adullam. The colony consisted of "every one that was in distress, and every one that was in debt, and every one that was discontented"—in brief, all the Socialists of Judah.

TRUCE, *n.* Friendship.

TRUTH, *n.* An ingenious compound of desirability and appearance. Discovery of truth is the sole purpose of philosophy, which is the most ancient occupation of the human mind and has a fair prospect of existing with increasing activity to the end of time.

TRUTHFUL, *adj.* Dumb and illiterate.

TRUST, *n.* In American politics, a large corporation composed in greater part of thrifty working men, widows of small means, orphans in the care of guardians and the courts, with many similar malefactors and public enemies.

TURKEY, *n.* A large bird whose flesh when eaten on certain religious anniversaries has the peculiar property of attesting piety and gratitude. Incidentally, it is pretty good eating.

TWICE, *adv.* Once too often.

TYPE, *n.* Pestilent bits of metal suspected of destroying civilization and enlightenment, despite their obvious agency in this incomparable dictionary.

TZETZE (or TSETSE) FLY, *n.* An African insect (*Glossina morsitans*) whose bite is commonly regarded as nature's most efficacious remedy for insomnia, though some patients prefer that of the American novelist (*Mendax interminabilis.*)

U

UBIQUITY, *n.* The gift or power of being in all places at one time, but not in all places at all times, which is omnipresence, an attribute of God and the luminiferous ether only. This important distinction between ubiquity and omnipresence was not clear to the mediæval Church and there was much bloodshed about it. Certain Lutherans, who affirmed the presence everywhere of Christ's body were known as Ubiquitarians. For this error they were doubtless damned, for Christ's body is present only in the eucharist, though that sacrament may be performed in more than one place simultaneously. In recent times ubiquity has not always been understood—not even by Sir Boyle Roche, for example, who held that a man cannot be in two places at once unless he is a bird.

UGLINESS, *n.* A gift of the gods to certain women, entailing virtue without humility.

ULTIMATUM, *n.* In diplomacy, a last demand before resorting to concessions.

Having received an ultimatum from Austria, the Turkish Ministry met to consider it.

"O servant of the Prophet," said the Sheik of the Imperial Chibouk to the Mamoosh of the Invincible Army, "how many unconquerable soldiers have we in arms?"

"Upholder of the Faith," that dignitary replied after examining his memoranda, "they are in numbers as the leaves of the forest!"

"And how many impenetrable battleships strike terror to the hearts of all Christian swine?" he asked the Imaum of the Ever Victorious Navy.

"Uncle of the Full Moon," was the reply, "deign to know that they are as the waves of the ocean, the sands of the desert and the stars of Heaven!"

For eight hours the broad brow of the Sheik of the Imperial Chibouk was corrugated with evidences of deep thought: he was calculating the chances of war. Then, "Sons of angels," he said, "the die is cast! I shall suggest to the Ulema of the Imperial Ear that he advise inaction. In the name of Allah, the council is adjourned."

UN-AMERICAN, *adj.* Wicked, intolerable, heathenish.

UNCTION, *n.* An oiling, or greasing. The rite of extreme unction consists in touching with oil consecrated by a bishop several parts of the body of one engaged in dying. Marbury relates that after the rite had been administered to a certain wicked English nobleman it was discovered that the oil had not been properly consecrated and no other could be obtained. When informed of this the sick man said in anger: "Then I'll be damned if I die!"

"My son," said the priest, "that is what we fear."

UNDERSTANDING, *n.* A cerebral secretion that enables one having it to know a house from a horse by the roof on the house. Its nature and laws have been exhaustively expounded by Locke, who rode a house, and Kant, who lived in a horse.

> His understanding was so keen
> That all things which he'd felt, heard, seen,
> He could interpret without fail
> If he was in or out of jail.
> He wrote of Inspiration's call
> Deep disquisitions on them all,
> Then, pent at last in an asylum,
> Performed the service to compile 'em.
> So great a writer, all men swore,
> They never had not read before.
> > *Jorrock Wormley.*

UNITARIAN, *n*. One who denies the divinity of a Trinitarian.

UNIVERSALIST, *n*. One who foregoes the advantage of a Hell for persons of another faith.

URBANITY, *n*. The kind of civility that urban observers ascribe to dwellers in all cities but New York. Its commonest expression is heard in the words, "I beg your pardon," and it is not inconsistent with disregard of the rights of others.

> The owner of a powder mill
> Was musing on a distant hill—
>   Something his mind foreboded—
> When from the cloudless sky there fell
> A deviled human kidney! Well,
>   The man's mill had exploded.
> His hat he lifted from his head;
> "I beg your pardon, sir," he said;
> "I didn't know 'twas loaded."
>   *Swatkin.*

USAGE, *n*. The First Person of the literary Trinity, the Second and Third being Custom and Conventionality. Imbued with a decent reverence for this Holy Triad an industrious writer may hope to produce books that will live as long as the fashion.

UXORIOUSNESS, *n*. A perverted affection that has strayed to one's own wife.

V

VALOR, *n*. A soldierly compound of vanity, duty and the gambler's hope.
"Why have you halted?" roared the commander of a division at Chickamauga, who had ordered a charge; "move forward, sir, at once."

"General," said the commander of the delinquent brigade, "I am persuaded that any further display of valor by my troops will bring them into collision with the enemy."

VANITY, *n.* The tribute of a fool to the worth of the nearest ass.

> They say that hens do cackle loudest when
> There's nothing vital in the eggs they've laid;
> And there are hens, professing to have made
> A study of mankind, who say that men
> Whose business 'tis to drive the tongue or pen
> Make the most clamorous fanfaronade
> O'er their most worthless work; and I'm afraid
> They're not entirely different from the hen.
> Lo! the drum-major in his coat of gold,
> His blazing breeches and high-towering cap—
> Imperiously pompous, grandly bold,
> Grim, resolute, an awe-inspiring chap!
> Who'd think this gorgeous creature's only virtue
> Is that in battle he will never hurt you?
> *Hannibal Hunsiker.*

VIRTUES, *n. pl.* Certain abstentions.

VITUPERATION, *n.* Satire, as understood by dunces and all such as suffer from an impediment in their wit.

VOTE, *n.* The instrument and symbol of a freeman's power to make a fool of himself and a wreck of his country.

W

w (double U) has, of all the letters in our alphabet, the only cumbrous name, the names of the others being monosyllabic. This advantage of the Roman alphabet over the Grecian is the more valued after audibly spelling out some simple Greek word, like ἐπιχοριαμβιχός. Still, it is now thought by the learned that other agencies than the difference of the two alphabets may have been concerned in the decline of "the glory that was Greece" and the rise of "the grandeur that was Rome." There can be no doubt, however, that by simplifying the name of W (calling it "wow," for example) our civilization could be, if not promoted, at least better endured.

WALL STREET, *n.* A symbol of sin for every devil to rebuke. That Wall Street is a den of thieves is a belief that serves every unsuccessful thief in place of a hope in Heaven. Even the great and good Andrew Carnegie has made his profession of faith in the matter.

> Carnegie the dauntless has uttered his call
> To battle: "The brokers are parasites all!"
> Carnegie, Carnegie, you'll never prevail;
> Keep the wind of your slogan to belly your sail,
> Go back to your isle of perpetual brume,
> Silence your pibroch, doff tartan and plume:
> Ben Lomond is calling his son from the fray—
> Fly, fly from the region of Wall Street away!
> While still you're possessed of a single baubee
> (I wish it were pledged to endowment of me)
> 'Twere wise to retreat from the wars of finance
> Lest its value decline ere your credit advance.
> For a man 'twixt a king of finance and the sea,
> Carnegie, Carnegie, your tongue is too free!
> *Anonymus Bink.*

WAR, *n.* A by-product of the arts of peace. The most menacing political condition is a period of international amity. The student of history who has not been taught to expect the unexpected may justly boast himself inaccessible to the light. "In time of peace prepare for war" has a deeper meaning than is commonly discerned; it means, not merely that all things earthly have an end—that change is the one immutable and eternal law—but that the soil of peace is thickly sown with seeds of war and singularly suited to their germination and growth. It was when Kubla Khan had decreed his "stately pleasure dome"—when, that is to say, there were peace and fat feasting in Xanadu—that he

> heard from far
> Ancestral voices prophesying war.

One of the greatest of poets, Coleridge was one of the wisest of men, and it was not for nothing that he read us this parable. Let us have a little less of "hands across the sea," and a little more of that elemental distrust that is the security of nations. War loves to come like a thief in the night; professions of eternal amity provide the night.

WASHINGTONIAN, *n.* A Potomac tribesman who exchanged the privilege of governing himself for the advantage of good government. In justice to him it should be said that he did not want to.

> They took away his vote and gave instead
> The right, when he had earned, to *eat* his bread.
> In vain—he clamors for his "boss," poor soul,
> To come again and part him from his roll.
>> *Offenbach Stutz.*

WEAKNESSES, *n. pl.* Certain primal powers of Tyrant Woman wherewith she holds dominion over the male of her species, binding him to the service of her will and paralyzing his rebellious energies.

WEATHER, *n.* The climate of an hour. A permanent topic of conversation among persons whom it does not interest, but who have inherited the tendency to chatter about it from naked arboreal ancestors whom it keenly concerned. The setting up of official weather bureaus and their maintenance in mendacity prove that even governments are accessible to suasion by the rude forefathers of the jungle.

> Once I dipt into the future far as human eye could see,
> And I saw the Chief Forecaster, dead as any one can be—
> Dead and damned and shut in Hades as a liar from his birth,
> With a record of unreason seldom paralleled on earth.
> While I looked he reared him solemnly, that incandescent youth,
> From the coals that he'd preferred to the advantages of truth.
> He cast his eyes about him and above him; then he wrote
> On a slab of thin asbestos what I venture here to quote—
> For I read it in the rose-light of the everlasting glow:
> "Cloudy; variable winds, with local showers; cooler; snow."
>> *Halcyon Jones.*

WEDDING, *n.* A ceremony at which two persons undertake to become one,

one undertakes to become nothing, and nothing undertakes to become supportable.

WEREWOLF, *n.* A wolf that was once, or is sometimes, a man. All werewolves are of evil disposition, having assumed a bestial form to gratify a bestial appetite, but some, transformed by sorcery, are as humane as is consistent with an acquired taste for human flesh.

Some Bavarian peasants having caught a wolf one evening, tied it to a post by the tail and went to bed. The next morning nothing was there! Greatly perplexed, they consulted the local priest, who told them that their captive was undoubtedly a werewolf and had resumed its human form during the night. "The next time that you take a wolf," the good man said, "see that you chain it by the leg, and in the morning you will find a Lutheran."

WHANGDEPOOTENAWAH, *n.* In the Ojibwa tongue, disaster; an unexpected affliction that strikes hard.

> Should you ask me whence this laughter,
> Whence this audible big-smiling,
> With its labial extension,
> With its maxillar distortion
> And its diaphragmic rhythmus
> Like the billowing of ocean,
> Like the shaking of a carpet,
> I should answer, I should tell you:
> From the great deeps of the spirit,
> From the unplummeted abysmus
> Of the soul this laughter welleth
> As the fountain, the gug-guggle,
> Like the river from the cañon,
> To entoken and give warning
> That my present mood is sunny.
> Should you ask me further question—
> Why the great deeps of the spirit,
> Why the unplummeted abysmus
> Of the soul extrudes this laughter,
> This all audible big-smiling,
> I should answer, I should tell you
> With a white heart, tumpitumpy,
> With a true tongue, honest Injun:
> William Bryan, he has Caught It,
> Caught the Whangdepootenawah!

Is't the sandhill crane, the shankank,
Standing in the marsh, the kneedeep,
Standing silent in the kneedeep
With his wing-tips crossed behind him
And his neck close-reefed before him,
With his bill, his william, buried
In the down upon his bosom,
With his head retracted inly,
While his shoulders overlook it?
Does the sandhill crane, the shankank,
Shiver grayly in the north wind,
Wishing he had died when little,
As the sparrow, the chipchip, does?
No 'tis not the Shankank standing,
Standing in the gray and dismal
Marsh, the gray and dismal kneedeep.
No, 'tis peerless William Bryan
Realizing that he's Caught It,
Caught the Whangdepootenawah!

WHEAT, *n.* A cereal from which a tolerably good whisky can with some difficulty be made, and which is used also for bread. The French are said to eat more bread *per capita* of population than any other people, which is natural, for only they know how to make the stuff palatable.

WHITE, *adj.* and *n.* Black.

WIDOW, *n.* A pathetic figure that the Christian world has agreed to take humorously, although Christ's tenderness towards widows was one of the most marked features of his character.

WINE, *n.* Fermented grape-juice known to the Women's Christian Union as "liquor," sometimes as "rum." Wine, madam, is God's next best gift to man.

WIT, *n.* The salt with which the American humorist spoils his intellectual cookery by leaving it out.

WITCH, *n.* (1) An ugly and repulsive old woman, in a wicked league with the devil. (2) A beautiful and attractive young woman, in wickedness a league beyond the devil.

WITTICISM, *n*. A sharp and clever remark, usually quoted, and seldom noted; what the Philistine is pleased to call a "joke."

WOMAN, *n*. An animal usually living in the vicinity of Man, and having a rudimentary susceptibility to domestication. It is credited by many of the elder zoölogists with a certain vestigial docility acquired in a former state of seclusion, but naturalists of the postsusananthony period, having no knowledge of the seclusion, deny the virtue and declare that such as creation's dawn beheld, it roareth now. The species is the most widely distributed of all beasts of prey, infesting all habitable parts of the globe, from Greenland's spicy mountains to India's moral strand. The popular name (wolf-man) is incorrect, for the creature is of the cat kind. The woman is lithe and graceful in its movements, especially the American variety (*Felis pugnans*), is omnivorous and can be taught not to talk.—*Balthasar Pober.*

WORMS'-MEAT, *n*. The finished product of which we are the raw material. The contents of the Taj Mahal, the Tombeau Napoleon and the Grantarium. Worms'-meat is usually outlasted by the structure that houses it, but "this too must pass away." Probably the silliest work in which a human being can engage is construction of a tomb for himself. The solemn purpose cannot dignify, but only accentuates by contrast the foreknown futility.

> Ambitious fool! so mad to be a show!
> How profitless the labor you bestow
>   Upon a dwelling whose magnificence
> The tenant neither can admire nor know.
>
> Build deep, build high, build massive as you can,
> The wanton grass-roots will defeat the plan
>   By shouldering asunder all the stones
> In what to you would be a moment's span.
>
> Time to the dead so all unreckoned flies
> That when your marble all is dust, arise,
>   If wakened, stretch your limbs and yawn—
> You'll think you scarcely can have closed your eyes.
>
> What though of all man's works your tomb alone
> Should stand till Time himself be overthrown?
>   Would it advantage you to dwell therein
> Forever as a stain upon a stone?
>
>   *Joel Huck.*

WORSHIP, *n.* Homo Creator's testimony to the sound construction and fine finish of Deus Creatus. A popular form of abjection, having an element of pride.

WRATH, *n.* Anger of a superior quality and degree, appropriate to exalted characters and momentous occasions; as, "the wrath of God," "the day of wrath," etc. Amongst the ancients the wrath of kings was deemed sacred, for it could usually command the agency of some god for its fit manifestation, as could also that of a priest. The Greeks before Troy were so harried by Apollo that they jumped out of the frying-pan of the wrath of Chryses into the fire of the wrath of Achilles, though Agamemnon, the sole offender, was neither fried nor roasted. A similar noted immunity was that of David when he incurred the wrath of Yahveh by numbering his people, seventy thousand of whom paid the penalty with their lives. God is now Love, and a director of the census performs his work without apprehension of disaster.

X

x in our alphabet being a needless letter has an added invincibility to the attacks of the spelling reformers, and like them, will doubtless last as long as the language. X is the sacred symbol of ten dollars, and in such words as Xmas, Xn, etc., stands for Christ, not, as is popularly supposed, because it represents a cross, but because the corresponding letter in the Greek alphabet is the initial of his name—Χριστός. If it represented a cross it would stand for St. Andrew, who "testified" upon one of that shape. In the algebra of psychology *x* stands for Woman's mind. Words beginning with X are Grecian and will not be defined in this standard English dictionary.

Y

YANKEE, *n.* In Europe, an American. In the Northern States of our Union, a New Englander. In the Southern States the word is unknown. (See DAMYANK.)

YEAR, *n.* A period of three hundred and sixty-five disappointments.

YESTERDAY, *n.* The infancy of youth, the youth of manhood, the entire past of age.

> But yesterday I should have thought me blest
> To stand high-pinnacled upon the peak
> Of middle life and look adown the bleak
> And unfamiliar foreslope to the West,
> Where solemn shadows all the land invest
> And stilly voices, half-remembered, speak
> Unfinished prophecy, and witch-fires freak
> The haunted twilight of the Dark of Rest.
> Yea, yesterday my soul was all aflame
> To stay the shadow on the dial's face
> At manhood's noonmark! Now, in God His name
> I chide aloud the little interspace
> Disparting me from Certitude, and fain
> Would know the dream and vision ne'er again.
> *Baruch Arnegriff.*

It is said that in his last illness the poet Arnegriff was attended at different times by seven doctors.

YOKE, *n.* An implement, madam, to whose Latin name, *jugum,* we owe one of the most illuminating words in our language—a word that defines the matrimonial situation with precision, point and poignancy. A thousand apologies for withholding it.

YOUTH, *n.* The Period of Possibility, when Archimedes finds a fulcrum, Cassandra has a following and seven cities compete for the honor of endowing a living Homer.

Youth is the true Saturnian Reign, the Golden Age on earth again, when figs are grown on thistles, and pigs betailed with whistles and, wearing silken bristles, live ever in clover, and cows fly over, delivering milk at every door, and Justice never is heard to snore, and every assassin is made a ghost and, howling, is cast into Baltimost!

Polydore Smith.

Z

ZANZIBARI, *n.* An inhabitant of the Sultanate of Zanzibar, off the eastern coast of Africa. The Zanzibaris, a warlike people, are best known in this country through a threatening diplomatic incident that occurred a few years ago. The American consul at the capital occupied a dwelling that faced the sea, with a sandy beach between. Greatly to the scandal of this official's family, and against repeated remonstrances of the official himself, the people of the city persisted in using the beach for bathing. One day a woman came down to the edge of the water and was stooping to remove her attire (a pair of sandals) when the consul, incensed beyond restraint, fired a charge of bird-shot into the most conspicuous part of her person. Unfortunately for the existing *entente cordiale* between two great nations, she was the Sultana.

ZEAL, *n.* A certain nervous disorder afflicting the young and inexperienced. A passion that goeth before a sprawl.

> When Zeal sought Gratitude for his reward
> He went away exclaiming: "O my Lord!"
> "What do you want?" the Lord asked, bending down.
> "An ointment for my cracked and bleeding crown."
>
> *Jum Coople.*

ZENITH, *n.* A point in the heavens directly overhead to a standing man or a growing cabbage. A man in bed or a cabbage in the pot is not considered as having a zenith, though from this view of the matter there was once a considerable dissent among the learned, some holding that the posture of the body was immaterial. These were called Horizontalists, their opponents, Verticalists. The Horizontalist heresy was finally extinguished by Xanobus, the philosopher-king of Abara, a zealous Verticalist. Entering an assembly of philosophers who were debating the matter, he cast a severed human head at the feet of his opponents and asked them to determine its zenith, explaining that its body was hanging by the heels outside. Observing that it was the head of their leader, the Horizontalists hastened to profess themselves converted to whatever opinion the Crown might be pleased to hold, and Horizontalism took its place among *fides defuncti*.

ZEUS, *n.* The chief of Grecian gods, adored by the Romans as Jupiter and by the modern Americans as God, Gold, Mob and Dog. Some explorers who have touched upon the shores of America, and one who professes to have penetrated a considerable distance into the interior, have thought that these four names stand for as many distinct deities, but in his monumental work on Surviving Faiths, Frumpp insists that the natives are monotheists, each having no other god than himself, whom he worships under many sacred names.

ZIGZAG, *v. t.* To move forward uncertainly, from side to side, as one carrying the white man's burden. (From *zed, z* and *jag,* an Icelandic word of unknown meaning.)

> He zedjagged so uncomen wyde
> Thet non coude pas on eyder syde;
> So, to com saufly thruh, I been
> Constreynet for to doodge betwene.
> *Munwele.*

ZOOLOGY, *n.* The science and history of the animal kingdom, including its king, the House Fly (*Musca maledicta.*) The father of Zoology was Aristotle, as is universally conceded, but the name of its mother has not come down to us. Two of the science's most illustrious expounders were Buffon and Oliver Goldsmith, from both of whom we learn (*L'Histoire générale des animaux* and *A History of Animated Nature*) that the domestic cow sheds its horns every two years.

CAN SUCH THINGS BE?

THE DEATH OF HALPIN FRAYSER

I

For by death is wrought greater change than hath been shown. Whereas in general the spirit that removed cometh back upon occasion, and is sometimes seen of those in flesh (appearing in the form of the body it bore) yet it hath happened that the veritable body without the spirit hath walked. And it is attested of those encountering who have lived to speak thereon that a lich so raised up hath no natural affection, nor remembrance thereof, but only hate. Also, it is known that some spirits which in life were benign become by death evil altogether.—*Hali.*

ONE dark night in midsummer a man waking from a dreamless sleep in a forest lifted his head from the earth, and staring a few moments into the blackness, said: "Catherine Larue." He said nothing more; no reason was known to him why he should have said so much.

The man was Halpin Frayser. He lived in St. Helena, but where he lives now is uncertain, for he is dead. One who practices sleeping in the woods with nothing under him but the dry leaves and the damp earth, and nothing over him but the branches from which the leaves have fallen and the sky from which the earth has fallen, cannot hope for great longevity, and Frayser had already attained the age of thirty-two. There are persons in this world, millions of persons, and far and away the best persons, who regard that as a very advanced age. They are the children. To those who view the voyage of life from the port of departure the bark that has accomplished any considerable distance appears already in close approach to the farther shore. However, it is not certain that Halpin Frayser came to his death by exposure.

He had been all day in the hills west of the Napa Valley, looking for doves and such small game as was in season. Late in the afternoon it had come on to be cloudy, and he had lost his bearings; and although he had only to go always downhill—everywhere the way to safety when one is lost—the absence of trails had so impeded him that he was overtaken by night while still in the forest. Unable in the darkness to penetrate the thickets of manzanita and other undergrowth, utterly bewildered and overcome with fatigue, he had lain down near the root of a large madroño and fallen into a dreamless sleep. It was hours later, in the very middle of the night, that one of God's mysterious messengers, gliding ahead of the incalculable host of his companions sweeping westward with the dawn line, pronounced the awakening word in the ear of the sleeper, who sat upright and spoke, he knew not why, a name, he knew not whose.

Halpin Frayser was not much of a philosopher, nor a scientist. The circumstance that, waking from a deep sleep at night in the midst of a forest, he had spoken aloud a name that he had not in memory and hardly had in mind did not arouse an enlightened curiosity to investigate the phenomenon. He thought it odd, and with a little perfunctory shiver, as if in deference to a seasonal presumption that the night was chill, he lay down again and went to sleep. But his sleep was no longer dreamless.

He thought he was walking along a dusty road that showed white in the gathering darkness of a summer night. Whence and whither it led, and why he traveled it, he did not know, though all seemed simple and natural, as is the way in dreams; for in the Land Beyond the Bed surprises cease from troubling and the judgment is at rest. Soon he came to a parting of the ways; leading from the highway was a road less traveled, having the appearance, indeed, of having been long abandoned, because, he thought, it led to something evil; yet he turned into it without hesitation, impelled by some imperious necessity.

As he pressed forward he became conscious that his way was haunted by invisible existences whom he could not definitely figure to his mind. From among the trees on either side he caught broken and incoherent whispers in a strange tongue which yet he partly understood. They seemed to him fragmentary utterances of a monstrous conspiracy against his body and soul.

It was now long after nightfall, yet the interminable forest through which he journeyed was lit with a wan glimmer having no point of diffusion, for in its mysterious lumination nothing cast a shadow. A shallow pool in the guttered depression of an old wheel rut, as from a recent rain, met his eye with a crimson gleam. He stooped and plunged his hand into it. It stained his fingers; it was blood! Blood, he then observed, was about him everywhere. The weeds growing rankly by the roadside showed it in blots and splashes on their big, broad leaves. Patches of dry dust between the wheelways were pitted and spattered as with a red rain. Defiling the trunks of the trees were broad maculations of crimson, and blood dripped like dew from their foliage.

All this he observed with a terror which seemed not incompatible with the fulfillment of a natural expectation. It seemed to him that it was all in expiation of some crime which, though conscious of his guilt, he could not rightly remember. To the menaces and mysteries of his surroundings the consciousness was an added horror. Vainly he sought by tracing life backward in memory, to reproduce the moment of his sin; scenes and incidents came crowding tumultuously into his mind, one picture effacing another, or commingling with it in confusion and obscurity, but nowhere could he catch a glimpse of what he sought. The failure augmented his terror; he felt as one who has murdered in the dark, not knowing whom nor why. So frightful was the situation—the mysterious light burned with so silent and awful a menace; the noxious plants, the trees that by common consent are invested with a melancholy or baleful character, so openly in his sight conspired against his peace; from overhead and all about came so audible and startling whispers and the sighs of creatures so obviously not of earth—that he could endure it no longer, and with a great effort to break some malign spell that bound his faculties to silence and inaction, he shouted with the full strength of his lungs! His voice broken, it seemed, into an infinite multitude of unfamiliar sounds, went babbling and stammering away into the distant reaches of the forest, died into silence, and all was as before. But he had made a beginning at resistance and was encouraged. He said:

"I will not submit unheard. There may be powers that are not malignant traveling this accursed road. I shall leave them a record and an appeal. I shall relate my wrongs, the persecutions that I endure—I, a helpless mortal, a penitent, an unoffending poet!" Halpin Frayser was a poet only as he was a penitent: in his dream.

Taking from his clothing a small red-leather pocketbook, one-half of which was leaved for memoranda, he discovered that he was without a pencil. He broke a twig from a bush, dipped it into a pool of blood and wrote rapidly. He had hardly touched the paper with the point of his twig when a low, wild peal of laughter broke out at a measureless distance away, and growing ever louder, seemed approaching ever nearer; a soulless, heartless, and unjoyous laugh, like that of the loon, solitary by the lakeside at midnight; a laugh which culminated in an unearthly shout close at hand, then died away by slow gradations, as if the accursed being that uttered it had withdrawn over the verge of the world whence it had come. But the man felt that this was not so—that it was near by and had not moved.

A strange sensation began slowly to take possession of his body and his mind. He could not have said which, if any, of his senses was affected; he felt it rather as a consciousness—a mysterious mental assurance of some overpowering presence—some supernatural malevolence different in kind from the invisible existences that swarmed about him, and superior to them in power. He knew that it had uttered that hideous laugh. And now it seemed to be approaching him; from what direction he did not know—dared not conjecture. All his former fears were forgotten or merged in the gigantic terror that now held him in thrall. Apart from that, he had but one thought: to complete his written appeal to the benign powers who, traversing the haunted wood, might some time rescue him if he should be denied the blessing of annihilation. He wrote with terrible rapidity, the twig in his fingers rilling blood without renewal; but in the middle of a sentence his hands denied their service to his will, his arms fell to his sides, the book to the earth; and powerless to move or cry out, he found himself staring into the sharply drawn face and blank, dead eyes of his own mother, standing white and silent in the garments of the grave!

II

In his youth Halpin Frayser had lived with his parents in Nashville, Tennessee. The Fraysers were well-to-do, having a good position in such society as had survived the wreck wrought by civil war. Their children had the social and educational opportunities of their time and place, and had responded to good associations and instruction with agreeable manners and cultivated minds. Halpin being the youngest and not over robust was perhaps a trifle "spoiled." He had the double disadvantage of a mother's assiduity and a father's neglect. Frayser *père* was what no Southern man of means is not—a politician. His country, or rather his section and State, made demands upon his time and attention so exacting that to those of his family he was compelled to turn an ear partly deafened by the thunder of the political captains and the shouting, his own included.

Young Halpin was of a dreamy, indolent and rather romantic turn, somewhat more addicted to literature than law, the profession to which he was bred. Among those of his relations who professed the modern faith of heredity it was well understood that in him the character of the late Myron Bayne, a maternal great-grandfather, had revisited the glimpses of the moon—by which orb Bayne had in his lifetime been sufficiently affected to be a poet of no small Colonial distinction. If not specially observed, it was observable that while a Frayser who was not the proud possessor of a sumptuous copy of the ancestral "poetical works" (printed at the family expense, and long ago withdrawn from an inhospitable market) was a rare Frayser indeed, there was an illogical indisposition to honor the great deceased in the person of his spiritual successor. Halpin was pretty generally deprecated as an intellectual black sheep who was likely at any moment to disgrace the flock by bleating in meter. The Tennessee Fraysers were a practical folk—not practical in the popular sense of devotion to sordid pursuits, but having a robust contempt for any qualities unfitting a man for the wholesome vocation of politics.

In justice to young Halpin it should be said that while in him were pretty faithfully reproduced most of the mental and moral characteristics ascribed by history and family tradition to the famous Colonial bard, his succession to the gift and faculty divine was purely inferential. Not only had he never been known to court the muse, but in truth he could not have written correctly a line of verse to save himself from the Killer of the Wise. Still, there was no knowing when the dormant faculty might wake and smite the lyre.

In the meantime the young man was rather a loose fish, anyhow. Between him and his mother was the most perfect sympathy, for secretly the lady was herself a devout disciple of the late and great Myron Bayne, though with the tact so generally and justly admired in her sex (despite the hardy calumniators who insist that it is essentially the same thing as cunning) she had always taken care to conceal her weakness from all eyes but those of him who shared it. Their common guilt in respect of that was an added tie between them. If in Halpin's youth his mother had "spoiled" him, he had assuredly done his part toward being spoiled. As he grew to such manhood as is attainable by a Southerner who does not care which way elections go the attachment between him and his beautiful mother—whom from early childhood he had called Katy—became yearly stronger and more tender. In these two romantic natures was manifest in a signal way that neglected phenomenon, the dominance of the sexual element in all the relations of life, strengthening, softening, and beautifying even those of consanguinity. The two were nearly inseparable, and by strangers observing their manner were not infrequently mistaken for lovers.

Entering his mother's boudoir one day Halpin Frayser kissed her upon the forehead, toyed for a moment with a lock of her dark hair which had escaped from its confining pins, and said, with an obvious effort at calmness:

"Would you greatly mind, Katy, if I were called away to California for a few weeks?"

It was hardly needful for Katy to answer with her lips a question to which her telltale cheeks had made instant reply. Evidently she would greatly mind; and the tears, too, sprang into her large brown eyes as corroborative testimony.

"Ah, my son," she said, looking up into his face with infinite tenderness, "I should have known that this was coming. Did I not lie awake a half of the night weeping because, during the other half, Grandfather Bayne had come to me in a dream, and standing by his portrait—young, too, and handsome as that—pointed to yours on the same wall? And when I looked it seemed that I could not see the features; you had been painted with a face cloth, such as we put upon the dead. Your father has laughed at me, but you and I, dear, know that such things are not for nothing. And I saw below the edge of the cloth the marks of hands on your throat—forgive me, but we have not been used to keep such things from each other. Perhaps you have another interpretation. Perhaps it does not mean that you will go to California. Or maybe you will take me with you?"

It must be confessed that this ingenious interpretation of the dream in the light of newly discovered evidence did not wholly commend itself to the son's more logical mind; he had, for the moment at least, a conviction that it foreshadowed a more simple and immediate, if less tragic, disaster than a visit to the Pacific Coast. It was Halpin Frayser's impression that he was to be garroted on his native heath.

"Are there not medicinal springs in California?" Mrs. Frayser resumed before he had time to give her the true reading of the dream— "places where one recovers from rheumatism and neuralgia? Look— my fingers feel so stiff; and I am almost sure they have been giving me great pain while I slept."

She held out her hands for his inspection. What diagnosis of her case the young man may have thought it best to conceal with a smile the historian is unable to state, but for himself he feels bound to say that fingers looking less stiff, and showing fewer evidences of even insensible pain, have seldom been submitted for medical inspection by even the fairest patient desiring a prescription of unfamiliar scenes.

The outcome of it was that of these two odd persons having equally odd notions of duty, the one went to California, as the interest of his client required, and the other remained at home in compliance with a wish that her husband was scarcely conscious of entertaining.

While in San Francisco Halpin Frayser was walking one dark night along the water front of the city, when, with a suddenness that surprised and disconcerted him, he became a sailor. He was in fact "shanghaied" aboard a gallant, gallant ship, and sailed for a far countree. Nor did his misfortunes end with the voyage; for the ship was cast ashore on an island of the South Pacific, and it was six years afterward when the survivors were taken off by a venturesome trading schooner and brought back to San Francisco.

Though poor in purse, Frayser was no less proud in spirit than he had been in the years that seemed ages and ages ago. He would accept no assistance from strangers, and it was while living with a fellow survivor near the town of St. Helena, awaiting news and remittances from home, that he had gone gunning and dreaming.

III

The apparition confronting the dreamer in the haunted wood—the thing so like, yet so unlike his mother—was horrible! It stirred no love nor longing in his heart; it came unattended with pleasant memories of a golden past—inspired no sentiment of any kind; all the finer emotions were swallowed up in fear. He tried to turn and run from before it, but his legs were as lead; he was unable to lift his feet from the ground. His arms hung helpless at his sides; of his eyes only he retained control, and these he dared not remove from the lusterless orbs of the apparition, which he knew was not a soul without a body, but that most dreadful of all existences infesting that haunted wood—a body without a soul! In its blank stare was neither love, nor pity, nor intelligence— nothing to which to address an appeal for mercy. "An appeal will not lie," he thought, with an absurd reversion to professional slang, making the situation more horrible, as the fire of a cigar might light up a tomb.

For a time, which seemed so long that the world grew gray with age and sin, and the haunted forest, having fulfilled its purpose in this monstrous culmination of its terrors, vanished out of his consciousness with all its sights and sounds, the apparition stood within a pace, regarding him with the mindless malevolence of a wild brute; then thrust its hands forward and sprang upon him with appalling ferocity! The act released his physical energies without unfettering his will; his mind was still spellbound, but his powerful body and agile limbs, endowed with a blind, insensate life of their own, resisted stoutly and well. For an instant he seemed to see this unnatural contest between a dead intelligence and a breathing mechanism only as a spectator—such fancies are in dreams; then he regained his identity almost as if by a leap forward into his body, and the straining automaton had a directing will as alert and fierce as that of its hideous antagonist.

But what mortal can cope with a creature of his dream? The imagination creating the enemy is already vanquished; the combat's result is the combat's cause. Despite his struggles—despite his strength and activity, which seemed wasted in a void, he felt the cold fingers close upon his throat. Borne backward to the earth, he saw above him the dead and drawn face within a hand's breadth of his own, and then all was black. A sound as of the beating of distant drums—a murmur of swarming voices, a sharp, far cry signing all to silence, and Halpin Frayser dreamed that he was dead.

IV

A warm, clear night had been followed by a morning of drenching fog. At about the middle of the afternoon of the preceding day a little whiff of light vapor—a mere thickening of the atmosphere, the ghost of a cloud—had been observed clinging to the western side of Mount St. Helena, away up along the barren altitudes near the summit. It was so thin, so diaphanous, so like a fancy made visible, that one would have said: "Look quickly! in a moment it will be gone."

In a moment it was visibly larger and denser. While with one edge it clung to the mountain, with the other it reached farther and farther out into the air above the lower slopes. At the same time it extended itself to north and south, joining small patches of mist that appeared to come out of the mountainside on exactly the same level, with an intelligent design to be absorbed. And so it grew and grew until the summit was shut out of view from the valley, and over the valley itself was an ever-extending canopy, opaque and gray. At Calistoga, which lies near the head of the valley and the foot of the mountain, there were a starless night and a sunless morning. The fog, sinking into the valley, had reached southward, swallowing up ranch after ranch, until it had blotted out the town of St. Helena, nine miles away. The dust in the road was laid; trees were adrip with moisture; birds sat silent in their coverts; the morning light was wan and ghastly, with neither color nor fire.

Two men left the town of St. Helena at the first glimmer of dawn, and walked along the road northward up the valley toward Calistoga. They carried guns on their shoulders, yet no one having knowledge of such matters could have mistaken them for hunters of bird or beast. They were a deputy sheriff from Napa and a detective from San Francisco—Holker and Jaralson, respectively. Their business was man-hunting.

"How far is it?" inquired Holker, as they strode along, their feet stirring white the dust beneath the damp surface of the road.

"The White Church? Only a half mile farther," the other answered. "By the way," he added, "it is neither white nor a church; it is an abandoned schoolhouse, gray with age and neglect. Religious services were once held in it—when it was white, and there is a graveyard that would delight a poet. Can you guess why I sent for you, and told you to come heeled?"

"Oh, I never have bothered you about things of that kind. I've always found you communicative when the time came. But if I may hazard a guess, you want me to help you arrest one of the corpses in the grave-yard."

"You remember Branscom?" said Jaralson, treating his companion's wit with the inattention that it deserved.

"The chap who cut his wife's throat? I ought; I wasted a week's work on him and had my expenses for my trouble. There is a reward of five hundred dollars, but none of us ever got a sight of him. You don't mean to say—"

"Yes, I do. He has been under the noses of you fellows all the time. He comes by night to the old graveyard at the White Church."

"The devil! That's where they buried his wife."

"Well, you fellows might have had sense enough to suspect that he would return to her grave some time."

"The very last place that anyone would have expected him to return to."

"But you had exhausted all the other places. Learning your failure at them, I 'laid for him' there."

"And you found him?"

"Damn it! he found *me*. The rascal got the drop on me—regularly held me up and made me travel. It's God's mercy that he didn't go through me. Oh, he's a good one, and I fancy the half of that reward is enough for me if you're needy."

Holker laughed good humoredly, and explained that his creditors were never more importunate.

"I wanted merely to show you the ground, and arrange a plan with you," the detective explained. "I thought it as well for us to be heeled, even in daylight."

"The man must be insane," said the deputy sheriff. "The reward is for his capture and conviction. If he's mad he won't be convicted."

Mr. Holker was so profoundly affected by that possible failure of justice that he involuntarily stopped in the middle of the road, then resumed his walk with abated zeal.

"Well, he looks it," assented Jaralson. "I'm bound to admit that a more unshaven, unshorn, unkempt, and uneverything wretch I never saw outside the ancient and honorable order of tramps. But I've gone in for him, and can't make up my mind to let go. There's glory in it for us, anyhow. Not another soul knows that he is this side of the Mountains of the Moon."

"All right," Holker said; "we will go and view the ground," and he added, in the words of a once favorite inscription for tombstones:

"'where you must shortly lie'—I mean, if old Branscom ever gets tired of you and your impertinent intrusion. By the way, I heard the other day that 'Branscom' was not his real name."

"What is?"

"I can't recall it. I had lost all interest in the wretch, and it did not fix itself in my memory—something like Pardee. The woman whose throat he had the bad taste to cut was a widow when he met her. She had come to California to look up some relatives—there are persons who will do that sometimes. But you know all that."

"Naturally."

"But not knowing the right name, by what happy inspiration did you find the right grave? The man who told me what the name was said it had been cut on the headboard."

"I don't know the right grave." Jaralson was apparently a trifle reluctant to admit his ignorance of so important a point of his plan. "I have been watching about the place generally. A part of our work this morning will be to identify that grave. Here is the White Church."

For a long distance the road had been bordered by fields on both sides, but now on the left there was a forest of oaks, madroños, and gigantic spruces whose lower parts only could be seen, dim and ghostly in the fog. The undergrowth was, in places, thick, but nowhere impenetrable. For some moments Holker saw nothing of the building, but as they turned into the woods it revealed itself in faint gray outline through the fog, looking huge and far away. A few steps more, and it was within an arm's length, distinct, dark with moisture, and insignificant in size. It had the usual country-schoolhouse form—belonged to the packing-box order of architecture; had an underpinning of stones, a moss-grown roof, and blank window spaces, whence both glass and sash had long departed. It was ruined, but not a ruin—a typical Californian substitute for what are known to guide-bookers abroad as "monuments of the past." With scarcely a glance at this uninteresting structure Jaralson moved on into the dripping undergrowth beyond.

"I will show you where he held me up," he said. "This is the grave-yard."

Here and there among the bushes were small inclosures containing graves, sometimes no more than one. They were recognized as graves by the discolored stones or rotting boards at head and foot, leaning at all angles, some prostrate; by the ruined picket fences surrounding them;

or, infrequently, by the mound itself showing its gravel through the fallen leaves. In many instances nothing marked the spot where lay the vestiges of some poor mortal—who, leaving "a large circle of sorrowing friends," had been left by them in turn—except a depression in the earth, more lasting than that in the spirits of the mourners. The paths, if any paths had been, were long obliterated; trees of a considerable size had been permitted to grow up from the graves and thrust aside with root or branch the inclosing fences. Over all was that air of abandonment and decay which seems nowhere so fit and significant as in a village of the forgotten dead.

As the two men, Jaralson leading, pushed their way through the growth of young trees, that enterprising man suddenly stopped and brought up his shotgun to the height of his breast, uttered a low note of warning, and stood motionless, his eyes fixed upon something ahead. As well as he could, obstructed by brush, his companion, though seeing nothing, imitated the posture and so stood, prepared for what might ensue. A moment later Jaralson moved cautiously forward, the other following.

Under the branches of an enormous spruce lay the dead body of a man. Standing silent above it they noted such particulars as first strike the attention—the face, the attitude, the clothing; whatever most promptly and plainly answers the unspoken question of a sympathetic curiosity.

The body lay upon its back, the legs wide apart. One arm was thrust upward, the other outward; but the latter was bent acutely, and the hand was near the throat. Both hands were tightly clenched. The whole attitude was that of desperate but ineffectual resistance to—what?

Near by lay a shotgun and a game bag through the meshes of which was seen the plumage of shot birds. All about were evidences of a furious struggle; small sprouts of poison-oak were bent and denuded of leaf and bark; dead and rotting leaves had been pushed into heaps and ridges on both sides of the legs by the action of other feet than theirs; alongside the hips were unmistakable impressions of human knees.

The nature of the struggle was made clear by a glance at the dead man's throat and face. While breast and hands were white, those were purple—almost black. The shoulders lay upon a low mound, and the head was turned back at an angle otherwise impossible, the expanded eyes staring blankly backward in a direction opposite to that of the feet. From the froth filling the open mouth the tongue protruded, black and swollen. The throat showed horrible contusions; not mere finger-marks, but bruises and lacerations wrought by two strong hands that must have buried themselves in the yielding flesh, maintaining their terrible grasp until long after death. Breast, throat, face, were wet; the clothing was saturated; drops of water, condensed from the fog, studded the hair and mustache.

All this the two men observed without speaking—almost at a glance. Then Holker said:

"Poor devil! he had a rough deal."

Jaralson was making a vigilant circumspection of the forest, his shot-gun held in both hands and at full cock, his finger upon the trigger.

"The work of a maniac," he said, without withdrawing his eyes from the inclosing wood. "It was done by Branscom—Pardee."

Something half hidden by the disturbed leaves on the earth caught Holker's attention. It was a red-leather pocketbook. He picked it up and opened it. It contained leaves of white paper for memoranda, and upon the first leaf was the name "Halpin Frayser." Written in red on several succeeding leaves—scrawled as if in haste and barely legible—were the following lines, which Holker read aloud, while his companion con-tinued scanning the dim gray confines of their narrow world and hear-ing matter of apprehension in the drip of water from every burdened branch:

"Enthralled by some mysterious spell, I stood
    In the lit gloom of an enchanted wood.
        The cypress there and myrtle twined their boughs,
    Significant, in baleful brotherhood.

"The brooding willow whispered to the yew;
    Beneath, the deadly nightshade and the rue,
        With immortelles self-woven into strange
    Funereal shapes, and horrid nettles grew.

"No song of bird nor any drone of bees,
    Nor light leaf lifted by the wholesome breeze:
        The air was stagnant all, and Silence was
    A living thing that breathed among the trees.

"Conspiring spirits whispered in the gloom,
    Half-heard, the stilly secrets of the tomb.

With blood the trees were all adrip; the leaves
Shone in the witch-light with a ruddy bloom.

"I cried aloud!—the spell, unbroken still,
Rested upon my spirit and my will.
Unsouled, unhearted, hopeless and forlorn,
I strove with monstrous presages of ill!

"At last the viewless—"

Holker ceased reading; there was no more to read. The manuscript broke off in the middle of a line.

"That sounds like Bayne," said Jaralson, who was something of a scholar in his way. He had abated his vigilance and stood looking down at the body.

"Who's Bayne?" Holker asked rather incuriously.

"Myron Bayne, a chap who flourished in the early years of the nation—more than a century ago. Wrote mighty dismal stuff; I have his collected works. That poem is not among them, but it must have been omitted by mistake."

"It is cold," said Holker; "let us leave here; we must have up the coroner from Napa."

Jaralson said nothing, but made a movement in compliance. Passing the end of the slight elevation of earth upon which the dead man's head and shoulders lay, his foot struck some hard substance under the rotting forest leaves, and he took the trouble to kick it into view. It was a fallen headboard, and painted on it were the hardly decipherable words, "Catherine Larue."

"Larue, Larue!" exclaimed Holker, with sudden animation. "Why, that is the real name of Branscom—not Pardee. And—bless my soul! how it all comes to me—the murdered woman's name had been Frayser!"

"There is some rascally mystery here," said Detective Jaralson. "I hate anything of that kind."

There came to them out of the fog—seemingly from a great distance—the sound of a laugh, a low, deliberate, soulless laugh, which had no more of joy than that of a hyena night-prowling in the desert; a laugh that rose by slow gradation, louder and louder, clearer, more distinct and terrible, until it seemed barely outside the narrow circle of their vision; a laugh so unnatural, so unhuman, so devilish, that it filled those hardy man-hunters with a sense of dread unspeakable! They did not move their weapons nor think of them; the menace of that horrible sound was not of the kind to be met with arms. As it had grown out of silence, so now it died away; from a culminating shout which had seemed almost in their ears, it drew itself away into the distance, until its failing notes, joyless and mechanical to the last, sank to silence at a measureless remove.

THE SECRET OF MACARGER'S GULCH

NORTHWESTWARDLY from Indian Hill, about nine miles as the crow flies, is Macarger's Gulch. It is not much of a gulch—a mere depression between two wooded ridges of inconsiderable height. From its mouth up to its head—for gulches, like rivers, have an anatomy of their own—the distance does not exceed two miles, and the width at bottom is at only one place more than a dozen yards; for most of the distance on either side of the little brook which drains it in winter, and goes dry in the early spring, there is no level ground at all; the steep slopes of the hills, covered with an almost impenetrable growth of manzanita and chemisal, are parted by nothing but the width of the water course. No one but an occasional enterprising hunter of the vicinity ever goes into Macarger's Gulch, and five miles away it is unknown, even by name. Within that distance in any direction are far more conspicuous topographical features without names, and one might try in vain to ascertain by local inquiry the origin of the name of this one.

About midway between the head and the mouth of Macarger's Gulch, the hill on the right as you ascend is cloven by another gulch, a short dry one, and at the junction of the two is a level space of two or three acres, and there a few years ago stood an old board house containing one small room. How the component parts of the house, few and simple as they were, had been assembled at that almost inaccessible point is a problem in the solution of which there would be greater satisfaction than advantage. Possibly the creek bed is a reformed road. It is certain that the gulch was at one time pretty thoroughly prospected by miners, who must have had some means of getting in with at least pack animals carrying tools and supplies; their profits, apparently, were not such as would have justified any considerable outlay to connect Macarger's Gulch with any center of civilization enjoying the distinction of a sawmill. The house, however, was there, most of it. It lacked a door and a window frame, and the chimney of mud and stones had fallen into an unlovely heap, overgrown with rank weeds. Such humble furniture as there may once have been and much of the lower weatherboarding, had served as fuel in the camp fires of hunters; as had also, probably, the curbing of an old well, which at the time I write of existed in the form of a rather wide but not very deep depression near by.

One afternoon in the summer of 1874, I passed up Macarger's Gulch from the narrow valley into which it opens, by following the dry bed of the brook. I was quail-shooting and had made a bag of about a dozen birds by the time I had reached the house described, of whose existence I was until then unaware. After rather carelessly inspecting the ruin I resumed my sport, and having fairly good success prolonged it until near sunset, when it occurred to me that I was a long way from any human habitation—too far to reach one by nightfall. But in my game bag was food, and the old house would afford shelter, if shelter were needed on a warm and dewless night in the foothills of the Sierra Nevada, where one may sleep in comfort on the pine needles, without covering. I am fond of solitude and love the night, so my resolution to "camp out" was soon taken, and by the time that it was dark I had made my bed of boughs and grasses in a corner of the room and was roasting a quail at a fire that I had kindled on the hearth. The smoke escaped out of the ruined chimney, the light illuminated the room with a kindly glow, and as I ate my simple meal of plain bird and drank the remains of a bottle of red wine which had served me all the afternoon in place of the water, which the region did not supply, I experienced a sense of comfort which better fare and accommodations do not always give.

Nevertheless, there was something lacking. I had a sense of comfort, but not of security. I detected myself staring more frequently at the open doorway and blank window than I could find warrant for doing. Outside these apertures all was black, and I was unable to repress a certain feeling of apprehension as my fancy pictured the outer world and filled it with unfriendly entities, natural and supernatural—chief among which, in their respective classes, were the grizzly bear, which I knew was occasionally still seen in that region, and the ghost, which I had reason to think was not. Unfortunately, our feelings do not always respect the law of probabilities, and to me that evening, the possible and the impossible were equally disquieting.

Everyone who has had experience in the matter must have observed that one confronts the actual and imaginary perils of the night with far less apprehension in the open air than in a house with an open doorway. I felt this now as I lay on my leafy couch in a corner of the room next to the chimney and permitted my fire to die out. So strong became my sense of the presence of something malign and menacing in the place, that I found myself almost unable to withdraw my eyes from the opening, as in the deepening darkness it became more and more indistinct. And when the last little flame flickered and went out I grasped the shotgun which I had laid at my side and actually turned the muzzle in the direction of the now invisible entrance, my thumb on one of the hammers, ready to cock the piece, my breath suspended, my muscles rigid and tense. But later I laid down the weapon with a sense of shame and mortification. What did I fear, and why?—I, to whom the night had been

> a more familiar face
> Than that of man—

I, in whom that element of hereditary superstition from which none of us is altogether free had given to solitude and darkness and silence only a more alluring interest and charm! I was unable to comprehend my folly, and losing in the conjecture the thing conjectured of, I fell asleep. And then I dreamed.

I was in a great city in a foreign land—a city whose people were of my own race, with minor differences of speech and costume; yet precisely what these were I could not say; my sense of them was indistinct. The city was dominated by a great castle upon an overlooking height whose name I knew, but could not speak. I walked through many streets, some broad and straight with high, modern buildings, some narrow, gloomy, and tortuous, between the gables of quaint old houses whose overhanging stories, elaborately ornamented with carvings in wood and stone, almost met above my head.

I sought someone whom I had never seen, yet knew that I should recognize when found. My quest was not aimless and fortuitous; it had a definite method. I turned from one street into another without hesitation and threaded a maze of intricate passages, devoid of the fear of losing my way.

Presently I stopped before a low door in a plain stone house which might have been the dwelling of an artisan of the better sort, and without announcing myself, entered. The room, rather sparely furnished, and lighted by a single window with small diamond-shaped panes, had but two occupants; a man and a woman. They took no notice of my intrusion, a circumstance which, in the manner of dreams, appeared entirely natural. They were not conversing; they sat apart, unoccupied and sullen.

The woman was young and rather stout, with fine large eyes and a certain grave beauty; my memory of her expression is exceedingly vivid, but in dreams one does not observe the details of faces. About her shoulders was a plaid shawl. The man was older, dark, with an evil face made more forbidding by a long scar extending from near the left temple diagonally downward into the black mustache; though in my dreams it seemed rather to haunt the face as a thing apart—I can express it no otherwise—than to belong to it. The moment that I found the man and woman I knew them to be husband and wife.

What followed, I remember indistinctly; all was confused and inconsistent—made so, I think, by gleams of consciousness. It was as if two pictures, the scene of my dream, and my actual surroundings, had been blended, one overlying the other, until the former, gradually fading, disappeared, and I was broad awake in the deserted cabin, entirely and tranquilly conscious of my situation.

My foolish fear was gone, and opening my eyes I saw that my fire, not altogether burned out, had revived by the falling of a stick and was again lighting the room. I had probably slept only a few minutes, but my commonplace dream had somehow so strongly impressed me that I was no longer drowsy; and after a little while I rose, pushed the embers of my fire together, and lighting my pipe proceeded in a rather ludicrously methodical way to meditate upon my vision.

It would have puzzled me then to say in what respect it was worth attention. In the first moment of serious thought that I gave to the matter I recognized the city of my dream as Edinburgh, where I had never been; so if the dream was a memory it was a memory of pictures and description. The recognition somehow deeply impressed me; it was as if something in my mind insisted rebelliously against will and reason on the importance of all this. And that faculty, whatever it was, asserted also a control of my speech. "Surely," I said aloud, quite involuntarily, "the MacGregors must have come here from Edinburgh."

At the moment, neither the substance of this remark nor the fact of my making it, surprised me in the least; it seemed entirely natural that I should know the name of my dreamfolk and something of their history. But the absurdity of it all soon dawned upon me: I laughed aloud, knocked the ashes from my pipe and again stretched myself upon my bed of boughs and grass, where I lay staring absently into my failing fire, with no further thought of either my dream or my surroundings. Suddenly the single remaining flame crouched for a moment, then, springing upward, lifted itself clear of its embers and expired in air. The darkness was absolute.

At that instant—almost, it seemed, before the gleam of the blaze had faded from my eyes—there was a dull, dead sound, as of some heavy body falling upon the floor, which shook beneath me as I lay. I sprang to a sitting posture and groped at my side for my gun; my notion was that some wild beast had leaped in through the open window. While the flimsy structure was still shaking from the impact I heard the sound of blows, the scuffling of feet upon the floor, and then—it seemed to come from almost within reach of my hand, the sharp shrieking of a woman in mortal agony. So horrible a cry I had never heard nor conceived; it utterly unnerved me; I was conscious for a moment of nothing but my own terror! Fortunately my hand now found the weapon of which it was in search, and the familiar touch somewhat restored me. I leaped to my feet, straining my eyes to pierce the darkness. The violent sounds had ceased, but more terrible than these, I heard, at what seemed long intervals, the faint intermittent gasping of some living, dying thing!

As my eyes grew accustomed to the dim light of the coals in the fireplace, I saw first the shapes of the door and window, looking blacker than the black of the walls. Next, the distinction between wall and floor became discernible, and at last I was sensible to the form and full expanse of the floor from end to end and side to side. Nothing was visible and the silence was unbroken.

With a hand that shook a little, the other still grasping my gun, I restored my fire and made a critical examination of the place. There was nowhere any sign that the cabin had been entered. My own tracks were visible in the dust covering the floor, but there were no others. I relit my pipe, provided fresh fuel by ripping a thin board or two from the inside of the house—I did not care to go into the darkness out of doors— and passed the rest of the night smoking and thinking, and feeding my fire; not for added years of life would I have permitted that little flame to expire again.

Some years afterward I met in Sacramento a man named Morgan, to whom I had a note of introduction from a friend in San Francisco. Dining with him one evening at his home I observed various "trophies" upon the wall, indicating that he was fond of shooting. It turned out that he was, and in relating some of his feats he mentioned having been in the region of my adventure.

"Mr. Morgan," I asked abruptly, "do you know a place up there called Macarger's Gulch?"

"I have good reason to," he replied; "it was I who gave to the newspapers, last year, the accounts of the finding of the skeleton there."

I had not heard of it; the accounts had been published, it appeared, while I was absent in the East.

"By the way," said Morgan, "the name of the gulch is a corruption; it should have been called 'MacGregor's.' My dear," he added, speaking to his wife, "Mr. Elderson has upset his wine."

That was hardly accurate—I had simply dropped it, glass and all.

"There was an old shanty once in the gulch," Morgan resumed when the ruin wrought by my awkwardness had been repaired, "but just previously to my visit it had been blown down, or rather blown away, for its *débris* was scattered all about, the very floor being parted, plank from plank. Between two of the sleepers still in position I and my companion observed the remnant of a plaid shawl, and examining it found that it was wrapped about the shoulders of the body of a woman, of which but little remained besides the bones, partly covered with fragments of clothing, and brown dry skin. But we will spare Mrs. Morgan," he added with a smile. The lady had indeed exhibited signs of disgust rather than sympathy.

"It is necessary to say, however," he went on, "that the skull was fractured in several places, as by blows of some blunt instrument; and that instrument itself—a pick-handle, still stained with blood—lay under the boards near by."

Mr. Morgan turned to his wife. "Pardon me, my dear," he said with affected solemnity, "for mentioning these disagreeable particulars, the natural though regrettable incidents of a conjugal quarrel—resulting, doubtless, from the luckless wife's insubordination."

"I ought to be able to overlook it," the lady replied with composure; "you have so many times asked me to in those very words."

I thought he seemed rather glad to go on with his story.

"From these and other circumstances," he said, "the coroner's jury found that the deceased, Janet MacGregor, came to her death from blows inflicted by some person to the jury unknown; but it was added that the evidence pointed strongly to her husband, Thomas MacGregor, as the guilty person. But Thomas MacGregor has never been found nor heard of. It was learned that the couple came from Edinburgh, but not —my dear, do you not observe that Mr. Elderson's boneplate has water in it?"

I had deposited a chicken bone in my finger bowl.

"In a little cupboard I found a photograph of MacGregor, but it did not lead to his capture."

"Will you let me see it?" I said.

The picture showed a dark man with an evil face made more forbidding by a long scar extending from near the temple diagonally downward into the black mustache.

"By the way, Mr. Elderson," said my affable host, "may I know why you asked about 'Macarger's Gulch'?"

"I lost a mule near there once," I replied, "and the mischance has— has quite—upset me."

"My dear," said Mr. Morgan, with the mechanical intonation of an interpreter translating, "the loss of Mr. Elderson's mule has peppered his coffee."

ONE SUMMER NIGHT

THE fact that Henry Armstrong was buried did not seem to him to prove that he was dead: he had always been a hard man to convince. That he really was buried, the testimony of his senses compelled him to admit. His posture—flat upon his back, with his hands crossed upon his stomach and tied with something that he easily broke without profitably altering the situation—the strict confinement of his entire person, the black darkness and profound silence, made a body of evidence impossible to controvert and he accepted it without cavil.

But dead—no; he was only very, very ill. He had, withal, the invalid's apathy and did not greatly concern himself about the uncommon fate that had been allotted to him. No philosopher was he—just a plain, commonplace person gifted, for the time being, with a pathological indifference: the organ that he feared consequences with was torpid. So, with no particular apprehension for his immediate future, he fell asleep and all was peace with Henry Armstrong.

But something was going on overhead. It was a dark summer night, shot through with infrequent shimmers of lightning silently firing a cloud lying low in the west and portending a storm. These brief, stammering illuminations brought out with ghastly distinctness the monuments and headstones of the cemetery and seemed to set them dancing. It was not a night in which any credible witness was likely to be straying about a cemetery, so the three men who were there, digging into the grave of Henry Armstrong, felt reasonably secure.

Two of them were young students from a medical college a few miles away; the third was a gigantic Negro known as Jess. For many years Jess had been employed about the cemetery as a man-of-all-work and it was his favorite pleasantry that he knew "every soul in the place." From the nature of what he was now doing it was inferable that the place was not so populous as its register may have shown it to be.

Outside the wall, at the part of the grounds farthest from the public road, were a horse and a light wagon, waiting.

The work of excavation was not difficult: the earth with which the grave had been loosely filled a few hours before offered little resistance and was soon thrown out. Removal of the casket from its box was less easy, but it was taken out, for it was a perquisite of Jess, who carefully unscrewed the cover and laid it aside, exposing the body in black trousers and white shirt. At that instant the air sprang to flame, a cracking shock of thunder shook the stunned world and Henry Armstrong tranquilly sat up. With inarticulate cries the men fled in terror, each in a different direction. For nothing on earth could two of them have been persuaded to return. But Jess was of another breed.

In the gray of the morning the two students, pallid and haggard from anxiety and with the terror of their adventure still beating tumultuously in their blood, met at the medical college.

"You saw it?" cried one.

"God! yes—what are we to do?"

They went around to the rear of the building, where they saw a horse, attached to a light wagon, hitched to a gatepost near the door of the dissecting-room. Mechanically they entered the room. On a bench in the obscurity sat the Negro Jess. He rose, grinning, all eyes and teeth.

"I'm waiting for my pay," he said.

Stretched naked on a long table lay the body of Henry Armstrong, the head defiled with blood and clay from a blow with a spade.

THE MOONLIT ROAD

I

STATEMENT OF JOEL HETMAN, JR.

I AM the most unfortunate of men. Rich, respected, fairly well educated and of sound health—with many other advantages usually valued by those having them and coveted by those who have them not— I sometimes think that I should be less unhappy if they had been denied me, for then the contrast between my outer and my inner life would not be continually demanding a painful attention. In the stress of privation and the need of effort I might sometimes forget the somber secret ever baffling the conjecture that it compels.

I am the only child of Joel and Julia Hetman. The one was a well-to-do country gentleman, the other a beautiful and accomplished woman to whom he was passionately attached with what I now know to have been a jealous and exacting devotion. The family home was a few miles from Nashville, Tennessee, a large, irregularly built dwelling of no particular order of architecture, a little way off the road, in a park of trees and shrubbery.

At the time of which I write I was nineteen years old, a student at Yale. One day I received a telegram from my father of such urgency that in compliance with its unexplained demand I left at once for home. At the railway station in Nashville a distant relative awaited me to apprise me of the reason for my recall: my mother had been barbarously murdered—why and by whom none could conjecture, but the circumstances were these:

My father had gone to Nashville, intending to return the next afternoon. Something prevented his accomplishing the business in hand, so he returned on the same night, arriving just before the dawn. In his testimony before the coroner he explained that having no latchkey and not caring to disturb the sleeping servants, he had, with no clearly defined intention, gone round to the rear of the house. As he turned an angle of the building, he heard a sound as of a door gently closed, and saw in the darkness, indistinctly, the figure of a man, which instantly disappeared among the trees of the lawn. A hasty pursuit and brief search of the grounds in the belief that the trespasser was some one secretly visiting a servant proving fruitless, he entered at the unlocked door and mounted the stairs to my mother's chamber. Its door was open, and stepping into black darkness he fell headlong over some heavy object on the floor. I may spare myself the details; it was my poor mother, dead of strangulation by human hands!

Nothing had been taken from the house, the servants had heard no sound, and excepting those terrible finger-marks upon the dead woman's throat—dear God! that I might forget them!—no trace of the assassin was ever found.

I gave up my studies and remained with my father, who, naturally, was greatly changed. Always of a sedate, taciturn disposition, he now fell into so deep a dejection that nothing could hold his attention, yet anything—a footfall, the sudden closing of a door—aroused in him a fitful interest; one might have called it an apprehension. At any small surprise of the senses he would start visibly and sometimes turn pale, then relapse into a melancholy apathy deeper than before. I suppose he was what is called a "nervous wreck." As to me, I was younger then than now—there is much in that. Youth is Gilead, in which is balm for every wound. Ah, that I might again dwell in that enchanted land! Unacquainted with grief, I knew not how to appraise my bereavement; I could not rightly estimate the strength of the stroke.

One night, a few months after the dreadful event, my father and I walked home from the city. The full moon was about three hours above the eastern horizon; the entire countryside had the solemn stillness of a summer night; our footfalls and the ceaseless song of the katydids were the only sound aloof. Black shadows of bordering trees lay athwart the road, which, in the short reaches between, gleamed a ghostly white. As we approached the gate to our dwelling, whose front was in shadow, and in which no light shone, my father suddenly stopped and clutched my arm, saying, hardly above his breath:

"God! God! what is that?"

"I hear nothing," I replied.

"But see—see!" he said, pointing along the road, directly ahead.

I said: "Nothing is there. Come, father, let us go in—you are ill."

He had released my arm and was standing rigid and motionless in the center of the illuminated roadway, staring like one bereft of sense. His face in the moonlight showed a pallor and fixity inexpressibly distressing. I pulled gently at his sleeve, but he had forgotten my existence. Presently he began to retire backward, step by step, never for an instant removing his eyes from what he saw, or thought he saw. I turned half round to follow, but stood irresolute. I do not recall any feeling of fear, unless a sudden chill was its physical manifestation. It seemed as if an icy wind had touched my face and enfolded my body from head to foot; I could feel the stir of it in my hair.

At that moment my attention was drawn to a light that suddenly streamed from an upper window of the house: one of the servants, awakened by what mysterious premonition of evil who can say, and in obedience to an impulse that she was never able to name, had lit a lamp. When I turned to look for my father he was gone, and in all the years that have passed no whisper of his fate has come across the border-land of conjecture from the realm of the unknown.

II
STATEMENT OF CASPAR GRATTAN

To-day I am said to live; to-morrow, here in this room, will lie a senseless shape of clay that all too long was I. If anyone lift the cloth from the face of that unpleasant thing it will be in gratification of a mere morbid curiosity. Some, doubtless, will go further and inquire, "Who was he?" In this writing I supply the only answer that I am able to make—Caspar Grattan. Surely, that should be enough. The name has served my small need for more than twenty years of a life of unknown length. True, I gave it to myself, but lacking another I had the right. In this world one must have a name; it prevents confusion, even when it does not establish identity. Some, though, are known by numbers, which also seem inadequate distinctions.

One day, for illustration, I was passing along a street of a city, far from here, when I met two men in uniform, one of whom, half pausing and looking curiously into my face, said to his companion, "That man looks like 767." Something in the number seemed familiar and horrible. Moved by an uncontrollable impulse, I sprang into a side street and ran until I fell exhausted in a country lane.

I have never forgotten that number, and always it comes to memory attended by gibbering obscenity, peals of joyless laughter, the clang of iron doors. So I say a name, even if self-bestowed, is better than a number. In the register of the potter's field I shall soon have both. What wealth!

Of him who shall find this paper I must beg a little consideration. It is not the history of my life; the knowledge to write that is denied me. This is only a record of broken and apparently unrelated memories, some of them as distinct and sequent as brilliant beads upon a thread, others remote and strange, having the character of crimson dreams with interspaces blank and black—witch-fires glowing still and red in a great desolation.

Standing upon the shore of eternity, I turn for a last look landward over the course by which I came. There are twenty years of footprints fairly distinct, the impressions of bleeding feet. They lead through poverty and pain, devious and unsure, as of one staggering beneath a burden—

Remote, unfriended, melancholy, slow.

Ah, the poet's prophecy of Me—how admirable, how dreadfully admirable!

Backward beyond the beginning of this *via dolorosa*—this epic of suffering with episodes of sin—I see nothing clearly; it comes out of a cloud. I know that it spans only twenty years, yet I am an old man.

One does not remember one's birth—one has to be told. But with me it was different; life came to me full-handed and dowered me with all my faculties and powers. Of a previous existence I know no more than others, for all have stammering intimations that may be memories and may be dreams. I know only that my first consciousness was of maturity in body and mind—a consciousness accepted without surprise or conjecture. I merely found myself walking in a forest, half-clad, footsore, unutterably weary and hungry. Seeing a farmhouse, I approached and asked for food, which was given me by one who inquired my name. I did not know, yet knew that all had names. Greatly embarrassed, I retreated, and night coming on, lay down in the forest and slept.

The next day I entered a large town which I shall not name. Nor shall I recount further incidents of the life that is now to end—a life of wandering, always and everywhere haunted by an overmastering sense of crime in punishment of wrong and of terror in punishment of crime. Let me see if I can reduce it to narrative.

I seem once to have lived near a great city, a prosperous planter, married to a woman whom I loved and distrusted. We had, it sometimes seems, one child, a youth of brilliant parts and promise. He is at all times a vague figure, never clearly drawn, frequently altogether out of the picture.

One luckless evening it occurred to me to test my wife's fidelity in a vulgar, commonplace way familiar to everyone who has acquaintance with the literature of fact and fiction. I went to the city, telling my wife that I should be absent until the following afternoon. But I returned before daybreak and went to the rear of the house, purposing to enter by a door with which I had secretly so tampered that it would seem to lock, yet not actually fasten. As I approached it, I heard it gently open and close, and saw a man steal away into the darkness. With murder in my heart, I sprang after him, but he had vanished without even the bad luck of identification. Sometimes now I cannot even persuade myself that it was a human being.

Crazed with jealousy and rage, blind and bestial with all the elemental passions of insulted manhood, I entered the house and sprang up the stairs to the door of my wife's chamber. It was closed, but having tampered with its lock also, I easily entered and despite the black darkness soon stood by the side of her bed. My groping hands told me that although disarranged it was unoccupied.

"She is below," I thought, "and terrified by my entrance has evaded me in the darkness of the hall."

With the purpose of seeking her I turned to leave the room, but took a wrong direction—the right one! My foot struck her, cowering in a corner of the room. Instantly my hands were at her throat, stifling a shriek, my knees were upon her struggling body; and there in the darkness, without a word of accusation or reproach, I strangled her till she died!

There ends the dream. I have related it in the past tense, but the present would be the fitter form, for again and again the somber tragedy reenacts itself in my consciousness—over and over I lay the plan, I suffer the confirmation, I redress the wrong. Then all is blank; and afterward the rains beat against the grimy window-panes, or the snows fall upon my scant attire, the wheels rattle in the squalid streets where my life lies in poverty and mean employment. If there is ever sunshine I do not recall it; if there are birds they do not sing.

There is another dream, another vision of the night. I stand among the shadows in a moonlit road. I am aware of another presence, but whose I cannot rightly determine. In the shadow of a great dwelling I catch the gleam of white garments; then the figure of a woman confronts me in the road—my murdered wife! There is death in the face; there are marks upon the throat. The eyes are fixed on mine with an infinite gravity which is not reproach, nor hate, nor menace, nor anything less terrible than recognition. Before this awful apparition I retreat in terror—a terror that is upon me as I write. I can no longer rightly shape the words. See! they—

Now I am calm, but truly there is no more to tell: the incident ends where it began—in darkness and in doubt.

Yes, I am again in control of myself: "the captain of my soul." But that is not respite; it is another stage and phase of expiation. My penance, constant in degree, is mutable in kind: one of its variants is tranquillity. After all, it is only a life-sentence. "To Hell for life"—that is a foolish penalty: the culprit chooses the duration of his punishment. To-day my term expires.

To each and all, the peace that was not mine.

III
STATEMENT OF THE LATE JULIA HETMAN, THROUGH THE MEDIUM BAYROLLES

I had retired early and fallen almost immediately into a peaceful sleep, from which I awoke with that indefinable sense of peril which is, I think, a common experience in that other, earlier life. Of its unmeaning character, too, I was entirely persuaded, yet that did not banish it. My husband, Joel Hetman, was away from home; the servants slept in another part of the house. But these were familiar conditions; they had never before distressed me. Nevertheless, the strange terror grew so insupportable that conquering my reluctance to move I sat up and lit the lamp at my bedside. Contrary to my expectation this gave me no relief; the light seemed rather an added danger, for I reflected that it would shine out under the door, disclosing my presence to whatever evil thing might lurk outside. You that are still in the flesh, subject to horrors of the imagination, think what a monstrous fear that must be which seeks in darkness security from malevolent existences of the night. That is to spring to close quarters with an unseen enemy—the strategy of despair!

Extinguishing the lamp I pulled the bedclothing about my head and lay trembling and silent, unable to shriek, forgetful to pray. In this pitiable state I must have lain for what you call hours—with us there are no hours, there is no time.

At last it came—a soft, irregular sound of footfalls on the stairs! They were slow, hesitant, uncertain, as of something that did not see its way; to my disordered reason all the more terrifying for that, as the approach of some blind and mindless malevolence to which is no appeal. I even thought that I must have left the hall lamp burning and the groping of this creature proved it a monster of the night. This was foolish and inconsistent with my previous dread of the light, but what would you have? Fear has no brains; it is an idiot. The dismal witness that it bears and the cowardly counsel that it whispers are unrelated. We know this well, we who have passed into the Realm of Terror, who skulk in eternal dusk among the scenes of our former lives, invisible even to ourselves and one another, yet hiding forlorn in lonely places; yearning for speech with our loved ones, yet dumb, and as fearful of them as they of us. Sometimes the disability is removed, the law suspended: by the deathless power of love or hate we break the spell—we are seen by those whom we would warn, console, or punish. What form we seem to them to bear we know not; we know only that we terrify even those whom we most wish to comfort, and from whom we most crave tenderness and sympathy.

Forgive, I pray you, this inconsequent digression by what was once a woman. You who consult us in this imperfect way—you do not understand. You ask foolish questions about things unknown and things forbidden. Much that we know and could impart in our speech is meaningless in yours. We must communicate with you through a stammering intelligence in that small fraction of our language that you yourselves can speak. You think that we are of another world. No, we have knowledge of no world but yours, though for us it holds no sunlight, no warmth, no music, no laughter, no song of birds, nor any companionship. O God! what a thing it is to be a ghost, cowering and shivering in an altered world, a prey to apprehension and despair!

No, I did not die of fright: the Thing turned and went away. I heard it go down the stairs, hurriedly, I thought, as if itself in sudden fear. Then I rose to call for help. Hardly had my shaking hand found the doorknob when—merciful heaven!—I heard it returning. Its footfalls as it remounted the stairs were rapid, heavy and loud; they shook the house. I fled to an angle of the wall and crouched upon the floor. I tried to pray. I tried to call the name of my dear husband. Then I heard the door thrown open. There was an interval of unconsciousness, and when I revived I felt a strangling clutch upon my throat—felt my arms feebly beating against something that bore me backward—felt my tongue thrusting itself from between my teeth! And then I passed into this life.

No, I have no knowledge of what it was. The sum of what we knew at death is the measure of what we know afterward of all that went before. Of this existence we know many things, but no new light falls upon any page of that; in memory is written all of it that we can read.

Here are no heights of truth overlooking the confused landscape of that dubitable domain. We still dwell in the Valley of the Shadow, lurk in its desolate places, peering from brambles and thickets at its mad, malign inhabitants. How should we have new knowledge of that fading past?

What I am about to relate happened on a night. We know when it is night, for then you retire to your houses and we can venture from our places of concealment to move unafraid about our old homes, to look in at the windows, even to enter and gaze upon your faces as you sleep. I had lingered long near the dwelling where I had been so cruelly changed to what I am, as we do while any that we love or hate remain. Vainly I had sought some method of manifestation, some way to make my continued existence and my great love and poignant pity understood by my husband and son. Always if they slept they would wake, or if in my desperation I dared approach them when they were awake, would turn toward me the terrible eyes of the living, frightening me by the glances that I sought from the purpose that I held.

On this night I had searched for them without success, fearing to find them; they were nowhere in the house, nor about the moonlit lawn. For, although the sun is lost to us forever, the moon, full-orbed or slender, remains to us. Sometimes it shines by night, sometimes by day, but always it rises and sets, as in that other life.

I left the lawn and moved in the white light and silence along the road, aimless and sorrowing. Suddenly I heard the voice of my poor husband in exclamations of astonishment, with that of my son in reassurance and dissuasion; and there by the shadow of a group of trees they stood—near, so near! Their faces were toward me, the eyes of the elder man fixed upon mine. He saw me—at last, at last, he saw me! In the consciousness of that, my terror fled as a cruel dream. The death-spell was broken: Love had conquered Law! Mad with exultation I shouted—I *must* have shouted, "He sees, he sees: he will understand!" Then, controlling myself, I moved forward, smiling and consciously beautiful, to offer myself to his arms, to comfort him with endearments, and, with my son's hand in mine, to speak words that should restore the broken bonds between the living and the dead.

Alas! alas! his face went white with fear, his eyes were as those of a hunted animal. He backed away from me, as I advanced, and at last turned and fled into the wood—whither, it is not given to me to know.

To my poor boy, left doubly desolate, I have never been able to impart a sense of my presence. Soon he, too, must pass to this Life Invisible and be lost to me forever.

A DIAGNOSIS OF DEATH

"I AM not so superstitious as some of your physicians—men of science, as you are pleased to be called," said Hawver, replying to an accusation that had not been made. "Some of you—only a few, I confess—believe in the immortality of the soul, and in apparitions which you have not the honesty to call ghosts. I go no further than a conviction that the living are sometimes seen where they are not, but have been—where they have lived so long, perhaps so intensely, as to have left their impress on everything about them. I know, indeed, that one's environment may be so affected by one's personality as to yield, long afterward, an image of one's self to the eyes of another. Doubtless the impressing personality has to be the right kind of personality as the perceiving eyes have to be the right kind of eyes—mine, for example."

"Yes, the right kind of eyes, conveying sensations to the wrong kind of brain," said Dr. Frayley, smiling.

"Than you; one likes to have an expectation gratified; that is about the reply that I supposed you would have the civility to make."

"Pardon me. But you say that you know. That is a good deal to say, don't you think? Perhaps you will not mind the trouble of saying how you learned."

"You will call it an hallucination," Hawver said, "but that does not matter." And he told the story.

"Last summer I went, as you know, to pass the hot weather term in the town of Meridian. The relative at whose house I had intended to stay was ill, so I sought other quarters. After some difficulty I succeeded in renting a vacant dwelling that had been occupied by an eccentric doctor of the name of Mannering, who had gone away years before, no one knew where, not even his agent. He had built the house himself and had lived in it with an old servant for about ten years. His practice, never very extensive, had after a few years been given up entirely. Not only so, but he had withdrawn himself almost altogether from social life and become a recluse. I was told by the village doctor, about the only person with whom he held any relations, that during his retirement he had devoted himself to a single line of study, the result of which he had expounded in a book that did not commend itself to the approval of his professional brethren, who, indeed, considered him not entirely sane. I have not seen the book and cannot now recall the title of it, but I am told that it expounded a rather startling theory. He held that it was possible in the case of many a person in good health to forecast his death with precision, several months in advance of the event. The limit, I think, was eighteen months. There were local tales of his having exerted his powers of prognosis, or perhaps you would say diagnosis; and it was said that in every instance the person whose friends he had warned had died suddenly at the appointed time, and from no assignable cause. All this, however, has nothing to do with what I have to tell; I thought it might amuse a physician.

"The house was furnished, just as he had lived in it. It was a rather gloomy dwelling for one who was neither a recluse nor a student, and I think it gave something of its character to me—perhaps some of its former occupant's character; for always I felt in it a certain melancholy that was not in my natural disposition, nor, I think, due to loneliness. I had no servants that slept in the house, but I have always been, as you know, rather fond of my own society, being much addicted to reading, though little to study. Whatever was the cause, the effect was dejection and a sense of impending evil; this was especially so in Dr. Mannering's study, although that room was the lightest and most airy in the house. The doctor's life-size portrait in oil hung in that room, and seemed completely to dominate it. There was nothing unusual in the picture; the man was evidently rather good looking, about fifty years old, with iron-gray hair, a smooth-shaven face and dark, serious eyes. Something in the picture always drew and held my attention. The man's appearance became familiar to me, and rather 'haunted' me.

"One evening I was passing through this room to my bedroom, with a lamp—there is no gas in Meridian. I stopped as usual before the portrait, which seemed in the lamplight to have a new expression, not easily named, but distinctly uncanny. It interested but did not disturb me. I moved the lamp from one side to the other and observed the effects of the altered light. While so engaged I felt an impulse to turn round. As I did so I saw a man moving across the room directly toward me! As soon as he came near enough for the lamplight to illuminate the face I saw that it was Dr. Mannering himself; it was as if the portrait were walking!

" 'I beg your pardon,' I said, somewhat coldly, 'but if you knocked I did not hear.'

"He passed me, within an arm's length, lifted his right forefinger, as in warning, and without a word went on out of the room, though I observed his exit no more than I had observed his entrance.

"Of course, I need not tell you that this was what you will call an hallucination and I call an apparition. That room had only two doors, of which one was locked; the other led into a bedroom, from which there was no exit. My feeling on realizing this is not an important part of the incident.

"Doubtless this seems to you a very commonplace 'ghost story'—one constructed on the regular lines laid down by the old masters of the art. If that were so I should not have related it, even if it were true. The man was not dead; I met him to-day in Union street. He passed me in a crowd."

Hawver had finished his story and both men were silent. Dr. Frayley absently drummed on the table with his fingers.

"Did he say anything to-day?" he asked—"anything from which you inferred that he was not dead?"

Hawver stared and did not reply.

"Perhaps," continued Frayley, "he made a sign, a gesture—lifted a finger, as in warning. It's a trick he had—a habit when saying something serious—announcing the result of a diagnosis, for example."

"Yes, he did—just as his apparition had done. But, good God! did you ever know him?"

Hawver was apparently growing nervous.

"I knew him. I have read his book, as will every physician some day. It is one of the most striking and important of the century's contributions to medical science. Yes, I knew him; I attended him in an illness three years ago. He died."

Hawver sprang from his chair, manifestly disturbed. He strode forward and back across the room; then approached his friend, and in a voice not altogether steady, said: "Doctor, have you anything to say to me—as a physician?"

"No, Hawver; you are the healthiest man I ever knew. As a friend I advise you to go to your room. You play the violin like an angel. Play it; play something light and lively. Get this cursed bad business off your mind."

The next day Hawver was found dead in his room, the violin at his neck, the bow upon the strings, his music open before him at Chopin's funeral march.

MOXON'S MASTER

"ARE you serious?—do you really believe that a machine thinks?"

I got no immediate reply; Moxon was apparently intent upon the coals in the grate, touching them deftly here and there with the fire-poker till they signified a sense of his attention by a brighter glow. For several weeks I had been observing in him a growing habit of delay in answering even the most trivial of commonplace questions. His air, however, was that of preoccupation rather than deliberation: one might have said that he had "something on his mind."

Presently he said:

"What is a 'machine'? The word has been variously defined. Here is one definition from a popular dictionary: 'Any instrument or organization by which power is applied and made effective, or a desired effect produced.' Well, then, is not a man a machine? And you will admit that he thinks—or thinks he thinks."

"If you do not wish to answer my question," I said, rather testily, "why not say so?—all that you say is mere evasion. You know well enough that when I say 'machine' I do not mean a man, but something that man has made and controls."

"When it does not control him," he said, rising abruptly and looking out of a window, whence nothing was visible in the blackness of a stormy night. A moment later he turned about and with a smile said: "I beg your pardon; I had no thought of evasion. I considered the dictionary man's unconscious testimony suggestive and worth something in the discussion. I can give your question a direct answer easily enough: I do believe that a machine thinks about the work that it is doing."

That was direct enough, certainly. It was not altogether pleasing, for it tended to confirm a sad suspicion that Moxon's devotion to study and work in his machine-shop had not been good for him. I knew, for one thing, that he suffered from insomnia, and that is no light affliction. Had it affected his mind? His reply to my question seemed to me then evidence that it had; perhaps I should think differently about it now. I was younger then, and among the blessings that are not denied to youth is ignorance. Incited by that great stimulant to controversy, I said:

"And what, pray, does it think with—in the absence of a brain?"

The reply, coming with less than his customary delay, took his favorite form of counter-interrogation:

"With what does a plant think—in the absence of a brain?"

"Ah, plants also belong to the philosopher class! I should be pleased to know some of their conclusions; you may omit the premises."

"Perhaps," he replied, apparently unaffected by my foolish irony, "you may be able to infer their convictions from their acts. I will spare you the familiar examples of the sensitive mimosa, the several insectivorous flowers and those whose stamens bend down and shake their pollen upon the entering bee in order that he may fertilize their distant mates. But observe this. In an open spot in my garden I planted a climbing vine. When it was barely above the surface I set a stake into the soil a yard away. The vine at once made for it, but as it was about to reach it after several days I removed it a few feet. The vine at once altered its course, making an acute angle, and again made for the stake. This manœuvre was repeated several times, but finally, as if discouraged, the vine abandoned the pursuit and ignoring further attempts to divert it traveled to a small tree, further away, which it climbed.

"Roots of the eucalyptus will prolong themselves incredibly in search of moisture. A well-known horticulturist relates that one entered an old drain pipe and followed it until it came to a break, where a section of the pipe had been removed to make way for a stone wall that had been built across its course. The root left the drain and followed the wall until it found an opening where a stone had fallen out. It crept through and following the other side of the wall back to the drain, entered the unexplored part and resumed its journey."

"And all this?"

"Can you miss the significance of it? It shows the consciousness of plants. It proves that they think."

"Even if it did—what then? We were speaking, not of plants, but of machines. They may be composed partly of wood—wood that has no longer vitality—or wholly of metal. Is thought an attribute also of the mineral kingdom?"

"How else do you explain the phenomena, for example, of crystallization?"

"I do not explain them."

"Because you cannot without affirming what you wish to deny, namely, intelligent co-operation among the constituent elements of the crystals. When soldiers form lines, or hollow squares, you call it reason. When wild geese in flight take the form of a letter V you say instinct. When the homogeneous atoms of a mineral, moving freely in solution, arrange themselves into shapes mathematically perfect, or particles of frozen moisture into the symmetrical and beautiful forms of snowflakes, you have nothing to say. You have not even invented a name to conceal your heroic unreason."

Moxon was speaking with unusual animation and earnestness. As he paused I heard in an adjoining room known to me as his "machine-shop," which no one but himself was permitted to enter, a singular thumping sound, as of some one pounding upon a table with an open hand. Moxon heard it at the same moment and, visibly agitated, rose and hurriedly passed into the room whence it came. I thought it odd that any one else should be in there, and my interest in my friend— with doubtless a touch of unwarrantable curiosity—led me to listen intently, though, I am happy to say, not at the keyhole. There were confused sounds, as of a struggle or scuffle; the floor shook. I distinctly heard hard breathing and a hoarse whisper which said "Damn you!" Then all was silent, and presently Moxon reappeared and said, with a rather sorry smile:

"Pardon me for leaving you so abruptly. I have a machine in there that lost its temper and cut up rough."

Fixing my eyes steadily upon his left cheek, which was traversed by four parallel excoriations showing blood, I said:

"How would it do to trim its nails?"

I could have spared myself the jest; he gave it no attention, but seated himself in the chair that he had left and resumed the interrupted monologue as if nothing had occurred:

"Doubtless you do not hold with those (I need not name them to a man of your reading) who have taught that all matter is sentient, that every atom is a living, feeling, conscious being. *I* do. There is no such thing as dead, inert matter: it is all alive; all instinct with force, actual and potential; all sensitive to the same forces in its environment and susceptible to the contagion of higher and subtler ones residing in such superior organisms as it may be brought into relation with, as those of man when he is fashioning it into an instrument of his will. It absorbs something of his intelligence and purpose—more of them in proportion to the complexity of the resulting machine and that of its work.

"Do you happen to recall Herbert Spencer's definition of 'Life'? I read it thirty years ago. He may have altered it afterward, for anything I know, but in all that time I have been unable to think of a single word that could profitably be changed or added or removed. It seems to me not only the best definition, but the only possible one.

" 'Life,' he says, 'is a definite combination of heterogeneous changes, both simultaneous and successive, in correspondence with external co-existences and sequences.' "

"That defines the phenomenon," I said, "but gives no hint of its cause."

"That," he replied, "is all that any definition can do. As Mill points out, we know nothing of cause except as an antecedent—nothing of effect except as a consequent. Of certain phenomena, one never occurs without another, which is dissimilar: the first in point of time we call cause, the second, effect. One who had many times seen a rabbit pursued by a dog, and had never seen rabbits and dogs otherwise, would think the rabbit the cause of the dog.

"But I fear," he added, laughing naturally enough, "that my rabbit is leading me a long way from the track of my legitimate quarry: I'm indulging in the pleasure of the chase for its own sake. What I want you to observe is that in Herbert Spencer's definition of 'life' the activity of a machine is included—there is nothing in the definition that is not applicable to it. According to this sharpest of observers and deepest of thinkers, if a man during his period of activity is alive, so is a machine when in operation. As an inventor and constructor of machines I know that to be true."

Moxon was silent for a long time, gazing absently into the fire. It was growing late and I thought it time to be going, but somehow I did not like the notion of leaving him in that isolated house, all alone except for the presence of some person of whose nature my conjectures could go no further than that it was unfriendly, perhaps malign. Leaning toward him and looking earnestly into his eyes while making a motion with my hand through the door of his workshop, I said:

"Moxon, whom have you in there?"

Somewhat to my surprise he laughed lightly and answered without hesitation:

"Nobody; the incident that you have in mind was caused by my folly in leaving a machine in action with nothing to act upon, while I undertook the interminable task of enlightening your understanding. Do you happen to know that Consciousness is the creature of Rhythm?"

"O bother them both!" I replied, rising and laying hold of my overcoat. "I'm going to wish you good night; and I'll add the hope that the machine which you inadvertently left in action will have her gloves on the next time you think it needful to stop her."

Without waiting to observe the effect of my shot I left the house.

Rain was falling, and the darkness was intense. In the sky beyond the crest of a hill toward which I groped my way along precarious plank sidewalks and across miry, unpaved streets I could see the faint glow of the city's lights, but behind me nothing was visible but a single window of Moxon's house. It glowed with what seemed to me a mysterious and fateful meaning. I knew it was an uncurtained aperture in my friend's "machine-shop," and I had little doubt that he had resumed the studies interrupted by his duties as my instructor in mechanical consciousness and the fatherhood of Rhythm. Odd, and in some degree humorous, as his convictions seemed to me at that time, I could not wholly divest myself of the feeling that they had some tragic relation to his life and character—perhaps to his destiny—although I no longer entertained the notion that they were the vagaries of a disordered mind. Whatever might be thought of his views, his exposition of them was too logical for that. Over and over, his last words came back to me: "Consciousness is the creature of Rhythm." Bald and terse as the statement was, I now found it infinitely alluring. At each recurrence it broadened in meaning and deepened in suggestion. Why, here, (I thought) is something upon which to found a philosophy. If consciousness is the product of rhythm all things *are* conscious, for all have motion, and all motion is rhythmic. I wondered if Moxon knew the significance and breadth of his thought —the scope of this momentous generalization; or had he arrived at his philosophic faith by the tortuous and uncertain road of observation?

That faith was then new to me, and all Moxon's expounding had failed to make me a convert; but now it seemed as if a great light shone about me, like that which fell upon Saul of Tarsus; and out there in the storm and darkness and solitude I experienced what Lewes calls "the endless variety and excitement of philosophic thought." I exulted in a new sense of knowledge, a new pride of reason. My feet seemed hardly to touch the earth; it was as if I were uplifted and borne through the air by invisible wings.

Yielding to an impulse to seek further light from him whom I now recognized as my master and guide, I had unconsciously turned about, and almost before I was aware of having done so found myself again at Moxon's door. I was drenched with rain, but felt no discomfort. Unable in my excitement to find the doorbell I instinctively tried the knob. It turned and, entering, I mounted the stairs to the room that I had so recently left. All was dark and silent; Moxon, as I had supposed, was in the adjoining room—the "machine-shop." Groping along the wall until I found the communicating door I knocked loudly several times, but got no response, which I attributed to the uproar outside, for the wind was blowing a gale and dashing the rain against the thin walls in sheets. The drumming upon the shingle roof spanning the unceiled room was loud and incessant.

I had never been invited into the machine-shop—had, indeed, been denied admittance, as had all others, with one exception, a skilled metal worker, of whom no one knew anything except that his name was Haley and his habit silence. But in my spiritual exaltation, discretion and civility were alike forgotten and I opened the door. What I saw took all philosophical speculation out of me in short order.

Moxon sat facing me at the farther side of a small table upon which a single candle made all the light that was in the room. Opposite him, his back toward me, sat another person. On the table between the two was a chess-board; the men were playing. I knew little of chess, but as only a few pieces were on the board it was obvious that the game was near its close. Moxon was intensely interested—not so much, it seemed to me, in the game as in his antagonist, upon whom he had fixed so intent a look that, standing though I did directly in the line of his vision, I was altogether unobserved. His face was ghastly white, and his eyes glittered like diamonds. Of his antagonist I had only a back view, but that was sufficient; I should not have cared to see his face.

He was apparently not more than five feet in height, with porportions suggesting those of a gorilla—a tremendous breadth of shoulders, thick, short neck and broad, squat head, which had a tangled growth of black hair and was topped with a crimson fez. A tunic of the same color, belted tightly to the waist, reached the seat—apparently a box—upon which he sat; his legs and feet were not seen. His left forearm appeared to rest in his lap; he moved his pieces with his right hand, which seemed disproportionately long.

I had shrunk back and now stood a little to one side of the doorway and in shadow. If Moxon had looked farther than the face of his opponent he could have observed nothing now, except that the door was open. Something forbade me either to enter or to retire, a feeling—I know not how it came—that I was in the presence of an imminent tragedy and might serve my friend by remaining. With a scarcely conscious rebellion against the indelicacy of the act I remained.

The play was rapid. Moxon hardly glanced at the board before making his moves, and to my unskilled eye seemed to move the piece most convenient to his hand, his motions in doing so being quick, nervous and lacking in precision. The response of his antagonist, while equally prompt in the inception, was made with a slow, uniform, mechanical and, I thought, somewhat theatrical movement of the arm, that was a sore trial to my patience. There was something unearthly about it all, and I caught myself shuddering. But I was wet and cold.

Two or three times after moving a piece the stranger slightly inclined his head, and each time I observed that Moxon shifted his king. All at once the thought came to me that the man was dumb. And then that he was a machine—an automaton chess-player! Then I remembered that Moxon had once spoken to me of having invented such a piece of mechanism, though I did not understand that it had actually been constructed. Was all his talk about the consciousness and intelligence of machines merely a prelude to eventual exhibition of this device—only a trick to intensify the effect of its mechanical action upon me in my ignorance of its secret?

A fine end, this, of all my intellectual transports—my "endless variety and excitement of philosophic thought!" I was about to retire in disgust when something occurred to hold my curiosity. I observed a shrug of the thing's great shoulders, as if it were irritated: and so natural was this— so entirely human—that in my new view of the matter it startled me. Nor was that all, for a moment later it struck the table sharply with its clenched hand. At that gesture Moxon seemed even more startled than I: he pushed his chair a little backward, as in alarm.

Presently Moxon, whose play it was, raised his hand high above the board, pounced upon one of his pieces like a sparrow-hawk and with the exclamation "checkmate!" rose quickly to his feet and stepped behind his chair. The automaton sat motionless.

The wind had now gone down, but I heard, at lessening intervals and progressively louder, the rumble and roll of thunder. In the pauses between I now became conscious of a low humming or buzzing which, like the thunder, grew momentarily louder and more distinct. It seemed to come from the body of the automaton, and was unmistakably a whirring of wheels. It gave me the impression of a disordered mechanism which had escaped the repressive and regulating action of some controlling part—an effect such as might be expected if a pawl should be jostled from the teeth of a ratchet-wheel. But before I had time for much conjecture as to its nature my attention was taken by the strange motions of the automaton itself. A slight but continuous convulsion appeared to have possession of it. In body and head it shook like a man with palsy or an ague chill, and the motion augmented every moment until the entire figure was in violent agitation. Suddenly it sprang to its feet and with a movement almost too quick for the eye to follow shot forward across table and chair, with both arms thrust forth to their full length— the posture and lunge of a diver. Moxon tried to throw himself backward out of reach, but he was too late: I saw the horrible thing's hands close upon his throat, his own clutch its wrists. Then the table was overturned, the candle thrown to the floor and extinguished, and all was black dark. But the noise of the struggle was dreadfully distinct, and most terrible of all were the raucous, squawking sounds made by the strangled man's efforts to breathe. Guided by the infernal hubbub, I sprang to the rescue of my friend, but had hardly taken a stride in the darkness when the whole room blazed with a blinding white light that burned into my brain and heart and memory a vivid picture of the combatants on the floor, Moxon underneath, his throat still in the clutch of those iron hands, his head forced backward, his eyes protruding, his mouth wide open and his tongue thrust out; and—horrible contrast! —upon the painted face of his assassin an expression of tranquil and profound thought, as in the solution of a problem in chess! This I observed, then all was blackness and silence.

Three days later I recovered consciousness in a hospital. As the memory of that tragic night slowly evolved in my ailing brain I recognized in my attendant Moxon's confidential workman, Haley. Responding to a look he approached, smiling.

"Tell me about it," I managed to say, faintly—"all about it."

"Certainly," he said; "you were carried unconscious from a burning house—Moxon's. Nobody knows how you came to be there. You may have to do a little explaining. The origin of the fire is a bit mysterious, too. My own notion is that the house was struck by lightning."

"And Moxon?"

"Buried yesterday—what was left of him."

Apparently this reticent person could unfold himself on occasion. When imparting shocking intelligence to the sick he was affable enough. After some moments of the keenest mental suffering I ventured to ask another question:

"Who rescued me?"

"Well, if that interests you—I did."

"Thank you, Mr. Haley, and may God bless you for it. Did you rescue, also, that charming product of your skill, the automaton chess-player that murdered its inventor?"

The man was silent a long time, looking away from me. Presently he turned and gravely said:

"Do you know that?"

"I do," I replied; "I saw it done."

That was many years ago. If asked to-day I should answer less confidently.

A TOUGH TUSSLE

ONE night in the autumn of 1861 a man sat alone in the heart of a forest in western Virginia. The region was one of the wildest on the continent—the Cheat Mountain country. There was no lack of people close at hand, however; within a mile of where the man sat was the now silent camp of a whole Federal brigade. Somewhere about—it might be still nearer—was a force of the enemy, the numbers unknown. It was this uncertainty as to its numbers and position that accounted for the man's presence in that lonely spot; he was a young officer of a Federal infantry regiment and his business there was to guard his sleeping comrades in the camp against a surprise. He was in command of a detachment of men constituting a picket-guard. These men he had stationed just at nightfall in an irregular line, determined by the nature of the ground, several hundred yards in front of where he now sat. The line ran through the forest, among the rocks and laurel thickets, the men fifteen or twenty paces apart, all in concealment and under injunction of strict silence and unremitting vigilance. In four hours, if nothing occurred, they would be relieved by a fresh detachment from the reserve now resting in care of its captain some distance away to the left and rear. Before stationing his men the young officer of whom we are writing had pointed out to his two sergeants the spot at which he would be found if it should be necessary to consult him, or if his presence at the front line should be required.

It was a quiet enough spot—the fork of an old wood-road, on the two branches of which, prolonging themselves deviously forward in the dim moonlight, the sergeants were themselves stationed, a few paces in rear of the line. If driven sharply back by a sudden onset of the enemy—and pickets are not expected to make a stand after firing—the men would come into the converging roads and naturally following them to their point of intersection could be rallied and "formed." In his small way the author of these dispositions was something of a strategist; if Napoleon had planned as intelligently at Waterloo he would have won that memorable battle and been overthrown later.

Second-Lieutenant Brainerd Byring was a brave and efficient officer, young and comparatively inexperienced as he was in the business of killing his fellow-men. He had enlisted in the very first days of the war as a private, with no military knowledge whatever, had been made first-sergeant of his company on account of his education and engaging manner, and had been lucky enough to lose his captain by a Confederate bullet; in the resulting promotions he had gained a commission. He had been in several engagements, such as they were—at Philippi, Rich Mountain, Carrick's Ford and Greenbrier—and had borne himself with such gallantry as not to attract the attention of his superior officers. The exhilaration of battle was agreeable to him, but the sight of the dead, with their clay faces, blank eyes and stiff bodies, which when not unnaturally shrunken were unnaturally swollen, had always intolerably affected him. He felt toward them a kind of reasonless antipathy that was something more than the physical and spiritual repugnance common to us all. Doubtless this feeling was due to his unusually acute sensibilities—his keen sense of the beautiful, which these hideous things outraged. Whatever may have been the cause, he could not look upon a dead body without a loathing which had in it an element of resentment. What others have respected as the dignity of death had to him no existence—was altogether unthinkable. Death was a thing to be hated. It was not picturesque, it had no tender and solemn side—a dismal thing, hideous in all its manifestations and suggestions. Lieutenant Byring was a braver man than anybody knew, for nobody knew his horror of that which he was ever ready to incur.

Having posted his men, instructed his sergeants and retired to his station, he seated himself on a log, and with senses all alert began his vigil. For greater ease he loosened his sword-belt and taking his heavy revolver from his holster laid it on the log beside him. He felt very comfortable, though he hardly gave the fact a thought, so intently did he listen for any sound from the front which might have a menacing significance—a shout, a shot, or the footfall of one of his sergeants coming to apprise him of something worth knowing. From the vast, invisible ocean of moonlight overhead fell, here and there, a slender, broken stream that seemed to plash against the intercepting branches and trickle to earth, forming small white pools among the clumps of laurel. But these leaks were few and served only to accentuate the blackness of his environment, which his imagination found it easy to people with all manner of unfamiliar shapes, menacing, uncanny, or merely grotesque.

He to whom the portentous conspiracy of night and solitude and silence in the heart of a great forest is not an unknown experience needs not to be told what another world it all is—how even the most commonplace and familiar objects take on another character. The trees group themselves differently; they draw closer together, as if in fear. The very silence has another quality than the silence of the day. And it is full of half-heard whispers—whispers that startle—ghosts of sounds long dead. There are living sounds, too, such as are never heard under other conditions: notes of strange night-birds, the cries of small animals in sudden encounters with stealthy foes or in their dreams, a rustling in the dead leaves—it may be the leap of a wood-rat, it may be the footfall of a panther. What caused the breaking of that twig?—what the low, alarmed twittering in that bushful of birds? There are sounds without a name, forms without substance, translations in space of objects which have not been seen to move, movements wherein nothing is observed to change its place. Ah, children of the sunlight and the gaslight, how little you know of the world in which you live!

Surrounded at a little distance by armed and watchful friends, Byring felt utterly alone. Yielding himself to the solemn and mysterious spirit of the time and place, he had forgotten the nature of his connection with the visible and audible aspects and phases of the night. The forest was boundless; men and the habitations of men did not exist. The universe was one primeval mystery of darkness, without form and void, himself the sole, dumb questioner of its eternal secret. Absorbed in thoughts born of this mood, he suffered the time to slip away unnoted. Meantime the infrequent patches of white light lying amongst the tree-trunks had undergone changes of size, form and place. In one of them near by, just at the roadside, his eye fell upon an object that he had not previously observed. It was almost before his face as he sat; he could have sworn that it had not before been there. It was partly covered in shadow, but he could see that it was a human figure. Instinctively he adjusted the clasp of his sword-belt and laid hold of his pistol—again he was in a world of war, by occupation an assassin.

The figure did not move. Rising, pistol in hand, he approached. The figure lay upon its back, its upper part in shadow, but standing above it and looking down upon the face, he saw that it was a dead body. He shuddered and turned from it with a feeling of sickness and disgust, resumed his seat upon the log, and forgetting military prudence struck a match and lit a cigar. In the sudden blackness that followed the extinction of the flame he felt a sense of relief; he could no longer see the object of his aversion. Nevertheless, he kept his eyes set in that direction until it appeared again with growing distinctness. It seemed to have moved a trifle nearer.

"Damn the thing!" he muttered. "What does it want?"

It did not appear to be in need of anything but a soul.

Byring turned away his eyes and began humming a tune, but he broke off in the middle of a bar and looked at the dead body. Its presence annoyed him, though he could hardly have had a quieter neighbor. He was conscious, too, of a vague, indefinable feeling that was new to him. It was not fear, but rather a sense of the supernatural—in which he did not at all believe.

"I have inherited it," he said to himself. "I suppose it will require a thousand ages—perhaps ten thousand—for humanity to outgrow this feeling. Where and when did it originate? Away back, probably, in what is called the cradle of the human race—the plains of Central Asia. What we inherit as a superstition our barbarous ancestors must have held as a reasonable conviction. Doubtless they believed themselves justified by facts whose nature we cannot even conjecture in thinking a dead body a malign thing endowed with some strange power of mischief, with perhaps a will and a purpose to exert it. Possibly they had some awful form of religion of which that was one of the chief doctrines, sedulously taught by their priesthood, as ours teach the immortality of the soul. As the Aryans moved slowly on, to and through the Caucasus passes, and spread over Europe, new conditions of life must have resulted in the formulation of new religions. The old belief in the malevolence of the dead body was lost from the creeds and even perished from tradition, but it left its heritage of terror, which is transmitted from generation to generation—is as much a part of us as are our blood and bones."

In following out his thought he had forgotten that which suggested it; but now his eye fell again upon the corpse. The shadow had now altogether uncovered it. He saw the sharp profile, the chin in the air, the whole face, ghastly white in the moonlight. The clothing was gray, the uniform of a Confederate soldier. The coat and waistcoat, unbuttoned, had fallen away on each side, exposing the white shirt. The chest seemed unnaturally prominent, but the abdomen had sunk in, leaving a sharp projection at the line of the lower ribs. The arms were extended, the left knee was thrust upward. The whole posture impressed Byring as having been studied with a view to the horrible.

"Bah!" he exclaimed; "he was an actor—he knows how to be dead."

He drew away his eyes, directing them resolutely along one of the roads leading to the front, and resumed his philosophizing where he had left off.

"It may be that our Central Asian ancestors had not the custom of burial. In that case it is easy to understand their fear of the dead, who really were a menace and an evil. They bred pestilences. Children were taught to avoid the places where they lay, and to run away if by inadvertence they came near a corpse. I think, indeed, I'd better go away from this chap."

He half rose to do so, then remembered that he had told his men in front and the officer in the rear who was to relieve him that he could at any time be found at that spot. It was a matter of pride, too. If he abandoned his post he feared they would think he feared the corpse. He was no coward and he was unwilling to incur anybody's ridicule. So he again seated himself, and to prove his courage looked boldly at the body. The right arm—the one farthest from him—was now in shadow. He could barely see the hand which, he had before observed, lay at the root of a clump of laurel. There had been no change, a fact which gave him a certain comfort, he could not have said why. He did not at once remove his eyes; that which we do not wish to see has a strange fascination, sometimes irresistible. Of the woman who covers her eyes with her hands and looks between the fingers let it be said that the wits have dealt with her not altogether justly.

Byring suddenly became conscious of a pain in his right hand. He withdrew his eyes from his enemy and looked at it. He was grasping the hilt of his drawn sword so tightly that it hurt him. He observed, too, that he was leaning forward in a strained attitude—crouching like a gladiator ready to spring at the throat of an antagonist. His teeth were clenched and he was breathing hard. This matter was soon set right, and as his muscles relaxed and he drew a long breath he felt keenly enough the ludicrousness of the incident. It affected him to laughter. Heavens! what sound was that? what mindless devil was uttering an unholy glee in mockery of human merriment? He sprang to his feet and looked about him, not recognizing his own laugh.

He could no longer conceal from himself the horrible fact of his cowardice; he was thoroughly frightened! He would have run from the spot, but his legs refused their office; they gave way beneath him and he sat again upon the log, violently trembling. His face was wet, his whole body bathed in a chill perspiration. He could not even cry out. Distinctly he heard behind him a stealthy tread, as of some wild animal, and dared not look over his shoulder. Had the soulless living joined forces with the soulless dead?—was it an animal? Ah, if he could but be assured of that! But by no effort of will could he now unfix his gaze from the face of the dead man.

I repeat that Lieutenant Byring was a brave and intelligent man. But what would you have? Shall a man cope, single-handed, with so monstrous an alliance as that of night and solitude and silence and the dead,—while an incalculable host of his own ancestors shriek into the ear of his spirit their coward counsel, sing their doleful death-songs in his heart, and disarm his very blood of all its iron? The odds are too great—courage was not made for so rough use as that.

One sole conviction now had the man in possession: that the body had moved. It lay nearer to the edge of its plot of light—there could be no doubt of it. It had also moved its arms, for, look, they are both in the shadow! A breath of cold air struck Byring full in the face; the boughs of trees above him stirred and moaned. A strongly defined shadow passed across the face of the dead, left it luminous, passed back upon it and left it half obscured. The horrible thing was visibly moving! At that moment a single shot rang out upon the picket-line—a lonelier and louder, though more distant, shot than ever had been heard by mortal ear! It broke the spell of that enchanted man; it slew the silence and the solitude, dispersed the hindering host from Central Asia and released his modern manhood. With a cry like that of some great bird pouncing upon its prey he sprang forward, hot-hearted for action!

Shot after shot now came from the front. There were shoutings and confusion, hoof-beats and desultory cheers. Away to the rear, in the sleeping camp, were a singing of bugles and grumble of drums. Pushing through the thickets on either side the roads came the Federal pickets, in full retreat, firing backward at random as they ran. A straggling group that had followed back one of the roads, as instructed, suddenly sprang away into the bushes as half a hundred horsemen thundered by them, striking wildly with their sabres as they passed. At headlong speed these mounted madmen shot past the spot where Byring had sat, and vanished round an angle of the road, shouting and firing their pistols. A moment later there was a roar of musketry, followed by dropping shots—they had encountered the reserve-guard in line; and back they came in dire confusion, with here and there an empty saddle and many a maddened horse, bullet-stung, snorting and plunging with pain. It was all over—"an affair of out-posts."

The line was reëstablished with fresh men, the roll called, the stragglers were re-formed. The Federal commander with a part of his staff, imperfectly clad, appeared upon the scene, asked a few questions, looked exceedingly wise and retired. After standing at arms for an hour the brigade in camp "swore a prayer or two" and went to bed.

Early the next morning a fatigue-party, commanded by a captain and accompanied by a surgeon, searched the ground for dead and wounded. At the fork of the road, a little to one side, they found two bodies lying close together—that of a Federal officer and that of a Confederate private. The officer had died of a sword-thrust through the heart, but not, apparently, until he had inflicted upon his enemy no fewer than five dreadful wounds. The dead officer lay on his face in a pool of blood, the weapon still in his breast. They turned him on his back and the surgeon removed it.

"Gad!" said the captain—"It is Byring!"—adding, with a glance at the other, "They had a tough tussle."

The surgeon was examining the sword. It was that of a line officer of Federal infantry—exactly like the one worn by the captain. It was, in fact, Byring's own. The only other weapon discovered was an undischarged revolver in the dead officer's belt.

The surgeon laid down the sword and approached the other body. It was frightfully gashed and stabbed, but there was no blood. He took hold of the left foot and tried to straighten the leg. In the effort the body was displaced. The dead do not wish to be moved—it protested with a faint, sickening odor. Where it had lain were a few maggots, manifesting an imbecile activity.

The surgeon looked at the captain. The captain looked at the surgeon.

ONE OF TWINS

A Letter Found among the Papers
of the Late Mortimer Barr

YOU ask me if in my experience as one of a pair of twins I ever observed anything unaccountable by the natural laws with which we have acquaintance. As to that you shall judge; perhaps we have not all acquaintance with the same natural laws. You may know some that I do not, and what is to me unaccountable may be very clear to you.

You knew my brother John—that is, you knew him when you knew that I was not president; but neither you nor, I believe, any human being could distinguish between him and me if we chose to seem alike. Our parents could not; ours is the only instance of which I have any knowledge of so close resemblance as that. I speak of my brother John, but I am not at all sure that his name was not Henry and mine John. We were regularly christened, but afterward, in the very act of tattooing us with small distinguishing marks, the operator lost his reckoning; and although I bear upon my forearm a small "H" and he bore a "J," it is by no means certain that the letters ought not to have been transposed. During our boyhood our parents tried to distinguish us more obviously by our clothing and other simple devices, but we would so frequently exchange suits and otherwise circumvent the enemy that they abandoned all such ineffectual attempts, and during all the years that we lived together at home everybody recognized the difficulty of the situation and made the best of it by calling us both "Jehnry." I have often wondered at my father's forbearance in not branding us conspicuously upon our unworthy brows, but as we were tolerably good boys and used our power of embarrassment and annoyance with commendable moderation, we escaped the iron. My father was, in fact, a singularly good-natured man, and I think quietly enjoyed nature's practical joke.

Soon after we had come to California, and settled at San Jose (where the only good fortune that awaited us was our meeting with so kind a friend as you) the family, as you know, was broken up by the death of both my parents in the same week. My father died insolvent and the

445

homestead was sacrificed to pay his debts. My sisters returned to relatives in the East, but owing to your kindness John and I, then twenty-two years of age, obtained employment in San Francisco, in different quarters of the town. Circumstances did not permit us to live together, and we saw each other infrequently, sometimes not oftener than once a week. As we had few acquaintances in common, the fact of our extraordinary likeness was little known. I come now to the matter of your inquiry.

One day soon after we had come to this city I was walking down Market street late in the afternoon, when I was accosted by a well-dressed man of middle age, who after greeting me cordially said: "Stevens, I know, of course, that you do not go out much, but I have told my wife about you, and she would be glad to see you at the house. I have a notion, too, that my girls are worth knowing. Suppose you come out to-morrow at six and dine with us, *en famille;* and then if the ladies can't amuse you afterward I'll stand in with a few games of billiards."

This was said with so bright a smile and so engaging a manner that I had not the heart to refuse, and although I had never seen the man in my life, I promptly replied: "You are very good, sir, and it will give me great pleasure to accept the invitation. Please present my compliments to Mrs. Margovan and ask her to expect me."

With a shake of the hand and a pleasant parting word the man passed on. That he had mistaken me for my brother was plain enough. That was an error to which I was accustomed and which it was not my habit to rectify unless the matter seemed important. But how had I known that this man's name was Margovan? It certainly is not a name that one would apply to a man at random, with a probability that it would be right. In point of fact, the name was as strange to me as the man.

The next morning I hastened to where my brother was employed and met him coming out of the office with a number of bills that he was to collect. I told him how I had "committed" him and added that if he didn't care to keep the engagement I should be delighted to continue the impersonation.

"That's queer," he said thoughtfully. "Margovan is the only man in the office here whom I know well and like. When he came in this morning and we had passed the usual greetings some singular impulse prompted me to say: 'Oh, I beg your pardon, Mr. Margovan, but I neglected to ask your address.' I got the address, but what under the sun

I was to do with it, I did not know until now. It's good of you to offer to take the consequence of your impudence, but I'll eat that dinner myself, if you please."

He ate a number of dinners at the same place—more than were good for him, I may add without disparaging their quality; for he fell in love with Miss Margovan, proposed marriage to her and was heartlessly accepted.

Several weeks after I had been informed of the engagement, but before it had been convenient for me to make the acquaintance of the young woman and her family, I met one day on Kearney street a handsome but somewhat dissipated-looking man whom something prompted me to follow and watch, which I did without any scruple whatever. He turned up Geary street and followed it until he came to Union square. There he looked at his watch, then entered the square. He loitered about the paths for some time, evidently waiting for someone. Presently he was joined by a fashionably dressed and beautiful young woman and the two walked away up Stockton street, I following. I now felt the necessity of extreme caution, for although the girl was a stranger it seemed to me that she would recognize me at a glance. They made several turns from one street to another and finally, after both had taken a hasty look all about—which I narrowly evaded by stepping into a doorway—they entered a house of which I do not care to state the location. Its location was better than its character.

I protest that my action in playing the spy upon these two strangers was without assignable motive. It was one of which I might or might not be ashamed, according to my estimate of the character of the person finding it out. As an essential part of a narrative educed by your question it is related here without hesitancy or shame.

A week later John took me to the house of his prospective father-in-law, and in Miss Margovan, as you have already surmised, but to my profound astonishment, I recognized the heroine of that discreditable adventure. A gloriously beautiful heroine of a discreditable adventure I must in justice admit that she was; but that fact has only this importance: her beauty was such a surprise to me that it cast a doubt upon her identity with the young woman I had seen before; how could the marvelous fascination of her face have failed to strike me at that time? But no—there was no possibility of error; the difference was due to costume, light and general surroundings.

John and I passed the evening at the house, enduring, with the fortitude of long experience, such delicate enough banter as our likeness naturally suggested. When the young lady and I were left alone for a few minutes I looked her squarely in the face and said with sudden gravity:

"You, too, Miss Margovan, have a double: I saw her last Tuesday afternoon in Union square."

She trained her great gray eyes upon me for a moment, but her glance was a trifle less steady than my own and she withdrew it, fixing it on the tip of her shoe.

"Was she very like me?" she asked, with an indifference which I thought a little overdone.

"So like," said I, "that I greatly admired her, and being unwilling to lose sight of her I confess that I followed her until—Miss Margovan, are you sure that you understand?"

She was now pale, but entirely calm. She again raised her eyes to mine, with a look that did not falter.

"What do you wish me to do?" she asked. "You need not fear to name your terms. I accept them."

It was plain, even in the brief time given me for reflection, that in dealing with this girl ordinary methods would not do, and ordinary exactions were needless.

"Miss Margovan," I said, doubtless with something of the compassion in my voice that I had in my heart, "it is impossible not to think you the victim of some horrible compulsion. Rather than impose new embarrassments upon you I would prefer to aid you to regain your freedom."

She shook her head, sadly and hopelessly, and I continued, with agitation:

"Your beauty unnerves me. I am disarmed by your frankness and your distress. If you are free to act upon conscience you will, I believe, do what you conceive to be best; if you are not—well, Heaven help us all! You have nothing to fear from me but such opposition to this marriage as I can try to justify on—on other grounds."

These were not my exact words, but that was the sense of them, as nearly as my sudden and conflicting emotions permitted me to express it. I rose and left her without another look at her, met the others as they reentered the room and said, as calmly as I could: "I have been bidding Miss Margovan good evening; it is later than I thought."

John decided to go with me. In the street he asked if I had observed anything singular in Julia's manner.

"I thought her ill," I replied; "that is why I left." Nothing more was said.

The next evening I came late to my lodgings. The events of the previous evening had made me nervous and ill; I had tried to cure myself and attain to clear thinking by walking in the open air, but I was oppressed with a horrible presentiment of evil—a presentiment which I could not formulate. It was a chill, foggy night; my clothing and hair were damp and I shook with cold. In my dressing-gown and slippers before a blazing grate of coals I was even more uncomfortable. I no longer shivered but shuddered—there is a difference. The dread of some impending calamity was so strong and dispiriting that I tried to drive it away by inviting a real sorrow—tried to dispel the conception of a terrible future by substituting the memory of a painful past. I recalled the death of my parents and endeavored to fix my mind upon the last sad scenes at their bedsides and their graves. It all seemed vague and unreal, as having occurred ages ago and to another person. Suddenly, striking through my thought and parting it as a tense cord is parted by the stroke of steel—I can think of no other comparison—I heard a sharp cry as of one in mortal agony! The voice was that of my brother and seemed to come from the street outside my window. I sprang to the window and threw it open. A street lamp directly opposite threw a wan and ghastly light upon the wet pavement and the fronts of the houses. A single policeman, with upturned collar, was leaning against a gatepost, quietly smoking a cigar. No one else was in sight. I closed the window and pulled down the shade, seated myself before the fire and tried to fix my mind upon my surroundings. By way of assisting, by performance of some familiar act, I looked at my watch; it marked half-past eleven. Again I heard that awful cry! It seemed in the room—at my side. I was frightened and for some moments had not the power to move. A few minutes later—I have no recollection of the intermediate time—I found myself hurrying along an unfamilar street as fast as I could walk. I did not know where I was, nor whither I was going, but presently sprang up the steps of a house before which were two or three carriages and in which were moving lights and a subdued confusion of voices. It was the house of Mr. Margovan.

You know, good friend, what had occurred there. In one chamber lay

Julia Margovan, hours dead by poison; in another John Stevens, bleeding from a pistol wound in the chest, inflicted by his own hand. As I burst into the room, pushed aside the physicians and laid my hand upon his forehead he unclosed his eyes, stared blankly, closed them slowly and died without a sign.

I knew no more until six weeks afterward, when I had been nursed back to life by your own saintly wife in your own beautiful home. All of that you know, but what you do not know is this—which, however, has no bearing upon the subject of your psychological researches—at least not upon that branch of them in which, with a delicacy and consideration all your own, you have asked for less assistance than I think I have given you:

One moonlight night several years afterward I was passing through Union square. The hour was late and the square deserted. Certain memories of the past naturally came into my mind as I came to the spot where I had once witnessed that fateful assignation, and with that unaccountable perversity which prompts us to dwell upon thoughts of the most painful character I seated myself upon one of the benches to indulge them. A man entered the square and came along the walk toward me. His hands were clasped behind him, his head was bowed; he seemed to observe nothing. As he approached the shadow in which I sat I recognized him as the man whom I had seen meet Julia Margovan years before at that spot. But he was terribly altered—gray, worn and haggard. Dissipation and vice were in evidence in every look; illness was no less apparent. His clothing was in disorder, his hair fell across his forehead in a derangement which was at once uncanny and picturesque. He looked fitter for restraint than liberty—the restraint of a hospital.

With no defined purpose I rose and confronted him. He raised his head and looked me full in the face. I have no words to describe the ghastly change that came over his own; it was a look of unspeakable terror—he thought himself eye to eye with a ghost. But he was a courageous man. "Damn you, John Stevens!" he cried, and lifting his trembling arm he dashed his fist feebly at my face and fell headlong upon the gravel as I walked away.

Somebody found him there, stone-dead. Nothing more is known of him, not even his name. To know of a man that he is dead should be enough.

THE HAUNTED VALLEY

I
HOW TREES ARE FELLED IN CHINA

A HALF-MILE north from Jo. Dunfer's, on the road from Hutton's to Mexican Hill, the highway dips into a sunless ravine which opens out on either hand in a half-confidential manner, as if it had a secret to impart at some more convenient season. I never used to ride through it without looking first to the one side and then to the other, to see if the time had arrived for the revelation. If I saw nothing—and I never did see anything—there was no feeling of disappointment, for I knew the disclosure was merely withheld temporarily for some good reason which I had no right to question. That I should one day be taken into full confidence I no more doubted than I doubted the existence of Jo. Dunfer himself, through whose premises the ravine ran.

It was said that Jo. had once undertaken to erect a cabin in some remote part of it, but for some reason had abandoned the enterprise and constructed his present hermaphrodite habitation, half residence and half groggery, at the roadside, upon an extreme corner of his estate; as far away as possible, as if on purpose to show how radically he had changed his mind.

This Jo. Dunfer—or, as he was familiarly known in the neighborhood, Whisky Jo.—was a very important personage in those parts. He was apparently about forty years of age, a long, shock-headed fellow, with a corded face, a gnarled arm and a knotty hand like a bunch of prison-keys. He was a hairy man, with a stoop in his walk, like that of one who is about to spring upon something and rend it.

Next to the peculiarity to which he owed his local appellation, Mr. Dunfer's most obvious characteristic was a deep-seated antipathy to the Chinese. I saw him once in a towering rage because one of his herdsmen had permitted a travel-heated Asian to slake his thirst at the horse-trough in front of the saloon end of Jo.'s establishment. I ventured faintly to remonstrate with Jo. for his unchristian spirit, but he merely explained that there was nothing about Chinamen in the New Testa-

451

ment, and strode away to wreak his displeasure upon his dog, which also, I suppose, the inspired scribes had overlooked.

Some days afterward, finding him sitting alone in his barroom, I cautiously approached the subject, when, greatly to my relief, the habitual austerity of his expression visibly softened into something that I took for condescension.

"You young Easterners," he said, "are a mile-and-a-half too good for this country, and you don't catch on to our play. People who don't know a Chileño from a Kanaka can afford to hang out liberal ideas about Chinese immigration, but a fellow that has to fight for his bone with a lot of mongrel coolies hasn't any time for foolishness."

This long consumer, who had probably never done an honest day's work in his life, sprung the lid of a Chinese tobacco-box and with thumb and forefinger forked out a wad like a small haycock. Holding this reinforcement within supporting distance he fired away with renewed confidence.

"They're a flight of devouring locusts, and they're going for everything green in this God blest land, if you want to know."

Here he pushed his reserve into the breach and when his gabble-gear was again disengaged resumed his uplifting discourse.

"I had one of them on this ranch five years ago, and I'll tell you about it, so that you can see the nub of this whole question. I didn't pan out particularly well those days—drank more whisky than was prescribed for me and didn't seem to care for my duty as a patriotic American citizen; so I took that pagan in, as a kind of cook. But when I got religion over at the Hill and they talked of running me for the Legislature it was given to me to see the light. But what was I to do? If I gave him the go somebody else would take him, and mightn't treat him white. *What* was I to do? What would any good Christian do, especially one new to the trade and full to the neck with the brotherhood of Man and the fatherhood of God?"

Jo. paused for a reply, with an expression of unstable satisfaction, as of one who has solved a problem by a distrusted method. Presently he rose and swallowed a glass of whisky from a full bottle on the counter, then resumed his story.

"Besides, he didn't count for much—didn't know anything and gave himself airs. They all do that. I said him nay, but he muled it through on that line while he lasted; but after turning the other cheek seventy and seven times I doctored the dice so that he didn't last forever. And I'm almighty glad I had the sand to do it."

Jo.'s gladness, which somehow did not impress me, was duly and ostentatiously celebrated at the bottle.

"About five years ago I started in to stick up a shack. That was before this one was built, and I put it in another place. I set Ah Wee and a little cuss named Gopher to cutting the timber. Of course I didn't expect Ah Wee to help much, for he had a face like a day in June and big black eyes—I guess maybe they were the damn'dest eyes in this neck o' woods."

While delivering this trenchant thrust at common sense Mr. Dunfer absently regarded a knot-hole in the thin board partition separating the bar from the living-room, as if that were one of the eyes whose size and color had incapacitated his servant for good service.

"Now you Eastern galoots won't believe anything against the yellow devils," he suddenly flamed out with an appearance of earnestness not altogether convincing, "but I tell you that Chink was the perversest scoundrel outside San Francisco. The miserable pig-tail Mongolian went to hewing away at the saplings all round the stems, like a worm o' the dust gnawing a radish. I pointed out his error as patiently as I knew how, and showed him how to cut them on two sides, so as to make them fall right; but no sooner would I turn my back on him, like this"—and he turned it on me, amplifying the illustration by taking some more liquor—"than he was at it again. It was just this way: while I looked at him, *so*"—regarding me rather unsteadily and with evident complexity of vision—"he was all right; but when I looked away, *so*" —taking a long pull at the bottle—"he defied me. Then I'd gaze at him reproachfully, *so,* and butter wouldn't have melted in his mouth."

Doubtless Mr. Dunfer honestly intended the look that he fixed upon me to be merely reproachful, but it was singularly fit to arouse the gravest apprehension in any unarmed person incurring it; and as I had lost all interest in his pointless and interminable narrative, I rose to go. Before I had fairly risen, he had again turned to the counter, and with a barely audible "so," had emptied the bottle at a gulp.

Heavens! what a yell! It was like a Titan in his last, strong agony. Jo. staggered back after emitting it, as a cannon recoils from its own thunder, and then dropped into his chair, as if he had been "knocked in the head" like a beef—his eyes drawn sidewise toward the wall, with a

stare of terror. Looking in the same direction, I saw that the knot-hole
in the wall had indeed become a human eye—a full, black eye, that
glared into my own with an entire lack of expression more awful than
the most devilish glitter. I think I must have covered my face with my
hands to shut out the horrible illusion, if such it was, and Jo.'s little
white man-of-all-work coming into the room broke the spell, and I
walked out of the house with a sort of dazed fear that *delirium tremens*
might be infectious. My horse was hitched at the watering-trough, and
untying him I mounted and gave him his head, too much troubled in
mind to note whither he took me.

I did not know what to think of all this, and like every one who does
not know what to think I thought a great deal, and to little purpose. The
only reflection that seemed at all satisfactory, was, that on the morrow I
should be some miles away, with a strong probability of never returning.

A sudden coolness brought me out of my abstraction, and looking up
I found myself entering the deep shadows of the ravine. The day was
stifling; and this transition from the pitiless, visible heat of the parched
fields to the cool gloom, heavy with pungency of cedars and vocal with
twittering of the birds that had been driven to its leafy asylum, was
exquisitely refreshing. I looked for my mystery, as usual, but not finding the ravine in a communicative mood, dismounted, led my sweating
animal into the undergrowth, tied him securely to a tree and sat down
upon a rock to meditate.

I began bravely by analyzing my pet superstition about the place.
Having resolved it into its constituent elements I arranged them in
convenient troops and squadrons, and collecting all the forces of my
logic bore down upon them from impregnable premises with the thunder
of irresistible conclusions and a great noise of chariots and general intellectual shouting. Then, when my big mental guns had overturned all
opposition, and were growling almost inaudibly away on the horizon of
pure speculation, the routed enemy straggled in upon their rear, massed
silently into a solid phalanx, and captured me, bag and baggage. An indefinable dread came upon me. I rose to shake it off, and began thread-
ing the narrow dell by an old, grass-grown cow-path that seemed to
flow along the bottom, as a substitute for the brook that Nature had
neglected to provide.

The trees among which the path straggled were ordinary, well-
behaved plants, a trifle perverted as to trunk and eccentric as to bough,

but with nothing unearthly in their general aspect. A few loose bowlders, which had detached themselves from the sides of the depression to set up an independent existence at the bottom, had dammed up the pathway, here and there, but their stony repose had nothing in it of the stillness of death. There was a kind of death-chamber hush in the valley, it is true, and a mysterious whisper above: the wind was just fingering the tops of the trees—that was all.

I had not thought of connecting Jo. Dunfer's drunken narrative with what I now sought, and only when I came into a clear space and stumbled over the level trunks of some small trees did I have the revelation. This was the site of the abandoned "shack." The discovery was verified by noting that some of the rotting stumps were hacked all round, in a most unwoodmanlike way, while others were cut straight across, and the butt ends of the corresponding trunks had the blunt wedge-form given by the axe of a master.

The opening among the trees was not more than thirty paces across. At one side was a little knoll—a natural hillock, bare of shrubbery but covered with wild grass, and on this, standing out of the grass, the headstone of a grave!

I do not remember that I felt anything like surprise at this discovery. I viewed that lonely grave with something of the feeling that Columbus must have had when he saw the hills and headlands of the new world. Before approaching it I leisurely completed my survey of the surroundings. I was even guilty of the affectation of winding my watch at that unusual hour, and with needless care and deliberation. Then I approached my mystery.

The grave—a rather short one—was in somewhat better repair than was consistent with its obvious age and isolation, and my eyes, I dare say, widened a trifle at a clump of unmistakable garden flowers showing evidence of recent watering. The stone had clearly enough done duty once as a doorstep. In its front was carved, or rather dug, an inscription. It read thus:

AH WEE—CHINAMAN.
Age unknown. Worked for Jo. Dunfer.
This monument is erected by him to keep the Chink's
memory green. Likewise as a warning to Celestials
not to take on airs. Devil take 'em!
She Was a Good Egg.

I cannot adequately relate my astonishment at this uncommon inscription! The meagre but sufficient identification of the deceased; the impudent candor of confession; the brutal anathema; the ludicrous change of sex and sentiment—all marked this record as the work of one who must have been at least as much demented as bereaved. I felt that any further disclosure would be a paltry anti-climax, and with an unconscious regard for dramatic effect turned squarely about and walked away. Nor did I return to that part of the county for four years.

II

WHO DRIVES SANE OXEN SHOULD HIMSELF BE SANE

"Gee-up, there, old Fuddy-Duddy!"

This unique adjuration came from the lips of a queer little man perched upon a wagonful of firewood, behind a brace of oxen that were hauling it easily along with a simulation of mighty effort which had evidently not imposed on their lord and master. As that gentleman happened at the moment to be staring me squarely in the face as I stood by the roadside it was not altogether clear whether he was addressing me or his beasts; nor could I say if they were named Fuddy and Duddy and were both subjects of the imperative verb "to gee-up." Anyhow the command produced no effect on us, and the queer little man removed his eyes from mine long enough to spear Fuddy and Duddy alternately with a long pole, remarking, quietly but with feeling: "Dern your skin," as if they enjoyed that integument in common. Observing that my request for a ride took no attention, and finding myself falling slowly astern, I placed one foot upon the inner circumference of a hind wheel and was slowly elevated to the level of the hub, whence I boarded the concern, *sans cérémonie,* and scrambling forward seated myself beside the driver—who took no notice of me until he had administered another indiscriminate castigation to his cattle, accompanied with the advice to "buckle down, you derned Incapable!" Then, the master of the outfit (or rather the former master, for I could not suppress a whimsical feeling that the entire establishment was my lawful prize) trained his big, black eyes upon me with an expression strangely, and somewhat unpleasantly, familiar, laid down his rod—which neither blossomed nor turned into a serpent, as I half expected—folded his arms, and gravely demanded, "W'at did you do to W'isky?"

My natural reply would have been that I drank it, but there was something about the query that suggested a hidden significance, and something about the man that did not invite a shallow jest. And so, having no other answer ready, I merely held my tongue, but felt as if I were resting under an imputation of guilt, and that my silence was being construed into a confession.

Just then a cold shadow fell upon my cheek, and caused me to look up. We were descending into my ravine! I can not describe the sensation that came upon me: I had not seen it since it unbosomed itself four years before, and now I felt like one to whom a friend has made some sorrowing confession of crime long past, and who has basely deserted him in consequence. The old memories of Jo. Dunfer, his fragmentary revelation, and the unsatisfying explanatory note by the headstone, came back with singular distinctness. I wondered what had become of Jo., and—I turned sharply round and asked my prisoner. He was intently watching his cattle, and without withdrawing his eyes replied:

"Gee-up, old Terrapin! He lies aside of Ah Wee up the gulch. Like to see it? They always come back to the spot—I've been expectin' you. H-woa!"

At the enunciation of the aspirate, Fuddy-Duddy, the incapable terrapin, came to a dead halt, and before the vowel had died away up the ravine had folded up all his eight legs and lain down in the dusty road, regardless of the effect upon his derned skin. The queer little man slid off his seat to the ground and started up the dell without deigning to look back to see if I was following. But I was.

It was about the same season of the year, and at near the same hour of the day, of my last visit. The jays clamored loudly, and the trees whispered darkly, as before; and I somehow traced in the two sounds a fanciful analogy to the open boastfulness of Mr. Jo. Dunfer's mouth and the mysterious reticence of his manner, and to the mingled hardihood and tenderness of his sole literary production—the epitaph. All things in the valley seemed unchanged, excepting the cow-path, which was almost wholly overgrown with weeds. When we came out into the "clearing," however, there was change enough. Among the stumps and trunks of the fallen saplings, those that had been hacked "China fashion" were no longer distinguishable from those that were cut " 'Melican way." It was as if the Old-World barbarism and the New-World civilization had reconciled their differences by the arbitration of an impartial decay

—as is the way of civilizations. The knoll was there, but the Hunnish brambles had overrun and all but obliterated its effete grasses; and the patrician garden-violet had capitulated to his plebeian brother—perhaps had merely reverted to his original type. Another grave—a long, robust mound—had been made beside the first, which seemed to shrink from the comparison; and in the shadow of a new headstone the old one lay prostrate, with its marvelous inscription illegible by accumulation of leaves and soil. In point of literary merit the new was inferior to the old—was even repulsive in its terse and savage jocularity:

JO. DUNFER.   DONE FOR.

I turned from it with indifference, and brushing away the leaves from the tablet of the dead pagan restored to light the mocking words which, fresh from their long neglect, seemed to have a certain pathos. My guide, too, appeared to take on an added seriousness as he read it, and I fancied that I could detect beneath his whimsical manner something of manliness, almost of dignity. But while I looked at him his former aspect, so subtly unhuman, so tantalizingly familiar, crept back into his big eyes, repellant and attractive. I resolved to make an end of the mystery if possible.

"My friend," I said, pointing to the smaller grave, "did Jo. Dunfer murder that Chinaman?"

He was leaning against a tree and looking across the open space into the top of another, or into the blue sky beyond. He neither withdrew his eyes, nor altered his posture as he slowly replied:

"No, sir; he justifiably homicided him."

"Then he really did kill him."

"Kill 'im? I should say he did, rather. Doesn't everybody know that? Didn't he stan' up before the coroner's jury and confess it? And didn't they find a verdict of 'Came to 'is death by a wholesome Christian sentiment workin' in the Caucasian breast'? An' didn't the church at the Hill turn W'isky down for it? And didn't the sovereign people elect him Justice of the Peace to get even on the gospelers? I don't know where you were brought up."

"But did Jo. do that because the Chinaman did not, or would not, learn to cut down trees like a white man?"

"Sure!—it stan's so on the record, which makes it true an' legal. My knowin' better doesn't make any difference with legal truth; it wasn't my funeral and I wasn't invited to deliver an oration. But the fact is, W'isky was jealous o' *me"*—and the little wretch actually swelled out like a turkeycock and made a pretense of adjusting an imaginary neck-tie, noting the effect in the palm of his hand, held up before him to represent a mirror.

"Jealous of *you!*" I repeated with ill-mannered astonishment.

"That's what I said. Why not?—don't I look all right?"

He assumed a mocking attitude of studied grace, and twitched the wrinkles out of his threadbare waistcoat. Then, suddenly dropping his voice to a low pitch of singular sweetness, he continued:

"W'isky thought a lot o' that Chink; nobody but me knew how 'e doted on 'im. Couldn't bear 'im out 'is sight, the derned protoplasm! And w'en 'e came down to this clearin' one day an' found him an' me neglectin' our work—him asleep an' me grapplin' a tarantula out of 'is sleeve—W'isky laid hold of my axe and let us have it, good an' hard! I dodged just then, for the spider bit me, but Ah Wee got it bad in the side an' tumbled about like anything. W'isky was just weighin' me out one w'en 'e saw the spider fastened on my finger; then 'e knew he'd made a jack ass of 'imself. He threw away the axe and got down on 's knees alongside of Ah Wee, who gave a last little kick and opened 'is eyes—he had eyes like mine—an' puttin' up 'is hands drew down W'isky's ugly head and held it there w'ile 'e stayed. That wasn't long, for a tremblin' ran through 'im and 'e gave a bit of a moan an' beat the game."

During the progress of the story the narrator had become transfigured. The comic, or rather, the sardonic element was all out of him, and as he painted that strange scene it was with difficulty that I kept my composure. And this consummate actor had somehow so managed me that the sympathy due to his *dramatis personæ* was given to himself. I stepped forward to grasp his hand, when suddenly a broad grin danced across his face and with a light, mocking laugh he continued:

"W'en W'isky got 'is nut out o' that 'e was a sight to see! All his fine clothes—'e dressed mighty blindin' those days—were spoiled ever-lastin'! 'Is hair was towsled and 'is face—what I could see of it—was whiter than the ace of lilies. 'E stared once at me, and looked away as if I didn't count; an' then there were shootin' pains chasin' one another from my bitten finger into my head, and it was Gopher to the dark. That's why I wasn't at the inquest."

"But why did you hold your tongue afterward?" I asked.

"It's that kind of tongue," he replied, and not another word would he say about it.

"After that W'isky took to drinkin' harder an' harder, and was rabider an' rabider anti-coolie, but I don't think 'e was ever particularly glad that 'e dispelled Ah Wee. He didn't put on so much dog about it w'en we were alone as w'en he had the ear of a derned Spectacular Extravaganza like you. 'E put up that headstone and gouged the inscription accordin' to his varyin' moods. It took 'im three weeks, workin' between drinks. I gouged his in one day."

"When did Jo. die?" I asked rather absently. The answer took my breath:

"Pretty soon after I looked at him through that knot-hole, w'en you had put something in his w'isky, you derned Borgia!"

Recovering somewhat from my surprise at this astounding charge, I was half-minded to throttle the audacious accuser, but was restrained by a sudden conviction that came to me in the light of a revelation. I fixed a grave look upon him and asked, as calmly as I could: "And when did you go luny?"

"Nine years ago!" he shrieked, throwing out his clenched hands—"nine years ago, w'en that big brute killed the woman who loved him better than she did me!—me who had followed 'er from San Francisco, where 'e won 'er at draw poker!—me who had watched over 'er for years w'en the scoundrel she belonged to was ashamed to acknowledge 'er and treat 'er white!—me who for her sake kept 'is cussed secret till it ate 'im up!—me who w'en you poisoned the beast fulfilled 'is last request to lay 'im alongside 'er and give 'im a stone to the head of 'im! And I've never since seen 'er grave till now, for I didn't want to meet 'im here."

"Meet him? Why, Gopher, my poor fellow, he is dead!"

"That's why I'm afraid of 'im."

I followed the little wretch back to his wagon and wrung his hand at parting. It was now nightfall, and as I stood there at the roadside in the deepening gloom, watching the blank outlines of the receding wagon, a sound was borne to me on the evening wind—a sound as of a series of vigorous thumps—and a voice came out of the night:

"Gee-up, there, you derned old Geranium."

A JUG OF SIRUP

THIS narrative begins with the death of its hero. Silas Deemer died on the 16th day of July, 1863, and two days later his remains were buried. As he had been personally known to every man, woman and well-grown child in the village, the funeral, as the local newspaper phrased it, "was largely attended." In accordance with a custom of the time and place, the coffin was opened at the graveside and the entire assembly of friends and neighbors filed past, taking a last look at the face of the dead. And then, before the eyes of all, Silas Deemer was put into the ground. Some of the eyes were a trifle dim, but in a general way it may be said that at that interment there was lack of neither observance nor observation; Silas was indubitably dead, and none could have pointed out any ritual delinquency that would have justified him in coming back from the grave. Yet if human testimony is good for anything (and certainly it once put an end to witch-craft in and about Salem) he came back.

I forgot to state that the death and burial of Silas Deemer occurred in the little village of Hillbrook, where he had lived for thirty-one years. He had been what is known in some parts of the Union (which is admittedly a free country) as a "merchant"; that is to say, he kept a retail shop for the sale of such things as are commonly sold in shops of that character. His honesty had never been questioned, so far as is known, and he was held in high esteem by all. The only thing that could be urged against him by the most censorious was a too close attention to business. It was not urged against him, though many another, who manifested it in no greater degree, was less leniently judged. The business to which Silas was devoted was mostly his own—that, possibly, may have made a difference.

At the time of Deemer's death nobody could recollect a single day, Sundays excepted, that he had not passed in his "store," since he had opened it more than a quarter-century before. His health having been perfect during all that time, he had been unable to discern any validity in whatever may or might have been urged to lure him astray from his counter; and it is related that once when he was summoned to the county seat as a witness in an important law case and did not attend, the lawyer who had the hardihood to move that he be "admonished" was solemnly informed that the Court regarded the proposal with "surprise." Judicial surprise being an emotion that attorneys are not commonly ambitious to arouse, the motion was hastily withdrawn and an agreement with the other side effected as to what Mr. Deemer would have said if he had been there—the other side pushing its advantage to the extreme and making the supposititious testimony distinctly damaging to the interests of its proponents. In brief, it was the general feeling in all that region that Silas Deemer was the one immobile verity of Hillbrook, and that his translation in space would precipitate some dismal public ill or strenuous calamity.

Mrs. Deemer and two grown daughters occupied the upper rooms of the building, but Silas had never been known to sleep elsewhere than on a cot behind the counter of the store. And there, quite by accident, he was found one night, dying, and passed away just before the time for taking down the shutters. Though speechless, he appeared conscious, and it was thought by those who knew him best that if the end had unfortunately been delayed beyond the usual hour for opening the store the effect upon him would have been deplorable.

Such had been Silas Deemer—such the fixity and invariety of his life and habit, that the village humorist (who had once attended college) was moved to bestow upon him the sobriquet of "Old Ibidem," and, in the first issue of the local newspaper after the death, to explain without offence that Silas had taken "a day off." It was more than a day, but from the record it appears that well within a month Mr. Deemer made it plain that he had not the leisure to be dead.

One of Hillbrook's most respected citizens was Alvan Creede, a banker. He lived in the finest house in town, kept a carriage and was a most estimable man variously. He knew something of the advantages of travel, too, having been frequently in Boston, and once, it was thought, in New York, though he modestly disclaimed that glittering distinction. The matter is mentioned here merely as a contribution to an understanding of Mr. Creede's worth, for either way it is creditable to him—to his intelligence if he had put himself, even temporarily, into contact with metropolitan culture; to his candor if he had not.

One pleasant summer evening at about the hour of ten Mr. Creede, entering at his garden gate, passed up the gravel walk, which looked very white in the moonlight, mounted the stone steps of his fine house and pausing a moment inserted his latchkey in the door. As he pushed this open he met his wife, who was crossing the passage from the parlor to the library. She greeted him pleasantly and pulling the door further back held it for him to enter. Instead he turned and, looking about his feet in front of the threshold, uttered an exclamation of surprise.

"Why!—what the devil," he said, "has become of that jug?"

"What jug, Alvan?" his wife inquired, not very sympathetically.

"A jug of maple sirup— I brought it along from the store and set it down here to open the door. What the—"

"There, there, Alvan, please don't swear again," said the lady, interrupting. Hillbrook, by the way, is not the only place in Christendom where a vestigial polytheism forbids the taking in vain of the Evil One's name.

The jug of maple sirup which the easy ways of village life had permitted Hillbrook's foremost citizen to carry home from the store was not there.

"Are you quite sure, Alvan?"

"My dear, do you suppose a man does not know when he is carrying a jug? I bought that sirup at Deemer's as I was passing. Deemer himself drew it and lent me the jug, and I—"

The sentence remains to this day unfinished. Mr. Creede staggered into the house, entered the parlor and dropped into an arm-chair, trembling in every limb. He had suddenly remembered that Silas Deemer was three weeks dead.

Mrs. Creede stood by her husband, regarding him with surprise and anxiety.

"For Heaven's sake," she said, "what ails you?"

Mr. Creede's ailment having no obvious relation to the interests of the better land he did not apparently deem it necessary to expound it on that demand; he said nothing—merely stared. There were long moments of silence broken by nothing but the measured ticking of the clock, which seemed somewhat slower than usual, as if it were civilly granting them an extension of time in which to recover their wits.

"Jane, I have gone mad—that is it." He spoke thickly and hurriedly. "You should have told me; you must have observed my symptoms before they became so pronounced that I have observed them myself. I thought I was passing Deemer's store; it was open and lit up—that is what I thought; of course it is never open now. Silas Deemer stood at his desk behind the counter. My God, Jane, I saw him as distinctly as I see you. Remembering that you had said you wanted some maple sirup, I went in and bought some—that is all— I bought two quarts of maple sirup from Silas Deemer, who is dead and underground, but nevertheless drew that sirup from a cask and handed it to me in a jug. He talked with me, too, rather gravely, I remember, even more so than was his way, but not a word of what he said can I now recall. But I saw him— good Lord, I saw and talked with him—and he is dead! So I thought, but I'm mad, Jane, I'm as crazy as a beetle; and you have kept it from me."

This monologue gave the woman time to collect what faculties she had.

"Alvan," she said, "you have given no evidence of insanity, believe me. This was undoubtedly an illusion—how should it be anything else? That would be too terrible! But there is no insanity; you are working too hard at the bank. You should not have attended the meeting of directors this evening; any one could see that you were ill; I knew something would occur."

It may have seemed to him that the prophecy had lagged a bit, awaiting the event, but he said nothing of that, being concerned with his own condition. He was calm now, and could think coherently.

"Doubtless the phenomenon was subjective," he said, with a somewhat ludicrous transition to the slang of science. "Granting the possibility of spiritual apparition and even materialization, yet the apparition and materialization of a half-gallon brown clay jug—a piece of coarse, heavy pottery evolved from nothing—that is hardly thinkable."

As he finished speaking, a child ran into the room—his little daughter. She was clad in a bedgown. Hastening to her father she threw her arms about his neck, saying: "You naughty papa, you forgot to come in and kiss me. We heard you open the gate and got up and looked out. And, papa dear, Eddy says mayn't he have the little jug when it is empty?"

As the full import of that revelation imparted itself to Alvan Creede's understanding he visibly shuddered. For the child could not have heard a word of the conversation.

The estate of Silas Deemer being in the hands of an administrator who had thought it best to dispose of the "business" the store had been closed ever since the owner's death, the goods having been removed by another "merchant" who had purchased them *en bloc*. The rooms above were vacant as well, for the widow and daughters had gone to another town.

On the evening immediately after Alvan Creede's adventure (which had somehow "got out") a crowd of men, women and children thronged the sidewalk opposite the store. That the place was haunted by the spirit of the late Silas Deemer was now well known to every resident of Hillbrook, though many affected disbelief. Of these the hardiest, and in a general way the youngest, threw stones against the front of the building, the only part accessible, but carefully missed the unshuttered windows. Incredulity had not grown to malice. A few venturesome souls crossed the street and rattled the door in its frame; struck matches and held them near the window; attempted to view the black interior. Some of the spectators invited attention to their wit by shouting and groaning and challenging the ghost to a footrace.

After a considerable time had elapsed without any manifestation, and many of the crowd had gone away, all those remaining began to observe that the interior of the store was suffused with a dim, yellow light. At this all demonstrations ceased; the intrepid souls about the door and windows fell back to the opposite side of the street and were merged in the crowd; the small boys ceased throwing stones. Nobody spoke above his breath; all whispered excitedly and pointed to the now steadily growing light. How long a time had passed since the first faint glow had been observed none could have guessed, but eventually the illumination was bright enough to reveal the whole interior of the store; and there, standing at his desk behind the counter, Silas Deemer was distinctly visible!

The effect upon the crowd was marvelous. It began rapidly to melt away at both flanks, as the timid left the place. Many ran as fast as their legs would let them; others moved off with greater dignity, turning occasionally to look backward over the shoulder. At last a score or more, mostly men, remained where they were, speechless, staring, excited. The apparition inside gave them no attention; it was apparently occupied with a book of accounts.

Presently three men left the crowd on the sidewalk as if by a common impulse and crossed the street. One of them, a heavy man, was about to set his shoulder against the door when it opened, apparently without human agency, and the courageous investigators passed in. No sooner had they crossed the threshold than they were seen by the awed observers outside to be acting in the most unaccountable way. They thrust out their hands before them, pursued devious courses, came into violent collision with the counter, with boxes and barrels on the floor, and with one another. They turned awkwardly hither and thither and seemed trying to escape, but unable to retrace their steps. Their voices were heard in exclamations and curses. But in no way did the apparition of Silas Deemer manifest an interest in what was going on.

By what impulse the crowd was moved none ever recollected, but the entire mass—men, women, children, dogs—made a simultaneous and tumultuous rush for the entrance. They congested the doorway, pushing for precedence—resolving themselves at length into a line and moving up step by step. By some subtle spiritual or physical alchemy observation had been transmuted into action—the sightseers had become participants in the spectacle—the audience had usurped the stage.

To the only spectator remaining on the other side of the street—Alvan Creede, the banker—the interior of the store with its inpouring crowd continued in full illumination; all the strange things going on there were clearly visible. To those inside all was black darkness. It was as if each person as he was thrust in at the door had been stricken blind, and was maddened by the mischance. They groped with aimless imprecision, tried to force their way out against the current, pushed and elbowed, struck at random, fell and were trampled, rose and trampled in their turn. They seized one another by the garments, the hair, the beard —fought like animals, cursed, shouted, called one another approbrious and obscene names. When, finally, Alvan Creede had seen the last person of the line pass into that awful tumult the light that had illuminated it was suddenly quenched and all was as black to him as to those within. He turned away and left the place.

In the early morning a curious crowd had gathered about "Deemer's." It was composed partly of those who had run away the night before, but now had the courage of sunshine, partly of honest folk going to their daily toil. The door of the store stood open; the place was vacant, but on the walls, the floor, the furniture, were shreds of clothing and tangles of hair. Hillbrook militant had managed somehow to pull itself out and had gone home to medicine its hurts and swear that it had been all night in bed. On the dusty desk, behind the counter, was the salesbook. The entries in it, in Deemer's handwriting, had ceased on the 16th day of July, the last of his life. There was no record of a later sale to Alvan Creede.

That is the entire story—except that men's passions having subsided and reason having resumed its immemorial sway, it was confessed in Hillbrook that, considering the harmless and honorable character of his first commercial transaction under the new conditions, Silas Deemer, deceased, might properly have been suffered to resume business at the old stand without mobbing. In that judgment the local historian from whose unpublished work these facts are compiled had the thoughtfulness to signify his concurrence.

STALEY FLEMING'S HALLUCINATION

OF two men who were talking one was a physician.

"I sent for you, Doctor," said the other, "but I don't think you can do me any good. May be you can recommend a specialist in psychopathy. I fancy I'm a bit loony."

"You look all right," the physician said.

"You shall judge—I have hallucinations. I wake every night and see in my room, intently watching me, a big black Newfoundland dog with a white forefoot."

"You say you wake; are you sure about that? 'Hallucinations' are sometimes only dreams."

"Oh, I wake, all right. Sometimes I lie still a long time, looking at the dog as earnestly as the dog looks at me—I always leave the light going. When I can't endure it any longer I sit up in bed—and nothing is there!"

"'M, 'm—what is the beast's expression?"

"It seems to me sinister. Of course I know that, except in art, an animal's face in repose has always the same expression. But this is not a real animal. Newfoundland dogs are pretty mild looking, you know; what's the matter with this one?"

"Really, my diagnosis would have no value: I am not going to treat the dog."

The physician laughed at his own pleasantry, but narrowly watched his patient from the corner of his eye. Presently he said: "Fleming, your description of the beast fits the dog of the late Atwell Barton."

Fleming half-rose from his chair, sat again and made a visible attempt at indifference. "I remember Barton," he said; "I believe he was—it was reported that—wasn't there something suspicious in his death?"

Looking squarely now into the eyes of his patient, the physician said: "Three years ago the body of your old enemy, Atwell Barton, was found in the woods near his house and yours. He had been stabbed to death. There have been no arrests; there was no clew. Some of us had 'theories.' I had one. Have you?"

"I? Why, bless your soul, what could I know about it? You remember that I left for Europe almost immediately afterward—a considerable time afterward. In the few weeks since my return you could not expect me to construct a 'theory.' In fact, I have not given the matter a thought. What about his dog?"

"It was first to find the body. It died of starvation on his grave."

We do not know the inexorable law underlying coincidences. Staley Fleming did not, or he would perhaps not have sprung to his feet as the night wind brought in through the open window the long wailing howl of a distant dog. He strode several times across the room in the steadfast gaze of the physician; then, abruptly confronting him, almost shouted: "What has all this to do with my trouble, Dr. Halderman? You forget why you were sent for."

Rising, the physician laid his hand upon his patient's arm and said, gently: "Pardon me. I cannot diagnose your disorder off-hand—to-morrow, perhaps. Please go to bed, leaving your door unlocked; I will pass the night here with your books. Can you call me without rising?"

"Yes, there is an electric bell."

"Good. If anything disturbs you push the button without sitting up. Good night."

Comfortably installed in an armchair the man of medicine stared into the glowing coals and thought deeply and long, but apparently to little purpose, for he frequently rose and opening a door leading to the staircase, listened intently; then resumed his seat. Presently, however, he fell asleep, and when he woke it was past midnight. He stirred the failing fire, lifted a book from the table at his side and looked at the title. It was Denneker's "Meditations." He opened it at random and began to read:

"Forasmuch as it is ordained of God that all flesh hath spirit and thereby taketh on spiritual powers, so, also, the spirit hath powers of the flesh, even when it is gone out of the flesh and liveth as a thing apart, as many a violence performed by wraith and lemure sheweth. And there be who say that man is not single in this, but the beasts have the like evil inducement, and—"

The reading was interrupted by a shaking of the house, as by the fall of a heavy object. The reader flung down the book, rushed from the room and mounted the stairs to Fleming's bed-chamber. He tried the door, but contrary to his instructions it was locked. He set his shoulder against it with such force that it gave way. On the floor near the disordered bed, in his night clothes, lay Fleming gasping away his life.

The physician raised the dying man's head from the floor and observed a wound in the throat. "I should have thought of this," he said, believing it suicide.

When the man was dead an examination disclosed the unmistakable marks of an animal's fangs deeply sunken into the jugular vein.

But there was no animal.

A RESUMED IDENTITY

I

THE REVIEW AS A FORM OF WELCOME

ONE summer night a man stood on a low hill overlooking a wide expanse of forest and field. By the full moon hanging low in the west he knew that he might not have known otherwise: that it was near the hour of dawn. A light mist lay along the earth, partly veiling the lower features of the landscape, but above it the taller trees showed in well-defined masses against a clear sky. Two or three farmhouses were visible through the haze, but in none of them, naturally, was a light. Nowhere, indeed, was any sign or suggestion of life except the barking of a distant dog, which, repeated with mechanical iteration, served rather to accentuate than dispel the loneliness of the scene.

The man looked curiously about him on all sides, as one who among familiar surroundings is unable to determine his exact place and part in the scheme of things. It is so, perhaps, that we shall act when, risen from the dead, we await the call to judgment.

A hundred yards away was a straight road, showing white in the moonlight. Endeavoring to orient himself, as a surveyor or navigator might say, the man moved his eyes slowly along its visible length and at a distance of a quarter-mile to the south of his station saw, dim and gray in the haze, a group of horsemen riding to the north. Behind them were men afoot, marching in column, with dimly gleaming rifles aslant above their shoulders. They moved slowly and in silence. Another group of horsemen, another regiment of infantry, another and another—all in unceasing motion toward the man's point of view, past it, and beyond. A battery of artillery followed, the cannoneers riding with folded arms on limber and caisson. And still the interminable procession came out of the obscurity to south and passed into the obscurity to north, with never a sound of voice, nor hoof, nor wheel.

The man could not rightly understand: he thought himself deaf; said so, and heard his own voice, although it had an unfamiliar quality that almost alarmed him; it disappointed his ear's expectancy in the matter of *timbre* and resonance. But he was not deaf, and that for the moment sufficed.

Then he remembered that there are natural phenomena to which some one has given the name "acoustic shadows." If you stand in an acoustic shadow there is one direction from which you will hear nothing. At the battle of Gaines's Mill, one of the fiercest conflicts of the Civil War, with a hundred guns in play, spectators a mile and a half away on the opposite side of the Chickahominy valley heard nothing of what they clearly saw. The bombardment of Port Royal, heard and felt at St. Augustine, a hundred and fifty miles to the south, was inaudible two miles to the north in a still atmosphere. A few days before the surrender at Appomattox a thunderous engagement between the commands of Sheridan and Pickett was unknown to the latter commander, a mile in the rear of his own line.

These instances were not known to the man of whom we write, but less striking ones of the same character had not escaped his observation. He was profoundly disquieted, but for another reason than the uncanny silence of that moonlight march.

"Good Lord!" he said to himself—and again it was as if another had spoken his thought—"if those people are what I take them to be we have lost the battle and they are moving on Nashville!"

Then came a thought of self—an apprehension—a strong sense of personal peril, such as in another we call fear. He stepped quickly into the shadow of a tree. And still the silent battalions moved slowly forward in the haze.

The chill of a sudden breeze upon the back of his neck drew his attention to the quarter whence it came, and turning to the east he saw a faint gray light along the horizon—the first sign of returning day. This increased his apprehension.

"I must get away from here," he thought, "or I shall be discovered and taken."

He moved out of the shadow, walking rapidly toward the graying east. From the safer seclusion of a clump of cedars he looked back. The entire column had passed out of sight: the straight white road lay bare and desolate in the moonlight!

Puzzled before, he was now inexpressibly astonished. So swift a passing of so slow an army!—he could not comprehend it. Minute after minute passed unnoted; he had lost his sense of time. He sought with a terrible earnestness a solution of the mystery, but sought in vain. When at last he roused himself from his abstraction the sun's rim was visible above the hills, but in the new conditions he found no other light than that of day; his understanding was involved as darkly in doubt as before.

On every side lay cultivated fields showing no sign of war and war's ravages. From the chimneys of the farmhouses thin ascensions of blue smoke signaled preparations for a day's peaceful toil. Having stilled its immemorial allocution to the moon, the watch-dog was assisting a Negro who, prefixing a team of mules to the plow, was flatting and sharping contentedly at his task. The hero of this tale stared stupidly at the pastoral picture as if he had never seen such a thing in all his life; then he put his hand to his head, passed it through his hair and, withdrawing it, attentively considered the palm—a singular thing to do. Apparently reassured by the act, he walked confidently toward the road.

II

WHEN YOU HAVE LOST YOUR LIFE CONSULT A PHYSICIAN

Dr. Stilling Malson, of Murfreesboro, having visited a patient six or seven miles away, on the Nashville road, had remained with him all night. At daybreak he set out for home on horseback, as was the custom of doctors of the time and region. He had passed into the neighborhood of Stone's River battlefield when a man approached him from the roadside and saluted in the military fashion, with a movement of the right hand to the hat-brim. But the hat was not a military hat, the man was not in uniform and had not a martial bearing. The doctor nodded civilly, half thinking that the stranger's uncommon greeting was perhaps in deference to the historic surroundings. As the stranger evidently desired speech with him he courteously reined in his horse and waited.

"Sir," said the stranger, "although a civilian, you are perhaps an enemy."

"I am a physician," was the non-committal reply.

"Thank you," said the other. "I am a lieutenant, of the staff of General Hazen." He paused a moment and looked sharply at the person whom he was addressing, then added, "Of the Federal army."

The physician merely nodded.

"Kindly tell me," continued the other, "what has happened here. Where are the armies? Which has won the battle?"

The physician regarded his questioner curiously with half-shut eyes. After a professional scrutiny, prolonged to the limit of politeness, "Pardon me," he said; "one asking information should be willing to impart it. Are you wounded?" he added, smiling.

"Not seriously—it seems."

The man removed the unmilitary hat, put his hand to his head, passed it through his hair and, withdrawing it, attentively considered the palm.

"I was struck by a bullet and have been unconscious. It must have been a light, glancing blow: I find no blood and feel no pain. I will not trouble you for treatment, but will you kindly direct me to my command —to any part of the Federal army—if you know?"

Again the doctor did not immediately reply: he was recalling much that is recorded in the books of his profession—something about lost identity and the effect of familiar scenes in restoring it. At length he looked the man in the face, smiled, and said:

"Lieutenant, you are not wearing the uniform of your rank and service."

At this the man glanced down at his civilian attire, lifted his eyes, and said with hesitation:

"That is true. I—I don't quite understand."

Still regarding him sharply but not unsympathetically the man of science bluntly inquired:

"How old are you?"

"Twenty-three—if that has anything to do with it."

"You don't look it; I should hardly have guessed you to be just that."

The man was growing impatient. "We need not discuss that," he said; "I want to know about the army. Not two hours ago I saw a column of troops moving northward on this road. You must have met them. Be good enough to tell me the color of their clothing, which I was unable to make out, and I'll trouble you no more."

"You are quite sure that you saw them?"

"Sure? My God, sir, I could have counted them!"

"Why, really," said the physician, with an amusing consciousness of his own resemblance to the loquacious barber of the Arabian Nights, "this is very interesting. I met no troops."

The man looked at him coldly, as if he had himself observed the likeness to the barber. "It is plain," he said, "that you do not care to assist me. Sir, you may go to the devil!"

He turned and strode away, very much at random, across the dewy fields, his half-penitent tormentor quietly watching him from his point of vantage in the saddle till he disappeared beyond an array of trees.

III

THE DANGER OF LOOKING INTO A POOL
OF WATER

After leaving the road the man slackened his pace, and now went forward, rather deviously, with a distinct feeling of fatigue. He could not account for this, though truly the interminable loquacity of that country doctor offered itself in explanation. Seating himself upon a rock, he laid one hand upon his knee, back upward, and casually looked at it. It was lean and withered. He lifted both hands to his face. It was seamed and furrowed; he could trace the lines with the tips of his fingers. How strange!—a mere bullet-stroke and a brief unconsciousness should not make one a physical wreck.

"I must have been a long time in hospital," he said aloud. "Why, what a fool I am! The battle was in December, and it is now summer!" He laughed. "No wonder that fellow thought me an escaped lunatic. He was wrong: I am only an escaped patient."

At a little distance a small plot of ground enclosed by a stone wall caught his attention. With no very definite intent he rose and went to it. In the center was a square, solid monument of hewn stone. It was brown with age, weather-worn at the angles, spotted with moss and lichen. Between the massive blocks were strips of grass the leverage of whose roots had pushed them apart. In answer to the challenge of this ambitious structure Time had laid his destroying hand upon it, and it would soon be "one with Nineveh and Tyre." In an inscription on one side his eye caught a familiar name. Shaking with excitement, he craned his body across the wall and read:

HAZEN'S BRIGADE
to
The Memory of Its Soldiers
who fell at
Stone River, Dec. 31, 1862.

The man fell back from the wall, faint and sick. Almost within an arm's length was a little depression in the earth; it had been filled by a recent rain—a pool of clear water. He crept to it to revive himself, lifted the upper part of his body on his trembling arms, thrust forward his head and saw the reflection of his face, as in a mirror. He uttered a terrible cry. His arms gave way; he fell, face downward, into the pool and yielded up the life that had spanned another life.

A BABY TRAMP

IF you had seen little Jo standing at the street corner in the rain, you would hardly have admired him. It was apparently an ordinary autumn rainstorm, but the water which fell upon Jo (who was hardly old enough to be either just or unjust, and so perhaps did not come under the law of impartial distribution) appeared to have some property peculiar to itself: one would have said it was dark and adhesive—sticky. But that could hardly be so, even in Blackburg, where things certainly did occur that were a good deal out of the common.

For example, ten or twelve years before, a shower of small frogs had fallen, as is credibly attested by a contemporaneous chronicle, the record concluding with a somewhat obscure statement to the effect that the chronicler considered it good growing-weather for Frenchmen.

Some years later Blackburg had a fall of crimson snow; it is cold in Blackburg when winter is on, and the snows are frequent and deep. There can be no doubt of it—the snow in this instance was of the color of blood and melted into water of the same hue, if water it was, not blood. The phenomenon had attracted wide attention, and science had as many explanations as there were scientists who knew nothing about it. But the men of Blackburg—men who for many years had lived right there where the red snow fell, and might be supposed to know a good deal about the matter—shook their heads and said something would come of it.

And something did, for the next summer was made memorable by the prevalence of a mysterious disease—epidemic, endemic, or the Lord knows what, though the physicians didn't—which carried away a full half of the population. Most of the other half carried themselves away and were slow to return, but finally came back, and were now increasing and multiplying as before, but Blackburg had not since been altogether the same.

Of quite another kind, though equally "out of the common," was the incident of Hetty Parlow's ghost. Hetty Parlow's maiden name had been Brownon, and in Blackburg that meant more than one would think.

The Brownons had from time immemorial—from the very earliest of the old colonial days—been the leading family of the town. It was the richest and it was the best, and Blackburg would have shed the last drop of its plebeian blood in defense of the Brownon fair fame. As few of the family's members had ever been known to live permanently away from Blackburg, although most of them were educated elsewhere and nearly all had traveled, there was quite a number of them. The men held most of the public offices, and the women were foremost in all good works. Of these latter, Hetty was most beloved by reason of the sweetness of her disposition, the purity of her character and her singular personal beauty. She married in Boston a young scapegrace named Parlow, and like a good Brownon brought him to Blackburg forthwith and made a man and a town councilman of him. They had a child which they named Joseph and dearly loved, as was then the fashion among parents in all that region. Then they died of the mysterious disorder already mentioned, and at the age of one whole year Joseph set up as an orphan.

Unfortunately for Joseph the disease which had cut off his parents did not stop at that; it went on and extirpated nearly the whole Brownon contingent and its allies by marriage; and those who fled did not return. The tradition was broken, the Brownon estates passed into alien hands and the only Brownons remaining in that place were underground in Oak Hill Cemetery, where, indeed, was a colony of them powerful enough to resist the encroachment of surrounding tribes and hold the best part of the grounds. But about the ghost:

One night, about three years after the death of Hetty Parlow, a number of the young people of Blackburg were passing Oak Hill Cemetery in a wagon—if you have been there you will remember that the road to Greenton runs alongside it on the south. They had been attending a May Day festival at Greenton; and that serves to fix the date. Altogether there may have been a dozen, and a jolly party they were, considering the legacy of gloom left by the town's recent somber experiences. As they passed the cemetery the man driving suddenly reined in his team with an exclamation of surprise. It was sufficiently surprising, no doubt, for just ahead, and almost at the roadside, though inside the cemetery, stood the ghost of Hetty Parlow. There could be no doubt of it, for she had been personally known to every youth and maiden in the party. That established the thing's identity; its character as ghost was signified by all the customary signs—the shroud, the long, undone hair, the "far-away look"—everything. This disquieting apparition was stretching out its arms toward the west, as if in supplication for the evening star, which, certainly, was an alluring object, though obviously out of reach. As they all sat silent (so the story goes) every member of that party of merrymakers—they had merry-made on coffee and lemonade only—distinctly heard that ghost call the name "Joey, Joey!" A moment later nothing was there. Of course one does not have to believe all that.

Now, at that moment, as was afterward ascertained, Joey was wandering about in the sagebrush on the opposite side of the continent, near Winnemucca, in the State of Nevada. He had been taken to that town by some good persons distantly related to his dead father, and by them adopted and tenderly cared for. But on that evening the poor child had strayed from home and was lost in the desert.

His after history is involved in obscurity and has gaps which conjecture alone can fill. It is known that he was found by a family of Piute Indians, who kept the little wretch with them for a time and then sold him—actually sold him for money to a woman on one of the eastbound trains, at a station a long way from Winnemucca. The woman professed to have made all manner of inquiries, but all in vain: so, being childless and a widow, she adopted him herself. At this point of his career Jo seemed to be getting a long way from the condition of orphanage; the interposition of a multitude of parents between himself and that woeful state promised him a long immunity from its disadvantages.

Mrs. Darnell, his newest mother, lived in Cleveland, Ohio. But her adopted son did not long remain with her. He was seen one afternoon by a policeman, new to that beat, deliberately toddling away from her house, and being questioned answered that he was "a doin' home." He must have traveled by rail, somehow, for three days later he was in the town of Whiteville, which, as you know, is a long way from Blackburg. His clothing was in pretty fair condition, but he was sinfully dirty. Unable to give any account of himself he was arrested as a vagrant and sentenced to imprisonment in the Infants' Sheltering Home—where he was washed.

Jo ran away from the Infants' Sheltering Home at Whiteville—just took to the woods one day, and the Home knew him no more forever.

We find him next, or rather get back to him, standing forlorn in the cold autumn rain at a suburban street corner in Blackburg; and it seems right to explain now that the raindrops falling upon him there were really not dark and gummy; they only failed to make his face and hands less so. Jo was indeed fearfully and wonderfully besmirched, as by the hand of an artist. And the forlorn little tramp had no shoes; his feet were bare, red, and swollen, and when he walked he limped with both legs. As to clothing—ah, you would hardly have had the skill to name any single garment that he wore, or say by what magic he kept it upon him. That he was cold all over and all through did not admit of a doubt; he knew it himself. Anyone would have been cold there that evening; but, for that reason, no one else was there. How Jo came to be there himself, he could not for the flickering little life of him have told, even if gifted with a vocabulary exceeding a hundred words. From the way he stared about him one could have seen that he had not the faintest notion of where (nor why) he was.

Yet he was not altogether a fool in his day and generation; being cold and hungry, and still able to walk a little by bending his knees very much indeed and putting his feet down toes first, he decided to enter one of the houses which flanked the street at long intervals and looked so bright and warm. But when he attempted to act upon that very sensible decision a burly dog came bowsing out and disputed his right. Inexpressibly frightened and believing, no doubt (with some reason, too) that brutes without meant brutality within, he hobbled away from all the houses, and with gray, wet fields to right of him and gray, wet fields to left of him—with the rain half blinding him and the night coming in mist and darkness, held his way along the road that leads to Greenton. That is to say, the road leads those to Greenton who succeed in passing the Oak Hill Cemetery. A considerable number every year do not.

Jo did not.

They found him there the next morning, very wet, very cold, but no longer hungry. He had apparently entered the cemetery gate—hoping, perhaps, that it led to a house where there was no dog—and gone blundering about in the darkness, falling over many a grave, no doubt, until he had tired of it all and given up. The little body lay upon one side, with one soiled cheek upon one soiled hand, the other hand tucked away among the rags to make it warm, the other cheek washed clean and white at last, as for a kiss from one of God's great angels. It was observed—though nothing was thought of it at the time, the body being as yet unidentified—that the little fellow was lying upon the grave of

Hetty Parlow. The grave, however, had not opened to receive him. That is a circumstance which, without actual irreverence, one may wish had been ordered otherwise.

THE NIGHT-DOINGS AT "DEADMAN'S"
A Story That Is Untrue

IT was a singularly sharp night, and clear as the heart of a diamond. Clear nights have a trick of being keen. In darkness you may be cold and not know it; when you see, you suffer. This night was bright enough to bite like a serpent. The moon was moving mysteriously along behind the giant pines crowning the South Mountain, striking a cold sparkle from the crusted snow, and bringing out against the black west the ghostly outlines of the Coast Range, beyond which lay the invisible Pacific. The snow had piled itself, in the open spaces along the bottom of the gulch, into long ridges that seemed to heave, and into hills that appeared to toss and scatter spray. The spray was sunlight, twice reflected: dashed once from the moon, once from the snow.

In this snow many of the shanties of the abandoned mining camp were obliterated (a sailor might have said they had gone down), and at irregular intervals it had overtopped the tall trestles which had once supported a river called a flume; for, of course, "flume" is *flumen*. Among the advantages of which the mountains cannot deprive the goldhunter is the privilege of speaking Latin. He says of his dead neighbor, "He has gone up the flume." This is not a bad way to say, "His life has returned to the Fountain of Life."

While putting on its armor against the assaults of the wind, this snow had neglected no coign of vantage. Snow pursued by the wind is not wholly unlike a retreating army. In the open field it ranges itself in ranks and battalions; where it can get a foothold it makes a stand; where it can take cover it does so. You may see whole platoons of snow cowering behind a bit of broken wall. The devious old road, hewn out of the mountain side, was full of it. Squadron upon squadron had struggled to escape by this line, when suddenly pursuit had ceased. A more desolate and dreary spot than Deadman's Gulch in a winter midnight it is impossible to imagine. Yet Mr. Hiram Beeson elected to live there, the sole inhabitant.

Away up the side of the North Mountain his little pine-log shanty projected from its single pane of glass a long, thin beam of light, and looked not altogether unlike a black beetle fastened to the hillside with a bright new pin. Within it sat Mr. Beeson himself, before a roaring fire, staring into its hot heart as if he had never before seen such a thing in all his life. He was not a comely man. He was gray; he was ragged and slovenly in his attire; his face was wan and haggard; his eyes were too bright. As to his age, if one had attempted to guess it, one might have said forty-seven, then corrected himself and said seventy-four. He was really twenty-eight. Emaciated he was; as much, perhaps, as he dared be, with a needy undertaker at Bentley's Flat and a new and enterprising coroner at Sonora. Poverty and zeal are an upper and a nether millstone. It is dangerous to make a third in that kind of sandwich.

As Mr. Beeson sat there, with his ragged elbows on his ragged knees, his lean jaws buried in his lean hands, and with no apparent intention of going to bed, he looked as if the slightest movement would tumble him to pieces. Yet during the last hour he had winked no fewer than three times.

There was a sharp rapping at the door. A rap at that time of night and in that weather might have surprised an ordinary mortal who had dwelt two years in the gulch without seeing a human face, and could not fail to know that the country was impassable; but Mr. Beeson did not so much as pull his eyes out of the coals. And even when the door was pushed open he only shrugged a little more closely into himself, as one does who is expecting something that he would rather not see. You may observe this movement in women when, in a mortuary chapel, the coffin is borne up the aisle behind them.

But when a long old man in a blanket overcoat, his head tied up in a handkerchief and nearly his entire face in a muffler, wearing green goggles and with a complexion of glittering whiteness where it could be seen, strode silently into the room, laying a hard, gloved hand on Mr. Beeson's shoulder, the latter so far forgot himself as to look up with an appearance of no small astonishment; whomever he may have been expecting, he had evidently not counted on meeting anyone like this. Nevertheless, the sight of this unexpected guest produced in Mr. Beeson the following sequence: a feeling of astonishment; a sense of gratification; a sentiment of profound good will. Rising from his seat, he took the knotty hand from his shoulder, and shook it up and down with a fervor quite unaccountable; for in the old man's aspect was nothing to attract, much to repel. However, attraction is too general a property for repulsion to be without it. The most attractive object in the world is the face we instinctively cover with a cloth. When it becomes still more attractive—fascinating—we put seven feet of earth above it.

"Sir," said Mr. Beeson, releasing the old man's hand, which fell passively against his thigh with a quiet clack, "it is an extremely disagreeable night. Pray be seated; I am very glad to see you."

Mr. Beeson spoke with an easy good breeding that one would hardly have expected, considering all things. Indeed, the contrast between his appearance and his manner was sufficiently surprising to be one of the commonest of social phenomena in the mines. The old man advanced a step toward the fire, glowing cavernously in the green goggles. Mr. Beeson resumed:

"You bet your life I am!"

Mr. Beeson's elegance was not too refined; it had made reasonable concessions to local taste. He paused a moment, letting his eyes drop from the muffled head of his guest, down along the row of moldy buttons confining the blanket overcoat, to the greenish cowhide boots powdered with snow, which had begun to melt and run along the floor in little rills. He took an inventory of his guest, and appeared satisfied. Who would not have been? Then he continued:

"The cheer I can offer you is, unfortunately, in keeping with my surroundings; but I shall esteem myself highly favored if it is your pleasure to partake of it, rather than seek better at Bentley's Flat."

With a singular refinement of hospitable humility Mr. Beeson spoke as if a sojourn in his warm cabin on such a night, as compared with walking fourteen miles up to the throat in snow with a cutting crust, would be an intolerable hardship. By way of reply, his guest unbuttoned the blanket overcoat. The host laid fresh fuel on the fire, swept the hearth with the tail of a wolf, and added:

"But *I* think you'd better skedaddle."

The old man took a seat by the fire, spreading his broad soles to the heat without removing his hat. In the mines the hat is seldom removed except when the boots are. Without further remark Mr. Beeson also seated himself in a chair which had been a barrel, and which, retaining much of its original character, seemed to have been designed with a view to preserving his dust if it should please him to crumble. For a moment there was silence; then, from somewhere among the pines, came the snarling yelp of a coyote; and simultaneously the door rattled in its frame. There was no other connection between the two incidents than that the coyote has an aversion to storms, and the wind was rising; yet there seemed somehow a kind of supernatural conspiracy between the two, and Mr. Beeson shuddered with a vague sense of terror. He recovered himslf in a moment and again addressed his guest.

"There are strange doings here. I will tell you everything, and then if you decide to go I shall hope to accompany you over the worst of the way; as far as where Baldy Peterson shot Ben Hike—I dare say you know the place."

The old man nodded emphatically, as intimating not merely that he did, but that he did indeed.

"Two years ago," began Mr. Beeson, "I, with two companions, occupied this house; but when the rush to the Flat occurred we left, along with the rest. In ten hours the Gulch was deserted. That evening, however, I discovered I had left behind me a valuable pistol (that is it) and returned for it, passing the night here alone, as I have passed every night since. I must explain that a few days before we left, our Chinese domestic had the misfortune to die while the ground was frozen so hard that it was impossible to dig a grave in the usual way. So, on the day of our hasty departure, we cut through the floor there, and gave him such burial as we could. But before putting him down I had the extremely bad taste to cut off his pigtail and spike it to that beam above his grave, where you may see it at this moment, or preferably, when warmth has given you leisure for observation.

"I stated, did I not, that the Chinaman came to his death from natural causes? I had, of course, nothing to do with that, and returned through no irresistible attraction, or morbid fascination, but only because I had forgotten a pistol. This is clear to you, is it not, sir?"

The visitor nodded gravely. He appeared to be a man of few words, if any. Mr. Beeson continued:

"According to the Chinese faith, a man is like a kite: he cannot go to heaven without a tail. Well, to shorten this tedious story—which, however, I thought it my duty to relate—on that night, while I was here alone and thinking of anything but him, that Chinaman came back for his pigtail.

"He did not get it."

At this point Mr. Beeson relapsed into blank silence. Perhaps he was fatigued by the unwonted exercise of speaking; perhaps he had conjured up a memory that demanded his undivided attention. The wind was now fairly abroad, and the pines along the mountain-side sang with singular distinctness. The narrator continued:

"You say you do not see much in that, and I must confess I do not myself.

"But he keeps coming!"

There was another long silence, during which both stared into the fire without the movement of a limb. Then Mr. Beeson broke out, almost fiercely, fixing his eyes on what he could see of the impassive face of his auditor:

"Give it him? Sir, in this matter I have no intention of troubling anyone for advice. You will pardon me, I am sure"—here he became singularly persuasive—"but I have ventured to nail that pigtail fast, and have assumed the somewhat onerous obligation of guarding it. So it is quite impossible to act on your considerate suggestion.

"Do you play me for a Modoc?"

Nothing could exceed the sudden ferocity with which he thrust this indignant remonstrance into the ear of his guest. It was as if he had struck him on the side of the head with a steel gauntlet. It was a protest, but it was a challenge. To be mistaken for a coward—to be played for a Modoc: these two expressions are one. Sometimes it is a Chinaman. Do you play me for a Chinaman? is a question frequently addressed to the ear of the suddenly dead.

Mr. Beeson's buffet produced no effect, and after a moment's pause, during which the wind thundered in the chimney like the sound of clods upon a coffin, he resumed:

"But, as you say, it is wearing me out. I feel that the life of the last two years has been a mistake—a mistake that corrects itself; you see how. The grave! No; there is no one to dig it. The ground is frozen, too. But you are very welcome. You may say at Bentley's—but that is not important. It was very tough to cut: they braid silk into their pigtails. Kwaagh."

Mr. Beeson was speaking with his eyes shut, and he wandered. His last word was a snore. A moment later he drew a long breath, opened his eyes with an effort, made a single remark, and fell into a deep sleep. What he said was this:

"They are swiping my dust!"

Then the aged stranger, who had not uttered one word since his arrival, arose from his seat and deliberately laid off his outer clothing, looking as angular in his flannels as the late. Signorina Festorazzi, an Irish woman, six feet in height, and weighing fifty-six pounds, who used to exhibit herself in her chemise to the people of San Francisco. He then crept into one of the "bunks," having first placed a revolver in easy reach, according to the custom of the country. This revolver he took from a shelf, and it was the one which Mr. Beeson had mentioned as that for which he had returned to the Gulch two years before.

In a few moments Mr. Beeson awoke, and seeing that his guest had retired he did likewise. But before doing so he approached the long, plaited wisp of pagan hair and gave it a powerful tug, to assure himself that it was fast and firm. The two beds—mere shelves covered with blankets not overclean—faced each other from opposite sides of the room, the little square trapdoor that had given access to the Chinaman's grave being midway between. This, by the way, was crossed by a double row of spike-heads. In his resistance to the supernatural, Mr. Beeson had not disdained the use of material precautions.

The fire was now low, the flames burning bluely and petulantly, with occasional flashes, projecting spectral shadows on the walls—shadows that moved mysteriously about, now dividing, now uniting. The shadow of the pendent queue, however, kept moodily apart, near the roof at the further end of the room, looking like a note of admiration. The song of the pines outside had now risen to the dignity of a triumphal hymn. In the pauses the silence was dreadful.

It was during one of these intervals that the trap in the floor began to lift. Slowly and steadily it rose, and slowly and steadily rose the swaddled head of the old man in the bunk to observe it. Then, with a clap that shook the house to its foundation, it was thrown clean back, where it lay with its unsightly spikes pointing threateningly upward. Mr. Beeson awoke, and without rising, pressed his fingers into his eyes. He shuddered; his teeth chattered. His guest was now reclining on one elbow, watching the proceedings with the goggles that glowed like lamps.

Suddenly a howling gust of wind swooped down the chimney, scattering ashes and smoke in all directions, for a moment obscuring everything. When the firelight again illuminated the room there was seen, sitting gingerly on the edge of a stool by the hearthside, a swarthy little man of prepossessing appearance and dressed with faultless taste, nodding to the old man with a friendly and engaging smile. "From San Francisco, evidently," thought Mr. Beeson, who having somewhat recovered from his fright was groping his way to a solution of the evening's events.

But now another actor appeared upon the scene. Out of the square black hole in the middle of the floor protruded the head of the departed Chinaman, his glassy eyes turned upward in their angular slits and fastened on the dangling queue above with a look of yearning unspeakable. Mr. Becson groaned, and again spread his hands upon his face. A mild odor of opium pervaded the place. The phantom, clad only in a short blue tunic quilted and silken but covered with grave-mold, rose slowly, as if pushed by a weak spiral spring. Its knees were at the level of the floor, when with a quick upward impulse like the silent leaping of a flame it grasped the queue with both hands, drew up its body and took the tip in its horrible yellow teeth. To this it clung in a seeming frenzy, grimacing ghastly, surging and plunging from side to side in its efforts to disengage its property from the beam, but uttering no sound. It was like a corpse artificially convulsed by means of a galvanic battery. The contrast between its superhuman activity and its silence was no less than hideous!

Mr. Beeson cowered in his bed. The swarthy little gentleman uncrossed his legs, beat an impatient tattoo with the toe of his boot and consulted a heavy gold watch. The old man sat erect and quietly laid hold of the revolver.

Bang!

Like a body cut from the gallows the Chinaman plumped into the black hole below, carrying his tail in his teeth. The trapdoor turned over, shutting down with a snap. The swarthy little gentleman from San Francisco sprang nimbly from his perch, caught something in the air with his hat, as a boy catches a butterfly, and vanished into the chimney as if drawn up by suction.

From away somewhere in the outer darkness floated in through the open door a faint, far cry—a long, sobbing wail, as of a child death-strangled in the desert, or a lost soul borne away by the Adversary. It may have been the coyote.

In the early days of the following spring a party of miners on their way to new diggings passed along the Gulch, and straying through the deserted shanties found in one of them the body of Hiram Beeson, stretched upon a bunk, with a bullet hole through the heart. The ball had evidently been fired from the opposite side of the room, for in one of the oaken beams overhead was a shallow blue dint, where it had struck a knot and been deflected downward to the breast of its victim. Strongly attached to the same beam was what appeared to be an end of a rope of braided horsehair, which had been cut by the bullet in its passage to the knot. Nothing else of interest was noted, excepting a suit of moldy and incongruous clothing, several articles of which were afterward identified by respectable witnesses as those in which certain deceased citizens of Deadman's had been buried years before. But it is not easy to understand how that could be, unless, indeed, the garments had been worn as a disguise by Death himself—which is hardly credible.

BEYOND THE WALL

Many years ago, on my way from Hongkong to New York, I passed a week in San Francisco. A long time had gone by since I had been in that city, during which my ventures in the Orient had prospered beyond my hope; I was rich and could afford to revisit my own country to renew my friendship with such of the companions of my youth as still lived and remembered me with the old affection. Chief of these, I hoped, was Mohun Dampier, an old schoolmate with whom I had held a desultory correspondence which had long ceased, as is the way of correspondence between men. You may have observed that the indisposition to write a merely social letter is in the ratio of the square of the distance between you and your correspondent. It is a law.

I remembered Dampier as a handsome, strong young fellow of scholarly tastes, with an aversion to work and a marked indifference to many of the things that the world cares for, including wealth, of which, however, he had inherited enough to put him beyond the reach of want. In his family, one of the oldest and most aristocratic in the country, it was, I think, a matter of pride that no member of it had ever been in trade nor politics, nor suffered any kind of distinction. Mohun was a trifle sentimental, and had in him a singular element of superstition, which led him to the study of all manner of occult subjects, although his sane mental health safeguarded him against fantastic and perilous faiths. He made daring incursions into the realm of the unreal without renouncing his residence in the partly surveyed and charted region of what we are pleased to call certitude.

The night of my visit to him was stormy. The Californian winter was on, and the incessant rain plashed in the deserted streets, or, lifted by irregular gusts of wind, was hurled against the houses with incredible fury. With no small difficulty my cabman found the right place, away out toward the ocean beach, in a sparsely populated suburb. The dwelling, a rather ugly one, apparently, stood in the center of its grounds, which as nearly as I could make out in the gloom were destitute of either flowers or grass. Three or four trees, writhing and moaning in the torment of the tempest, appeared to be trying to escape from their dismal environment and take the chance of finding a better one out at sea. The house was a two-story brick structure with a tower, a story higher, at one corner. In a window of that was the only visible light. Something in the appearance of the place made me shudder, a performance that may have been assisted by a rill of rain-water down my back as I scuttled to cover in the doorway.

In answer to my note apprising him of my wish to call, Dampier had written, "Don't ring—open the door and come up." I did so. The staircase was dimly lighted by a single gas-jet at the top of the second flight. I managed to reach the landing without disaster and entered by an open door into the lighted square room of the tower. Dampier came forward in gown and slippers to receive me, giving me the greeting that I wished, and if I had held a thought that it might more fitly have been accorded me at the front door the first look at him dispelled any sense of his inhospitality.

He was not the same. Hardly past middle age, he had gone gray and had acquired a pronounced stoop. His figure was thin and angular, his face deeply lined, his complexion dead-white, without a touch of color. His eyes, unnaturally large, glowed with a fire that was almost uncanny.

He seated me, proffered a cigar, and with grave and obvious sincerity assured me of the pleasure that it gave him to meet me. Some unimportant conversation followed, but all the while I was dominated by a melancholy sense of the great change in him. This he must have perceived, for he suddenly said with a bright enough smile, "You are disappointed in me—*non sum qualis eram.*"

I hardly knew what to reply, but managed to say: "Why, really, I don't know: your Latin is about the same."

He brightened again. "No," he said, "being a dead language, it grows in appropriateness. But please have the patience to wait: where I am going there is perhaps a better tongue. Will you care to have a message in it?"

The smile faded as he spoke, and as he concluded he was looking into my eyes with a gravity that distressed me. Yet I would not surrender myself to his mood, nor permit him to see how deeply his prescience of death affected me.

"I fancy that it will be long," I said, "before human speech will cease to serve our need; and then the need, with its possibilities of service, will have passed."

He made no reply, and I too was silent, for the talk had taken a dispiriting turn, yet I knew not how to give it a more agreeable character. Suddenly, in a pause of the storm, when the dead silence was almost startling by contrast with the previous uproar, I heard a gentle tapping, which appeared to come from the wall behind my chair. The sound was such as might have been made by a human hand, not as upon a door by one asking admittance, but rather, I thought, as an agreed signal, an assurance of someone's presence in an adjoining room; most of us, I fancy, have had more experience of such communications than we should care to relate. I glanced at Dampier. If possibly there was something of amusement in the look he did not observe it. He appeared to have forgotten my presence, and was staring at the wall behind me with an expression in his eyes that I am unable to name, although my memory of it is as vivid to-day as was my sense of it then. The situation was embarrassing; I rose to take my leave. At this he seemed to recover himself.

"Please be seated," he said; "it is nothing—no one is there."

But the tapping was repeated, and with the same gentle, slow insistence as before.

"Pardon me," I said, "it is late. May I call to-morrow?"

He smiled—a little mechanically, I thought. "It is very delicate of you," said he, "but quite needless. Really, this is the only room in the tower, and no one is there. At least—" He left the sentence incomplete, rose, and threw up a window, the only opening in the wall from which the sound seemed to come. "See."

Not clearly knowing what else to do I followed him to the window and looked out. A street-lamp some little distance away gave enough light through the murk of the rain that was again falling in torrents to make it entirely plain that "no one was there." In truth there was nothing but the sheer blank wall of the tower.

Dampier closed the window and signing me to my seat resumed his own.

The incident was not in itself particularly mysterious; any one of a dozen explanations was possible (though none has occurred to me), yet it impressed me strangely, the more, perhaps, from my friend's effort to reassure me, which seemed to dignify it with a certain significance and importance. He had proved that no one was there, but in that fact lay all the interest; and he proffered no explanation. His silence was irritating and made me resentful.

"My good friend," I said, somewhat ironically, I fear, "I am not disposed to question your right to harbor as many spooks as you find agreeable to your taste and consistent with your notions of companionship; that is no business of mine. But being just a plain man of affairs, mostly of this world, I find spooks needless to my peace and comfort. I am going to my hotel, where my fellow-guests are still in the flesh."

It was not a very civil speech, but he manifested no feeling about it. "Kindly remain," he said. "I am grateful for your presence here. What you have heard to-night I believe myself to have heard twice before. Now I *know* it was no illusion. That is much to me—more than you know. Have a fresh cigar and a good stock of patience while I tell you the story."

The rain was now falling more steadily, with a low, monotonous susurration, interrupted at long intervals by the sudden slashing of the boughs of the trees as the wind rose and failed. The night was well advanced, but both sympathy and curiosity held me a willing listener to my friend's monologue, which I did not interrupt by a single word from beginning to end.

"Ten years ago," he said, "I occupied a ground-floor apartment in one of a row of houses, all alike, away at the other end of the town, on what we call Rincon Hill. This had been the best quarter of San Francisco, but had fallen into neglect and decay, partly because the primitive character of its domestic architecture no longer suited the maturing tastes of our wealthy citizens, partly because certain public improvements had made a wreck of it. The row of dwellings in one of which I lived stood a little way back from the street, each having a miniature garden, separated from its neighbors by low iron fences and bisected with mathematical precision by a box-bordered gravel walk from gate to door.

"One morning as I was leaving my lodging I observed a young girl entering the adjoining garden on the left. It was a warm day in June, and she was lightly gowned in white. From her shoulders hung a broad straw hat profusely decorated with flowers and wonderfully beribboned in the fashion of the time. My attention was not long held by the exquisite simplicity of her costume, for no one could look at her face and think of anything earthly. Do not fear; I shall not profane it by description; it was beautiful exceedingly. All that I had ever seen or dreamed of loveliness was in that matchless living picture by the hand of the Divine Artist. So deeply did it move me that, without a thought of the impropriety of the act, I unconsciously bared my head, as a devout Catholic or well-bred Protestant uncovers before an image of the Blessed Virgin. The maiden showed no displeasure; she merely turned her glorious dark eyes upon me with a look that made me catch my breath, and without other recognition of my act passed into the house. For a moment I stood motionless, hat in hand, painfully conscious of my rudeness, yet so dominated by the emotion inspired by that vision of incomparable beauty that my penitence was less poignant than it should have been. Then I went my way, leaving my heart behind. In the natural course of things I should probably have remained away until nightfall, but by the middle of the afternoon I was back in the little garden, affecting an interest in the few foolish flowers that I had never before observed. My hope was vain; she did not appear.

"To a night of unrest succeeded a day of expectation and disappointment, but on the day after, as I wandered aimlessly about the neighborhood, I met her. Of course I did not repeat my folly of uncovering, nor venture by even so much as too long a look to manifest an interest in her; yet my heart was beating audibly. I trembled and consciously colored as she turned her big black eyes upon me with a look of obvious recognition entirely devoid of boldness or coquetry.

"I will not weary you with particulars; many times afterward I met the maiden, yet never either addressed her or sought to fix her attention. Nor did I take any action toward making her acquaintance. Perhaps my forbearance, requiring so supreme an effort of self-denial, will not be entirely clear to you. That I was heels over head in love is true, but who can overcome his habit of thought, or reconstruct his character?

"I was what some foolish persons are pleased to call, and others, more foolish, are pleased to be called—an aristocrat; and despite her beauty, her charms and graces, the girl was not of my class. I had learned her name—which it is needless to speak—and something of her family. She was an orphan, a dependent niece of the impossible elderly fat woman in whose lodging-house she lived. My income was small and I lacked the talent for marrying; it is perhaps a gift. An alliance with that family would condemn me to its manner of life, part me from my books and studies, and in a social sense reduce me to the ranks. It is easy to deprecate such considerations as these and I have not retained myself for the defense. Let judgment be entered against me, but in strict justice all my ancestors for generations should be made co-defendants and I be permitted to plead in mitigation of punishment the imperious mandate of heredity. To a mésalliance of that kind every globule of my ancestral blood spoke in opposition. In brief, my tastes, habits, instinct, with whatever of reason my love had left me—all fought against it. Moreover, I was an irreclaimable sentimentalist, and found a subtle charm in an impersonal and spiritual relation which acquaintance might vulgarize and marriage would certainly dispel. No woman, I argued, is what this lovely creature seems. Love is a delicious dream; why should I bring about my own awakening?

"The course dictated by all this sense and sentiment was obvious. Honor, pride, prudence, preservation of my ideals—all commanded me to go away, but for that I was too weak. The utmost that I could do by a mighty effort of will was to cease meeting the girl, and that I did. I even avoided the chance encounters of the garden, leaving my lodging only when I knew that she had gone to her music lessons, and returning after nightfall. Yet all the while I was as one in a trance, indulging the most fascinating fancies and ordering my entire intellectual life in accordance with my dream. Ah, my friend, as one whose actions have a traceable relation to reason, you cannot know the fool's paradise in which I lived.

"One evening the devil put it into my head to be an unspeakable idiot. By apparently careless and purposeless questioning I learned from my gossipy landlady that the young woman's bedroom adjoined my own, a party-wall between. Yielding to a sudden and coarse impulse I gently rapped on the wall. There was no response, naturally, but I was in no mood to accept a rebuke. A madness was upon me and I repeated the folly, the offense, but again ineffectually, and I had the decency to desist.

"An hour later, while absorbed in some of my infernal studies, I heard, or thought I heard, my signal answered. Flinging down my books I sprang to the wall and as steadily as my beating heart would permit gave three slow taps upon it. This time the response was distinct, unmistakable: one, two, three—an exact repetition of my signal. That was all I could elicit, but it was enough—too much.

"The next evening, and for many evenings afterward, that folly went on, I always having 'the last word.' During the whole period I was deliriously happy, but with the perversity of my nature I persevered in my resolution not to see her. Then, as I should have expected, I got no further answers. 'She is disgusted,' I said to myself, 'with what she thinks my timidity in making no more definite advances'; and I resolved to seek her and make her acquaintance and—what? I did not know, nor do I now know, what might have come of it. I know only that I passed days and days trying to meet her, and all in vain; she was invisible as well as inaudible. I haunted the streets where we had met, but she did not come. From my window I watched the garden in front of her house, but she passed neither in nor out. I fell into the deepest dejection, believing that she had gone away, yet took no steps to resolve my doubt by inquiry of my landlady, to whom, indeed, I had taken an unconquerable aversion from her having once spoken of the girl with less of reverence then I thought befitting.

"There came a fateful night. Worn out with emotion, irresolution and despondency, I had retired early and fallen into such sleep as was still possible to me. In the middle of the night something—some malign power bent upon the wrecking of my peace forever—caused me to open my eyes and sit up, wide awake and listening intently for I knew not what. Then I thought I heard a faint tapping on the wall—the mere ghost of the familiar signal. In a few moments it was repeated: one, two, three—no louder than before, but addressing a sense alert and strained to receive it. I was about to reply when the Adversary of Peace again intervened in my affairs with a rascally suggestion of retaliation. She had long and cruelly ignored me; now I would ignore her. Incredible fatuity—may God forgive it! All the rest of the night I lay awake, fortifying my obstinacy with shameless justifications and—listening.

"Late the next morning, as I was leaving the house, I met my landlady, entering.

"'Good morning, Mr. Dampier,' she said. 'Have you heard the news?'

"I replied in words that I had heard no news; in manner, that I did not care to hear any. The manner escaped her observation.

"'About the sick young lady next door,' she babbled on. 'What! you did not know? Why, she has been ill for weeks. And now—'

"I almost sprang upon her. 'And now,' I cried, 'now what?'

"'She is dead.'

"That is not the whole story. In the middle of the night, as I learned later, the patient, awakening from a long stupor after a week of delirium, had asked—it was her last utterance—that her bed be moved to the opposite side of the room. Those in attendance had thought the request a vagary of her delirium, but had complied. And there the poor passing soul had exerted its failing will to restore a broken connection—a golden thread of sentiment between its innocence and a monstrous baseness owning a blind, brutal allegiance to the Law of Self.

"What reparation could I make? Are there masses that can be said for the repose of souls that are abroad such nights as this—spirits 'blown about by the viewless winds'—coming in the storm and darkness with signs and portents, hints of memory and presages of doom?

"This is the third visitation. On the first occasion I was too skeptical to do more than verify by natural methods the character of the incident;

on the second, I responded to the signal after it had been several times repeated, but without result. To-night's recurrence completes the 'fatal triad' expounded by Parapelius Necromantius. There is no more to tell."

When Dampier had finished his story I could think of nothing relevant that I cared to say, and to question him would have been a hideous impertinence. I rose and bade him good night in a way to convey to him a sense of my sympathy, which he silently acknowledged by a pressure of the hand. That night, alone with his sorrow and remorse, he passed into the Unknown.

A PSYCHOLOGICAL SHIPWRECK

In the summer of 1874 I was in Liverpool, whither I had gone on business for the mercantile house of Bronson & Jarrett, New York. I am William Jarrett; my partner was Zenas Bronson. The firm failed last year, and unable to endure the fall from affluence to poverty he died.

Having finished my business, and feeling the lassitude and exhaustion incident to its dispatch, I felt that a protracted sea voyage would be both agreeable and beneficial, so instead of embarking for my return on one of the many fine passenger steamers I booked for New York on the sailing vessel *Morrow,* upon which I had shipped a large and valuable invoice of the goods I had bought. The *Morrow* was an English ship with, of course, but little accommodation for passengers, of whom there were only myself, a young woman and her servant, who was a middle-aged Negress. I thought it singular that a traveling English girl should be so attended, but she afterward explained to me that the woman had been left with her family by a man and his wife from South Carolina, both of whom had died on the same day at the house of the young lady's father in Devonshire—a circumstance in itself sufficiently uncommon to remain rather distinctly in my memory, even had it not afterward transpired in conversation with the young lady that the name of the man was William Jarrett, the same as my own. I knew that a branch of my family had settled in South Carolina, but of them and their history I was ignorant.

The *Morrow* sailed from the mouth of the Mersey on the 15th of June and for several weeks we had fair breezes and unclouded skies. The skipper, an admirable seaman but nothing more, favored us with very little of his society, except at his table; and the young woman, Miss Janette Harford, and I became very well acquainted. We were, in truth, nearly always together, and being of an introspective turn of mind I often endeavored to analyze and define the novel feeling with which she inspired me—a secret, subtle, but powerful attraction which constantly impelled me to seek her; but the attempt was hopeless. I could only be sure that at least it was not love. Having assured myself of this and being certain that she was quite as whole-hearted, I ventured one evening (I remember it was on the 3d of July) as we sat on deck to ask her, laughingly, if she could assist me to resolve my psychological doubt.

For a moment she was silent, with averted face, and I began to fear I had been extremely rude and indelicate; then she fixed her eyes gravely on my own. In an instant my mind was dominated by as strange a fancy as ever entered human consciousness. It seemed as if she were looking at me, not *with,* but *through,* those eyes—from an immeasurable distance behind them—and that a number of other persons, men, women and children, upon whose faces I caught strangely familiar evanescent expressions, clustered about her, struggling with gentle eagerness to look at me through the same orbs. Ship, ocean sky—all had vanished. I was conscious of nothing but the figures in this extraordinary and fantastic scene. Then all at once darkness fell upon me, and anon from out of it, as to one who grows accustomed by degrees to a dimmer light, my former surroundings of deck and mast and cordage slowly resolved themselves. Miss Harford had closed her eyes and was leaning back in her chair, apparently asleep, the book she had been reading open in her lap. Impelled by surely I cannot say what motive, I glanced at the top of the page; it was a copy of that rare and curious work, "Denneker's Meditations," and the lady's index finger rested on this passage:

"To sundry it is given to be drawn away, and to be apart from the body for a season; for, as concerning rills which would flow across each other the weaker is borne along by the stronger, so there be certain of kin whose paths intersecting, their souls do bear company, the while their bodies go fore-appointed ways, unknowing."

Miss Harford arose, shuddering; the sun had sunk below the horizon, but it was not cold. There was not a breath of wind; there were no clouds in the sky, yet not a star was visible. A hurried tramping sounded on the deck; the captain, summoned from below, joined the first officer, who stood looking at the barometer. "Good God!" I heard him exclaim.

An hour later the form of Janette Harford, invisible in the darkness and spray, was torn from my grasp by the cruel vortex of the sinking ship, and I fainted in the cordage of the floating mast to which I had lashed myself.

It was by lamplight that I awoke. I lay in a berth amid the familiar surroundings of the stateroom of a steamer. On a couch opposite sat a man, half undressed for bed, reading a book. I recognized the face of my friend Gordon Doyle, whom I had met in Liverpool on the day of my embarkation, when he was himself about to sail on the steamer *City of Prague,* on which he had urged me to accompany him.

After some moments I now spoke his name. He simply said, "Well," and turned a leaf in his book without removing his eyes from the page.

"Doyle," I repeated, "did they save *her?*"

He now deigned to look at me and smiled as if amused. He evidently thought me but half awake.

"Her? Whom do you mean?"

"Janette Harford."

His amusement turned to amazement; he stared at me fixedly, saying nothing.

"You will tell me after a while," I continued; "I suppose you will tell me after a while."

A moment later I asked: "What ship is this?"

Doyle stared again. "The steamer *City of Prague,* bound from Liverpool to New York, three weeks out with a broken shaft. Principal passenger, Mr. Gordon Doyle; ditto lunatic, Mr. William Jarrett. These two distinguished travelers embarked together, but they are about to part, it being the resolute intention of the former to pitch the latter overboard."

I sat bolt upright. "Do you mean to say that I have been for three weeks a passenger on this steamer?"

"Yes, pretty nearly; this is the 3d of July."

"Have I been ill?"

"Right as a trivet all the time, and punctual at your meals."

"My God! Doyle, there is some mystery here; do have the goodness to be serious. Was I not rescued from the wreck of the ship *Morrow?*"

Doyle changed color, and approaching me, laid his fingers on my wrist. A moment later, "What do you know of Janette Harford?" he asked very calmly.

"First tell me what *you* know of her?"

Mr. Doyle gazed at me for some moments as if thinking what to do, then seating himself again on the couch, said:

"Why should I not? I am engaged to marry Janette Harford, whom I met a year ago in London. Her family, one of the wealthiest in Devonshire, cut up rough about it, and we eloped—are eloping rather, for on the day that you and I walked to the landing stage to go aboard this steamer she and her faithful servant, a Negress, passed us, driving to the ship *Morrow*. She would not consent to go in the same vessel with me, and it had been deemed best that she take a sailing vessel in order to avoid observation and lessen the risk of detection. I am now alarmed lest this cursed breaking of our machinery may detain us so long that the *Morrow* will get to New York before us, and the poor girl will not know where to go."

I lay still in my berth—so still I hardly breathed. But the subject was evidently not displeasing to Doyle, and after a short pause he resumed:

"By the way, she is only an adopted daughter of the Harfords. Her mother was killed at their place by being thrown from a horse while hunting, and her father, mad with grief, made away with himself the same day. No one ever claimed the child, and after a reasonable time they adopted her. She has grown up in the belief that she is their daughter."

"Doyle, what book are you reading?"

"Oh, it's called 'Denneker's Meditations.' It's a rum lot, Janette gave it to me; she happened to have two copies. Want to see it?"

He tossed me the volume, which opened as it fell. On one of the exposed pages was a marked passage:

"To sundry it is given to be drawn away, and to be apart from the body for a season; for, as concerning rills which would flow across each other the weaker is borne along by the stronger, so there be certain of kin whose paths intersecting, their souls do bear company, the while their bodies go fore-appointed ways, unknowing."

"She had—she has—a singular taste in reading," I managed to say, mastering my agitation.

"Yes. And now perhaps you will have the kindness to explain how you knew her name and that of the ship she sailed in."

"You talked of her in your sleep," I said.

A week later we were towed into the port of New York. But the *Morrow* was never heard from.

THE MIDDLE TOE OF THE RIGHT FOOT

I

It is well known that the old Manton house is haunted. In all the rural district near about, and even in the town of Marshall, a mile away, not one person of unbiased mind entertains a doubt of it; incredulity is confined to those opinionated persons who will be called "cranks" as soon as the useful word shall have penetrated the intellectual demesne of the Marshall *Advance*. The evidence that the house is haunted is of two kinds: the testimony of disinterested witnesses who have had ocular proof, and that of the house itself. The former may be disregarded and ruled out on any of the various grounds of objection which may be urged against it by the ingenious; but facts within the observation of all are material and controlling.

In the first place, the Manton house has been unoccupied by mortals for more than ten years, and with its outbuildings is slowly falling into decay—a circumstance which in itself the judicious will hardly venture to ignore. It stands a little way off the loneliest reach of the Marshall and Harriston road, in an opening which was once a farm and is still disfigured with strips of rotting fence and half covered with brambles overrunning a stony and sterile soil long unacquainted with the plow. The house itself is in tolerably good condition, though badly weatherstained and in dire need of attention from the glazier, the smaller male population of the region having attested in the manner of its kind its disapproval of dwelling without dwellers. It is two stories in height, nearly square, its front pierced by a single doorway flanked on each side by a window boarded up to the very top. Corresponding windows above, not protected, serve to admit light and rain to the rooms of the upper floor. Grass and weeds grow pretty rankly all about, and a few shade trees, somewhat the worse for wind, and leaning all in one direction, seem to be making a concerted effort to run away. In short, as the Marshall town humorist explained in the columns of the *Advance,* "the proposition that the Manton house is badly haunted is the only logical conclusion from the premises." The fact that in this dwelling Mr. Manton thought it expedient one night some ten years ago to rise and cut the throats of his wife and two small children, removing at once to another part of the country, has no doubt done its share in directing public attention to the fitness of the place for supernatural phenomena.

To this house, one summer evening, came four men in a wagon. Three of them promptly alighted, and the one who had been driving hitched the team to the only remaining post of what had been a fence. The fourth remained seated in the wagon. "Come," said one of his companions, approaching him, while the others moved away in the direction of the dwelling—"this is the place."

The man addressed did not move. "By God!" he said harshly, "this is a trick, and it looks to me as if you were in it."

"Perhaps I am," the other said, looking him straight in the face and speaking in a tone which had something of contempt in it. "You will remember, however, that the choice of place was with your own assent left to the other side. Of course if you are afraid of spooks—"

"I am afraid of nothing," the man interrupted with another oath, and sprang to the ground. The two then joined the others at the door, which one of them had already opened with some difficulty, caused by rust of lock and hinge. All entered. Inside it was dark, but the man who had unlocked the door produced a candle and matches and made a light. He then unlocked a door on their right as they stood in the passage. This gave them entrance to a large, square room that the candle but dimly lighted. The floor had a thick carpeting of dust, which partly muffled their footfalls. Cobwebs were in the angles of the walls and depended from the ceiling like strips of rotting lace, making undulatory movements in the disturbed air. The room had two windows in adjoining sides, but from neither could anything be seen except the rough inner surfaces of boards a few inches from the glass. There was no fireplace, no furniture; there was nothing: besides the cobwebs and the dust, the four men were the only objects there which were not a part of the structure.

Strange enough they looked in the yellow light of the candle. The one who had so reluctantly alighted was especially spectacular—he might have been called sensational. He was of middle age, heavily built, deep chested and broad shouldered. Looking at his figure, one would have said that he had a giant's strength; at his features, that he would use it like a giant. He was clean shaven, his hair rather closely cropped and gray. His low forehead was seamed with wrinkles above the eyes, and over the nose these became vertical. The heavy black brows followed the same law, saved from meeting only by an upward turn at what would otherwise have been the point of contact. Deeply sunken beneath these, glowed in the obscure light a pair of eyes of uncertain color, but obviously enough too small. There was something forbidding in their expression, which was not bettered by the cruel mouth and wide jaw. The nose was well enough, as noses go; one does not expect much of noses. All that was sinister in the man's face seemed accentuated by an unnatural pallor—he appeared altogether bloodless.

The appearance of the other men was sufficiently commonplace: they were such persons as one meets and forgets that he met. All were younger than the man described, between whom and the eldest of the others, who stood apart, there was apparently no kindly feeling. They avoided looking at each other.

"Gentlemen," said the man holding the candle and keys, "I believe everything is right. Are you ready, Mr. Rosser?"

The man standing apart from the group bowed and smiled.

"And you, Mr. Grossmith?"

The heavy man bowed and scowled.

"You will be pleased to remove your outer clothing."

Their hats, coats, waistcoats and neckwear were soon removed and thrown outside the door, in the passage. The man with the candle now nodded, and the fourth man—he who had urged Grossmith to leave the wagon—produced from the pocket of his overcoat two long, murderous-looking bowie-knives, which he drew now from their leather scabbards.

"They are exactly alike," he said, presenting one to each of the two principals—for by this time the dullest observer would have understood the nature of this meeting. It was to be a duel to the death.

Each combatant took a knife, examined it critically near the candle and tested the strength of blade and handle across his lifted knee. Their persons were then searched in turn, each by the second of the other.

"If it is agreeable to you, Mr. Grossmith," said the man holding the light, "you will place yourself in that corner."

He indicated the angle of the room farthest from the door, whither Grossmith retired, his second parting from him with a grasp of the hand which had nothing of cordiality in it. In the angle nearest the door Mr. Rosser stationed himself, and after a whispered consultation his second left him, joining the other near the door. At that moment the candle was suddenly extinguished, leaving all in profound darkness. This may have been done by a draught from the opened door; whatever the cause, the effect was startling.

"Gentlemen," said a voice which sounded strangely unfamiliar in the altered condition affecting the relations of the senses—"gentlemen, you will not move until you hear the closing of the outer door."

A sound of trampling ensued, then the closing of the inner door; and finally the outer one closed with a concussion which shook the entire building.

A few minutes afterward a belated farmer's boy met a light wagon which was being driven furiously toward the town of Marshall. He declared that behind the two figures on the front seat stood a third, with its hands upon the bowed shoulders of the others, who appeared to struggle vainly to free themselves from its grasp. This figure, unlike the others, was clad in white, and had undoubtedly boarded the wagon as it passed the haunted house. As the lad could boast a considerable former experience with the supernatural thereabouts his word had the weight justly due to the testimony of an expert. The story (in connection with the next day's events) eventually appeared in the *Advance,* with some slight literary embellishments and a concluding intimation that the gentlemen referred to would be allowed the use of the paper's columns for their version of the night's adventure. But the privilege remained without a claimant.

II

The events that led up to this "duel in the dark" were simple enough. One evening three young men of the town of Marshall were sitting in a quiet corner of the porch of the village hotel, smoking and discussing such matters as three educated young men of a Southern village would naturally find interesting. Their names were King, Sancher and Rosser. At a little distance, within easy hearing, but taking no part in the conversation, sat a fourth. He was a stranger to the others. They merely knew that on his arrival by the stage-coach that afternoon he had written in the hotel register the name Robert Grossmith. He had not been observed to speak to anyone except the hotel clerk. He seemed, indeed, singularly fond of his own company—or, as the *personnel* of the *Advance* expressed it, "grossly addicted to evil associations." But then it should be said in justice to the stranger that the *personnel* was himself of a too convivial disposition fairly to judge one differently gifted, and had, moreover, experienced a slight rebuff in an effort at an "interview."

"I hate any kind of deformity in a woman," said King, "whether natural or—acquired. I have a theory that any physical defect has its correlative mental and moral defect."

"I infer, then," said Rosser, gravely, "that a lady lacking the moral advantage of a nose would find the struggle to become Mrs. King an arduous enterprise."

"Of course you may put it that way," was the reply; "but, seriously, I once threw over a most charming girl on learning quite accidentally that she had suffered amputation of a toe. My conduct was brutal if you like, but if I had married that girl I should have been miserable for life and should have made her so."

"Whereas," said Sancher, with a light laugh, "by marrying a gentleman of more liberal views she escaped with a parted throat."

"Ah, you know to whom I refer. Yes, she married Manton, but I don't know about his liberality; I'm not sure but he cut her throat because he discovered that she lacked that excellent thing in woman, the middle toe of the right foot."

"Look at that chap!" said Rosser in a low voice, his eyes fixed upon the stranger.

That chap was obviously listening intently to the conversation.

"Damn his impudence!" muttered King—"what ought we to do?"

"That's an easy one," Rosser replied, rising. "Sir," he continued, addressing the stranger, "I think it would be better if you would remove your chair to the other end of the veranda. The presence of gentlemen is evidently an unfamiliar situation to you."

The man sprang to his feet and strode forward with clenched hands, his face white with rage. All were now standing. Sancher stepped between the belligerents.

"You are hasty and unjust," he said to Rosser; "this gentleman has done nothing to deserve such language."

But Rosser would not withdraw a word. By the custom of the country and the time there could be but one outcome to the quarrel.

"I demand the satisfaction due to a gentleman," said the stranger, who had become more calm. "I have not an acquaintance in this region. Perhaps you, sir," bowing to Sancher, "will be kind enough to represent me in this matter."

Sancher accepted the trust—somewhat reluctantly it must be confessed, for the man's appearance and manner were not at all to his liking. King, who during the colloquy had hardly removed his eyes from the stranger's face and had not spoken a word, consented with a nod to act for Rosser, and the upshot of it was that, the principals having retired, a meeting was arranged for the next evening. The nature of the arrangements has been already disclosed. The duel with knives in a dark room was once a commoner feature of Southwestern life than it is likely to be again. How thin a veneering of "chivalry" covered the essential brutality of the code under which such encounters were possible we shall see.

III

In the blaze of a midsummer noonday the old Manton house was hardly true to its traditions. It was of the earth, earthy. The sunshine caressed it warmly and affectionately, with evident disregard of its bad reputation. The grass greening all the expanse in its front seemed to grow, not rankly, but with a natural and joyous exuberance, and the weeds blossomed quite like plants. Full of charming lights and shadows and populous with pleasant-voiced birds, the neglected shade trees no longer struggled to run away, but bent reverently beneath their burdens of sun and song. Even in the glassless upper windows was an expression of peace and contentment, due to the light within. Over the stony fields the visible heat danced with a lively tremor incompatible with the gravity which is an attribute of the supernatural.

Such was the aspect under which the place presented itself to Sheriff Adams and two other men who had come out from Marshall to look at it. One of these men was Mr. King, the sheriff's deputy; the other, whose name was Brewer, was a brother of the late Mrs. Manton. Under a beneficent law of the State relating to property which has been for a certain period abandoned by an owner whose residence cannot be ascertained, the sheriff was legal custodian of the Manton farm and appurtenances thereunto belonging. His present visit was in mere perfunctory compliance with some order of a court in which Mr. Brewer had an action to get possession of the property as heir to his deceased sister. By a mere coincidence, the visit was made on the day after the night that Deputy King had unlocked the house for another and very different purpose. His presence now was not of his own choosing: he had been ordered to accompany his superior and at the moment could think of nothing more prudent than simulated alacrity in obedience to the command.

Carelessly opening the front door, which to his surprise was not locked, the sheriff was amazed to see, lying on the floor of the passage into which it opened, a confused heap of men's apparel. Examination showed it to consist of two hats, and the same number of coats, waistcoats and scarves, all in a remarkably good state of preservation, albeit somewhat defiled by the dust in which they lay. Mr. Brewer was equally astonished, but Mr. King's emotion is not of record. With a new and lively interest in his own actions the sheriff now unlatched and pushed open a door on the right, and the three entered. The room was apparently vacant—no; as their eyes became accustomed to the dimmer light something was visible in the farthest angle of the wall. It was a human figure—that of a man crouching close in the corner. Something in the attitude made the intruders halt when they had barely passed the threshold. The figure more and more clearly defined itself. The man was upon one knee, his back in the angle of the wall, his shoulders elevated to the level of his ears, his hands before his face, palms outward, the fingers spread and crooked like claws; the white face turned upward on the retracted neck had an expression of unutterable fright, the mouth half open, the eyes incredibly expanded. He was stone dead. Yet, with the exception of a bowie-knife, which had evidently fallen from his own hand, not another object was in the room.

In thick dust that covered the floor were some confused footprints near the door and along the wall through which it opened. Along one of the adjoining walls, too, past the boarded-up windows, was the trail made by the man himself in reaching his corner. Instinctively in approaching the body the three men followed that trail. The sheriff grasped one of the outthrown arms; it was as rigid as iron, and the application of a gentle force rocked the entire body without altering the relation of its parts. Brewer, pale with excitement, gazed intently into the distorted face. "God of mercy!" he suddenly cried, "it is Manton!"

"You are right," said King, with an evident attempt at calmness: "I knew Manton. He then wore a full beard and his hair long, but this is he."

He might have added: "I recognized him when he challenged Rosser. I told Rosser and Sancher who he was before we played him this horrible trick. When Rosser left this dark room at our heels, forgetting his outer clothing in the excitement, and driving away with us in his shirt sleeves —all through the discreditable proceedings we knew whom we were dealing with, murderer and coward that he was!"

But nothing of this did Mr. King say. With his better light he was trying to penetrate the mystery of the man's death. That he had not once moved from the corner where he had been stationed; that his posture was that of neither attack nor defense; that he had dropped his weapon; that he had obviously perished of sheer horror of something that he *saw*—these were circumstances which Mr. King's disturbed intelligence could not rightly comprehend.

Groping in intellectual darkness for a clew to his maze of doubt, his gaze, directed mechanically downward in the way of one who ponders momentous matters, fell upon something which, there, in the light of day and in the presence of living companions, affected him with terror. In the dust of years that lay thick upon the floor—leading from the door by which they had entered, straight across the room to within a yard of Manton's crouching corpse—were three parallel lines of footprints— light but definite impressions of bare feet, the outer ones those of small children, the inner a woman's. From the point at which they ended they did not return; they pointed all one way. Brewer, who had observed them at the same moment, was leaning forward in an attitude of rapt attention, horribly pale.

"Look at that!" he cried, pointing with both hands at the nearest print of the woman's right foot, where she had apparently stopped and stood. "The middle toe is missing—it was Gertrude!"

Gertrude was the late Mrs. Manton, sister to Mr. Brewer.

JOHN MORTONSON'S FUNERAL *

J OHN MORTONSON was dead: his lines in "the tragedy of 'Man' " had all been spoken and he had left the stage.

The body rested in a fine mahogany coffin fitted with a plate of glass. All arrangements for the funeral had been so well attended to that had the deceased known he would doubtless have approved. The face, as it showed under the glass, was not disagreeable to look upon: it bore a faint smile, and as the death had been painless, had not been distorted beyond the repairing power of the undertaker. At two o'clock of the afternoon the friends were to assemble to pay their last tribute of respect to one who had no further need of friends and respect. The surviving members of the family came severally every few minutes to the casket and wept above the placid features beneath the glass. This did them no good; it did no good to John Mortonson; but in the presence of death reason and philosophy are silent.

As the hour of two approached the friends began to arrive and after offering such consolation to the stricken relatives as the proprieties of the occasion required, solemnly seated themselves about the room with an augmented consciousness of their importance in the scheme funereal. Then the minister came, and in that overshadowing presence the lesser lights went into eclipse. His entrance was followed by that of the widow, whose lamentations filled the room. She approached the casket and after leaning her face against the cold glass for a moment was gently led to a seat near her daughter. Mournfully and low the man of God began his eulogy of the dead, and his doleful voice, mingled with the sobbing which it was its purpose to stimulate and sustain, rose and fell, seemed to come and go, like the sound of a sullen sea. The gloomy day grew darker as he spoke; a curtain of cloud underspread the sky and a few drops of rain fell audibly. It seemed as if all nature were weeping for John Mortonson.

* Rough notes of this tale were found among the papers of the late Leigh Bierce. It is printed here with such revision only as the author might himself have made in transcription.

When the minister had finished his eulogy with prayer a hymn was sung and the pallbearers took their places beside the bier. As the last notes of the hymn died away the widow ran to the coffin, cast herself upon it and sobbed hysterically. Gradually, however, she yielded to dissuasion, becoming more composed; and as the minister was in the act of leading her away her eyes sought the face of the dead beneath the glass. She threw up her arms and with a shriek fell backward insensible.

The mourners sprang forward to the coffin, the friends followed, and as the clock on the mantel solemnly struck three all were staring down upon the face of John Mortonson, deceased.

They turned away, sick and faint. One man, trying in his terror to escape the awful sight, stumbled against the coffin so heavily as to knock away one of its frail supports. The coffin fell to the floor, the glass was shattered to bits by the concussion.

From the opening crawled John Mortonson's cat, which lazily leapt to the floor, sat up, tranquilly wiped its crimson muzzle with a forepaw, then walked with dignity from the room.

THE REALM OF THE UNREAL

I

For a part of the distance between Auburn and Newcastle the road—first on one side of a creek and then on the other—occupies the whole bottom of the ravine, being partly cut out of the steep hillside, and partly built up with bowlders removed from the creek-bed by the miners. The hills are wooded, the course of the ravine is sinuous. In a dark night careful driving is required in order not to go off into the water. The night that I have in memory was dark, the creek a torrent, swollen by a recent storm. I had driven up from Newcastle and was within about a mile of Auburn in the darkest and narrowest part of the ravine, looking intently ahead of my horse for the roadway. Suddenly I saw a man almost under the animal's nose, and reined in with a jerk that came near setting the creature upon its haunches.

"I beg your pardon," I said; "I did not see you, sir."

"You could hardly be expected to see me," the man replied, civilly, approaching the side of the vehicle; "and the noise of the creek prevented my hearing you."

I at once recognized the voice, although five years had passed since I had heard it. I was not particularly well pleased to hear it now.

"You are Dr. Dorrimore, I think," said I.

"Yes; and you are my good friend Mr. Manrich. I am more than glad to see you—the excess," he added, with a light laugh, "being due to the fact that I am going your way, and naturally expect an invitation to ride with you."

"Which I extend with all my heart."

That was not altogether true.

Dr. Dorrimore thanked me as he seated himself beside me, and I drove cautiously forward, as before. Doubtless it is fancy, but it seems to me now that the remaining distance was made in a chill fog; that I was uncomfortably cold; that the way was longer than ever before, and the town, when we reached it, cheerless, forbidding, and desolate. It must have been early in the evening, yet I do not recollect a light in any of the houses nor a living thing in the streets. Dorrimore explained at some length how he happened to be there, and where he had been during the years that had elapsed since I had seen him. I recall the fact of the narrative, but none of the facts narrated. He had been in foreign countries and had returned—this is all that my memory retains, and this I already knew. As to myself I cannot remember that I spoke a word, though doubtless I did. Of one thing I am distinctly conscious: the man's presence at my side was strangely distasteful and disquieting—so much so that when I at last pulled up under the lights of the Putnam House I experienced a sense of having escaped some spiritual peril of a nature peculiarly forbidding. This sense of relief was somewhat modified by the discovery that Dr. Dorrimore was living at the same hotel.

II

In partial explanation of my feelings regarding Dr. Dorrimore I will relate briefly the circumstances under which I had met him some years before. One evening a half-dozen men of whom I was one were sitting in the library of the Bohemian Club in San Francisco. The conversation had turned to the subject of sleight-of-hand and the feats of the *prestidigitateurs,* one of whom was then exhibiting at a local theatre.

"These fellows are pretenders in a double sense," said one of the party; "they can do nothing which it is worth one's while to be made a dupe by. The humblest wayside juggler in India could mystify them to the verge of lunacy."

"For example, how?" asked another, lighting a cigar.

"For example, by all their common and familiar performances— throwing large objects into the air which never come down; causing plants to sprout, grow visibly and blossom, in bare ground chosen by spectators; putting a man into a wicker basket, piercing him through and through with a sword while he shrieks and bleeds, and then—the basket being opened nothing is there; tossing the free end of a silken ladder into the air, mounting it and disappearing."

"Nonsense!" I said, rather uncivilly, I fear. "You surely do not believe such things?"

"Certainly not: I have seen them too often."

"But I do," said a journalist of considerable local fame as a picturesque reporter. "I have so frequently related them that nothing but observation could shake my conviction. Why, gentlemen, I have my own word for it."

Nobody laughed—all were looking at something behind me. Turning in my seat I saw a man in evening dress who had just entered the room. He was exceedingly dark, almost swarthy, with a thin face, black-bearded to the lips, an abundance of coarse black hair in some disorder, a high nose and eyes that glittered with as soulless an expression as those of a cobra. One of the group rose and introduced him as Dr. Dorrimore, of Calcutta. As each of us was presented in turn he acknowledged the fact with a profound bow in the Oriental manner, but with nothing of Oriental gravity. His smile impressed me as cynical and a trifle contemptuous. His whole demeanor I can describe only as disagreeably engaging.

His presence led the conversation into other channels. He said little— I do not recall anything of what he did say. I thought his voice singularly rich and melodious, but it affected me in the same way as his eyes and smile. In a few minutes I rose to go. He also rose and put on his overcoat.

"Mr. Manrich," he said, "I am going your way."

"The devil you are!" I thought. "How do you know which way I am going?" Then I said, "I shall be pleased to have your company."

We left the building together. No cabs were in sight, the street cars had gone to bed, there was a full moon and the cool night air was delightful; we walked up the California street hill. I took that direction thinking he would naturally wish to take another, toward one of the hotels.

"You do not believe what is told of the Hindu jugglers," he said abruptly.

"How do you know that?" I asked.

Without replying he laid his hand lightly upon my arm and with the other pointed to the stone sidewalk directly in front. There, almost at our feet, lay the dead body of a man, the face upturned and white in the moonlight! A sword whose hilt sparkled with gems stood fixed and upright in the breast; a pool of blood had collected on the stones of the sidewalk.

I was startled and terrified—not only by what I saw, but by the circumstances under which I saw it. Repeatedly during our ascent of the hill my eyes, I thought, had traversed the whole reach of that sidewalk, from street to street. How could they have been insensible to this dreadful object now so conspicuous in the white moonlight?

As my dazed faculties cleared I observed that the body was in evening dress; the overcoat thrown wide open revealed the dresscoat, the white tie, the broad expanse of shirt front pierced by the sword. And—horrible revelation!—the face, except for its pallor, was that of my companion! It was to the minutest detail of dress and feature Dr. Dorrimore himself. Bewildered and horrified, I turned to look for the living man. He was nowhere visible, and with an added terror I retired from the place, down the hill in the direction whence I had come. I had taken but a few strides when a strong grasp upon my shoulder arrested me. I came near crying out with terror: the dead man, the sword still fixed in his breast, stood beside me! Pulling out the sword with his disengaged hand, he flung it from him, the moonlight glinting upon the jewels of its hilt and the unsullied steel of its blade. It fell with a clang upon the sidewalk ahead and—vanished! The man, swarthy as before, relaxed his grasp upon my shoulder and looked at me with the same cynical regard that I had observed on first meeting him. The dead have not that look—it partly restored me, and turning my head backward, I saw the smooth white expanse of sidewalk, unbroken from street to street.

"What is all this nonsense, you devil?" I demanded, fiercely enough, though weak and trembling in every limb.

"It is what some are pleased to call jugglery," he answered, with a light, hard laugh.

He turned down Dupont street and I saw him no more until we met in the Auburn ravine.

III

On the day after my second meeting with Dr. Dorrimore I did not see him: the clerk in the Putnam House explained that a slight illness confined him to his rooms. That afternoon at the railway station I was surprised and made happy by the unexpected arrival of Miss Margaret Corray and her mother, from Oakland.

This is not a love story. I am no story-teller, and love as it is cannot be portrayed in a literature dominated and enthralled by the debasing tyranny which "sentences letters" in the name of the Young Girl. Under the Young Girl's blighting reign—or rather under the rule of those false Ministers of the Censure who have appointed themselves to the custody of her welfare—love

> veils her sacred fires,
> And, unaware, Morality expires,

famished upon the sifted meal and distilled water of a prudish purveyance.

Let it suffice that Miss Corray and I were engaged in marriage. She and her mother went to the hotel at which I lived, and for two weeks I saw her daily. That I was happy needs hardly be said; the only bar to my perfect enjoyment of those golden days was the presence of Dr. Dorrimore, whom I had felt compelled to introduce to the ladies.

By them he was evidently held in favor. What could I say? I knew absolutely nothing to his discredit. His manners were those of a cultivated and considerate gentleman; and to women a man's manner is the man. On one or two occasions when I saw Miss Corray walking with him I was furious, and once had the indiscretion to protest. Asked for reasons, I had none to give and fancied I saw in her expression a shade of contempt for the vagaries of a jealous mind. In time I grew morose and consciously disagreeable, and resolved in my madness to return to San Francisco the next day. Of this, however, I said nothing.

IV

There was at Auburn an old, abandoned cemetery. It was nearly in the heart of the town, yet by night it was as gruesome a place as the most dismal of human moods could crave. The railings about the plats were prostrate, decayed, or altogether gone. Many of the graves were sunken, from others grew sturdy pines, whose roots had committed unspeakable sin. The headstones were fallen and broken across; brambles overran the ground; the fence was mostly gone, and cows and pigs wandered there at will; the place was a dishonor to the living, a calumny on the dead, a blasphemy against God.

The evening of the day on which I had taken my madman's resolution to depart in anger from all that was dear to me found me in that congenial spot. The light of the half moon fell ghostly through the foliage of trees in spots and patches, revealing much that was unsightly, and the black shadows seemed conspiracies withholding to the proper time revelations of darker import. Passing along what had been a gravel path, I saw emerging from shadow the figure of Dr. Dorrimore. I was myself in shadow, and stood still with clenched hands and set teeth, trying to control the impulse to leap upon and strangle him. A moment later a second figure joined him and clung to his arm. It was Margaret Corray!

I cannot rightly relate what occurred. I know that I sprang forward, bent upon murder; I know that I was found in the gray of the morning, bruised and bloody, with finger marks upon my throat. I was taken to the Putnam House, where for days I lay in a delirium. All this I know, for I have been told. And of my own knowledge I know that when consciousness returned with convalescence I sent for the clerk of the hotel.

"Are Mrs. Corray and her daughter still here?" I asked.

"What name did you say?"

"Corray."

"Nobody of that name has been here."

"I beg you will not trifle with me," I said petulantly. "You see that I am all right now; tell me the truth."

"I give you my word," he replied with evident sincerity, "we have had no guests of that name."

His words stupefied me. I lay for a few moments in silence; then I asked: "Where is Dr. Dorrimore?"

"He left on the morning of your fight and has not been heard of since. It was a rough deal he gave you."

V

Such are the facts of this case. Margaret Corray is now my wife. She has never seen Auburn, and during the weeks whose history as it shaped itself in my brain I have endeavored to relate, was living at her home in Oakland, wondering where her lover was and why he did not write. The other day I saw in the Baltimore *Sun* the following paragraph:

"Professor Valentine Dorrimore, the hypnotist, had a large audience last night. The lecturer, who has lived most of his life in India, gave some marvelous exhibitions of his power, hypnotizing anyone who chose to submit himself to the experiment, by merely looking at him. In fact, he twice hypnotized the entire audience (reporters alone exempted), making all entertain the most extraordinary illusions. The most valuable feature of the lecture was the disclosure of the methods of the Hindu jugglers in their famous performances, familiar in the mouths of travelers. The professor declares that these thaumaturgists have acquired such skill in the art which he learned at their feet that they perform their miracles by simply throwing the 'spectators' into a state of hypnosis and telling them what to see and hear. His assertion that a peculiarly susceptible subject may be kept in the realm of the unreal for weeks, months, and even years, dominated by whatever delusions and hallucinations the operator may from time to time suggest, is a trifle disquieting."

JOHN BARTINE'S WATCH

A Story by a Physician

"THE exact time? Good God! my friend, why do you insist? One would think—but what does it matter; it is easily bedtime—isn't that near enough? But, here, if you must set your watch, take mine and see for yourself."

With that he detached his watch—a tremendously heavy, old-fashioned one—from the chain, and handed it to me; then turned away, and walking across the room to a shelf of books, began an examination of their backs. His agitation and evident distress surprised me; they appeared reasonless. Having set my watch by his, I stepped over to where he stood and said, "Thank you."

As he took his timepiece and reattached it to the guard I observed that his hands were unsteady. With a tact upon which I greatly prided myself, I sauntered carelessly to the sideboard and took some brandy and water; then, begging his pardon for my thoughtlessness, asked him to have some and went back to my seat by the fire, leaving him to help himself, as was our custom. He did so and presently joined me at the hearth, as tranquil as ever.

This odd little incident occurred in my apartment, where John Bartine was passing an evening. We had dined together at the club, had come home in a cab and—in short, everything had been done in the most prosaic way; and why John Bartine should break in upon the natural and established order of things to make himself spectacular with a display of emotion, apparently for his own entertainment, I could nowise understand. The more I thought of it, while his brilliant conversational gifts were commending themselves to my inattention, the more curious I grew, and of course had no difficulty in persuading myself that my curiosity was friendly solicitude. That is the disguise that curiosity usually assumes to evade resentment. So I ruined one of the finest sentences of his disregarded monologue by cutting it short without ceremony.

"John Bartine," I said, "you must try to forgive me if I am wrong,

514

but with the light that I have at present I cannot concede your right to go all to pieces when asked the time o' night. I cannot admit that it is proper to experience a mysterious reluctance to look your own watch in the face and to cherish in my presence, without explanation, painful emotions which are denied to me, and which are none of my business."

To this ridiculous speech Bartine made no immediate reply, but sat looking gravely into the fire. Fearing that I had offended I was about to apologize and beg him to think no more about the matter, when looking me calmly in the eyes he said:

"My dear fellow, the levity of your manner does not at all disguise the hideous impudence of your demand; but happily I had already decided to tell you what you wish to know, and no manifestation of your unworthiness to hear it shall alter my decision. Be good enough to give me your attention and you shall hear all about the matter.

"This watch," he said, "had been in my family for three generations before it fell to me. Its original owner, for whom it was made, was my great-grandfather, Bramwell Olcott Bartine, a wealthy planter of Colonial Virginia, and as stanch a Tory as ever lay awake nights contriving new kinds of maledictions for the head of Mr. Washington, and new methods of aiding and abetting good King George. One day this worthy gentleman had the deep misfortune to perform for his cause a service of capital importance which was not recognized as legitimate by those who suffered its disadvantages. It does not matter what it was, but among its minor consequences was my excellent ancestor's arrest one night in his own house by a party of Mr. Washington's rebels. He was permitted to say farewell to his weeping family, and was then marched away into the darkness which swallowed him up forever. Not the slenderest clew to his fate was ever found. After the war the most diligent inquiry and the offer of large rewards failed to turn up any of his captors or any fact concerning his disappearance. He had disappeared, and that was all."

Something in Bartine's manner that was not in his words—I hardly knew what it was—prompted me to ask:

"What is your view of the matter—of the justice of it?"

"My view of it," he flamed out, bringing his clenched hand down upon the table as if he had been in a public house dicing with blackguards—"my view of it is that it was a characteristically dastardly assassination by that damned traitor, Washington, and his ragamuffin rebels!"

For some minutes nothing was said: Bartine was recovering his temper, and I waited. Then I said:

"Was that all?"

"No—there was something else. A few weeks after my great-grandfather's arrest his watch was found lying on the porch at the front door of his dwelling. It was wrapped in a sheet of letter paper bearing the name of Rupert Bartine, his only son, my grandfather. I am wearing that watch."

Bartine paused. His usually restless black eyes were staring fixedly into the grate, a point of red light in each, reflected from the glowing coals. He seemed to have forgotten me. A sudden threshing of the branches of a tree outside one of the windows, and almost at the same instant a rattle of rain against the glass, recalled him to a sense of his surroundings. A storm had risen, heralded by a single gust of wind, and in a few moments the steady plash of the water on the pavement was distinctly heard. I hardly know why I relate this incident; it seemed somehow to have a certain significance and relevancy which I am unable now to discern. It at least added an element of seriousness, almost solemnity. Bartine resumed:

"I have a singular feeling toward this watch—a kind of affection for it; I like to have it about me, though partly from its weight, and partly for a reason I shall now explain, I seldom carry it. The reason is this: Every evening when I have it with me I feel an unaccountable desire to open and consult it, even if I can think of no reason for wishing to know the time. But if I yield to it, the moment my eyes rest upon the dial I am filled with a mysterious apprehension—a sense of imminent calamity. And this is the more insupportable the nearer it is to eleven o'clock—· by this watch, no matter what the actual hour may be. After the hands have registered eleven the desire to look is gone; I am entirely indifferent. Then I can consult the thing as often as I like, with no more emotion than you feel in looking at your own. Naturally I have trained myself not to look at that watch in the evening before eleven; nothing could induce me. Your insistence this evening upset me a trifle. I felt very much as I suppose an opium-eater might feel if his yearning for his special and particular kind of hell were re-enforced by opportunity and advice.

"Now that is my story, and I have told it in the interest of your trumpery science; but if on any evening hereafter you observe me wearing this damnable watch, and you have the thoughtfulness to ask me the hour, I shall beg leave to put you to the inconvenience of being knocked down."

His humor did not amuse me. I could see that in relating his delusion he was again somewhat disturbed. His concluding smile was positively ghastly, and his eyes had resumed something more than their old restlessness; they shifted hither and thither about the room with apparent aimlessness and I fancied had taken on a wild expression, such as is sometimes observed in cases of dementia. Perhaps this was my own imagination, but at any rate I was now persuaded that my friend was afflicted with a most singular and interesting monomania. Without, I trust, any abatement of my affectionate solicitude for him as a friend, I began to regard him as a patient, rich in possibilities of profitable study. Why not? Had he not described his delusion in the interest of science? Ah, poor fellow, he was doing more for science than he knew: not only his story but himself was in evidence. I should cure him if I could, of course, but first I should make a little experiment in psychology—nay, the experiment itself might be a step in his restoration.

"That is very frank and friendly of you, Bartine," I said cordially, "and I'm rather proud of your confidence. It is all very odd, certainly. Do you mind showing me the watch?"

He detached it from his waistcoat, chain and all, and passed it to me without a word. The case was of gold, very thick and strong, and singularly engraved. After closely examining the dial and observing that it was nearly twelve o'clock, I opened it at the back and was interested to observe an inner case of ivory, upon which was painted a miniature portrait in that exquisite and delicate manner which was in vogue during the eighteenth century.

"Why, bless my soul!" I exclaimed, feeling a sharp artistic delight—"how under the sun did you get that done? I thought miniature painting on ivory was a lost art."

"That," he replied, gravely smiling, "is not I; it is my excellent great-grandfather, the late Bramwell Olcott Bartine, Esquire, of Virginia. He was younger then than later—about my age, in fact. It is said to resemble me; do you think so?"

"Resemble you? I should say so! Barring the costume, which I supposed you to have assumed out of compliment to the art—or for *vraisemblance,* so to say—and the no mustache, that portrait is you in every feature, line, and expression."

No more was said at that time. Bartine took a book from the table and began reading. I heard outside the incessant plash of the rain in the street. There were occasional hurried footfalls on the sidewalks; and once a slower, heavier tread seemed to cease at my door—a policeman, I thought, seeking shelter in the doorway. The boughs of the trees tapped significantly on the window panes, as if asking for admittance. I remember it all through these years and years of a wiser, graver life.

Seeing myself unobserved, I took the old-fashioned key that dangled from the chain and quickly turned back the hands of the watch a full hour; then, closing the case, I handed Bartine his property and saw him replace it on his person.

"I think you said," I began, with assumed carelessness, "that after eleven the sight of the dial no longer affects you. As it is now nearly twelve"—looking at my own timepiece—"perhaps, if you don't resent my pursuit of proof, you will look at it now."

He smiled good-humoredly, pulled out the watch again, opened it, and instantly sprang to his feet with a cry that Heaven has not had the mercy to permit me to forget! His eyes, their blackness strikingly intensified by the pallor of his face, were fixed upon the watch, which he clutched in both hands. For some time he remained in that attitude without uttering another sound; then, in a voice that I should not have recognized as his, he said:

"Damn you! it is two minutes to eleven!"

I was not unprepared for some such outbreak, and without rising replied, calmly enough:

"I beg your pardon; I must have misread your watch in setting my own by it."

He shut the case with a sharp snap and put the watch in his pocket. He looked at me and made an attempt to smile, but his lower lip quivered and he seemed unable to close his mouth. His hands, also, were shaking, and he thrust them, clenched, into the pockets of his sack-coat. The courageous spirit was manifestly endeavoring to subdue the coward body. The effort was too great; he began to sway from side to side, as from vertigo, and before I could spring from my chair to support him his knees gave way and he pitched awkwardly forward and fell upon his face. I sprang to assist him to rise; but when John Bartine rises we shall all rise.

The *post-mortem* examination disclosed nothing; every organ was normal and sound. But when the body had been prepared for burial a faint dark circle was seen to have developed around the neck; at least I was so assured by several persons who said they saw it, but of my own knowledge I cannot say if that was true.

Nor can I set limitations to the law of heredity. I do not know that in the spiritual world a sentiment or emotion may not survive the heart that held it, and seek expression in a kindred life, ages removed. Surely, if I were to guess at the fate of Bramwell Olcott Bartine, I should guess that he was hanged at eleven o'clock in the evening, and that he had been allowed several hours in which to prepare for the change.

As to John Bartine, my friend, my patient for five minutes, and—Heaven forgive me!—my victim for eternity, there is no more to say. He is buried, and his watch with him—I saw to that. May God rest his soul in Paradise, and the soul of his Virginian ancestor, if, indeed, they are two souls.

THE DAMNED THING

I
ONE DOES NOT ALWAYS EAT WHAT IS ON THE TABLE

BY the light of a tallow candle which had been placed on one end of a rough table a man was reading something written in a book. It was an old account book, greatly worn; and the writing was not, apparently, very legible, for the man sometimes held the page close to the flame of the candle to get a stronger light on it. The shadow of the book would then throw into obscurity a half of the room, darkening a number of faces and figures; for besides the reader, eight other men were present. Seven of them sat against the rough log walls, silent, motionless, and the room being small, not very far from the table. By extending an arm any one of them could have touched the eighth man, who lay on the table, face upward, partly covered by a sheet, his arms at his sides. He was dead.

The man with the book was not reading aloud, and no one spoke; all seemed to be waiting for something to occur; the dead man only was without expectation. From the blank darkness outside came in, through the aperture that served for a window, all the ever unfamiliar noises of night in the wilderness—the long nameless note of a distant coyote; the stilly pulsing thrill of tireless insects in trees; strange cries of night birds, so different from those of the birds of day; the drone of great blundering beetles, and all that mysterious chorus of small sounds that seem always to have been but half heard when they have suddenly ceased, as if conscious of an indiscretion. But nothing of all this was noted in that company; its members were not overmuch addicted to idle interest in matters of no practical importance; that was obvious in every line of their rugged faces—obvious even in the dim light of the single candle. They were evidently men of the vicinity—farmers and woodsmen.

The person reading was a trifle different; one would have said of him that he was of the world, worldly, albeit there was that in his attire which attested a certain fellowship with the organisms of his environment. His coat would hardly have passed muster in San Francisco; his foot-gear was not of urban origin, and the hat that lay by him on the floor (he was the only one uncovered) was such that if one had considered it as an article of mere personal adornment he would have missed its meaning. In countenance the man was rather prepossessing, with just a hint of sternness; though that he may have assumed or cultivated, as appropriate to one in authority. For he was a coroner. It was by virtue of his office that he had possession of the book in which he was reading; it had been found among the dead man's effects—in his cabin, where the inquest was now taking place.

When the coroner had finished reading he put the book into his breast pocket. At that moment the door was pushed open and a young man entered. He, clearly, was not of mountain birth and breeding: he was clad as those who dwell in cities. His clothing was dusty, however, as from travel. He had, in fact, been riding hard to attend the inquest.

The coroner nodded; no one else greeted him.

"We have waited for you," said the coroner. "It is necessary to have done with this business to-night."

The young man smiled. "I am sorry to have kept you," he said. "I went away, not to evade your summons, but to post to my newspaper an account of what I suppose I am called back to relate."

The coroner smiled.

"The account that you posted to your newspaper," he said, "differs, probably, from that which you will give here under oath."

"That," replied the other, rather hotly and with a visible flush, "is as you please. I used manifold paper and have a copy of what I sent. It was not written as news, for it is incredible, but as fiction. It may go as a part of my testimony under oath."

"But you say it is incredible."

"That is nothing to you, sir, if I also swear that it is true."

The coroner was silent for a time, his eyes upon the floor. The men about the sides of the cabin talked in whispers, but seldom withdrew their gaze from the face of the corpse. Presently the coroner lifted his eyes and said: "We will resume the inquest."

The men removed their hats. The witness was sworn.

"What is your name?" the coroner asked.

"William Harker."

"Age?"

"Twenty-seven."

"You knew the deceased, Hugh Morgan?"

"Yes."

"You were with him when he died?"

"Near him."

"How did that happen—your presence, I mean?"

"I was visiting him at this place to shoot and fish. A part of my purpose, however, was to study him and his odd, solitary way of life. He seemed a good model for a character in fiction. I sometimes write stories."

"I sometimes read them."

"Thank you."

"Stories in general—not yours."

Some of the jurors laughed. Against a sombre background humor shows high lights. Soldiers in the intervals of battle laugh easily, and a jest in the death chamber conquers by surprise.

"Relate the circumstances of this man's death," said the coroner. "You may use any notes or memoranda that you please."

The witness understood. Pulling a manuscript from his breast pocket he held it near the candle and turning the leaves until he found the passage that he wanted began to read.

II
WHAT MAY HAPPEN IN A FIELD OF WILD OATS

". . . The sun had hardly risen when we left the house. We were looking for quail, each with a shotgun, but we had only one dog. Morgan said that our best ground was beyond a certain ridge that he pointed out, and we crossed it by a trail through the *chaparral*. On the other side was comparatively level ground, thickly covered with wild oats. As we emerged from the *chaparral* Morgan was but a few yards in advance. Suddenly we heard, at a little distance to our right and partly in front, a noise as of some animal thrashing about in the bushes, which we could see were violently agitated.

" 'We've started a deer,' I said. 'I wish we had brought a rifle.'

"Morgan, who had stopped and was intently watching the agitated *chaparral,* said nothing, but had cocked both barrels of his gun and was holding it in readiness to aim. I thought him a trifle excited, which surprised me, for he had a reputation for exceptional coolness, even in moments of sudden and imminent peril.

" 'O, come,' I said. 'You are not going to fill up a deer with quail-shot, are you?'

"Still he did not reply; but catching a sight of his face as he turned it slightly toward me I was struck by the intensity of his look. Then I understood that we had serious business in hand and my first conjecture was that we had 'jumped' a grizzly. I advanced to Morgan's side, cocking my piece as I moved.

"The bushes were now quiet and the sounds had ceased, but Morgan was as attentive to the place as before.

" 'What is it? What the devil is it?' I asked.

" 'That Damned Thing!' he replied, without turning his head. His voice was husky and unnatural. He trembled visibly.

"I was about to speak further, when I observed the wild oats near the place of the disturbance moving in the most inexplicable way. I can hardly describe it. It seemed as if stirred by a streak of wind, which not only bent it, but pressed it down—crushed it so that it did not rise; and this movement was slowly prolonging itself directly toward us.

"Nothing that I had ever seen had affected me so strangely as this unfamiliar and unaccountable phenomenon, yet I am unable to recall any sense of fear. I remember—and tell it here because, singularly enough, I recollected it then—that once in looking carelessly out of an open window I momentarily mistook a small tree close at hand for one of a group of larger trees at a little distance away. It looked the same size as the others, but being more distinctly and sharply defined in mass and detail seemed out of harmony with them. It was a mere falsification of the law of aërial perspective, but it startled, almost terrified me. We so rely upon the orderly operation of familiar natural laws that any seeming suspension of them is noted as a menace to our safety, a warning of unthinkable calamity. So now the apparently causeless movement of the herbage and the slow, undeviating approach of the line of disturbance were distinctly disquieting. My companion appeared actually frightened, and I could hardly credit my senses when I saw him suddenly throw his gun to his shoulder and fire both barrels at the agitated grain! Before the smoke of the discharge had cleared away I heard a loud savage cry—a scream like that of a wild animal—and flinging his gun upon the ground Morgan sprang away and ran swiftly from the spot. At the same instant I was thrown violently to the ground by the impact of something unseen in the smoke—some soft, heavy substance that seemed thrown against me with great force.

"Before I could get upon my feet and recover my gun, which seemed to have been struck from my hands, I heard Morgan crying out as if in mortal agony, and mingling with his cries were such hoarse, savage sounds as one hears from fighting dogs. Inexpressibly terrified, I struggled to my feet and looked in the direction of Morgan's retreat; and may Heaven in mercy spare me from another sight like that! At a distance of less than thirty yards was my friend, down upon one knee, his head thrown back at a frightful angle, hatless, his long hair in disorder and his whole body in violent movement from side to side, backward and forward. His right arm was lifted and seemed to lack the hand—at least, I could see none. The other arm was invisible. At times, as my memory now reports this extraordinary scene, I could discern but a part of his body; it was as if he had been partly blotted out—I cannot otherwise express it—then a shifting of his position would bring it all into view again.

"All this must have occurred within a few seconds, yet in that time Morgan assumed all the postures of a determined wrestler vanquished by superior weight and strength. I saw nothing but him, and him not always distinctly. During the entire incident his shouts and curses were heard, as if through an enveloping uproar of such sounds of rage and fury as I had never heard from the throat of man or brute!

"For a moment only I stood irresolute, then throwing down my gun I ran forward to my friend's assistance. I had a vague belief that he was suffering from a fit, or some form of convulsion. Before I could reach his side he was down and quiet. All sounds had ceased, but with a feeling of such terror as even these awful events had not inspired I now saw again the mysterious movement of the wild oats, prolonging itself from the trampled area about the prostrate man toward the edge of a wood. It was only when it had reached the wood that I was able to withdraw my eyes and look at my companion. He was dead."

III
A MAN THOUGH NAKED MAY BE IN RAGS

The coroner rose from his seat and stood beside the dead man. Lifting an edge of the sheet he pulled it away, exposing the entire body, altogether naked and showing in the candle-light a claylike yellow. It had, however, broad maculations of bluish black, obviously caused by extravasated blood from contusions. The chest and sides looked as if they had been beaten with a bludgeon. There were dreadful lacerations; the skin was torn in strips and shreds.

The coroner moved round to the end of the table and undid a silk handkerchief which had been passed under the chin and knotted on the top of the head. When the handkerchief was drawn away it exposed what had been the throat. Some of the jurors who had risen to get a better view repented their curiosity and turned away their faces. Witness Harker went to the open window and leaned out across the sill, faint and sick. Dropping the handkerchief upon the dead man's neck the coroner stepped to an angle of the room and from a pile of clothing produced one garment after another, each of which he held up a moment for inspection. All were torn, and stiff with blood. The jurors did not make a closer inspection. They seemed rather uninterested. They had, in truth, seen all this before; the only thing that was new to them being Harker's testimony.

"Gentlemen," the coroner said, "we have no more evidence, I think. Your duty has been already explained to you; if there is nothing you wish to ask you may go outside and consider your verdict."

The foreman rose—a tall, bearded man of sixty, coarsely clad.

"I should like to ask one question, Mr. Coroner," he said. "What asylum did this yer last witness escape from?"

"Mr. Harker," said the coroner, gravely and tranquilly, "from what asylum did you last escape?"

Harker flushed crimson again, but said nothing, and the seven jurors rose and solemnly filed out of the cabin.

"If you have done insulting me, sir," said Harker, as soon as he and the officer were left alone with the dead man, "I suppose I am at liberty to go?"

"Yes."

Harker started to leave, but paused, with his hand on the door latch. The habit of his profession was strong in him—stronger than his sense of personal dignity. He turned about and said:

"The book that you have there—I recognize it as Morgan's diary. You seemed greatly interested in it; you read in it while I was testifying. May I see it? The public would like—"

"The book will cut no figure in this matter," replied the official, slipping it into his coat pocket; "all the entries in it were made before the writer's death."

As Harker passed out of the house the jury reëntered and stood about the table, on which the now covered corpse showed under the sheet with sharp definition. The foreman seated himself near the candle, produced from his breast pocket a pencil and scrap of paper and wrote rather laboriously the following verdict, which with various degrees of effort all signed:

"We, the jury, do find that the remains come to their death at the hands of a mountain lion, but some of us thinks, all the same, they had fits."

IV

AN EXPLANATION FROM THE TOMB

In the diary of the late Hugh Morgan are certain interesting entries having, possibly, a scientific value as suggestions. At the inquest upon his body the book was not put in evidence; possibly the coroner thought it not worth while to confuse the jury. The date of the first of the entries mentioned cannot be ascertained; the upper part of the leaf is torn away; the part of the entry remaining follows:

". . . would run in a half-circle, keeping his head turned always toward the centre, and again he would stand still, barking furiously. At last he ran away into the brush as fast as he could go. I thought at first that he had gone mad, but on returning to the house found no other alteration in his manner than what was obviously due to fear of punishment.

"Can a dog see with his nose? Do odors impress some cerebral centre with images of the thing that emitted them? . . .

"Sept. 2.—Looking at the stars last night as they rose above the crest of the ridge east of the house, I observed them successively disappear— from left to right. Each was eclipsed but an instant, and only a few at the same time, but along the entire length of the ridge all that were within a degree or two of the crest were blotted out. It was as if something had passed along between me and them; but I could not see it, and the stars were not thick enough to define its outline. Ugh! I don't like this."

Several weeks' entries are missing, three leaves being torn from the book.

"Sept. 27.—It has been about here again— I find evidences of its presence every day. I watched again all last night in the same cover, gun in hand, double-charged with buckshot. In the morning the fresh footprints were there, as before. Yet I would have sworn that I did not sleep—indeed, I hardly sleep at all. It is terrible, insupportable! If these amazing experiences are real I shall go mad; if they are fanciful I am mad already.

"Oct. 3.—I shall not go—it shall not drive me away. No, this is *my* house, *my* land. God hates a coward. . . .

"Oct. 5.—I can stand it no longer; I have invited Harker to pass a few weeks with me—he has a level head. I can judge from his manner if he thinks me mad.

"Oct. 7.—I have the solution of the mystery; it came to me last night— suddenly, as by revelation. How simple—how terribly simple!

"There are sounds that we cannot hear. At either end of the scale are notes that stir no chord of that imperfect instrument, the human ear. They are too high or too grave. I have observed a flock of blackbirds occupying an entire tree-top—the tops of several trees—and all in full song. Suddenly—in a moment—at absolutely the same instant—all spring into the air and fly away. How? They could not all see one another—whole tree-tops intervened. At no point could a leader have been visible to all. There must have been a signal of warning or command, high and shrill above the din, but by me unheard. I have observed, too, the same simultaneous flight when all were silent, among not only blackbirds, but other birds—quail, for example, widely separated by bushes—even on opposite sides of a hill.

"It is known to seamen that a school of whales basking or sporting on the surface of the ocean, miles apart, with the convexity of the earth between, will sometimes dive at the same instant—all gone out of sight in a moment. The signal has been sounded—too grave for the ear of the sailor at the masthead and his comrades on the deck—who nevertheless feel its vibrations in the ship as the stones of a cathedral are stirred by the bass of the organ.

"As with sounds, so with colors. At each end of the solar spectrum the chemist can detect the presence of what are known as 'actinic' rays. They represent colors—integral colors in the composition of light—which we are unable to discern. The human eye is an imperfect instrument; its range is but a few octaves of the real 'chromatic scale.' I am not mad; there are colors that we cannot see.

"And, God help me! the Damned Thing is of such a color!"

HAÏTA THE SHEPHERD

IN the heart of Haïta the illusions of youth had not been supplanted by those of age and experience. His thoughts were pure and pleasant, for his life was simple and his soul devoid of ambition. He rose with the sun and went forth to pray at the shrine of Hastur, the god of shepherds, who heard and was pleased. After performance of this pious rite Haïta unbarred the gate of the fold and with a cheerful mind drove his flock afield, eating his morning meal of curds and oat cake as he went, occasionally pausing to add a few berries, cold with dew, or to drink of the waters that came away from the hills to join the stream in the middle of the valley and be borne along with it, he knew not whither.

During the long summer day, as his sheep cropped the good grass which the gods had made to grow for them, or lay with their forelegs doubled under their breasts and chewed the cud, Haïta, reclining in the shadow of a tree, or sitting upon a rock, played so sweet music upon his reed pipe that sometimes from the corner of his eye he got accidental glimpses of the minor sylvan deities, leaning forward out of the copse to hear; but if he looked at them directly they vanished. From this—for he must be thinking if he would not turn into one of his own sheep— he drew the solemn inference that happiness may come if not sought, but if looked for will never be seen; for next to the favor of Hastur, who never disclosed himself, Haïta most valued the friendly interest of his neighbors, the shy immortals of the wood and stream. At nightfall he drove his flock back to the fold, saw that the gate was secure and retired to his cave for refreshment and for dreams.

So passed his life, one day like another, save when the storms uttered the wrath of an offended god. Then Haïta cowered in his cave, his face hidden in his hands, and prayed that he alone might be punished for his sins and the world saved from destruction. Sometimes when there was a great rain, and the stream came out of its banks, compelling him to urge his terrified flock to the uplands, he interceded for the people in the cities which he had been told lay in the plain beyond the two blue hills forming the gateway of his valley.

"It is kind of thee, O Hastur," so he prayed, "to give me mountains so near to my dwelling and my fold that I and my sheep can escape the angry torrents; but the rest of the world thou must thyself deliver in some way that I know not of, or I will no longer worship thee."

And Hastur, knowing that Haïta was a youth who kept his word, spared the cities and turned the waters into the sea.

So he had lived since he could remember. He could not rightly conceive any other mode of existence. The holy hermit who dwelt at the head of the valley, a full hour's journey away, from whom he had heard the tale of the great cities where dwelt people—poor souls!—who had no sheep, gave him no knowledge of that early time, when, so he reasoned, he must have been small and helpless like a lamb.

It was through thinking on these mysteries and marvels, and on that horrible change to silence and decay which he felt sure must some time come to him, as he had seen it come to so many of his flock—as it came to all living things except the birds—that Haïta first became conscious how miserable and hopeless was his lot.

"It is necessary," he said, "that I know whence and how I came; for how can one perform his duties unless able to judge what they are by the way in which he was intrusted with them? And what contentment can I have when I know not how long it is going to last? Perhaps before another sun I may be changed, and then what will become of the sheep? What, indeed, will have become of me?"

Pondering these things Haïta became melancholy and morose. He no longer spoke cheerfully to his flock, nor ran with alacrity to the shrine of Hastur. In every breeze he heard whispers of malign deities whose existence he now first observed. Every cloud was a portent signifying disaster, and the darkness was full of terrors. His reed pipe when applied to his lips gave out no melody, but a dismal wail; the sylvan and riparian intelligences no longer thronged to the thicket-side to listen, but fled from the sound, as he knew by the stirred leaves and bent flowers. He relaxed his vigilance and many of his sheep strayed away into the hills and were lost. Those that remained became lean and ill for lack of good pasturage, for he would not seek it for them, but conducted them day after day to the same spot, through mere abstraction, while puzzling about life and death—of immortality he knew not.

One day while indulging in the gloomiest reflections he suddenly sprang from the rock upon which he sat, and with a determined gesture exclaimed: "I will no longer be a suppliant for knowledge which the gods withhold. Let them look to it that they do me no wrong. I will do my duty as best I can and if I err upon their own heads be it!"

Suddenly, as he spoke, a great brightness fell about him, causing him to look upward, thinking the sun had burst through a rift in the clouds; but there were no clouds. No more than an arm's length away stood a beautiful maiden. So beautiful she was that the flowers about her feet folded their petals in despair and bent their heads in token of submission; so sweet her look that the humming birds thronged her eyes, thrusting their thirsty bills almost into them, and the wild bees were about her lips. And such was her brightness that the shadows of all objects lay divergent from her feet, turning as she moved.

Haïta was entranced. Rising, he knelt before her in adoration, and she laid her hand upon his head.

"Come," she said in a voice that had the music of all the bells of his flock—"come, thou art not to worship me, who am no goddess, but if thou art truthful and dutiful I will abide with thee."

Haïta seized her hand, and stammering his joy and gratitude arose, and hand in hand they stood and smiled into each other's eyes. He gazed on her with reverence and rapture. He said: "I pray thee, lovely maid, tell me thy name and whence and why thou comest."

At this she laid a warning finger on her lip and began to withdraw. Her beauty underwent a visible alteration that made him shudder, he knew not why, for still she was beautiful. The landscape was darkened by a giant shadow sweeping across the valley with the speed of a vulture. In the obscurity the maiden's figure grew dim and indistinct and her voice seemed to come from a distance, as she said, in a tone of sorrowful reproach: "Presumptuous and ungrateful youth! must I then so soon leave thee? Would nothing do but thou must at once break the eternal compact?"

Inexpressibly grieved, Haïta fell upon his knees and implored her to remain—rose and sought her in the deepening darkness—ran in circles, calling to her aloud, but all in vain. She was no longer visible, but out of the gloom he heard her voice saying: "Nay, thou shalt not have me by seeking. Go to thy duty, faithless shepherd, or we shall never meet again."

Night had fallen; the wolves were howling in the hills and the terrified sheep crowding about Haïta's feet. In the demands of the hour he forgot his disappointment, drove his sheep to the fold and repairing to the place of worship poured out his heart in gratitude to Hastur for permitting him to save his flock, then retired to his cave and slept.

When Haïta awoke the sun was high and shone in at the cave, illuminating it with a great glory. And there, beside him, sat the maiden. She smiled upon him with a smile that seemed the visible music of his pipe of reeds. He dared not speak, fearing to offend her as before, for he knew not what he could venture to say.

"Because," she said, "thou didst thy duty by the flock, and didst not forget to thank Hastur for staying the wolves of the night, I am come to thee again. Wilt thou have me for a companion?"

"Who would not have thee forever?" replied Haïta. "Oh! never again leave me until—until I—change and become silent and motionless."

Haïta had no word for death.

"I wish, indeed," he continued, "that thou wert of my own sex, that we might wrestle and run races and so never tire of being together."

At these words the maiden arose and passed out of the cave, and Haïta, springing from his couch of fragrant boughs to overtake and detain her, observed to his astonishment that the rain was falling and the stream in the middle of the valley had come out of its banks. The sheep were bleating in terror, for the rising waters had invaded their fold. And there was danger for the unknown cities of the distant plain.

It was many days before Haïta saw the maiden again. One day he was returning from the head of the valley, where he had gone with ewe's milk and oat cakes and berries for the holy hermit, who was too old and feeble to provide himself with food.

"Poor old man!" he said aloud, as he trudged along homeward. "I will return to-morrow and bear him on my back to my own dwelling, where I can care for him. Doubtless it is for this that Hastur has reared me all these many years, and gives me health and strength."

As he spoke, the maiden, clad in glittering garments, met him in the path with a smile that took away his breath.

"I am come again," she said, "to dwell with thee if thou wilt now have me, for none else will. Thou mayest have learned wisdom, and art willing to take me as I am, nor care to know."

Haïta threw himself at her feet. "Beautiful being," he cried, "if thou wilt but deign to accept all the devotion of my heart and soul—after Hastur be served—it is thine forever. But, alas! thou are capricious and wayward. Before to-morrow's sun I may lose thee again. Promise, I beseech thee, that however in my ignorance I may offend, thou wilt forgive and remain always with me."

Scarcely had he finished speaking when a troop of bears came out of the hills, racing toward him with crimson mouths and fiery eyes. The maiden again vanished, and he turned and fled for his life. Nor did he stop until he was in the cot of the holy hermit, whence he had set out. Hastily barring the door against the bears he cast himself upon the ground and wept.

"My son," said the hermit from his couch of straw, freshly gathered that morning by Haïta's hands, "it is not like thee to weep for bears— tell me what sorrow hath befallen thee, that age may minister to the hurts of youth with such balms as it hath of its wisdom."

Haïta told him all: how thrice he had met the radiant maid, and thrice she had left him forlorn. He related minutely all that had passed between them, omitting no word of what had been said.

When he had ended, the holy hermit was a moment silent, then said: "My son, I have attended to thy story, and I know the maiden. I have myself seen her, as have many. Know, then, that her name, which she would not even permit thee to inquire, is Happiness. Thou saidst the truth to her, that she is capricious for she imposeth conditions that man can not fulfill, and delinquency is punished by desertion. She cometh only when unsought, and will not be questioned. One manifestation of curiosity, one sign of doubt, one expression of misgiving, and she is away! How long didst thou have her at any time before she fled?"

"Only a single instant," answered Haïta, blushing with shame at the confession. "Each time I drove her away in one moment."

"Unfortunate youth!" said the holy hermit, "but for thine indiscretion thou mightst have had her for two."

AN INHABITANT OF CARCOSA

For there be divers sorts of death—some wherein the body remaineth; and in some it vanisheth quite away with the spirit. This commonly occurreth only in solitude (such is God's will) and, none seeing the end, we say the man is lost, or gone on a long journey— which indeed he hath; but sometimes it hath happened in sight of many, as abundant testimony showeth. In one kind of death the spirit also dieth, and this it hath been known to do while yet the body was in vigor for many years. Sometimes, as is veritably attested, it dieth with the body, but after a season is raised up again in that place where the body did decay.

PONDERING these words of Hali (whom God rest) and questioning their full meaning, as one who, having an intimation, yet doubts if there be not something behind, other than that which he has discerned, I noted not whither I had strayed until a sudden chill wind striking my face revived in me a sense of my surroundings. I observed with astonishment that everything seemed unfamiliar. On every side of me stretched a bleak and desolate expanse of plain, covered with a tall overgrowth of sere grass, which rustled and whistled in the autumn wind with heaven knows what mysterious and disquieting suggestion. Protruded at long intervals above it, stood strangely shaped and somber-colored rocks, which seemed to have an understanding with one another and to exchange looks of uncomfortable significance, as if they had reared their heads to watch the issue of some foreseen event. A few blasted trees here and there appeared as leaders in this malevolent conspiracy of silent expectation.

The day, I thought, must be far advanced, though the sun was invisible; and although sensible that the air was raw and chill my consciousness of that fact was rather mental than physical— I had no feeling of discomfort. Over all the dismal landscape a canopy of low, lead-colored clouds hung like a visible curse. In all this there were a menace and a portent—a hint of evil, an intimation of doom. Bird, beast, or insect there was none. The wind sighed in the bare branches of the dead trees and the gray grass bent to whisper its dread secret to the earth; but no other sound nor motion broke the awful repose of that dismal place.

I observed in the herbage a number of weather-worn stones, evidently shaped with tools. They were broken, covered with moss and half sunken in the earth. Some lay prostrate, some leaned at various angles, none was vertical. They were obviously headstones of graves, though the graves themselves no longer existed as either mounds or depressions; the years had leveled all. Scattered here and there, more massive blocks showed where some pompous tomb or ambitious monument had once flung its feeble defiance at oblivion. So old seemed these relics, these vestiges of vanity and memorials of affection and piety, so battered and worn and stained—so neglected, deserted, forgotten the place, that I could not help thinking myself the discoverer of the burial-ground of a prehistoric race of men whose very name was long extinct.

Filled with these reflections, I was for some time heedless of the sequence of my own experiences, but soon I thought, "How came I hither?" A moment's reflection seemed to make this all clear and explain at the same time, though in a disquieting way, the singular character with which my fancy had invested all that I saw or heard. I was ill.

I remembered now that I had been prostrated by a sudden fever, and that my family had told me that in my periods of delirium I had constantly cried out for liberty and air, and had been held in bed to prevent my escape out-of-doors. Now I had eluded the vigilance of my attendants and had wandered hither to—to where? I could not conjecture. Clearly I was at a considerable distance from the city where I dwelt—the ancient and famous city of Carcosa.

No signs of human life were anywhere visible nor audible; no rising smoke, no watchdog's bark, no lowing of cattle, no shouts of children at play—nothing but that dismal burial-place, with its air of mystery and dread, due to my own disordered brain. Was I not becoming again delirious, there beyond human aid? Was it not indeed *all* an illusion of my madness? I called aloud the names of my wives and sons, reached out my hands in search of theirs, even as I walked among the crumbling stones and in the withered grass.

A noise behind me caused me to turn about. A wild animal—a lynx—was approaching. The thought came to me: If I break down here in the desert—if the fever return and I fail, this beast will be at my throat. I sprang toward it, shouting. It trotted tranquilly by within a hand's breadth of me and disappeared behind a rock.

A moment later a man's head appeared to rise out of the ground a short distance away. He was ascending the farther slope of a low hill whose crest was hardly to be distinguished from the general level. His whole figure soon came into view against the background of gray cloud. He was half naked, half clad in skins. His hair was unkempt, his beard long and ragged. In one hand he carried a bow and arrow; the other held a blazing torch with a long trail of black smoke. He walked slowly and with caution, as if he feared falling into some open grave concealed by the tall grass. This strange apparition surprised but did not alarm, and taking such a course as to intercept him with the familiar salutation, "God keep you."

He gave no heed, nor did he arrest his pace.

"Good stranger," I continued, "I am ill and lost. Direct me, I beseech you, to Carcosa."

The man broke into a barbarous chant in an unknown tongue, passing on and away.

An owl on the branch of a decayed tree hooted dismally and was answered by another in the distance. Looking upward, I saw through a sudden rift in the clouds Aldebaran and the Hyades! In all this there was a hint of night—the lynx, the man with the torch, the owl. Yet I saw— I saw even the stars in absence of darkness. I saw, but was apparently not seen nor heard. Under what awful spell did I exist.

I seated myself at the root of a great tree, seriously to consider what it were best to do. That I was mad I could no longer doubt, yet recognized a ground of doubt in the conviction. Of fever I had no trace. I had, withal, a sense of exhilaration and vigor altogether unknown to me—a feeling of mental and physical exaltation. My senses seemed all alert; I could feel the air as a ponderous substance; I could hear the silence.

A great root of the giant tree against whose trunk I leaned as I sat held inclosed in its grasp a slab of stone, a part of which protruded into a recess formed by another root. The stone was thus partly protected from the weather, though greatly decomposed. Its edges were worn round, its corners eaten away, its surface deeply furrowed and scaled. Glittering particles of mica were visible in the earth about it—vestiges of its decomposition. This stone had apparently marked the grave out of which the tree had sprung ages ago. The tree's exacting roots had robbed the grave and made the stone a prisoner.

A sudden wind pushed some dry leaves and twigs from the uppermost face of the stone; I saw the low-relief letters of an inscription and bent to read it. God in Heaven! *my* name in full!—the date of *my* birth!—the date of *my* death!

A level shaft of light illuminated the whole side of the tree as I sprang to my feet in terror. The sun was rising in the rosy east. I stood between the tree and his broad red disk—no shadow darkened the trunk!

A chorus of howling wolves saluted the dawn. I saw them sitting on their haunches, singly and in groups, on the summits of irregular mounds and tumuli filling a half of my desert prospect and extending to the horizon. And then I knew that these were ruins of the ancient and famous city of Carcosa.

———

Such are the facts imparted to the medium Bayrolles by the spirit Hoseib Alar Robardin.

THE STRANGER

A MAN stepped out of the darkness into the little illuminated circle about our failing campfire and seated himself upon a rock.

"You are not the first to explore this region," he said, gravely.

Nobody controverted his statement; he was himself proof of its truth, for he was not of our party and must have been somewhere near when we camped. Moreover, he must have companions not far away; it was not a place where one would be living or traveling alone. For more than a week we had seen, besides ourselves and our animals, only such living things as rattlesnakes and horned toads. In an Arizona desert one does not long coexist with only such creatures as these: one must have pack animals, supplies, arms—"an outfit." And all these imply comrades. It was perhaps a doubt as to what manner of men this unceremonious stranger's comrades might be, together with something in his words interpretable as a challenge, that caused every man of our half-dozen "gentlemen adventurers" to rise to a sitting posture and lay his hand upon a weapon—an act signifying, in that time and place, a policy of expectation. The stranger gave the matter no attention and began again to speak in the same deliberate, uninflected monotone in which he had delivered his first sentence:

"Thirty years ago Ramon Gallegos, William Shaw, George W. Kent and Berry Davis, all of Tucson, crossed the Santa Catalina mountains and traveled due west, as nearly as the configuration of the country permitted. We were prospecting and it was our intention, if we found nothing, to push through to the Gila River at some point near Big Bend, where we understood there was a settlement. We had a good outfit but no guide—just Ramon Gallegos, William Shaw, George W. Kent and Berry Davis."

The man repeated the names slowly and distinctly, as if to fix them in the memories of his audience, every member of which was now attentively observing him, but with a slackened apprehension regarding his possible companions somewhere in the darkness that seemed to enclose us like a black wall; in the manner of this volunteer historian was no suggestion of an unfriendly purpose. His act was rather that of a harmless lunatic than an enemy. We were not so new to the country as not to know that the solitary life of many a plainsman had a tendency to develop eccentricities of conduct and character not always easily distinguishable from mental aberration. A man is like a tree: in a forest of his fellows he will grow as straight as his generic and individual nature permits; alone in the open, he yields to the deforming stresses and tortions that environ him. Some such thoughts were in my mind as I watched the man from the shadow of my hat, pulled low to shut out the firelight. A witless fellow, no doubt, but what could he be doing there in the heart of a desert?

Having undertaken to tell this story, I wish that I could describe the man's appearance; that would be a natural thing to do. Unfortunately, and somewhat strangely, I find myself unable to do so with any degree of confidence, for afterward no two of us agreed as to what he wore and how he looked; and when I try to set down my own impressions they elude me. Anyone can tell some kind of story; narration is one of the elemental powers of the race. But the talent for description is a gift.

Nobody having broken silence the visitor went on to say:

"This country was not then what it is now. There was not a ranch between the Gila and the Gulf. There was a little game here and there in the mountains, and near the infrequent water-holes grass enough to keep our animals from starvation. If we should be so fortunate as to encounter no Indians we might get through. But within a week the purpose of the expedition had altered from discovery of wealth to preservation of life. We had gone too far to go back, for what was ahead could be no worse than what was behind; so we pushed on, riding by night to avoid Indians and the intolerable heat, and concealing ourselves by day as best we could. Sometimes, having exhausted our supply of wild meat and emptied our casks, we were days without food or drink; then a water-hole or a shallow pool in the bottom of an *arroyo* so restored our strength and sanity that we were able to shoot some of the wild animals that sought it also. Sometimes it was a bear, sometimes an antelope, a coyote, a cougar—that was as God pleased; all were food.

"One morning as we skirted a mountain range, seeking a practicable pass, we were attacked by a band of Apaches who had followed our trail up a gulch—it is not far from here. Knowing that they outnumbered us ten to one, they took none of their usual cowardly precautions, but dashed upon us at a gallop, firing and yelling. Fighting was out of the question: we urged our feeble animals up the gulch as far as there was footing for a hoof, then threw ourselves out of our saddles and took to the *chaparral* on one of the slopes, abandoning our entire outfit to the enemy. But we retained our rifles, every man—Ramon Gallegos, William Shaw, George W. Kent and Berry Davis."

"Same old crowd," said the humorist of our party. He was an Eastern man, unfamiliar with the decent observances of social intercourse. A gesture of disapproval from our leader silenced him and the stranger proceeded with his tale:

"The savages dismounted also, and some of them ran up the gulch beyond the point at which we had left it, cutting off further retreat in that direction and forcing us on up the side. Unfortunately the *chaparral* extended only a short distance up the slope, and as we came into the open ground above we took the fire of a dozen rifles; but Apaches shoot badly when in a hurry, and God so willed it that none of us fell. Twenty yards up the slope, beyond the edge of the brush, were vertical cliffs, in which, directly in front of us, was a narrow opening. Into that we ran, finding ourselves in a cavern about as large as an ordinary room in a house. Here for a time we were safe: a single man with a repeating rifle could defend the entrance against all the Apaches in the land. But against hunger and thirst we had no defense. Courage we still had, but hope was a memory.

"Not one of those Indians did we afterward see, but by the smoke and glare of their fires in the gulch we knew that by day and by night they watched with ready rifles in the edge of the bush—knew that if we made a sortie not a man of us would live to take three steps into the open. For three days, watching in turn, we held out before our suffering became insupportable. Then—it was the morning of the fourth day—Ramon Gallegos said:

" 'Senores, I know not well of the good God and what please him. I have live without religion, and I am not acquaint with that of you. Pardon, senores, if I shock you, but for me the time is come to beat the game of the Apache.'

"He knelt upon the rock floor of the cave and pressed his pistol against his temple. 'Madre de Dios,' he said, 'comes now the soul of Ramon Gallegos.'

"And so he left us—William Shaw, George W. Kent and Berry Davis.

"I was the leader: it was for me to speak.

" 'He was a brave man,' I said—'he knew when to die, and how. It is foolish to go mad from thirst and fall by Apache bullets, or be skinned alive—it is in bad taste. Let us join Ramon Gallegos.'

" 'That is right,' said William Shaw.

" 'That is right,' said George W. Kent.

"I straightened the limbs of Ramon Gallegos and put a handkerchief over his face. Then William Shaw said: 'I should like to look like that— a little while.'

"And George W. Kent said that he felt that way, too.

" 'It shall be so,' I said: 'the red devils will wait a week. William Shaw and George W. Kent, draw and kneel.'

"They did so and I stood before them.

" 'Almighty God, our Father,' said I.

" 'Almighty God, our Father,' said William Shaw.

" 'Almighty God, our Father,' said George W. Kent.

" 'Forgive us our sins,' said I.

" 'Forgive us our sins,' said they.

" 'And receive our souls.'

" 'And receive our souls.'

" 'Amen!'

" 'Amen!'

"I laid them beside Ramon Gallegos and covered their faces."

There was a quick commotion on the opposite side of the campfire: one of our party had sprung to his feet, pistol in hand.

"And you!" he shouted—"*you* dared to escape?—you dare to be alive? You cowardly hound, I'll send you to join them if I hang for it!"

But with the leap of a panther the captain was upon him, grasping his wrist. "Hold it in, Sam Yountsey, hold it in!"

We were now all upon our feet—except the stranger, who sat motionless and apparently inattentive. Some one seized Yountsey's other arm.

"Captain," I said, "there is something wrong here. This fellow is either a lunatic or merely a liar—just a plain, every-day liar whom Yountsey has no call to kill. If this man was of that party it had five members, one of whom—probably himself—he has not named."

"Yes," said the captain, releasing the insurgent, who sat down, "there is something—unusual. Years ago four dead bodies of white men, scalped and shamefully mutilated, were found about the mouth of that cave.

They are buried there; I have seen the graves—we shall all see them tomorrow."

The stranger rose, standing tall in the light of the expiring fire, which in our breathless attention to his story we had neglected to keep going.

"There were four," he said—"Ramon Gallegos, William Shaw, George W. Kent and Berry Davis."

With this reiterated roll-call of the dead he walked into the darkness and we saw him no more.

At that moment one of our party, who had been on guard, strode in among us, rifle in hand and somewhat excited.

"Captain," he said, "for the last half-hour three men have been standing out there on the *mesa.*" He pointed in the direction taken by the stranger. "I could see them distinctly, for the moon is up, but as they had no guns and I had them covered with mine I thought it was their move. They have made none, but, damn it! they have got on to my nerves."

"Go back to your post, and stay till you see them again," said the captain. "The rest of you lie down again, or I'll kick you all into the fire."

The sentinel obediently withdrew, swearing, and did not return. As we were arranging our blankets the fiery Yountsey said: "I beg your pardon, Captain, but who the devil do you take them to be?"

"Ramon Gallegos, William Shaw and George W. Kent."

"But how about Berry Davis? I ought to have shot him."

"Quite needless; you couldn't have made him any deader. Go to sleep."

FANTASTIC FABLES
WITH
Fables from "Fun"
Æsopus Emendatus
Old Saws with New Teeth
Fables in Rhyme

MORAL PRINCIPLE AND MATERIAL INTEREST

A MORAL PRINCIPLE met a Material Interest on a bridge wide enough for but one.

"Down, you base thing!" thundered the Moral Principle, "and let me pass over you!"

The Material Interest merely looked in the other's eyes without saying anything.

"Ah," said the Moral Principle, hesitatingly, "let us draw lots to see which one of us shall retire till the other has crossed."

The Material Interest maintained an unbroken silence and an unwavering stare.

"In order to avoid a conflict," the Moral Principle resumed, somewhat uneasily, "I shall myself lie down and let you walk over me."

Then the Material Interest found his tongue. "I don't think you are very good walking," he said. "I am a little particular about what I have underfoot. Suppose you get off into the water."

It occurred that way.

THE CRIMSON CANDLE

A MAN lying at the point of death called his wife to his bedside and said:

"I am about to leave you forever; give me, therefore, one last proof of your affection and fidelity. In my desk you will find a crimson candle, which has been blessed by the High Priest and has a peculiar mystical significance. Swear to me that while it is in existence you will not remarry."

The Woman swore and the Man died. At the funeral the Woman stood at the head of the bier, holding a lighted crimson candle till it was wasted entirely away.

ESCUTCHEON AND ERMINE

A BLOTTED ESCUTCHEON, rising to a question of privilege, said:

"Mr. Speaker, I wish to hurl back an allegation and explain that the spots upon me are the natural markings of one who is a direct descendant of the sun and a spotted fawn. They come of no accident of character, but inhere in the divine order and constitution of things."

When the Blotted Escutcheon had resumed his seat a Soiled Ermine rose and said:

"Mr. Speaker, I have heard with profound attention and entire approval the explanation of the honorable member, and wish to offer a few remarks on my own behalf. I, too, have been foully calumniated by our ancient enemy, the Infamous Falsehood, and I wish to point out that I am made of the fur of the *Mustela maculata,* which is dirty from birth."

THE INGENIOUS PATRIOT

HAVING obtained an audience of the King an Ingenious Patriot pulled a paper from his pocket, saying:

"May it please your Majesty, I have here a formula for constructing armor plating that no gun can pierce. If these plates are adopted in the Royal Navy our warships will be invulnerable and therefore invincible. Here, also, are reports of your Majesty's Ministers, attesting the value of the invention. I will part with my right in it for a million tumtums."

After examining the papers, the King put them away and promised him an order on the Lord High Treasurer of the Extortion Department for a million tumtums.

"And here," said the Ingenious Patriot, pulling another paper from another pocket, "are the working plans of a gun that I have invented, which will pierce that armor. Your Majesty's royal brother, the Emperor of Bang, is eager to purchase it, but loyalty to your Majesty's throne and person constrains me to offer it first to your Majesty. The price is one million tumtums."

Having received the promise of another check, he thrust his hand into still another pocket, remarking:

"The price of the irresistible gun would have been much greater, your Majesty, but for the fact that its missiles can be so effectively averted by my peculiar method of treating the armor plates with a new—"

The King signed to the Great Head Factotum to approach.

"Search this man," he said, "and report how many pockets he has."

"Forty-three, Sire," said the Great Head Factotum, completing the scrutiny.

"May it please your Majesty," cried the Ingenious Patriot, in terror, "one of them contains tobacco."

"Hold him up by the ankles and shake him," said the King; "then give him a check for forty-two million tumtums and put him to death. Let a decree issue making ingenuity a capital offence."

OFFICER AND THUG

A CHIEF OF POLICE who had seen an Officer beating a Thug was very indignant, and said he must not do so any more on pain of dismissal.

"Don't be too hard on me," said the Officer, smiling; "I was beating him with a stuffed club."

"Nevertheless," persisted the Chief of Police, "it was a liberty that must have been very disagreeable, though it may not have hurt. Please do not repeat it."

"But," said the Officer, still smiling, "it was a stuffed Thug."

In attempting to express his gratification the Chief of Police thrust out his right hand with such violence that his skin was ruptured at the armpit and a stream of sawdust poured from the wound. He was a stuffed Chief of Police.

TWO KINGS

THE King of Madagao, being engaged in a dispute with the King of Bornegascar, wrote him as follows:

"Before proceeding further in this matter I demand the recall of your Minister from my capital."

Greatly enraged by this impossible demand, the King of Bornegascar replied:

"I shall not recall my Minister. Moreover, if you do not immediately retract your demand I shall withdraw him!"

This threat so terrified the King of Madagao that in hastening to comply he fell over his own feet, breaking the Third Commandment.

THE CONSCIENTIOUS OFFICIAL

WHILE a Division Superintendent of a railway was attending closely to his business of placing obstructions on the track and tampering with the switches he received word that the President of the road was about to discharge him for incompetency.

"Good Heavens!" he cried; "there are more accidents on my division than on all the rest of the line."

"The President is very particular," said the Man who brought him the news; "he thinks the same loss of life might be effected with less damage to the company's property."

"Does he expect me to shoot passengers through the car windows?" exclaimed the indignant official, spiking a loose tie across the rails. "Does he take me for an assassin?"

THE MORAL SENTIMENT

A PUGILIST met the Moral Sentiment of the Community, who was carrying a hat-box. "What have you in the hat-box my friend?" inquired the Pugilist.

"A new frown," was the answer. "I am bringing it from the frownery —the one over there with the gilded steeple."

"And what are you going to do with the nice new frown?" the Pugilist asked.

"Put down pugilism—if I have to wear it night and day," said the Moral Sentiment of the Community, sternly.

"That's right," said the Pugilist, "that is right, my good friend; if pugilism had been put down yesterday, I wouldn't have this kind of nose to-day. I had a rattling hot fight last evening with—"

"Is that so?" cried the Moral Sentiment of the Community, with sudden animation. "Which licked? Sit down here on the hat-box and tell me all about it!"

HOW LEISURE CAME

A MAN to Whom Time Was Money, and who was bolting his breakfast in order to catch a train, had leaned his newspaper against the sugar-bowl and was reading as he ate. In his haste and abstraction he stuck a pickle-fork into his right eye, and on removing the fork the eye came with it. In buying spectacles the needless outlay for the right lens soon reduced him to poverty, and the Man to Whom Time Was Money had to sustain life by fishing from the end of a wharf.

THE THOUGHTFUL WARDEN

THE Warden of a Penitentiary was one day putting locks on the doors of all the cells when a mechanic said to him:
"Those locks can all be opened from the inside—you are very imprudent."
The Warden did not look up from his work, but said:
"If that is called imprudence I wonder what would be called a thoughtful provision against the vicissitudes of fortune."

TREASURY AND ARMS

A PUBLIC TREASURY, feeling Two Arms lifting out its contents, exclaimed:
"Mr. Shareman, I move for a division."
"You seem to know something about parliamentary forms of speech," said the Two Arms.
"Yes," replied the Public Treasury, "I am familiar with the hauls of legislation."

THE CHRISTIAN SERPENT

A RATTLESNAKE came home to his brood and said: "My children, gather about and receive your father's last blessing, and see how a Christian dies."

"What ails you, Father?" asked the Small Snakes.

"I have been bitten by the editor of a partisan journal," was the reply, accompanied by the ominous death-rattle.

THE POLITICIANS

An Old Politician and a Young Politician were traveling through a beautiful country, by the dusty highway which leads to the City of Prosperous Obscurity. Lured by the flowers and the shade and charmed by the songs of birds which invited to woodland paths and green fields, his imagination fired by glimpses of golden domes and glittering palaces in the distance on either hand, the Young Politician said:

"Let us, I beseech thee, turn aside from this comfortless road, leading, thou knowest whither, but not I. Let us turn our backs upon duty and abandon ourselves to the delights and advantages beckoning from every grove and calling to us from every shining hill. Let us, if so thou wilt, follow this beautiful path, which, as thou seest, hath a guide-board saying, 'Turn in here all ye who seek the Palace of Popular Attention.'"

"It is a beautiful path, my son," said the Old Politician, without either slackening his pace or turning his head, "and it leadeth among pleasant scenes. But the search for the Palace of Popular Attention is beset with one mighty peril."

"What is that?" said the Young Politician.

"The peril of finding it," the Old Politician replied, pushing on.

THE BROOM OF THE TEMPLE

The city of Gakwak being about to lose its character of capital of the province of Ukwuk, the Wampog issued a proclamation convening all the male residents in council in the Temple of Ul to devise means of defence. The first speaker thought the best policy would be to offer a fried jackass to the gods. The second suggested a public procession headed by the Wampog himself, bearing the Holy Poker on a cushion of cloth-of-brass. Another thought that a scarlet mole should be buried alive in the public park and a suitable incantation chanted over the remains. The advice of the fourth was that the columns of the capitol be rubbed with oil of dog by a person having a moustache on the calf of his leg. When all the others had spoken an Aged Man rose and said:

"High and mighty Wampog and fellow-citizens, I have listened attentively to all the plans proposed. All seem wise, and I do not suffer myself to doubt that any one of them would be efficacious. Nevertheless, I cannot help thinking that if we would put an improved breed of polliwogs in our drinking water, drain our roadways, groom the street cows, offer the stranger within our gates a free choice between the poniard and the potion and relinquish our private system of morals, the other measures of public safety would be needless."

The Aged Man was about to speak further, but the meeting informally adjourned in order to sweep the floor of the temple—for the men of Gakwak are the tidiest housewives in all that province. The Aged Man was the broom.

THE DISCONTENTED MALEFACTOR

A JUDGE having sentenced a Malefactor to the penitentiary was proceeding to point out to him the disadvantages of crime and the profit of reformation.

"Your Honor," said the Malefactor, interrupting, "would you be kind enough to alter my punishment to ten years in the penitentiary and nothing else?"

"Why," said the Judge, surprised, "I have given you only three years!"

"Yes, I know," assented the Malefactor—"three years' imprisonment and the preaching. If you please, I should like to commute the preaching."

FATHER AND SON

"MY BOY," said an aged Father to his fiery and disobedient Son, "a hot temper is the soil of remorse. Promise me that when next you are angry you will count one hundred before you move or speak."

No sooner had the Son promised than he received a stinging blow from the paternal walking-stick, and by the time he had counted to seventy-five had the unhappiness to see the old man jump into a waiting cab and whirl away.

A CALL TO QUIT

SEEING that his audiences were becoming smaller every Sunday, a Minister of the Gospel broke off in the midst of a sermon, descended the pulpit stairs and walked on his hands down the central aisle of the church. He then remounted his feet, ascended to the pulpit and resumed his discourse, making no allusion to the incident.

"Now," said he to himself, as he went home, "I shall have, henceforth, a large attendance and no snoring."

But on the following Friday he was waited upon by the Pillars of the Church, who informed him that in order to be in harmony with the New Theology and get full advantage of modern methods of Gospel interpretation they had deemed it advisable to make a change. They had therefore sent a call to Brother Jowjeetum-Fallal, the world-renowned Hindoo human pin-wheel, then holding forth in Hoopitup's circus. They were happy to say that the reverend gentleman had been moved by the Spirit to accept the call, and on the ensuing Sabbath would break the bread of life for the brethren or break his neck in the attempt.

THE CRITICS

WHILE bathing, Antinoüs was seen by Minerva, who was so enamoured of his beauty that, all armed as she happened to be, she descended from Olympus to woo him; but unluckily displaying her shield with the head of Medusa on it, she had the unhappiness to see the beautiful mortal turn to stone from catching a glimpse of it. She straightway ascended to ask Jove to restore him; but before this could be done a Sculptor and a Critic passed that way and espied him.

"This is a very bad Apollo," said the Sculptor: "the chest is too narrow, and one arm is at least a half-inch shorter than the other. The attitude is unnatural, and I may say impossible. Ah! my friend, you should see my statue of Antinoüs."

"In my judgment," said the Critic, "the figure is tolerably good, though rather Etrurian, but the expression of the face is decidedly Tuscan, and therefore false to nature. By the way, have you read my work on 'The Fallaciousness of the Aspectual in Art'?"

THE FOOLISH WOMAN

A MARRIED WOMAN, whose lover was about to reform by running away, procured a pistol and shot him dead.

"Why did you do that, madam?" inquired a Policeman, sauntering by.

"Because," replied the Married Woman, "he was a wicked man, and had purchased a ticket to Chicago."

"My sister," said an adjacent Man of God, solemnly, "you cannot stop the wicked from going to Chicago by killing them."

MAN AND LIGHTNING

A MAN Running for Office was overtaken by Lightning.

"You see," said the Lightning, as it crept past him inch by inch, "I can travel considerably faster than you."

"Yes," the Man Running for Office replied, "but think how much longer I keep going!"

THE LITERARY ASTRONOMER

THE Director of an Observatory, who, with a thirty-six inch refractor, had discovered the moon, hastened to an Editor, with a four-column account of the event.

"How much?" said the Editor, sententiously, without looking up from his essay on the circularity of the political horizon.

"One hundred and sixty dollars," replied the man who had discovered the moon.

"Not half enough," was the Editor's comment.

"Generous man!" cried the Astronomer, glowing with warm and elevated sentiments, "pay me, then, what you will."

"Great and good friend," said the Editor, blandly, looking up from his work, "we are far asunder, it seems. The paying is to be done by you."

The Director of the Observatory gathered up the manuscript and went away, explaining that it needed correction—that he had neglected to dot an m.

THE LASSOED BEAR

A HUNTER who had lassoed a Bear was trying to disengage himself from the rope, but the slip-knot about his wrist would not yield, for the Bear was all the time pulling in the slack with his paws. In the midst of his trouble the Hunter saw a Showman passing by and managed to attract his attention.

"What will you give me," he said, "for my Bear?"

"It will be some five or ten minutes," said the Showman, "before I shall want a bear, and it looks to me as if prices would fall during that time. I think I'll wait and watch the market."

"The price of this animal," the Hunter replied, "is down to bed-rock; you can have him for a cent a pound, spot cash, and I'll throw in the next one that I lasso. But the purchaser must remove the goods from the premises forthwith, to make room for three man-eating tigers, a cat-headed gorilla and an armful of rattlesnakes."

But the Showman passed on in maiden meditation, fancy free, and being joined soon afterward by the Bear, who was absently picking his teeth, it was inferred that they were not unacquainted.

A PROTAGONIST OF SILVER

SOME Financiers were whetting their tongues on their teeth because the Government had "struck down" silver. They were about to "inaugurate" a season of sweatshed, when they were addressed by a Member of their honorable and warlike body:

"Comrades of the thunder and companions of death, I can but regard it as singularly fortunate that we who by conviction and sympathy are designated by nature as the champions of that fairest of her products, the white metal, should also, by a happy chance, be engaged mostly in the business of mining it. Nothing could be more just than that those who from unselfish motives and elevated sentiments are doing battle for the people's rights and interests should themselves be the chief beneficiaries of success. Therefore, O children of the earthquake and the storm, let us stand shoulder to shoulder, heart to heart and pocket to pocket!"

This speech so pleased the other Members of the convention that actuated by a magnanimous impulse they sprang to their feet and left the hall. It was the first time they had ever been known to leave anything having value.

THE WOODEN GUNS

An Artillery Regiment of a State Militia applied to the Governor for wooden guns to practice with.

"Those," they explained, "will be cheaper than real ones."

"It shall not be said that I sacrificed efficiency to economy," said the Governor. "You shall have real guns."

"Thank you, thank you," cried the warriors, effusively. "We will take good care of them, and in the event of war return them to the arsenal."

THE HOLY DEACON

An Itinerant Preacher who had wrought hard in the moral vineyard for several hours whispered to a Holy Deacon of the local church:

"Brother, these people know you, and your active support will bear fruit abundantly. Please pass the plate for me, and you shall have one fourth."

The Holy Deacon did so, and putting the money into his pocket waited till the congregation was dismissed, then said good-night.

"But the money, brother, the money that you collected!" said the Itinerant Preacher.

"Nothing is coming to you," was the reply; "the Adversary has hardened their hearts and one fourth is all they gave."

THE INEFFECTIVE ROOTER

A Drunken Man was lying in the road with a bleeding nose, upon which he had fallen, when a Pig passed that way.

"You wallow fairly well," said the Pig, "but, my fine fellow, you have much to learn about rooting."

A HASTY SETTLEMENT

"Your Honor," said an Attorney, rising, "what is the present status of this case—as far as it has gone?"

"I have given a judgment for the residuary legatee under the will," said the Court, "put the costs upon the contestants, decided all questions relating to fees and other charges; and, in short, the estate in litigation has been settled, with all controversies, disputes, misunderstandings and differences of opinion thereunto appertaining."

"Ah, yes, I see," said the Attorney, thoughtfully, "we are making progress—we are getting on famously."

"Progress?" echoed the Judge—"progress? Why, sir, the matter is concluded!"

"Exactly, exactly; it had to be concluded in order to give relevancy to the motion that I am about to make. Your Honor, I move that the judgment of the Court be set aside and the case reopened."

"Upon what ground, sir?" the Judge asked in surprise.

"Upon the ground," said the Attorney, "that after paying all fees and expenses of litigation and all charges against the estate there will still be something left."

"There may have been an error," said his Honor, thoughtfully—"the Court may have underestimated the value of the estate. The motion is taken under advisement."

THE POET'S DOOM

An Object was walking along the King's highway wrapped in meditation and with little else on, when he suddenly found himself at the gates of a strange city. On applying for admittance, he was arrested as a necessitator of ordinances and taken before the King.

"Who are you," said the King, "and what is your business in life?"

"Snouter the Sneak," replied the Object, with ready invention—"pickpocket."

The King was about to command him to be released when the Prime Minister suggested that the prisoner's fingers be examined. They were found greatly flattened and calloused at the ends.

"Ha!" cried the King; "I told you so!—he is addicted to counting syllables. He is a poet. Turn him over to the Lord High Dissuader from the Head Habit."

"My liege," said the Inventor-in-Ordinary of Ingenious Penalties, "I venture to suggest a keener affliction."

"Name it," the King said.

"Let him retain that head!"

It was so ordered.

LION AND RATTLESNAKE

A MAN having found a Lion in his path undertook to subdue him by the power of the human eye; and near by was a Rattlesnake engaged in fascinating a small bird.

"How are you getting on, brother?" the Man called out to the other reptile, without removing his eyes from those of the Lion.

"Admirably," replied the serpent. "My success is assured; my victim draws nearer and nearer in spite of her efforts."

"And mine," said the Man, "draws nearer and nearer in spite of mine. Are you sure it is all right?"

"If you don't think so," the reptile replied as well as he then could, with his mouth full of bird, "you'd better give it up."

A half-hour later the Lion, thoughtfully picking his teeth with his claws, told the Rattlesnake that he had never in all his varied experience in being subdued, seen a subduer try so earnestly to give it up. "But," he added, with a wide, significant smile, "I looked him into countenance."

LEGISLATOR AND SOAP

A MEMBER of the Kansas Legislature meeting a Cake of Soap was passing it by without recognition, but the Cake of Soap insisted on stopping and shaking hands. Thinking it might possibly be in the enjoyment of the elective franchise, he gave it a cordial and earnest grasp. On letting it go he observed that a part of it adhered to his fingers, and running to a brook in great alarm, proceeded to wash it off. In doing so he necessarily got some on the other hand, and when he had finished washing both were so white that he went to bed and sent for a physician.

THE THISTLES UPON THE GRAVE

A MIND READER made a wager that he would be buried alive and remain so for six months, then be dug up alive. In order to secure the grave against secret disturbance, it was sown with thistles. At the end of three months the Mind Reader lost his bet. He had come up to eat the thistles.

ALARM AND PRIDE

"GOOD morning, my friend," said Alarm to Pride; "how are you this morning?"

"Very tired," answered Pride, seating himself on a stone by the wayside and mopping his steaming brow. "The politicians are wearing me out by pointing to their dirty records with *me,* when they could as well use a stick."

Alarm sighed sympathetically and said:

"It is pretty much the same way here. Instead of using an opera-glass they view the acts of their opponents with *me!*"

As these patient drudges were mingling their tears, they were notified that they must go on duty again, for one of the political parties had nominated a thief and was about to hold a gratification meeting.

THE REFORM SCHOOL BOARD

THE members of the School Board in Doosnoswair being suspected of appointing female teachers for an improper consideration, the people elected a Board composed wholly of women. In a few years the scandal was at an end; there were no female teachers in the Department.

ALDERMAN AND RACCOON

"I SEE quite a number of rings on your tail," said an Alderman to a Raccoon that he met in a zoological garden.

"Yes," replied the Raccoon, "and I hear quite a number of tales on your ring."

The Alderman, being of a sensitive, retiring disposition, shrank from further comparison, and strolling to another part of the garden stole the camel.

CAT AND KING

A Cat was looking at a King, as permitted by the proverb.

"Well," said the monarch, observing her inspection of the royal person, "how do you like me?"

"I can imagine a King," said the Cat, "whom I should like better."

"For example?"

"The King of Mice."

The sovereign was so pleased with the wit of the reply that he gave her permission to scratch his Prime Minister's eyes out.

THE MAN WITH NO ENEMIES

An Inoffensive Person walking in a public place was assaulted by a Stranger with a Club, and severely beaten.

When the Stranger with a Club was brought to trial, the complainant said to the Judge:

"I do not know why I was assaulted; I have not an enemy in the world."

"That," said the defendant, "is why I struck him."

"Let the prisoner be discharged," said the Judge; "a man who has no enemies has no friends. The courts are not for such."

THE FLYING-MACHINE

An Ingenious Man who had built a flying-machine invited a great concourse of people to see it go up. At the appointed moment, everything being ready, he boarded the car and turned on the power. The machine immediately broke through the massive substructure upon which it was builded, and sank out of sight into the earth, the aeronaut springing out barely in time to save himself.

"Well," said he, "I have done enough to demonstrate the correctness of my details. The defects," he added, with a look at the ruined brick-work, "are merely basic and fundamental."

On this assurance the people came forward with subscriptions to build a second machine.

THE ANGEL'S TEAR

An Unworthy Man who had laughed at the woes of a Woman whom he loved, was bewailing his indiscretion in sack-cloth-of-gold and ashes-of-roses, when the Angel of Compassion looked down upon him, saying:

"Poor mortal!—how unblest not to know the wickedness of laughing at another's misfortune!"

So saying, he let fall a great tear, which, encountering in its descent a current of cold air, was congealed into a hail-stone. This struck the Unworthy Man upon the head and set him rubbing that bruised organ vigorously with one hand while vainly attempting to expand an umbrella with the other.

Thereat the Angel of Compassion did most shamelessly and wickedly laugh.

THE CITY OF POLITICAL DISTINCTION

Jamrach the Rich, being anxious to reach the City of Political Distinction before nightfall, arrived at a fork of the road and was undecided which branch to follow; so he consulted a Wise-Looking Person who sat by the wayside.

"Take *that* road," said the Wise-Looking Person, pointing it out; "it is known as the Political Highway."

"Thank you," said Jamrach, and was about to proceed.

"About how much do you thank me?" was the reply. "Do you suppose I am here for my health?"

As Jamrach had not become rich by stupidity he handed something to his guide and hastening on soon came to a toll-gate kept by a Benevolent Gentleman, to whom he gave something and was suffered to pass. A little farther along he came to a bridge across an imaginary stream, where a Civil Engineer (who had built the bridge) demanded something for interest on his investment, and it was forthcoming. It was growing late when Jamrach came to the margin of what appeared to be a lake of black ink, and there the road terminated. Seeing a Ferryman in his boat he paid something for his passage and was about to embark.

"No," said the Ferryman. "Put your neck in this noose, and I will tow you over. It is the only way," he added, seeing that the passenger was about to complain of the accommodations.

In due time he was dragged across, half strangled and dreadfully beslubbered by the feculent waters. "There," said the Ferryman, hauling him ashore and disengaging him, "you are now in the City of Political Distinction. It has fifty millions of inhabitants, and as the color of the Filthy Pool does not wash off, they all look exactly alike."

"Alas!" exclaimed Jamrach, weeping and bewailing the loss of all his possessions, paid out in tips and tolls; "I will go back with you."

"I don't think you will," said the Ferryman, pushing off; "this city is situated on the Island of the Unreturning."

THE PARTY OVER THERE

A MAN in a Hurry, whose watch was at his lawyer's, asked a Grave Person the time of day.

"I heard you ask that Party Over There the same question," said the Grave Person. "What answer did he give you?"

"He said it was about three o'clock," replied the Man in a Hurry; "but he did not look at his watch, and as the sun is nearly down I think it is later."

"The fact that the sun is nearly down," the Grave Person said, "is immaterial, but the fact that he did not consult his timepiece and make answer after due deliberation and consideration is fatal. The answer given," continued the Grave Person, consulting his own timepiece, "is of no effect, invalid, and void."

"What, then," said the Man in a Hurry, eagerly, "is the time of day?"

"The question is remanded to the Party Over There for a new answer," replied the Grave Person, returning his watch to his pocket and moving away with great dignity.

He was a Judge of an Appellate Court.

THE POET OF REFORM

ONE pleasant day in the latter part of eternity, as the Shades of all the great writers were reposing upon beds of asphodel and moly in the Elysian fields, each happy in hearing from the lips of others nothing but copious quotation from his own works (for so Jove had kindly bedeviled their ears) there came in among them with triumphant mien a Shade whom none knew. She (for the new-comer showed such evidences of sex as cropped hair and a manly stride) took a seat in their midst and smiling a superior smile explained:

"After centuries of oppression I have wrested my rights from the grasp of the jealous gods. On earth I was the Poetess of Reform and sang to inattentive ears. Now for an eternity of honor and glory."

But it was not to be so, and soon she was the unhappiest of immortals, vainly desirous to wander again in gloom by the infernal lakes. For Jove had not bedeviled her ears, and she heard from the lips of each blessed Shade an incessant flow of quotation from his own works. Moreover, she was denied the happiness of repeating her poems. She could not recall a line of them, for Jove had decreed that the memory of them abide in Pluto's painful domain as a part of the apparatus.

THE UNCHANGED DIPLOMATIST

THE republic of Madagonia had been long and well represented at the court of the King of Patagascar by an officer called a Dazie, but one day the Madagonian Parliament conferred upon him the superior rank of Dandee. The next day after being apprised of his new dignity he hastened to inform the King of Patagascar.

"Ah, yes, I understand," said the King; "you have been promoted and given increased pay and allowances. There was an appropriation?"

"Yes, your Majesty."

"And you have now two heads, have you not?"

"Oh, no, your Majesty—only one, I assure you."

"Indeed? And how many legs and arms?"

"Two of each, Sire—only two of each."

"And only one body?"

"Just a single body, as you perceive."

Thoughtfully removing his crown and scratching the royal head, the monarch was silent a moment, and then he said:

"I fancy that appropriation has been misapplied. You seem to be about the same kind of damned fool that you were before."

AN INVITATION

A Pious Person who had overcharged his paunch with dead bird by way of attesting his gratitude for escaping the many calamities which Heaven had sent upon others fell asleep at table and dreamed. He thought he lived in a country where turkeys were the ruling class, and every year they held a feast to manifest their sense of Heaven's goodness in sparing their lives, to kill them later. One day, about a week before one of these feasts, he met the Supreme Gobbler, who said:

"You will please get yourself into good condition for the Thanksgiving dinner."

"Yes, your Excellency," replied the Pious Person, delighted, "I shall come hungry, I assure you. It is no small privilege to dine with your Excellency."

The Supreme Gobbler eyed him for a moment in silence; then said:

"As one of the lower domestic animals, you cannot be expected to know much, but you might know something. Since you do not, you will permit me to point out that being asked to dinner is one thing; being asked to dine is another and different thing."

With this significant remark the Supreme Gobbler left him, and thenceforward the Pious Person dreamed of himself as white meat and dark until rudely awakened by terror.

THE ASHES OF MADAME BLAVATSKY

The brightest two Lights of Theosophy being in the same place at once in company with the Ashes of Madame Blavatsky, an Inquiring Soul thought the time propitious to learn something worth while. So he sat at the feet of one awhile, and then he sat awhile at the feet of the other, and at last he applied his ear to the keyhole of the casket containing the Ashes of Madame Blavatsky. When the Inquiring Soul had completed his course of instruction he declared himself the Ahkoond of Swat, fell into the baleful habit of standing on his head and swore that the mother who bore him was a pragmatic paralogism. Wherefore he was held in so high reverence that when the two other gentlemen were hanged for lying the Theosophists elected him to the leadership of their Disastral Body, and after a quiet life and an honorable death by the kick of a jackass he was reincarnated as a Yellow Dog. As such he ate the Ashes of Madame Blavatsky, and Theosophy was no more.

THE OPOSSUM OF THE FUTURE

ONE day an Opossum who had gone to sleep hanging from the highest branch of a tree by the tail, awoke and saw a large Snake wound about the limb, between him and the trunk of the tree.

"If I hold on," he said to himself, "I shall be swallowed; if I let go I shall break my neck."

But suddenly he bethought himself to dissemble.

"My perfected friend," he said, "my parental instinct recognizes in you a noble evidence and illustration of the theory of development. You are the Opossum of the Future, the ultimate Fittest Survivor of our species, the ripe result of progressive prehensility—all tail!"

But the Snake, proud of his ancient eminence in Scriptural history, was strictly orthodox and did not accept the scientific view.

THE LIFE-SAVER

SEVENTY-FIVE Men presented themselves before the President of the Humane Society and demanded the great gold medal for life-saving.

"Why, yes," said the President; "by diligent efforts so many men must have saved a considerable number of lives. How many did you save?"

"Seventy-five, sir," replied their Spokesman.

"Ah, yes, that is one each—very good work—very good work, indeed," the President said. "You shall not only have the Society's great gold medal, but its recommendation for employment at the several life-boat stations along the coast. But how did you save so many lives?"

The Spokesman of the Men replied:

"We are officers of the law, and have just abandoned the pursuit of two murderous outlaws."

THE AUSTRALIAN GRASSHOPPER

A DISTINGUISHED NATURALIST was traveling in Australia, when he saw a Kangaroo in session and flung a stone at it. The Kangaroo immediately adjourned, tracing against the sunset sky a parabolic curve spanning seven provinces, and evanished below the horizon. The Distinguished Naturalist looked interested, but said nothing for an hour; then he said to his native Guide:

"You have pretty wide meadows here, I suppose?"

"No, not very wide," the Guide answered; "about the same as in England and America."

After another long silence the Distinguished Naturalist said:

"The hay which we shall purchase for our horses this evening—I shall expect to find the stalks about fifty feet long. Am I right?"

"Why, no," said the Guide; "a foot or two is about the usual length of our hay. What can you be thinking of?"

The Distinguished Naturalist made no immediate reply, but later, as in the shades of night they journeyed through the desolate vastness of the Great Lone Land, he broke the silence:

"I was thinking," he said, "of the uncommon magnitude of that grasshopper."

THE PAVIOR

AN Author saw a Laborer hammering stones into the pavement of a street, and approaching him said:

"My friend, you seem weary. Ambition is a hard taskmaster."

"I'm working for Mr. Jones, sir," the Laborer replied.

"Well, cheer up," the Author resumed; "fame comes at the most unexpected times. To-day you are poor, obscure and disheartened, but tomorrow the world may be ringing with your name."

"What are you telling me?" the Laborer said. "Can not an honest pavior perform his work in peace, and get his money for it, and his living by it, without others talking rot about ambition and hopes of fame?"

"Can not an honest writer?" said the Author.

THE TRIED ASSASSIN

AN Assassin being put upon trial in a New England court, his Counsel rose and said: "Your Honor, I move for a discharge on the ground of 'once in jeopardy': my client has been already tried for that murder and acquitted."

"In what court?" asked the Judge.

"In the Superior Court of San Francisco," the Counsel replied.

"Let the trial proceed—your motion is denied," said the Judge. "An Assassin is not in jeopardy when tried in California."

TWO POETS

Two Poets were quarreling for the Apple of Discord and the Bone of Contention, for they were very hungry.

"My sons," said Apollo, "I will part the prizes between you. You," he said to the First Poet, "excel in Art—take the Apple. And you," he said to the Second Poet, "in Imagination—take the Bone."

"To Art the best prize!" said the First Poet, triumphantly, and endeavouring to devour his award broke all his teeth. The Apple was a work of Art.

"That shows our master's contempt for mere Art," said the Second Poet, grinning.

Thereupon he attempted to gnaw his Bone, but his teeth passed through it without encountering resistance. It was an imaginary Bone.

THE WITCH'S STEED

A BROOMSTICK that had long served a witch as a steed complained of the nature of its employment, which it thought degrading.

"Very well," said the Witch, "I will give you work in which you will be associated with intellect—you will come in contact with brains. I shall present you to a housewife."

"What!" said the Broomstick, "do you consider the hands of a housewife intellectual?"

"I referred," said the Witch, "to the head of her good man."

THE SAGACIOUS RAT

A Rat that was about to emerge from his hole caught a glimpse of a Cat waiting for him, and descending to the colony at the bottom of the hole invited a Friend to join him in a visit to a neighboring corn-bin. "I would have gone alone," he said, "but could not deny myself the pleasure of such distinguished company."

"Very well," said the Friend, "I will go with you. Lead on."

"Lead?" exclaimed the other. "What! *I* precede so great and illustrious a rat as you? No, indeed—after you, sir, after you."

Pleased with this great show of deference, the Friend went ahead, and, leaving the hole first, was caught by the Cat, who trotted away with him. The other then went out unmolested.

THE BUMBO OF JIAM

The Pahdour of Patagascar and the Gookul of Madagonia were disputing about an island that both claimed. Finally, at the suggestion of the International League of Cannon Founders, which had important branches in both countries, they decided to refer their claims to the Bumbo of Jiam, and abide by his judgment. In settling the preliminaries of the arbitration they had, however, the misfortune to disagree, and appealed to arms. At the end of a long and disastrous war, when both sides were exhausted and bankrupt, the Bumbo of Jiam intervened in the interest of peace.

"My great and good friends," he said to his brother sovereigns, "it will be advantageous to you to learn that some questions are more complex and perilous than others, presenting a greater number of points upon which it is possible to differ. For four generations your royal predecessors disputed about possession of that island without falling out.

Beware, oh, beware the perils of international arbitration!—against which I feel it my duty to protect you henceforth."

So saying, he annexed both countries, and after a long, peaceful and happy reign was poisoned by his Prime Minister.

NOSER AND NOTE

THE Head Rifler of an insolvent bank, learning that it was about to be visited by the official Noser into Things, placed his own personal note for a large amount among its resources, and gaily touching his guitar awaited the inspection. When the Noser came to the note he asked, "What's this?"

"That," said the Assistant Pocketer of Deposits, "is one of our liabilities."

"A liability?" exclaimed the Noser. "Nay, nay, an asset. That is what you mean, doubtless."

"Therein you err," the Pocketer explained; "that note was written in the bank with our own pen, ink and paper, and we have not paid a stationery bill for six months."

"Ah, I see," the Noser said, thoughtfully; "it is a liability. May I ask how you expect to meet it?"

"With fortitude, please God," answered the Assistant Pocketer, his eyes to Heaven raising—"with fortitude and a firm reliance on the laxity of the law."

"Enough, enough," exclaimed the faithful servant of the State, choking with emotion; "here is a certificate of solvency."

"And here is a bottle of ink," the grateful financier said, slipping it into the other's pocket; "it is all that we have."

THE SHADOW OF THE LEADER

A POLITICAL LEADER was walking out one sunny day, when he observed his Shadow leaving him and walking rapidly away.

"Come back here, you scoundrel," he cried.

"If I had been a scoundrel," answered the Shadow, increasing its speed, "I should not have left you."

A CAUSEWAY

A RICH WOMAN having returned from abroad disembarked at the foot of Kneedeep Street, and was about to walk to her hotel through the mud.

"Madam," said a Policeman, "I cannot permit you to do that; you would soil your shoes and stockings."

"Oh, that is of no importance, really," replied the Rich Woman, with a cheerful smile.

"But, madam, it is needless; from the wharf to the hotel, as you observe, extends an unbroken line of prostrate newspaper men who crave the honor of having you walk upon them."

"In that case," she said, seating herself in a doorway and unlocking her satchel, "I shall have to put on my rubber boots."

THE ALL-DOG

A LION seeing a Poodle fell into laughter at the ridiculous spectacle. "Who ever saw so small a beast?" he said.

"It is very true," said the Poodle, with austere dignity, "that I am small; but, sir, I beg you to observe that I am all dog."

TWO POLITICIANS

Two Politicians were exchanging ideas regarding the rewards for public service.

"The reward that I most desire," said the First Politician, "is the gratitude of my fellow citizens."

"That would be very gratifying, no doubt," said the Second Politician, "but, alas! in order to obtain it one has to retire from politics."

For an instant they gazed upon each other with inexpressible tenderness; then the First Politician murmured, "God's will be done! Since we cannot hope for reward let us be content with what we have."

And lifting their right hands for a moment from the public treasury they swore to be content.

THE FARMER'S FRIEND

A GREAT PHILANTHROPIST who had thought of himself in connection with the Presidency and had introduced a bill into Congress requiring the Government to lend every voter all the money that he needed, on his personal security, was explaining to a Sunday-school at a railway station how much he had done for the country, when an angel looked down from Heaven and wept.

"For example," said the Great Philanthropist, watching the teardrops pattering in the dust, "these early rains are of incalculable advantage to the farmer."

PHYSICIANS TWO

A WICKED OLD MAN finding himself ill sent for a Physician, who prescribed for him and went away. Then the Wicked Old Man sent for Another Physician, saying nothing of the first, and an entirely different treatment was ordered. This continued for some weeks, the physicians visiting him on alternate days and treating him for two different disorders, with constantly enlarging doses of medicine and more and more rigorous nursing. But one day they accidentally met at his bedside while he slept and, the truth coming out, a violent quarrel ensued.

"My good friends," said the patient, awakened by the noise of the dispute, and apprehending the cause of it, "pray be more reasonable. If I could for weeks endure you both, can you not for a little while endure each other? I have been well for ten days, but have remained in bed in the hope of gaining by repose the strength that would justify me in taking your medicines. So far I have touched none of them."

THE HONEST CADI

A ROBBER who had plundered a merchant of one thousand pieces of gold was taken before the Cadi, who asked him if he had anything to say why he should not be decapitated.

"Your Honor," said the Robber, "I could do no otherwise than take the money, for Allah made me that way."

"Your defence is ingenious and sound," said the Cadi, "and I must acquit you of criminality. Unfortunately, Allah has also made me so that I must take off your head—unless," he added, thoughtfully, "you offer me a half of the gold; for He made me weak under temptation."

Thereupon the Robber put five hundred pieces of gold into the Cadi's hand.

"Good," said the Cadi. "I shall now remove only one-half your head. To show my trust in your discretion I shall leave intact the half that you talk with."

THE OVERLOOKED FACTOR

A Man that owned a fine Dog, and by a careful selection of its mate had bred a number of animals but a little lower than the angels, fell in love with his washerwoman, married her and reared a family of dolts.

"Alas!" he exclaimed, contemplating the melancholy result, "had I but chosen a mate for myself with half the care that I did for my Dog I should now be a proud and happy father."

"I'm not so sure of that," said the Dog, overhearing the lament. "There's a difference, certainly, between your whelps and mine, but I flatter myself that it is not due altogether to the mothers. You and I are not entirely alike ourselves."

SPORTSMAN AND SQUIRREL

A Sportsman who had wounded a Squirrel, which was making desperate efforts to drag itself away, ran after it with a stick, exclaiming:

"Poor thing! I will put it out of its misery."

At that moment the Squirrel stopped from exhaustion, and looking up at its enemy, said:

"I don't venture to doubt the sincerity of your compassion, though it comes rather late, but you seem to lack the faculty of observation. Do you not perceive by my actions that the dearest wish of my heart is to continue in my misery?"

At this exposure of his hypocrisy the Sportsman was so overcome with shame and remorse that he would not strike the Squirrel, but pointing it out to his dog, walked thoughtfully away.

KANGAROO AND ZEBRA

A Kangaroo hopping awkwardly along with some bulky object concealed in her pouch met a Zebra, and desirous of keeping his attention upon himself, said:

"Your costume looks as if you might have come out of the penitentiary."

"Appearances are deceitful," replied the Zebra, smiling in the consciousness of a more insupportable wit, "or I should have to think that you had come out of the Legislature."

A MATTER OF METHOD

A Philosopher seeing a Fool beating his Donkey, said:

"Abstain, my son, abstain, I implore. Those who resort to violence shall suffer from violence."

"That," said the Fool, diligently belaboring the animal, "is what I'm trying to teach this beast—which has kicked me."

"Doubtless," said the Philosopher to himself, as he walked away, "the wisdom of fools is no deeper nor truer than ours, but they really do seem to have a more impressive way of imparting it."

A MAN OF PRINCIPLE

During a shower of rain the Keeper of a Zoölogical garden observed a Man of Principle crouching beneath the belly of the ostrich, which had drawn itself up to its full height to sleep.

"Why, my dear sir," said the Keeper, "if you fear to get wet you'd better creep into the pouch of yonder female kangaroo—the *Saltatrix mackintosha*—for if that ostrich wakes he will kick you to death in a moment!"

"I can't help that," the Man of Principle replied, with that lofty scorn of practical considerations distinguishing his species. "He may kick me to death if he wish, but until he does he shall give me shelter from the storm. He has swallowed my umbrella."

THE RETURNED CALIFORNIAN

A MAN was hanged by the neck until he was dead. This was in 1893. "Whence do you come?" Saint Peter asked when the Man presented himself at the gate of Heaven.

"From California," replied the applicant.

"Enter, my son, enter; you bring joyous tidings."

When the Man had vanished inside, Saint Peter took his memorandum tablet and made the following entry:

"February 16, 1893. California settled by the Christians."

THE COMPASSIONATE PHYSICIAN

A KIND-HEARTED PHYSICIAN sitting at the bedside of a patient afflicted with an incurable and painful disease heard a noise behind him and turning saw a Cat laughing at the feeble efforts of a wounded Mouse to drag itself out of the room.

"You cruel beast!" he cried. "Why don't you kill it at once, like a lady?"

Rising, he kicked the Cat out of the door and picking up the Mouse compassionately put it out of its misery by pulling off its head. Recalled to the bedside by the moans of his patient, the Kind-Hearted Physician administered a stimulant, a tonic and a nutrient, and went away.

A PROPHET OF EVIL

AN Undertaker Who Was a Member of a Trust saw a Man Leaning on a Spade, and asked him why he was not at work.

"Because," said the Man Leaning on a Spade, "I belong to the Gravediggers' National Extortion Society, and we have decided to limit the production of graves and get more money for the reduced output. We have a corner in graves and purpose working it to the best advantage."

"My friend," said the Undertaker Who Was a Member of the Trust, "this is a most hateful and injurious scheme. If people can not be assured of graves I fear they will no longer die, and the best interests of civilization will wither like a frosted leaf."

And blowing his eyes upon his handkerchief, he walked away lamenting.

TWO OF THE DAMNED

Two Blighted Beings, haggard, lacrymose and detested, met on a blasted heath in the light of a struggling moon.

"I wish you a merry Christmas," said the First Blighted Being, in a voice like that of a singing tomb.

"And I you a happy New Year," responded the Second Blighted Being, with the accent of a penitent accordeon.

They then fell upon each other's neck and wept scalding rills down each other's spine in token of their banishment to the Realm of Ineffable Bosh. For one of these accursed creatures was the First of January, and the other the Twenty-fifth of December.

THE AUSTERE GOVERNOR

A GOVERNOR visiting a State prison was implored by a Convict to pardon him.

"What are you in for?" asked the Governor.

"I held a high office," the Convict humbly replied, "and sold subordinate appointments."

"Then I decline to interfere," said the Governor, with asperity; "a man who abuses his office by making it serve a private end and purvey a personal advantage is unfit to be free. By the way, Mr. Warden," he added to that official, as the Convict slunk away, "in appointing you to this position, I was given to understand that your friends could make the Shikane county delegation to the next State convention solid for— for the present Administration. Was I rightly informed?"

"You were, sir."

"Very well, then, I will bid you good-day. Please be so good as to appoint my nephew Night Chaplain and Reminder of Mothers and Sisters."

THE PENITENT ELECTOR

A PERSON belonging to the Society for Passing Resolutions of Respect for the Memory of Deceased Members having died received the customary attention.

"Good Heavens!" exclaimed a Sovereign Elector, on hearing the resolutions read, "what a loss to the nation! And to think that I once voted against that angel for Inspector of Gate-latches in Public Squares!"

In remorse the Sovereign Elector deprived himself of political influence by learning to read.

RELIGIONS OF ERROR

HEARING a sound of strife, a Christian in the Orient asked his Dragoman the cause of it.

"The Buddhists are cutting Mohammedan throats," the Dragoman replied, with Oriental composure.

"I did not know," remarked the Christian, with scientific interest, "that that would make so much noise."

"The Mohammedans are cutting Buddhist throats," added the Dragoman.

"It is astonishing," mused the Christian, "how violent and how general are religious animosities."

So saying he visibly smugged and went off to telegraph for a brigade of cut-throats to protect Christian interests.

THE TAIL OF THE SPHINX

A DOG of a taciturn disposition said to his Tail:

"Whenever I am angry you rise and bristle; when I am pleased you wag; when I am alarmed you tuck yourself in out of danger. You are too mercurial—you disclose all my emotions. My notion is that tails are given to conceal thought. It is my dearest ambition to be as impassive as the Sphinx."

"My friend, you must recognize the laws and limitations of your being," replied the Tail, with flexions appropriate to the sentiments uttered, "and try to be great some other way. The Sphinx has one hundred and fifty qualifications for impassiveness which you lack."

"What are they?" the Dog asked.

"One hundred and forty-nine tons of sand on its tail."

"And—?"

"A stone tail."

THE CREW OF THE LIFEBOAT

THE Gallant Crew at a life-saving station were about to launch their lifeboat for a spin along the coast when they discovered, a little distance away, a capsized vessel with a dozen men clinging to her keel.

"We are fortunate," said the Gallant Crew, "to have seen that in time. Our fate might have been the same as theirs."

So they hauled the lifeboat back into its house and were spared to the service of their country.

A TREATY OF PEACE

THROUGH massacres of each other's citizens China and the United States had been four times plunged into devastating wars, when, in the year 1994, arose a Philosopher in Madagascar, who laid before the Governments of the two distracted countries the following *modus vivendi:*

"Massacres are to be sternly forbidden as heretofore; but any citizen or subject of either country disobeying the injunction is to detach the scalps of all persons massacred and deposit them with a local officer designated to receive and preserve them and sworn to keep and render a true account thereof. At the conclusion of each massacre in either country, or as soon thereafter as practicable, or at stated regular periods, as may be provided by treaty, there shall be a counting of scalps, without regard to sex or age; the Government having the greatest number is to be taxed on the excess at the rate of $1000 a scalp, and the other Government credited with the amount. Once in every decade there shall be a general settlement, when the balance due shall be paid to the creditor nation in Mexican dollars."

The plan was adopted, the necessary treaty made, with legislation to carry out its provisions; the Madagascarene Philosopher took his seat in the Temple of Immortality and Peace spread her white wings over the two nations, to the unspeakable defiling of her plumage.

THE NIGHTSIDE OF CHARACTER

A GIFTED and Honorable Editor, who by practice of his profession had acquired wealth and distinction, applied to an Old Friend for the hand of his daughter in marriage.

"With all my heart, and God bless you!" said the Old Friend, grasping him by both hands. "It is a greater honor than I had dared to hope for."

"I knew what your answer would be," replied the Gifted and Honorable Editor. "And yet," he added, with a sly smile, "I feel that I ought to give you as much knowledge of my character as I possess. In this scrap-book is such testimony relating to my shady side as I have within the past ten years been able to cut from the columns of my competitors in the business of elevating humanity to a higher plane of mind and morals—my 'loathsome contemporaries.'"

Laying the book on a table, he withdrew in high spirits to make arrangements for the wedding. Three days later he received the scrap-book from a messenger, with a note warning him never again to darken his Old Friend's door.

"See!" the Gifted and Honorable Editor exclaimed, pointing to that injunction—"I am a painter and grainer!"

And he was led away to the Asylum for the Indiscreet.

THE FAITHFUL CASHIER

THE Cashier of a bank having defaulted was asked by the Directors what he had done with the money taken.

"I am greatly surprised by such a question," said the Cashier; "it sounds as if you suspected me of selfishness. Gentlemen, I applied that money to the purpose for which I took it; I paid it as an initiation fee and one year's dues in advance to the Treasurer of the Cashiers' Mutual Defence Association."

"What is the object of that organization?" the Directors inquired.

"When any one of its members is under suspicion," replied the Cashier, "the Association undertakes to clear his character by submitting evidence that he was never a prominent member of any church, nor foremost in Sunday-school work."

Recognizing the value to the bank of a spotless reputation for its officers, the President drew his check for the amount of the shortage and the Cashier was restored to favor.

THE CIRCULAR CLEW

A Detective searching for the murderer of a dead man was accosted by a Clew.

"Follow me," said the Clew, "and there's no knowing what you may discover."

So the Detective followed the Clew a whole year through a thousand sinuosities and at last found himself in the office of the Morgue.

"There!" said the Clew, pointing to the open register.

The Detective eagerly scanned the page and found an official statement that the deceased was dead. Thereupon he hastened to Police Headquarters to report progress. The Clew, meanwhile, sauntered among the busy haunts of men, arm in arm with an Ingenious Theory.

THE DEVOTED WIDOW

A Widow weeping on her husband's grave was approached by an Engaging Gentleman who, in a respectful manner, assured her that he had long entertained for her the most tender feelings.

"Wretch!" cried the Widow. "Leave me this instant! Is this a time to talk to me of love?"

"I assure you, madam, that I had not intended to disclose my affection," the Engaging Gentleman humbly explained, "but the power of your beauty has overcome my discretion."

"You should see me when I have not been weeping," said the Widow.

THE HARDY PATRIOTS

A DISPENSER-ELECT of Patronage gave notice through the newspapers that applicants for places would be given none until a certain date.

"You are exposing yourself to a grave danger," said a Lawyer.

"How so?" the Dispenser-Elect inquired.

"It will be nearly two months," the Lawyer answered, "before the day that you mention. Few patriots can live so long without eating, and some of the applicants will be compelled to go to work in the meantime. If that kills them, you will be liable to prosecution for murder."

"You underrate their powers of endurance," the official replied.

"What!" said the Lawyer, "you think they can endure work?"

"No," said the other—"hunger."

THE HUMBLE PEASANT

AN Office Seeker whom the President had ordered out of Washington was watering the homeward highway with his tears.

"Ah," he said, "how disastrous is ambition! how unsatisfying its rewards! how terrible its disappointments! Behold yonder peasant tilling his field in peace and contentment! He rises with the lark, passes the day in wholesome toil and lies down at night to pleasant dreams. In the mad struggle for place and power he has no part; the roar of the strife reaches his ear like the distant murmur of the ocean. Happy, thrice happy man! I will approach him and bask in the sunshine of his humble felicity. Peasant, hail!"

Leaning upon his rake, the Peasant returned the salutation with a nod, but said nothing.

"My friend," said the Office Seeker, "you see before you the wreck of an ambitious man—ruined by the pursuit of place and power. This morning when I set out from the national capital—"

"Stranger," the Peasant interrupted, "if you're going back there soon maybe you wouldn't mind using your influence to make me Postmaster at Smith's Corners."

The traveler passed on.

THE VARIOUS DELEGATION

The King of Wideout having been offered the sovereignty of Away-off, sent for the Three Persons who had made the offer, and said to them:

"I am extremely obliged to you, but before accepting so great a responsibility I must ascertain the sentiments of the people of Awayoff."

"Sire," said the Spokesman of the Three Persons, "they stand before you."

"Indeed!" said the King; "are you, then, the people of Awayoff?"

"Yes, your Majesty."

"There are not many of you," the King said, attentively regarding them with the royal eye, "and you are not so very large; I hardly think you are a quorum. Moreover, I never heard of you until you came here; whereas Awayoff is noted for the quality of its pork and contains hogs of distinction. I shall send a Commissioner to ascertain the sentiments of the hogs."

The Three Persons, bowing profoundly, backed out of the presence; but soon afterward they desired another audience, and on being readmitted said, through their Spokesman:

"May it please your Majesty, we are the hogs."

A HARMLESS VISITOR

At a meeting of the Golden League of Mystery a Woman was discovered, writing in a note-book. A member directed the attention of the Superb High Chairman to her, and she was asked to explain her presence there, and what she was doing.

"I came in for my own pleasure and instruction," she said, "and was so struck by the wisdom of the speakers that I could not help making a few notes."

"Madam," said the Superb High Chairman, "we have no objection to visitors if they will pledge themselves not to publish anything they hear. Are you—on your honor as a lady, now, madam—are you not connected with some newspaper or other publication?"

"Good gracious, no!" cried the Woman, earnestly. "Why, sir, I am an officer of the Women's Press Association!"

She was permitted to remain and presented with resolutions of apology.

AN INFLATED AMBITION

THE President of a great Corporation went into a dry-goods shop and saw a placard which read:

"If You Don't See What You Want Ask For It."

Approaching the shopkeeper, who had been narrowly observing him as he read the placard, he was about to speak, when the shopkeeper called to a salesman:

"John, show this gentleman the earth."

THE NO CASE

A STATESMAN who had been indicted by an unfeeling Grand Jury was arrested by a Sheriff and thrown into jail. As this was abhorrent to his fine spiritual nature, he sent for the District Attorney and asked that the case against him be dismissed.

"Upon what grounds?" asked the District Attorney.

"Lack of evidence to convict," replied the accused.

"Do you happen to have the lack with you?" the official asked. "I should like to see it."

"With pleasure," said the other; "here it is."

So saying he handed the other a check, which the District Attorney carefully examined, and then pronounced it the most complete absence of both proof and presumption that he had ever seen. He said it would acquit the poorest man in the world.

JUDGE AND RASH ACT

A JUDGE who had for years looked in vain for an opportunity for infamous distinction, but whom no litigant thought worth bribing, sat one day upon the Bench, lamenting his hard lot and threatening to put an end to his life if business did not improve. Suddenly he found himself confronted by a dreadful figure clad in a shroud, whose pallor and stony eyes smote him with a horrible apprehension.

"Who are you," he faltered, "and why do you come here?"

"I am the Rash Act," was the sepulchral reply; "you may commit me."

"No," the Judge said, thoughtfully, "no, that would be quite irregular. I do not sit to-day as a committing magistrate."

THE PREROGATIVE OF MIGHT

A SLANDER traveling rapidly through the land upon his joyous mission was accosted by a Retraction and commanded to halt and be killed.

"Your career of mischief is at an end," said the Retraction, drawing his club, rolling up his sleeves and spitting on his hands.

"Why should you slay me?" protested the Slander. "Whatever my intentions were, I have been innocuous, for you have dogged my strides and counteracted my influence."

"Dogged your grandmother!" said the Retraction, with contemptuous vulgarity of speech. "In the order of nature it is appointed that we two shall never travel the same road."

"How then," the Slander asked, triumphantly, "have you overtaken me?"

"I have not," replied the Retraction; "we have accidentally met. I came round the world the other way."

But when he tried to execute his fell purpose he found that in the order of nature it was appointed that he himself perish miserably in the encounter.

AT LARGE—ONE TEMPER

A TURBULENT PERSON was brought before a Judge to be tried for an assault with intent to commit murder, and it was proved that he had been variously obstreperous without apparent provocation, had affected the peripheries of several luckless fellow-citizens with the trunk of a small tree and afterward cleaned out the town. While trying to palliate these misdeeds, the Defendant's Attorney turned suddenly to the Judge, saying:

"Did your Honor ever lose your temper?"

"I fine you twenty-five dollars for contempt of court!" roared the Judge, in wrath. "How dare you mention the loss of my temper in connection with this case?"

After a moment's silence the Attorney said, meekly:

"I thought my client might perhaps have found it."

THE DIVIDED DELEGATION

A DELEGATION at Washington went to a New President, and said:

"Your Excellency, we are unable to agree upon a Favorite Son to represent us in your Cabinet."

"Then," said the New President, "I shall have to lock you up until you do agree."

So the Delegation was cast into the deepest dungeon beneath the moat, where it maintained a divided mind for many weeks, but finally reconciled its differences and asked to be taken before the New President.

"My children," said he, "nothing is so beautiful as harmony. My Cabinet selections were all made before our former interview, but you have supplied a noble instance of patriotism in subordinating your personal preferences to the general good. Go now to your beautiful homes and be happy."

REJECTED SERVICES

A HEAVY OPERATOR overtaken by a Reverse of Fortune was bewailing his sudden fall from affluence to indigence.

"Do not weep," said the Reverse of Fortune. "You need not suffer alone. Name any one of the men who have opposed your schemes, and I will overtake *him*."

"It is hardly worth while," said the victim, earnestly. "Not a soul of them has a cent. You have already visited them."

DECEASED AND HEIRS

A MAN died leaving a large estate and many sorrowful relations who claimed it. After some years, when all but one had had judgment given against them, that one was awarded the estate, which he asked his Attorney to have appraised.

"There is nothing to appraise," said the Attorney, pocketing his last fee.

"Then," said the Successful Claimant, "what good has all this litigation done me?"

"You have been a good client to me," the Attorney replied, gathering up his books and papers, "but I must say you betray a surprising ignorance of the purpose of litigation."

POLITICIANS AND PLUNDER

SEVERAL Political Entities were dividing the spoils.

"I will take the management of the prisons," said a Decent Respect for Public Opinion, "and make a radical change."

"And I," said the Blotted Escutcheon, "will retain my present general connection with affairs, while my friend here, the Soiled Ermine, will remain in the Judiciary."

The Political Pot said it would not boil any more unless replenished from the Filthy Pool.

The Cohesive Power of Public Plunder quietly remarked that the two bosses would, he supposed, naturally be his share.

"No," said the Lowest Depth of Degradation, "they have already fallen to me."

MAN AND WART

A PERSON with a Wart on His Nose met a Person Similarly Afflicted, and said:

"Let me propose your name for membership in the Imperial Order of Abnormal Proboscidians, of which I am the High Noble Toby and Surreptitious Treasurer. Two months ago I was the only member. One month ago there were two. To-day we number four Emperors of the Abnormal Proboscis in good standing—doubles every four weeks, see? That's geometrical progression—you know how that piles up. In a year and a half every man in the country will have a wart on his nose. Powerful Order! Initiation, five dollars."

"My friend," said the Person Similarly Afflicted, "here are five dollars. Keep my name off your books."

"Thank you kindly," the Man with a Wart on His Nose replied, pocketing the money; "it is just the same to us as if you joined. Good-bye."

He went away, but in a little while he was back.

"I quite forgot to mention the monthly dues," he said.

HIS FLY-SPECK MAJESTY

A Distinguished Advocate of Republican Institutions was seen pickling his shins in the ocean.

"Why don't you come out on dry land?" said the Spectator. "What are you in there for?"

"Sir," replied the Distinguished Advocate of Republican Institutions, "a ship is expected, bearing His Majesty the King of the Fly-Speck Islands, and I wish to be the first to grasp the crowned hand."

"But," said the Spectator, "you said in your famous speech before the Society for the Prevention of the Protrusion of Nail Heads from Plank Sidewalks that Kings are blood-smeared oppressors and hell-bound loafers."

"My dear sir," said the Distinguished Advocate of Republican Institutions, without removing his eyes from the horizon, "you wander away into the strangest irrelevancies! I spoke of Kings in general."

THE PUGILIST'S DIET

The Trainer of a Pugilist consulted a Physician regarding the champion's diet.

"Beef-steaks are too tender," said the Physician; "have his meat cut from the neck of a bull."

"I thought the steaks more digestible," the Trainer explained.

"That is very true," said the Physician; "but they do not sufficiently exercise the chin."

OLD MAN AND PUPIL

A Beautiful Old Man meeting a Sunday-school Pupil laid his hand tenderly upon the lad's head, saying: "Listen, my son, to the words of the wise and heed the advice of the righteous."

"All right," said the Sunday-school Pupil; "go ahead."

"Oh, I haven't anything to tell you, really," said the Beautiful Old Man. "I am only observing one of the customs of age. I am a pirate."

And when he had taken his hand from the lad's head the latter observed that his hair was full of clotted blood. Then the Beautiful Old Man went his way, instructing other youth.

FOGY AND SHEIK

A Fogy who lived in a cave near a great caravan route returned to his home one day and saw, near by, a great concourse of men and animals, and in their midst a tower, at the foot of which something with wheels smoked and panted like an exhausted horse. He sought the Sheik of the Outfit.

"What sin art thou committing now, O son of a Christian dog?" said the Fogy, with a truly Oriental politeness.

"Boring for water, you black-and-tan galoot!" replied the Sheik of the Outfit, with that ready repartee which distinguishes the Unbeliever.

"Knowest thou not, thou whelp of darkness and father of disordered livers," cried the Fogy, "that water will cause grass to spring up here, and trees and possibly even flowers? Knowest thou not that thou art, in truth, producing an oasis?"

"And don't you know," said the Sheik of the Outfit, "that caravans will then stop here for rest and refreshment, giving you a chance to steal the camels, the horses and the goods?"

"May the wild hog defile my grave, but thou speakest wisdom!" the Fogy replied, with the dignity of his race, extending his hand. "Sheik."

They shook.

REVENGE

An Insurance Agent was trying to induce a Hard Man to Deal With to take out a policy on his house. After listening to him for an hour, while he painted in vivid colors the extreme danger of fire consuming the house, the Hard Man to Deal With said:

"Do you really think it likely that my house will burn down inside the time that my policy will run?"

"Certainly," replied the Insurance Agent; "have I not been trying all this time to convince you that I do?"

"Then," said the Hard Man to Deal With, "why are you so eager to have your Company bet me money that it will not?"

The Agent was silent and thoughtful for a moment; then he drew the other apart into an unfrequented place and whispered in his ear:

"My friend, I will impart to you a dark secret. Years ago the Company betrayed my sweetheart by promise of marriage. Under an assumed name I have wormed myself into its service for revenge; and as there is a heaven above us, I will have its heart's blood!"

AN OPTIMIST

Two Frogs in the belly of a snake were considering their altered circumstances.

"This is pretty hard luck," said one.

"Don't jump to conclusions," the other said; "we are out of the wet and provided with board and lodging."

"With lodging, certainly," said the First Frog; "but I don't see the board."

"You are a croaker," the other explained. "We are the board."

TWO FOOTPADS

Two Footpads sat at their grog in a roadside resort, comparing the evening's adventures.

"I stood up the Chief of Police," said the First Footpad, "and got away with what he had."

"And I," said the Second Footpad, "stood up the United States District Attorney, and got away with—"

"Good Lord!" interrupted the other in astonishment and admiration, "you got away with what that fellow had?"

"No," the unfortunate narrator explained, "with a small part of what *I* had."

EQUIPPED FOR SERVICE

DURING the Civil War a Patriot was passing through the State of Maryland with a pass from the President to join Grant's army and see the fighting. Stopping a day at Annapolis, he visited the shop of a well-known optician and ordered seven powerful telescopes, one for every day in the week. In recognition of this munificent patronage of the State's languishing industries, the Governor commissioned him a colonel.

THE BASKING CYCLONE

A NEGRO in a boat, gathering driftwood, saw a sleeping Alligator and thinking it was a log, fell to estimating the number of shingles it would make for his new cabin. Having satisfied his mind on that point, he stuck his boat-hook into the beast's back to harvest his good fortune. Thereupon the saurian emerged from his dream and, greatly to the surprise of the man-and-brother, took to the water, making a terrible commotion!

"I never befo' seen sech a cyclone as dat," the Negro exclaimed as soon as he had recovered his breath. "It done carry away de ruf of my house!"

A VALUABLE SUGGESTION

A BIG NATION having a quarrel with a Little Nation, resolved to terrify its antagonist by a grand naval demonstration in the latter's principal port. So the Big Nation assembled all its ships of war from all over the world, and was about to send them three hundred and fifty thousand miles to the place of rendezvous, when the President of the Big Nation received the following note from the President of the Little Nation:

"My great and good friend, I hear that you are going to show us your navy in order to impress us with a sense of your power. How needless the expense! To prove to you that we already know all about it I inclose herewith a list and description of all the ships and guns that you have."

The great and good friend was so struck by the hard sense of the letter that he kept his navy at home, saving one thousand million dollars. This economy enabled him to buy a satisfactory decision when the cause of the quarrel was submitted to arbitration.

OPTIMIST AND CYNIC

A MAN who had experienced the favors of fortune and was an Optimist, met a man who had experienced an optimist and was a Cynic. So the Cynic turned out of the road to let the Optimist roll by in his gold carriage.

"My son," said the Optimist, stopping the gold carriage, "you look as if you had not a friend in the world."

"I don'- know if I have or not," replied the Cynic, "for you have the world."

THE TAKEN HAND

A SUCCESSFUL MAN of Business having occasion to write to a Thief expressed a wish to see him and shake hands.

"No," replied the Thief, "there are some things that I will not take —among them your hand."

"You must use a little strategy," said a Philosopher to whom the Successful Man of Business had reported the Thief's haughty reply. "Leave your hand out some night and he will take it."

So one night the Successful Man of Business left his hand out of a neighbor's pocket and the Thief took it with avidity.

POET AND EDITOR

"MY dear sir," said the Editor to the Poet who had called to see about his poem, "I regret to say that owing to an unfortunate altercation in this office the greater part of your manuscript is illegible; a bottle of ink was upset upon it, blotting out all but the first line—that is to say—

" 'The autumn leaves were falling, falling.'

"Unluckily, not having read the poem, I was unable to supply the incidents that followed; otherwise we could have given them in our own words. If the news is not stale, and has not already appeared in the other papers, perhaps you will kindly relate what occurred, while I make notes of it. 'The autumn leaves were falling, falling.' Go on."

"What!" said the Poet, "do you expect me to reproduce the entire poem from memory?"

"Only the substance of it—just the leading facts. We will add whatever is necessary in the way of amplification and embellishment. It will detain you but a moment. 'The autumn leaves were falling, falling—' Now, then."

There was a sound of a slow getting up and going away. The chronicler of passing events sat through it, motionless, with suspended pen; and when the movement was complete Poesy was represented in that place by nothing but a warm spot on a chair.

PARTY MANAGER AND GENTLEMAN

A PARTY MANAGER said to a Gentleman whom he saw minding his own business:

"How much will you pay for a nomination to office?"

"Nothing," the Gentleman replied.

"But you will contribute something to the campaign fund to assist in your election, will you not?" asked the Party Manager, winking.

"Oh, no," said the Gentleman, gravely. "If the people wish me to work for them they must hire me without solicitation. I am very comfortable without office."

"But," urged the Party Manager, "an election is a thing to be desired. It is a high honor to be a servant of the people."

"If servitude is a high honor," the Gentleman said, "it would be indecent for me to seek it; and if obtained by my own exertion it would be no honor."

"Well," persisted the Party Manager, "you will at least, I hope, indorse the party platform."

The Gentleman replied: "It is improbable that its authors have accurately expressed my views without consulting me; and if I indorsed their work without approving it I should be a liar."

"You are a detestable hypocrite and an idiot!" shouted the Party Manager.

"Even your good opinion of my fitness," replied the Gentleman, "shall not persuade me."

AT THE POLE

AFTER a great expenditure of life and treasure a Daring Explorer had succeeded in reaching the North Pole, when he was approached by a Native Galeut who lived there.

"Good morning," said the Native Galeut. "I'm very glad to see you, but why did you come here?"

"Glory," said the Daring Explorer, curtly.

"Yes, yes, I know," the other persisted; "but of what benefit to man is your discovery? To what truths does it give access which were inaccessible before?—facts, I mean, having a scientific value?"

"I'll be Tom scatted if I know," the great man replied frankly; "you will have to ask the Scientist of the Expedition."

But the Scientist of the Expedition explained that he had been so engrossed with the care of his instruments and the study of his tables that he had found no time to think of it.

AN UNSPEAKABLE IMBECILE

A JUDGE said to a Convicted Assassin:

"Prisoner at the bar, have you anything to say why the death-sentence should not be passed upon you?"

"Will what I say make any difference?" asked the Convicted Assassin.

"I do not see how it can," the Judge answered, reflectively. "No, it will not."

"Then," said the doomed one, "I should like to remark that you are the most unspeakable old imbecile in seven States and the District of Columbia."

MINE-OWNER AND JACKASS

WHILE the Owner of a Silver Mine was on his way to attend a convention of his species he was accosted by a Jackass, who said:

"By an unjust discrimination against quadrupeds I am made ineligible to a seat in your convention; so I am compelled to seek representation through you."

"It will give me great pleasure, sir," said the Owner of a Silver Mine, "to serve one so closely allied to me in—in—well, you know," he added, with a significant gesture of his two hands upward from the sides of his head. "What do you want?"

"Oh, nothing—nothing at all for myself individually," replied the Donkey; "but his country's welfare should be a patriot's supreme care. If Americans are to retain the sacred liberties for which their fathers strove Congress must declare our independence of European dictation by maintaining the price of mules."

A RADICAL PARALLEL

SOME White Christians engaged in driving Chinese Heathens out of an American town found a newspaper published in Peking in the Chinese tongue and compelled one of their victims to translate an editorial. It turned out to be an appeal to the people of the province of Pang Ki to drive the foreign devils out of the country and burn their dwellings and churches. At this evidence of Mongolian barbarity the White Christians were so greatly incensed that they carried out their original design.

DOG AND DOCTOR

A DOG that had seen a Doctor attending the burial of a wealthy patient, said: "When do you expect to dig it up?"

"Why should I dig it up?" the Doctor asked.

"When I bury a bone," said the Dog, "it is with an intention to uncover it later and pick it."

"The bones that I bury," said the Doctor, "are those that I can no longer pick."

LEGISLATOR AND CITIZEN

A FORMER Legislator asked a Most Respectable Citizen for a letter to the Governor, recommending him for appointment as Commissioner of Shrimps and Crabs.

"Sir," said the Most Respectable Citizen, austerely, "were you not once in the State Senate?"

"Not so bad as that, sir, I assure you," was the reply. "I was a member of the Slower House. I was expelled for selling my influence."

"And you dare to ask for mine!" shouted the Most Respectable Citizen. "You have the impudence? A man who will accept bribes will probably offer them. Do you mean to—"

"I should not think of making a corrupt proposal to you, sir; but if I were Commissioner of Shrimps and Crabs I might have some influence with the waterfront population, and be able to help you make your fight for Coroner."

"In that case I do not feel justified in denying you the letter."

CITIZEN AND SNAKES

A PUBLIC-SPIRITED CITIZEN who had failed miserably in trying to secure a National political convention for his city suffered acutely from dejection. While in that frame of mind he leaned thoughtlessly against a druggist's show-window, wherein were one hundred and fifty kinds of assorted snakes. The glass breaking, the reptiles all escaped into the street.

"When you can't do what you wish," said the Public-spirited Citizen, "it is worth while to do what you can."

THE RAINMAKER

AN Officer of the Government, with a great outfit of mule-wagons loaded with balloons, kites, dynamite bombs, and electrical apparatus, halted in the midst of a desert where there had been no rain for ten years and set up a camp. After several months of preparation and an expenditure of a million dollars all was in readiness, and a series of tremendous explosions occurred on the earth and in the sky. This was followed by a great downpour of rain, which washed the unfortunate Officer of the Government and the outfit off the face of creation and affected the agricultural heart with joy too deep for utterance. A Newspaper Reporter who had just arrived escaped by climbing a hill near by, and there he found the Sole Survivor of the expedition—a mule-driver—down on his knees behind a mesquite bush, praying with extreme fervor.

"Oh, you can't stop it that way," said the Reporter.

"My fellow-traveler to the bar of God," replied the Sole Survivor, looking up over his shoulder, "your understanding is in darkness. I am not stopping this great blessing; under Providence, I am bringing it."

"That is a pretty good joke," said the Reporter, laughing as well as he could in the strangling rain—"a mule driver's prayer answered!"

"Child of levity and scoffing," replied the other; "you err again, misled by these humble habiliments. I am the Rev. Ezekiel Thrifft, a minister of the gospel, now in the service of the great manufacturing firm of Skinn & Sheer. They make balloons, kites, dynamite bombs and electrical apparatus."

FORTUNE AND FABULIST

A WRITER of Fables was passing through a lonely forest, when he met a Fortune. Greatly alarmed, he tried to climb a tree, but the Fortune pulled him down and bestowed itself upon him with cruel persistence.

"Why did you try to run away?" said the Fortune, when his struggles had ceased and his screams were stilled. "Why do you glare at me so inhospitably?"

"I don't know what you are," replied the Writer of Fables, deeply disturbed.

"I am wealth; I am respectability," the Fortune explained; "I am elegant houses, a yacht and a clean shirt every day. I am leisure, I am travel, wine, a shiny hat and an unshiny coat. I am enough to eat."

"All right," said the Writer of Fables, in a whisper; "but for goodness' sake speak lower!"

"Why so?" the Fortune asked, in surprise.

"So as not to wake me," replied the Writer of Fables, a holy calm brooding upon his beautiful face.

A SMILING IDOL

An Idol said to a Missionary, "My friend, why do you seek to bring me into contempt? If it had not been for me what would you have been? Remember thy creator that thy days be long in the land."

"I confess," replied the Missionary, fingering a number of ten-cent pieces which a Sunday-school in his own country had forwarded to him, "that I am a product of you, but I protest that you cannot quote Scripture with accuracy and point. Therefore will I continue to go up against you with the sword of the Spirit."

Shortly afterwards the Idol's worshipers held a great religious ceremony at the base of his pedestal, and as a part of the rites the Missionary was roasted whole. As the tongue was removed for the high priest's table, "Ah," said the Idol to himself, "that is the sword of the Spirit—the only sword that is less dangerous when unsheathed."

And he smiled so pleasantly at his own wit that the provinces of M'gwana and Scowow were affected with a blight.

SIX AND ONE

The Committee on Gerrymander worked late into the night drawing intricate lines on a map of the State, and being weary sought repose in a game of poker. At the close of the game the six Republican members were bankrupt and the single Democrat had all the money. On the next day, when the Committee was called to order for business, one of the luckless six mounted his legs, and said:

"Mr. Chairman, before we bend to our noble task of purifying politics in the interest of good government I wish to say a word of the untoward events of last evening. If my memory serves me the disasters which overtook the Majority of this honorable body always befell when it was the Minority's deal. It is my solemn conviction, Mr. Chairman, and to its affirmation I pledge my life, my sacred fortune and my honor, that that wicked and unscrupulous Minority redistricted the cards!"

A TRANSPOSITION

TRAVELING through the sage-brush country a Jackass met a Rabbit, who exclaimed in great astonishment:

"Good heavens! how did you grow so big? You are doubtless the largest rabbit living."

"No," said the Jackass, "you are the smallest donkey."

After a good deal of fruitless argument the question was referred for decision to a passing Coyote, who was a bit of a demagogue and desirous to stand well with both.

"Gentlemen," said he, "you are both right, as was to have been expected of persons so gifted with appliances for receiving instruction from the wise. You, sir,"—turning to the superior animal—"are, as he has accurately observed, a rabbit. And you"—to the other—"are correctly described as a jackass. In transposing your names man has acted with incredible folly."

They were so pleased with the decision that they declared the Coyote their candidate for the Grizzly Bearship; but whether he ever obtained the office history does not relate.

A FORFEITED RIGHT

THE Chief of the Weather Bureau having predicted a fair day, a Thrifty Person hastened to lay in a large stock of umbrellas, which he exposed for sale on the sidewalk; but the weather remained clear and nobody would buy. Thereupon the Thrifty Person brought an action against the Chief of the Weather Bureau for the cost of the umbrellas.

"Your Honor," said the Defendant's Attorney, when the case was called, "I move that this astonishing action be dismissed. Not only is my client in no way responsible for the loss, but he distinctly forecast the fair weather that caused it."

"That is just it, your Honor," replied the Counsel for the Plaintiff; "by making a correct forecast the defendant fooled my client in the only way that he could do so. He has lied so much and so notoriously that he has no right to tell the truth."

Judgment for the plaintiff.

UNCALCULATING ZEAL

A MAN-EATING tiger was ravaging the Kingdom of Damnasia, and the King, greatly concerned for the lives and limbs of his subjects, promised his daughter Zodroulra to any man who would kill the animal. After some days Camaraladdin appeared before the King and demanded the reward.

"But where is the tiger?" the King asked.

"May jackasses sing above my uncle's grave," replied Camaraladdin, "if I dared go within a league of him!"

"Wretch!" cried the King, unsheathing his consoler-under-disappointment; "how dare you claim my daughter when you have done nothing to earn her?"

"Thou art wiser, O King, than Solyman the Great, and thy servant is as dust in the tomb of thy dog, yet thou errest. I did not, it is true, kill the tiger, but behold! I have brought thee the scalp of a man who had accumulated five million pieces of gold and was after more."

The King drew his consoler-under-disappointment, and flicking off Camaraladdin's head said:

"Learn, caitiff, the inexpediency of uncalculating zeal. If the millionaire had been let alone he would have devoured the tiger."

THE BONELESS KING

SOME Apes who had deposed their king fell at once into dissension and anarchy. In this strait they sent a Deputation to a neighboring tribe to consult the Oldest and Wisest Ape in All the World.

"My children," said the Oldest and Wisest Ape in All the World, when he had heard the Deputation, "you did right in ridding yourselves of tyranny, but your tribe is not sufficiently advanced to dispense with the forms of monarchy. Entice the tyrant back with fair promises, kill him and enthrone. The skeleton of even the most lawless despot makes a good constitutional sovereign."

At this the Deputation were greatly abashed. "It is impossible," they said, moving away; "our king has no skeleton; he was a stuffed king."

THE HONEST CITIZEN

A POLITICAL PREFERMENT, labeled with its price, was canvassing the State to find a purchaser. One day it offered itself to a Truly Good Man who after examining the label and finding that the price was twice as great as he was willing to pay spurned the Political Preferment from his door. Then the People said: "Behold, this is an honest citizen!" And the Truly Good Man humbly confessed that it was true.

A CREAKING TAIL

AN American Statesman who had twisted the tail of the British Lion until his arms ached was at last rewarded by a sharp, rasping sound.

"I knew your fortitude would give out after a while," said the American Statesman, delighted; "your agony attests my political power."

"Agony I know not!" said the British Lion, yawning; "the swivel in my tail needs a few drops of oil, that is all."

PHILOSOPHERS THREE

A BEAR, a Fox and an Opossum were attacked by an inundation.

"Death loves a coward," said the Bear, and went forward to fight the flood.

"What a fool!" said the Fox. "I know a trick worth two of that." And he slipped into a hollow stump.

"There are malevolent forces," said the Opossum, "which the wise will neither confront nor avoid. The thing is to know the nature of your antagonist."

So saying the Opossum lay down and pretended to be dead.

A NEEDFUL WAR

THE people of Kamzembla had an antipathy to the people of Novakatka and set upon some sailors of a Novakatkan vessel, killing two and wounding twelve. The King of Kamzembla having refused either to apologize or pay, the King of Novakatka made war upon him, saying that it was necessary to show that Novakatkans must not be slaughtered. In the battles that ensued the people of Kamzembla slaughtered two thousand Novakatkans and wounded twelve thousand. But the Kamzemblans were unsuccessful, which so chagrined them that never thereafter in all their land was a Novakatkan secure in property or life.

THE FUGITIVE OFFICE

A TRAVELER arriving at the capital of a nation saw a vast plain outside the wall, filled with struggling and shouting men. While he looked upon the alarming spectacle an Office broke away from the throng and took shelter in a tomb near to where he stood, the crowd being too intent upon hammering one another to observe that the cause of their contention had departed.

"Poor bruised and bleeding creature," said the compassionate Traveler, "what was your offense?"

"I 'sought the man,'" said the Office.

AT HEAVEN'S GATE

HAVING risen from the tomb, a Woman presented herself at the gate of Heaven, and knocked with a trembling hand.

"Madam," said Saint Peter, rising and approaching the wicket, "whence do you come?"

"From San Francisco," replied the Woman, with embarrassment, as great beads of perspiration spangled her spiritual brow.

"Never mind, my good girl!" the Saint said, compassionately. "Eternity is a long time; you can live that down."

"But that, if you please, is not all." The Woman was growing more and more confused. "I poisoned my husband. I chopped up my babies. I—"

"Ah," said the Saint, with a sudden austerity, "your confession suggests a grave possibility. Were you a member of the Women's Press Association?"

The lady drew herself up and replied with warmth:

"I was not."

The gates of pearl and jasper swung back upon their golden hinges, making the most ravishing music, and the Saint, stepping aside, bowed low, saying:

"Enter, then, into thine eternal rest."

But the Woman hesitated.

"The poisoning—the chopping—the—the—" she stammered.

"Of no consequence, I assure you. We are not going to be hard on a lady who did not belong to the Women's Press Association. Take a harp."

"But I applied for membership—I was blackballed."

"Take two harps."

WASTED SWEETS

A CANDIDATE canvassing his district met a Nurse wheeling a Baby in a carriage and, stooping, imprinted a kiss upon the Baby's clammy muzzle. Rising, he saw a Man, who laughed.

"Why do you laugh?" asked the Candidate.

"Because," replied the Man, "the Baby belongs to an Orphan Asylum."

"But the Nurse," said the Candidate—"the Nurse will surely relate the touching incident wherever she goes, and perhaps write to her former master."

"The Nurse," said the Man who had laughed, "is an illiterate mute."

THE CATTED ANARCHIST

AN Anarchist Orator who had been struck in the face with a Dead Cat by some Respecter of Law to him unknown, had the Dead Cat arrested and taken before a Magistrate.

"Why do you appeal to the law?" said the Magistrate—"you who go in for abolition of law."

"That," replied the Anarchist, who was not without a certain hardness of head, "that is none of your business; I am not bound to be consistent. You sit here to do justice between me and this Dead Cat."

"Very well," said the Magistrate, putting on the black cap and a solemn look; "as the accused makes no defence, and is undoubtedly guilty, I sentence her to be eaten by the public executioner; and as that position happens to be vacant, I appoint you to it, without bonds."

One of the most delighted spectators at the execution was the unknown Respecter of Law who had flung the condemned.

THE HONORABLE MEMBER

A MEMBER of a Legislature who had pledged himself to his Constituents not to steal brought him at the end of the session a large part of the dome of the Capitol. Thereupon the Constituents held an indignation meeting and passed a resolution of tar and feathers.

"You are most unjust," said the Member of the Legislature. "It is true I promised you that I would not steal; but had I ever promised you that I would not lie?"

The Constituents said he was an honorable man and elected him to the United States Congress, unpledged and unfledged.

THE EXPATRIATED BOSS

A Boss who had gone to Canada was taunted by a Citizen of Montreal with having fled to avoid prosecution.

"You do me a grave injustice," said the Boss, parting with a pair of tears. "I came to Canada solely because of its political attractions; its Government is said to be the most corrupt in the world."

"Pray forgive me," said the Citizen of Montreal.

They fell upon each other's neck, and at the conclusion of that touching rite the Boss had two watches.

AN INADEQUATE FEE

AN Ox unable to extricate himself from the mire into which he sank was advised to make use of a Political Pull. When the Political Pull had arrived the Ox said: "My good friend, please make fast to me and let nature take her course."

So the Political Pull made fast to the Ox's head and nature took her course: the Ox was drawn, first, from the mire and next from his skin. Then the Political Pull looked back upon the good fat carcass of beef that he was dragging to his lair and said, with a discontented spirit:

"That is hardly my customary fee; I'll take home this first instalment, then return for the skin."

A STATESMAN

A STATESMAN who attended a meeting of a Chamber of Commerce rose to speak, but was objected to on the ground that he had nothing to do with commerce.

"Mr. Chairman," said an Aged Member, rising, "I conceive that the objection is not well taken; the gentleman's connection with commerce is close and intimate. He is a commodity."

TWO DOGS

THE Dog as created had a rigid tail, but after some centuries of a cheerless existence, unappreciated by Man, who made him work for his living, he implored the Creator to endow him with a wag. This being done he was able to dissemble his resentment with a sign of affection, and the earth was his and the fulness thereof. Observing this, the Politician (an animal created later) petitioned that a wag might be given him too. As he was incaudate it was conferred upon his chin, which he now wags with great profit and gratification except when he is at his meals.

JUDGE AND PLAINTIFF

A MAN of Experience in Business was awaiting the judgment of the Court in an action for damages that he had brought against a railway company. The door opened and the Judge of the Court entered.

"Well," said he, "I am going to decide your case to-day. If I should decide in your favor I wonder how you would express your satisfaction."

"Sir," said the Man of Experience in Business, "I should risk your anger by offering you one-half the sum awarded."

"Did I say I was going to decide that case?" said the Judge, abruptly, as if awakening from a dream. "Dear me, how absent-minded I am! I mean I have already decided it, and judgment has been entered for the full amount that you sued for."

"Did I say I would give you one-half?" said the Man of Experience in Business, coldly. "Dear me, how near I came to being a rascal! I mean, that I am greatly obliged to you."

RETURN OF THE REPRESENTATIVE

HEARING that the Legislature had adjourned, the People of an Assembly District held a mass-meeting to devise a suitable punishment for their Dishonorable Representative. By one speaker it was proposed that he be disembowelled, by another that he be made to run the gauntlet. Some favored hanging, some thought that it would do him good to appear in a suit of tar and feathers. An Old Man famous for his wisdom and his habit of drooling on his shirt-front suggested that they first catch their hare. So the Chairman appointed a committee to watch for the victim at midnight and take him as he should attempt to sneak into town across-lots from the tamarack swamp. At this point in the proceedings they were interrupted by the sound of a brass band. Their Dishonorable Representative was driving up from the railway station in a coach-and-four, with music and a banner. A few moments later he entered the hall, went upon the platform and said it was the proudest moment of his life. (Cheers.)

THE MIRROR

A SILKEN-EARED Spaniel who traced his descent from King Charles the Second chanced to look into a mirror that was leaning against the wainscoting of a room on the ground floor of his mistress' house. Seeing his reflection, he supposed it to be another dog, outside, and said:

"I can chew up any such milksoppy pup as that, and I will."

So he ran out-of-doors and around to the side of the house where he fancied the enemy was. It so happened that at that moment a Bulldog sat there sunning his teeth. The Spaniel stopped short in dire consternation and after regarding the Bulldog a moment from a safe distance said:

"I don't know whether you cultivate the arts of peace or your flag is flung to the battle and the breeze and your voice is for war. If you are a civilian the windows of this house flatter you worse than a newspaper, but if you're a soldier they do you a grave injustice."

This speech being unintelligible to the Bulldog he only civilly smiled, which so terrified the Spaniel that he dropped dead in his tracks.

SAINT AND SINNER

"My friend," said a distinguished officer of the Salvation Army to a Most Wicked Sinner, "I was once a drunkard, a thief, an assassin. The Divine Grace has made me what I am."

The Most Wicked Sinner looked at him from head to foot. "Henceforth," he said, "the Divine Grace, I fancy, will let well enough alone."

A WEARY ECHO

A Convention of female writers, which for two days had been stuffing Woman's couch with goose-quills and hailing the down of a new era, adjourned with unabated enthusiasm, shouting, *"Place aux dames!"* And Echo wearily replied, "O, damn."

THREE RECRUITS

A Farmer, an Artisan and a Laborer went to the King of their country and complained that they were compelled to support a large standing army of consumers, who did nothing for their keep.

"Very well," said the King, "my subjects' wishes are the highest law."

So he disbanded his army and the consumers became producers also.

The sale of their products so brought down prices that farming was ruined and their skilled and unskilled labor drove artisans and laborers into almshouses and highways. In a few years the national distress was so great that the Farmer, the Artisan and the Laborer petitioned the King to restore the standing army.

"What!" said the King; "you wish to support those idle consumers again?"

"No, your Majesty," they replied—"we wish to enlist."

THE ANCIENT ORDER

HARDLY had that ancient order, the Sultans of Exceeding Splendor, been completely founded by the Grand Flashing Inaccessible, when a question arose as to what should be the title of address among the members. Some wanted it to be simply "my lord," others held out for "your dukeness," and still others preferred "my sovereign liege." Finally the gorgeous jewel of the order gleaming upon the breast of every member suggested "your badgesty," which was adopted and the order became popularly known as the Kings of Catarrh.

A FATAL DISORDER

A DYING MAN who had been shot was requested by officers of the law to make a statement and be quick about it.

"You were assaulted without provocation, of course," said the District Attorney preparing to set down the answer.

"No," replied the Dying Man, "I was the aggressor."

"Yes, I understand," said the District Attorney; "you committed the aggression—you were compelled to, as it were. You did it in self-defence."

"I don't think he would have hurt me if I had let him alone," said the other. "No, I fancy he was a man of peace and would not have hurt a fly. I brought such a pressure to bear on him that he naturally had to yield—he couldn't hold out. If he had refused to shoot me I don't see how I could decently have continued his acquaintance."

"Good Heavens!" exclaimed the District Attorney, throwing down his notebook and pencil; "this is all quite irregular. I can't make use of such an ante-mortem statement as that."

"I never before knew a man to tell the truth," said the Chief of Police, "when dying of violence."

"Violence nothing!" the Police Surgeon said, pulling out and inspecting the man's tongue—"it is the truth that is killing him."

A TALISMAN

HAVING been summoned to serve as a juror, a Prominent Citizen sent a physician's certificate stating that he was afflicted with softening of the brain.

"The gentleman is excused," said the Judge, handing back the certificate to the person who had brought it—"he has a brain."

AN ANTIDOTE

A YOUNG OSTRICH came to its Mother, groaning with pain and with its wings tightly crossed upon its stomach."

"What have you been eating?" the Mother asked, with solicitude.

"Nothing but a keg of nails," was the reply.

"What!" exclaimed the mother; "a whole keg of nails, at your age! Why, you will kill yourself that way. Go quickly, my child, and swallow a claw-hammer."

CONGRESS AND PEOPLE

SUCCESSIVE Congresses have greatly impoverished the People, they were discouraged and wept copiously.

"Why do you weep?" inquired an Angel who had perched upon a tree near by.

"They have taken all we have," replied the People—"excepting," they added, noting the suggestive visitant—"excepting our hope in Heaven. Thank God they cannot deprive us of that!"

But at last came the Congress of 1889!

SHIP AND MAN

SEEING a ship sailing by upon the sea of politics, toward the Presidency, an Ambitious Person started in hot pursuit along the strand; but the people's eyes being fixed upon the ship no one observed the pursuer. This greatly annoyed him and, recollecting that he was not aquatic, he stopped and shouted across the waves' tumultuous roar:

"Take my name off the passenger list."

Back to him over the waters, hollow and heartless, like laughter in a tomb, rang the voice of the Skipper:

" 'Tain't on!"

And there, in the focus of a million pairs of convergent eyes, the Ambitious Person sat him down between the sun and moon and murmured sadly to his own soul:

"Marooned, by thunder!"

THE JUSTICE AND HIS ACCUSER

AN eminent Justice of the Supreme Court of Gowk was accused of having obtained his appointment by fraud.

"You wander," he said to the Accuser; "it is of little importance how I obtained my power; it is only important how I have used it."

"I confess," said the Accuser, "that in comparison with the rascally way in which you have conducted yourself on the Bench the rascally way in which you got there does seem rather a trifle."

AN AEROPHOBE

A CELEBRATED DIVINE having affirmed the fallibility of the Bible, was asked why, then, he preached the religion founded on it.

"If it is fallible," he replied, "there is the greater reason that I explain it, lest it mislead."

"Then am I to infer," said his Questioner, "that *you* are not fallible?"

"You are to infer that I am not pneumophagous."

THE THRIFT OF STRENGTH

A WEAK MAN going down-hill met a Strong Man going up, and said: "I take this direction because it requires less exertion, not from choice. I pray you, sir, assist me to regain the summit."

"Gladly," said the Strong Man, his face illuminated with the glory of his thought. "I have always considered my strength a sacred gift in trust for my fellow-men. I will take you up with me. Go behind me and push."

THE TYRANT FROG

A SNAKE swallowing a frog head-first was approached by a Naturalist with a stick.

"Ah, my deliverer," said the Snake as well as he could, "you have arrived just in time; this reptile, you see, is pitching into me without provocation."

"Sir," replied the Naturalist, "I need a snakeskin for my collection, but if you had not explained I should not have molested you, for I thought you were at dinner."

HIGHWAYMAN AND TRAVELER

A HIGHWAYMAN confronted a Traveler, and covering him with a firearm, shouted: "Your money or your life!"

"My good friend," said the Traveler, "according to the terms of your demand my money will save my life, my life my money; you imply that you will take one or the other, but not both. If that is what you mean please be good enough to take my life."

"That is not what I mean," said the Highwayman; "you cannot save your money by giving up your life."

"Then take it anyhow," the Traveler said. "If it will not save my money it is good for nothing."

The Highwayman was so pleased with the Traveler's philosophy and wit that he took him into partnership and this splendid combination of talent started a newspaper.

THE ELIGIBLE SON-IN-LAW

A TRULY CLEVER PERSON who conducted a savings bank and lent money to his sisters and his cousins and his aunts was approached by a Tatterdemalion who applied for a loan of one hundred thousand dollars.

"What security have you to offer?" asked the Truly Clever Person.

"The best in the world," the applicant replied, confidentially; "I am about to become your son-in-law."

"That would indeed be gilt-edged," said the Banker, gravely; "but what claim have you to the hand of my daughter?"

"One that cannot be lightly denied," said the Tatterdemalion. "I am about to become worth one hundred thousand dollars."

Unable to detect a weak point in this scheme of mutual advantage, the Financier gave the Promoter in Disguise an order for the money and wrote a note to his wife directing her to count out the girl.

POLICEMAN AND CITIZEN

A POLICEMAN finding a man who had fallen in a fit said, "This man is drunk," and began beating him on the head with his club. A passing Citizen said:

"Why do you murder a man that is already harmless?"

Thereupon the Policeman left the man in a fit and attacked the Citizen, who after receiving several severe contusions ran away.

"Alas," said the Policeman, "why did I not attack the sober one before exhausting myself upon the other?"

Thenceforward he pursued that plan, and by zeal and diligence rose to be Chief, and sobriety is unknown in the region subject to his sway.

MAN AND BIRD

A MAN with a Shotgun said to a Bird:

"It is all nonsense, you know, about shooting being a cruel sport. I put my skill against your cunning—that is all there is of it. It is a fair game."

"True," said the Bird, "but I don't wish to play."

"Why not?" inquired the Man with a Shotgun.

"The game," the Bird replied, "is fair as you say; the chances are about even; but consider the stake. I am in it for you, but what is there in it for me?"

Not being prepared with an answer to the question, the Man with a Shotgun sagaciously removed the propounder.

WRITER AND TRAMPS

An Ambitious Writer distinguished for the condition of his linen was traveling the high road to fame, when he met a Tramp.

"What is the matter with your shirt?" inquired the Tramp.

"It bears the marks of that superb unconcern which is the characteristic of genius," replied the Ambitious Writer, contemptuously passing him by.

Resting by the wayside a little later, the Tramp carved upon the smooth bark of a birch-tree the words, "John Gump, Champion Genius."

STATESMAN AND HORSE

A Statesman who had saved his country was returning from Washington on foot, when he met a Race Horse going at full speed, and stopped him.

"Turn about and travel the other way," said the Statesman, "and I will keep you company as far as my home. The advantages of traveling together are obvious."

"I cannot do that," said the Race Horse; "I am following my master to Washington. I did not go fast enough to suit him, and he has gone on ahead."

"Who is your master?" inquired the Statesman.

"He is a Statesman who saved his country," answered the Race Horse.

"There appears to be some mistake," the other said. "Why did he wish to travel so fast?"

"So as to be there in time to get the country that he saved."

"I guess he got it," said the other, and limped along, sighing.

THE GOOD GOVERNMENT

"WHAT a happy land you are!" said a Republican Form of Government to a Sovereign State. "Be good enough to lie still while I walk upon you, singing the praises of universal suffrage and descanting upon the blessings of civil and religious liberty. In the meantime you can relieve your feelings by cursing the one-man power and the effete monarchies of Europe."

"My public servants have been fools and rogues from the date of your accession to power," replied the State; "my legislative bodies, both State and municipal, are bands of thieves; my taxes are insupportable; my courts are corrupt; my cities are a disgrace to civilization; my corporations have their hands at the throat of every private interest—all my affairs are in disorder and criminal confusion."

"That is all very true," said the Republican Form of Government, putting on its hobnail shoes; "but consider how I thrill you every Fourth of July."

THREE OF A KIND

A LAWYER was retained for the defence of a Burglar whom the police had taken after a desperate struggle with someone not in custody. In consultation with his client the Lawyer asked, "Have you accomplices?"

"Yes, sir," replied the Burglar. "I have two, but neither has been taken. I hired one to defend me against capture and you to defend me against conviction."

This answer deeply impressed the Lawyer, and having ascertained that the Burglar had accumulated no money in his profession he threw up the case.

THE LIFESAVER

AN Ancient Maiden, standing on the edge of a wharf near a Modern Swain, was overheard rehearsing the words:

"Noble preserver! The life that you have saved is yours!"

Having repeated them several times with various intonations, she sprang into the water, where she was suffered to drown.

"I am a noble preserver," said the Modern Swain, thoughtfully moving away; "the life that I have saved is indeed mine."

FROM THE MINUTES

An Orator afflicted with atrophy of the organ of common-sense rose in his place in the halls of legislation and pointed with pride to his Unblotted Escutcheon. Seeing what it supposed to be the finger of scorn pointed at it, the Unblotted Escutcheon turned black with rage. Seeing the Unblotted Escutcheon turning black with what he supposed to be the record of his own misdeeds showing through the whitewash, the orator fell dead of mortification. Seeing the Orator fall dead of what they supposed to be atrophy of the organ of common-sense, his colleagues resolved that whenever they should adjourn because they were tired it should be out of respect to the memory of him who had so frequently made them so.

THE FABULIST

An Illustrious Satirist was visiting a traveling menagerie with a view to collecting literary materials. As he was passing near the Elephant that animal said:

"How sad that so justly famous a censor should mar his work by ridicule of persons with pendulous noses—who are the salt of the earth!"

The Kangaroo said:

"I do so enjoy that great man's censure of the ridiculous—particularly his attacks on the proboscidæ; but, alas! he has no reverence for the marsupials, and laughs at our way of carrying our young in a pouch."

The Camel said:

"If he would only respect the Sacred Hump, he would be faultless. As it is, I can not permit his work to be read in the presence of my family."

The Ostrich, seeing his approach, thrust her head into the straw, saying:

"If I do not conceal myself, he may be reminded to write something disagreeable about my lack of a crest, or my appetite for scrap-iron; and although he is inexpressibly brilliant when he devotes himself to ridicule of folly and greed, his dullness is matchless when he transcends the limits of legitimate comment."

"That," said the Buzzard to his mate, "is the distinguished author of that glorious fable, 'The Ostrich and the Keg of Raw Nails.' I regret to add, that he wrote also, 'The Buzzard's Feast,' in which a carrion diet is contumeliously disparaged. A carrion diet is the foundation of sound health. If nothing but corpses were eaten, death would be unknown."

Seeing an attendant approaching, the Illustrious Satirist passed out of the tent and mingled with the crowd. It was afterward discovered that he had crept in under the canvas without paying.

A REVIVALIST REVIVED

A Revivalist who had fallen dead in the pulpit from too violent religious exercise was astonished to wake up in Hades. He promptly sent for the Adversary of Souls and demanded his freedom, explaining that he was entirely orthodox, and had always led a pious and holy life.

"That is all very true," said the Adversary, "but you taught by example that a verb should not agree with its subject in person and number, whereas the Good Book says that contention is worse than a dinner of herbs. You also tried to release the objective case from its thraldom to the preposition, and it is written that servants should obey their masters. You stay right here."

THE DEBATERS

A Hurled-back Allegation which after a brief rest had again started forth upon its mission of mischief met an Inkstand in mid-air.

"How did the Honorable Member whom you represent know that I was coming again?" inquired the Hurled-back Allegation.

"He did not," the Inkstand replied; "he isn't at all forehanded at repartee."

"Why, then, do you come, things being even when he had hurled me back?"

"He wanted to be a little ahead."

TWO OF THE PIOUS

A CHRISTIAN and a Heathen in His Blindness were disputing, when the Christian, with that charming consideration which serves to distinguish the truly pious from wolves that perish, exclaimed:

"If I could have my way I'd blow up all your gods with dynamite."

"And if I could have mine," retorted the Heathen in His Blindness, bitterly malevolent but oleaginously suave, "I'd fan all yours out of the universe."

THE DESPERATE OBJECT

A DISHONEST GAIN was driving in its luxurious carriage through its private park, when it saw something which frantically and repeatedly ran against a stone wall, endeavoring to butt out its brains.

"Hold, hold! thou desperate Object," cried the Dishonest Gain; "these beautiful private grounds are no place for such work as thine."

"True," said the Object, pausing; "I have other and better grounds for it."

"Then thou art a happy man," said the Dishonest Gain, "and thy bleeding head is but mere dissembling. Who art thou, great actor?"

"I am known," said the Object, dashing itself again at the wall, "as the Consciousness of Duty Well Performed."

A DEFECTIVE PETITION

AN Associate Justice of the Supreme Court was sitting by a river when a Traveler approached and said:

"I wish to cross. Will it be lawful to use this boat?"

"It will," was the reply; "it is my boat."

The Traveler thanked him, and pushing the boat into the water embarked and rowed away. But the boat sank and he was drowned.

"Heartless man!" said an Indignant Spectator. "Why did you not tell him that your boat had a hole in it?"

"The matter of the boat's condition," said the great jurist, "was not brought before me."

THE MOURNING BROTHERS

Observing that he was about to die, an Old Man called his two Sons to his bedside and expounded the situation.

"My children," said he, "you have not shown me many marks of respect during my life, but you will attest your sorrow for my death. To him who the longer wears a weed upon his hat in memory of me shall go my entire fortune. I have made a will to that effect."

So when the Old Man was dead each of the youths put a weed upon his hat and wore it until he was himself old, when, seeing that neither would give in, they agreed that the younger should leave off his weed and the elder give him half the estate. But when the elder applied for the property he found that there had been an Executor!

Thus were hypocrisy and obstinacy fitly punished.

A NEEDLESS LABOR

After waiting many a weary day to revenge himself upon a Lion for some unconsidered manifestation of contempt, a Skunk finally saw him coming and posting himself in the path ahead uttered the inaudible discord of his race. Observing that the Lion gave no attention to the matter, the Skunk, keeping carefully out of reach, said:

"Sir, I beg leave to point out that I have set on foot an implacable odor."

"My dear fellow," the Lion replied, "you have taken a needless trouble; I already knew that you are not a rose."

A FLOURISHING INDUSTRY

"Are the industries of this country in a flourishing condition?" asked a Traveler from a Foreign Land of the first Man he met in America.

"Splendid!" said the Man. "I have more orders than I can fill."

"What is your business?" the Traveler from a Foreign Land inquired.

The Man replied, "I make boxing-gloves for the tongues of pugilists."

PATRIOT AND BANKER

A PATRIOT who had taken office poor and retired rich was introduced at a bank where he desired to open an account.

"With pleasure," said the Honest Banker; "we shall be glad to do business with you; but first you must make yourself an honest man by restoring what you stole from the Government."

"Good heavens!" cried the Patriot; "if I do that, I shall have nothing to deposit with you."

"I don't see that," the Honest Banker replied. "We are not the whole American people."

"Ah, I understand," said the Patriot, musing. "At what sum do you estimate this bank's proportion of the country's loss by me?"

"About a dollar," answered the Honest Banker.

And with a proud consciousness of serving his country wisely and well he charged that sum to the account.

THE APPROPRIATE MEMORIAL

A HIGH PUBLIC FUNCTIONARY having died, the citizens of his town held a meeting to consider how to honor his memory, and Another High Public Functionary rose and addressed the meeting.

"Mr. Chairman and Gintlemen," said the Other, "it sames to me, and I'm hopin' yez wull approve the suggistion, that an appropriet way to honor the mimory of the deceased would be to erect an emolument sootably inscribed wid his vartues."

The soul of the great man looked down from Heaven and wept.

THE DISINTERESTED ARBITER

Two Dogs who had been fighting for a bone, without advantage to either, referred their dispute to a Sheep. The Sheep patiently heard their statements, then flung the bone into a pond.

"Why did you do that?" said the Dogs.

"Because," replied the Sheep, "I am a vegetarian."

THE REFORMED ANARCHIST

A FAMOUS Anarchist wrecked at sea was cast ashore upon the island of Gowqueechy, inhabited by the ancient and powerful tribe of Tumtums. He was found and taken before the Jamgrogrum, who asked him his political faith.

"We ask all strangers that," the Jamgrogrum explained, "in the hope that some day we shall hear of political principles that are superior to ours."

"I am an Anarchist," answered the stranger; "I hold that all government is wicked, all laws are oppressive. I teach that all Jamgrogra should be assassinated."

The monarch called his Prime Minister to his side and giving him some whispered instructions retired.

The next day, when the Prime Minister had presented himself at the palace and had eaten a handful of clay, as court etiquette required, he was asked by the Jamgrogrum for news of the Anarchist.

"May your Majesty's tomb stand forever," said the Prime Minister. "I had him taken to the baths and carefully washed all over."

"Well?"

"When asked, according to your Majesty's instructions, if he were still an Anarchist, he replied that no treatment, however harsh and cruel, could alter his convictions."

"Indeed," exclaimed the Jamgrogrum, with the dejected air of one deprived of a cherished illusion, "then my theory of the unity of dirt and anarchism is overthrown."

"No, your Majesty," said the Prime Minister; "he died ten minutes after the bath."

TWO SONS

A MAN had Two Sons. The elder was virtuous and dutiful, the younger wicked and crafty. When the father was about to die, he called them before him and said: "I have only two things of value—my herd of camels and my blessing. How shall I allot them?"

"Give to me," said the Younger Son, "thy blessing, for it may reform me. The camels I should be sure to sell and squander the money."

The Elder Son, disguising his joy, said that he would try to be content with the camels and a pious mind.

It was so arranged and the Man died. Then the wicked Younger Son went before the Cadi and said: "Behold, my brother has defrauded me of my lawful heritage. He is so bad that our father, as is well known, denied him his blessing; is it likely that he gave him the camels?"

So the Elder Son was compelled to give up the herd and was soundly bastinadoed for his rapacity.

THE FORTUNATE EXPLORER

An Emissary from the President of the United States to the Emperor of Abyssinia was taking leave of that sovereign, who, to attest his regret according to the custom of his country, let fall a flood of tears.

"My fame is assured," said the Emissary; "I have discovered the source of the Nile."

THE DUTIFUL SON

A Millionaire who had gone to an almshouse to visit his father met a Neighbor there, who was greatly surprised.

"What!" said the Neighbor, "you do sometimes visit your father?"

"If our situations were reversed," said the Millionaire, "I am sure he would visit me. The old man has always been rather proud of me. Besides," he added softly, "I had to have his signature; I am insuring his life."

WIDOW AND SOLDIER

A Widow whose husband had been hanged in chains was keeping vigil by the corpse the first night and tearfully beseeching the Sentinel who guarded it to let her steal it.

"Madam," he said, "I can no longer resist your entreaties; your beauty overcomes my sense of duty. I will deliver the body to you and take its place in the cage, where a stroke of my dagger will baffle justice and give me the happiness of dying for so lovely a lady."

"No," said the lady, "I cannot consent to the sacrifice of so noble a life.

If indeed you look upon me with favor, assist me and my servants to remove the sacred object to my chateau, where you shall remain in concealment until we can escape from the country."

"Nay," said the Sentinel, "I should surely be discovered and torn from your arms. In three days you can claim the body of your beloved husband; then you can confer upon an honorable soldier such happiness and distinction as you may think his devotion merits."

"Three days!" the lady exclaimed. "That is long for waiting and short for flight. If unincumbered we may reach the frontier. Already the day begins to break—let us leave the body and set out."

A NIGGARDLY OFFER

Two Soldiers lay dead upon the field of honor.

"What would you give to be alive again?" one asked the other.

"To the enemy, victory," was the reply, "to my country, a long life of disinterested service as a civilian. What would you give?"

"The plaudits of my countrymen."

"You are a pretty tight-fisted bargainer," said the other.

DIPLOMACY

"IF you do not submit my claim to arbitration," wrote the President of Omohu to the President of Modugy, "I shall take immediate steps to collect it in my own way!"

"Sir," replied the President of Modugy, "you may go to the devil with your threat of war."

"My great and good friend," wrote the other, "you mistake the character of my communication. It is an antepenultimatum."

TWO SCEPTICS

SOME heathens whose Idol was greatly weatherworn threw it into a river, and erecting a new one, engaged in public worship at its base.

"What is this all about?" inquired the New Idol.

"Father of Joy and Gore," said the High Priest, "be patient and I will instruct you in the doctrines and rites of our holy religion."

A year later, after a course of study in theology, the Idol asked to be thrown into the river, declaring himself an atheist.

"Do not let that trouble you," said the High Priest—"so am I."

A FAULTY PERFORMANCE

A PET Opossum belonging to a Great Critic stole his favorite kitten and was about to kill and eat it when she saw him approaching, and fearing detection she concealed it in her pouch.

"Well, my pretty one," said the Great Critic, with condescension, "what new charms and graces have you to-day?"

Before she could reply the kitten set up a diligent and persistent mewing. When at last the music had ceased the Opossum said:

"I've been dabbling a little in mimicry and ventriloquism; I thought it would please you, sir."

"The desire to please is ever pleasing," the Great Critic answered, not without a touch of professional dignity, "but you have much to learn about the mewing of kittens."

AFTERMATH

"WHAT is that great convulsion of nature?" Neptune asked, turning one ear upward toward the surface of the sea.

"That, sir," replied a Triton, "is a furious engagement by the heroes of the Senegambian Navy."

"So soon again?" said the sea god in surprise. "And whom, pray, are they fighting this time?"

"One another," the Triton explained. "They have fallen out over their recent exploit in sinking the Timbuctonese fleet."

Neptune rose from his couch of coral and paced the ocean's floor with the nervous, irregular strides of one in anger. "See here!" he thundered, "we can't have this kind of thing! When I saw those squadrons fighting I felt that trouble would come of it. A sea fight is pretty to look at, and the music of guns lulls like the evensong of a mermaid in the gloaming, but always the entertainment is prelude to a savage and insupportable uproar among the victors. The next time you see sailors fighting at sea please prevent a disagreeable result by sinking both fleets."

A HALF LOAF

HAVING found the Enemy's fleet in a harbor, the Scourge of the Seas sank a collier in the narrow entrance; and then from his cavernous helmet his merriment rang out over the waters like laughter from a tomb.

"Why this unseemly glee?" the Enemy signaled. "That hulk prevents my coming out."

"I know that, alas!" the Scourge wigwagged back; "but it prevents my going in. That is better than no bread."

BY THE RIVER MARGE

SEEING a Politician taking a bath an Observer, curious as to the singular habits of the lower animals, exclaimed:

"What! is nothing left for you to take more valuable than that? Why do you do this thing?"

"I have been in the hands of my friends," replied the Politician.

"Then I should suggest skinning," the Observer said.

"My friend, you are late: somebody suggested it to *them*. I am cleaning the finger marks off my bones."

THE MAIN THING

A POET proffering his work to an Editor said:

"This is a small poem, but quality is the main thing. I venture to think you'll find it true poetry."

Having read it the Editor put it into a drawer and handing the Poet a ten-cent piece said:

"This is a smallish coin, but I am so bold as to hope that you will be pleased with its purity. It is nearly all silver."

THE PLAUDITS OF THE PEOPLE

A Man who had been mentioned for high political preferment explained through the newspapers that he was "not a candidate." Thereupon he was lustily cheered by the populace.

"Why do you not cheer?" some one asked a Silent Person standing moodily apart.

"Because," answered the Silent Person, "I understand these plaudits to be given for his humility. Whenever you raise the shout for his knowledge of the English language you can count on the assistance of both my lungs."

"Why, how is that?" asked those who stood nearest.

"A 'candidate' is one who has been nominated," said the Silent Person. "He has not succeeded, as yet, in moving Heaven and Earth sufficiently to procure that distinction."

THE SECRET OF HAPPINESS

Having been told by an angel that Noureddin Becar was the happiest man in the world, the Sultan caused him to be brought to the palace and said:

"Impart to me, I command thee, the secret of thy happiness."

"O father of the sun and the moon," answered Noureddin Becar, "I did not know that I was happy."

"That," said the Sultan, "is the secret that I sought."

Noureddin Becar retired in deep dejection, fearing that his new-found happiness might forsake him.

ATONEMENT

Two Women in heaven claimed one Man newly arrived.

"I was his wife," said one.

"I his sweetheart," said the other.

St. Peter said to the Man: "Go down to the Other Place—you have suffered enough."

A PART OF THE WAGES

"Ours is a life of self-sacrifice," said a Clergyman. "While others pursue gain or pleasure we burn the midnight oil in studying how to crack the hardest theological nuts. And all for what earthly reward?"

"Well," said his Parishioner, thoughtfully, "there are, for example, the kernels."

TWO PARROTS

An Author who had made a fortune by writing slang had a Parrot. "Why have I not a gold cage?" asked the bird.

"Because," said its master, "you are a better thinker than repeater, as your question shows. And we have not the same audience."

TWIN INTOLERABLES

A Rattlesnake observing the approach of a Man with a Camera crept under a flat stone, leaving nothing exposed but the tip of his nose.

"I was not going to photograph you," the Man with a Camera explained with a touch of sadness in his voice. "Holding the ancient faith in the divine wisdom of serpents, I have come to ask you why I am hated and shunned by all mankind."

"Alas," said the Rattlesnake, "the gods have denied me that knowledge. Can you tell me why I am myself not very much sought after as a companion?"

CONSOLATION

A great country having vindicated its courage and prowess by fifteen defeats in which none of its enemy's troops suffered any damage, its Prime Minister sued for peace.

"I'll not be hard on you," said the Victor: "you shall keep everything except your colonies, your liberty, your credit and your self-respect."

"Ah," said the Prime Minister, "you are indeed magnanimous; you leave us our honor."

FAMINE VERSUS PESTILENCE

"It is hard on you, gallant friend," said the Victorious Besieger, "but I must say it. Pestilence was among my troops, and if you had not surrendered to me I should have surrendered to you."

"That is what I feared you would do," replied the Vanquished Commander. "My men were eating their belts and cartridge boxes; we could not properly provide for you."

THE MONARCHIST RECLAIMED

A recreant Citizen of a Great Republic went abroad, hoping to shine in "the fierce light that beats upon a throne." While intriguing to be presented at the court of a fly-speck principality, he fell asleep and dreamed that he was visited by an Angel wearing the robes of a lord high chamberlain.

"Come," said the Angel; "I will present you to all the crowned heads of Europe."

Miraculously conveyed through the air, they arrived at the portal of a vast building. The visitor's name and his rank in the order of the Dukes of Trade were announced, the great iron doors swung open and he found himself in the presence of all the crowned heads of Europe. The bodies had been carted away by the public scavenger.

The royal pageant so disappointed him that he awoke with a sigh, and returning to the land of the free, he plunged into patriotism, became a leader of the Mobocratic party and died an illustrious statesman with both hands in the public treasury.

DISAPPOINTMENT

A Dog that had been engaged in pursuit of his own tail abandoned the chase and lying down curled up for repose. In his new posture he found his tail within easy reach of his teeth and seized it with avidity, but immediately released it, wincing with pain.

"After all," he said, "there is more joy in pursuit than in possession."

SAINT AND SOUL

St. Peter was sitting at the gate of Heaven when a Soul approached, and, bowing civilly, handed him its card.

"I am very sorry, sir," said St. Peter, after reading the card, "but I really cannot admit you. You will have to go to the Other Place. Sorry, sir, very sorry."

"Don't mention it," said the Soul; "I have been all the month at a watering place, and it will be an agreeable change. I called only to ask if my friend Elihu Root is here."

"No, sir," the Saint replied; "Mr. Root is not dead."

"O, I know that," said the Soul. "I thought he might be visiting God."

THE STATUE AT BUMBOOGLE

On a high hill overlooking the ancient city of Bumboogle is a colossal statue, erected by the nation, to the memory of the illustrious Gaaka-Wolwol, "the best and wisest of mankind." A Traveler from a distant country said to the Custodian of the Statue, who is the highest officer of the realm: "The winds of the sea, O Most Exalted, have not blown the fame of your great countryman to my native shores. What did he do?"

"Nothing; that is how we know him to have been good."

"But his wisdom—what did he say?"

"Nothing; that is how we know him to have been wise."

IMPROVIDENCE

A Person who had fallen from wealth to indigence appealed to a Rich Man for alms.

"No," said the Rich Man, "you did not keep what you had. What assurance have I that you will keep what I may give you?"

"But I don't want it to keep," the beggar explained; "I want to exchange it for bread."

"That is just the same," said the Rich Man. "You would not keep the bread."

SHEEP AND LION

"You are a beast of war," said the Sheep to the Lion, "yet men go gunning for you. Me, a believer in non-resistance, they do not hunt."

"They do not need to," replied the son of the desert; "they can breed you."

THE INCONSOLABLE WIDOW

A Woman in widow's weeds was weeping upon a grave.

"Console yourself, madam," said a Sympathetic Stranger. "Heaven's mercies are infinite. There is another man somewhere, besides your husband, with whom you can still be happy."

"There was," she sobbed—"there was, but this is his grave."

AN INTRUSION

Morality put her toe into international politics and it was promptly chopped off.

"A thousand thanks," said Diplomacy, with an engaging bow; "we will keep it in memory of a most distinguished honor."

And Morality has limped a little ever since.

THE TOLERANT SOVEREIGN

The Gamdoodle of Moop summoned his Secretary of War to an audience and said:

"Sir, you cannot be unaware of the great outcry that my loyal subjects are making against you. They say that you are a rascal."

"Your Majesty," replied the Secretary of War, "it is untrue."

"I'm right glad to hear it," the Gamdoodle replied, rising to intimate that the interview was at an end. But observing that the official did not depart, he added: "Is there anything to say?"

"Yes, your Majesty," the Secretary of War answered; "I wish to surrender my portfolio; for while the public outcry is untrue it is not unjust. I am a fool."

At this the Gamdoodle was graciously pleased to smile. "My good man," he said, "return to your duties. I am that way myself."

THE MYSTERIOUS WORD

The Chief of a battalion of war correspondents read a manuscript account of a battle.

"My son," he said to its Author, "your story is distinctly unavailable. You say we lost only two men instead of a hundred; that the enemy's loss is unknown, instead of ten thousand, and that we were defeated and ran away. That is no way to write."

"But consider," expostulated the conscientious scribe, "my story may be tame with regard to the number of our casualties, disappointing as to the damage done to the enemy and shocking in its denouement, but it has the advantage of being the truth."

"I don't quite understand," said the Chief, scratching his head.

"Why, the advantage," the other exclaimed—"the merit—the distinction—the profitable excellence—the"—

"Oh," said the Chief, "I know very well the signification of 'advantage'; but what the devil do you mean by 'truth'?"

A BORN CAPTAIN

A Near-Sighted Man in Luzon met one day a Gorgeous Being whom he mistook for the American Commander.

"General," he said, "do you not find the United States volunteers difficult to manage?"

"I might," the Gorgeous Being replied, "if I were their commander; but, no, I am Aguinaldo."

REVELATION

A Lion was attacked by a pack of famishing Wolves, who circled about him, howling as loud as they could, though none dared approach him.

"These are very useful creatures," said the Lion, as he lay down for his afternoon nap—"they apprise me of my virtues. I never before knew that I was good to eat."

SOLDIER AND VULTURE

A Soldier struggling through a pestilential morass saw a Vulture perching on the branch of a tree and solemnly snapping its beak.

"What are you?" asked the Soldier, who had never seen a Vulture. "You look like the father of all chickens."

"Men call me all kinds of names," the bird replied, "according to the language that they speak. I called myself an Expansionist."

The soldier grew very grave. "I was that myself until now," he said, "but if you are the thing to be expanded I shall have to think about it."

But when he tried he found that heaven had not supplied him with a thinker.

HER HONOR THE MAYOR

A Statesman running for Office had the bad luck to fall and break his heart. As he lay bewailing his hard fate the Office of which he had been in pursuit came back to him, keeping just out of reach.

"My poor friend," said the Office, "what was your business with me?"

"I wanted to hold you," the sufferer explained.

"I should think," the Office said, reproachfully, "that it would be much easier to go home and hold the baby."

"Alas," said the unfortunate Statesman, "my home is in Colorado and my wife is Mayor of Maverick—there is no baby."

IN ADVANCE OF HIS TIME

Some rowdies, having savagely beaten an Unoffending Person, were haled before a Judge and prosecuted by their victim. "I seem to remember you," said the Judge to the prosecuting witness. "Did you not make a speech on a street corner recently, denouncing law and tyranny?"

"I did, your Honor."

"The very law to which you now appeal for protection?"

"Yes, your Honor, I hate all law."

"In short, you are an anarchist, are you not?"

"Yes, I am—but not a bigoted one."

"Well, I am not a bigoted enforcer of the law. The prisoners are discharged, and I invite attention to the fact that you are without standing in this court."

Soon afterward the Judge was removed from office, respected by all who knew him.

CAUSE AND EFFECT

A THIRTEEN-INCH gun having uttered a projectile relapsed into silence. Then sounded a Far, Faint Voice from beyond the earth's curvature: "Did you damage anything?"

"Did I damage anything?" echoed the portentous tube right scornfully. "If you are envious enough about that to investigate you will find a wide and ragged hole in the public treasury."

"Ah, permit me to introduce myself," said the Far, Faint Voice: "I am that hole. It is a wise child that knows its father—I had supposed myself due to the annual salary warrant of a Rear-Admiral."

ENVIRONMENT

"PRISONER," said the Judge, austerely, "you are justly convicted of murder. Are you guilty, or were you brought up in Kentucky?"

A CHAINED EAGLE

A PROVINCIAL STATESMAN newly elected to the parliament of Despotamia declared that he would introduce a resolution censuring the king. As he left the parliament house, he met a Stranger who warned him that if he persisted in his disloyal design he would lose his head.

"That," said he, "would be a smaller privation than the loss of my liberty."

"I do not know that," said the Stranger. "Liberty is something that I cannot rightly appraise, never having had it. I am the king."

THE POWERLESS POET

A POET whose lines never would scan was summoned before the King and commanded to show cause why he should not be put to death.

"If your ear is imperfect," said the King, "you could count your syllables on your fingers, like an honest workman."

"May your Majesty outlive your Prime Minister by as many years as remain to you," said the Poet, reverently. "I do count my syllables. But observe: my left hand lacks a finger—bitten off by a critic."

"Then," said the King, "why don't you count on the right hand?"

"Alas!" was the reply of the Poet, as he held up the mutilated left, "that is impossible—there is nothing to count with! It is the forefinger that is lacking."

"Unfortunate man!" exclaimed the sympathetic monarch. "We must make your limitations and disabilities immaterial. You shall write for the magazines."

THE INCREDULOUS SUBORDINATE

A COMMANDING GENERAL retreating after defeat came upon the camp of a Subordinate, who was playing cards with his men.

"Why did you not march to my assistance, sir?" thundered the Commanding General. "Did you not hear the reports of my guns?"

"Reports? O, yes," the Subordinate replied. "I heard them all right, but I did not believe them. I used to be a reporter."

WOLF AND TORTOISE

A WOLF meeting a Tortoise said: "My friend, you are the slowest thing out of doors. I do not see how you manage to escape from your enemies."

"As I lack the power to run away," replied the Tortoise, "Providence has thoughtfully supplied me with an impenetrable shell."

The Wolf reflected a long time, then he said:

"It seems to me that it would have been just as easy to give you long legs."

FROM GENERAL TO PARTICULAR

A Man of Candor said to his Wife: "I cannot permit you to think me better than I am. I have many vices and weaknesses."

"That is only natural," said she, smiling sweetly; "none of us is perfect."

Encouraged by her magnanimity, he confessed to a particular falsehood that he had once told her.

"Abominable wretch!" she cried, and clapped her hands thrice.

Thereupon a gigantic Nubian slave appeared and dispatched him with a scimitar.

A MONARCH FOREARMED

The Emperor of Jiam being dissatisfied with himself resolved to make war upon the King of Geylon.

"You'd better not," said the King.

"Why not?" the Emperor inquired, contemptuously—"in my realm every man is a soldier."

"That is why not," the King explained. "In mine every other man is a civilian."

Perceiving that in peace the King had prepared for war, the bellicose Emperor prudently sought a more military antagonist.

THE MERCIFUL ASPIRANT

A Person who had been made President was walking along a lonely road when he met an Aspirant to Office and called loudly for help. But nobody heard except the Aspirant, who said:

"I have here seven hundred and fifty recommendations for my appointment as National Inspector of Dead Dogs."

The President fell upon his knees and explained that he had a wife and twenty-nine small children. The Aspirant put away the papers, taking some more from another pocket.

"These documents," he said, "are affidavits of my neighbors; they attest my fitness for the office."

The President wrung his hands and wept audibly. He said:

"Eight Cabinet officers are dependent on me for their bread, and most of them are orphans."

The heart of the Aspirant to office was touched at last.

"I spare you," he said, putting away his papers and moving on, "for the sake of those who cannot. Keep your National Inspectorship of Dead Dogs. It shall not be said that I am a hard man to deal with."

The President rose and dusted his knees. "I could not have given it him without breaking my word," he said to himself. "I have promised it to sixteen others."

A DISCOMFITED PHILOSOPHER

THE King of Remotia had a favorite Philosopher to whom he said:

"Thou hast been so faithful a slave that I am desirous to reward thee. Ask of me anything that thou wouldst have."

"Give me," said the Philosopher, "a hair from the head of a man that hath never flattered thee."

The King promised and dismissed him. The next day he summoned him before the throne and handed him a hair.

"Thou art attempting to deceive me," said the Philosopher, carefully scrutinizing the gift. "This hair is from the head of a flatterer who assured thee that he would think it an honor to give thee his head also."

"Thou art not so astute as thou thinkest," the King replied. "That hair is from the head of the only deaf mute in my kingdom."

A CONDITION PRECEDENT

THE King of Dogs was petitioned by one of his subjects, a reformer, to command that strangers when meeting should treat one another with amity and forbearance. He issued a royal rescript to that effect and ordered the Petitioner to cry it through the world; but whenever the herald appeared he was set upon by the dogs of the locality and cruelly bitten before he could perform his duty.

"Alas!" he said, "I perceive that reform must be preceded by reformation."

THE AMBITIOUS STATESMAN

A MAN Out of Office applied for relief to the King of the Quakers. "What can you do?" his Majesty asked.

"I have been a Secretary of War," the Man Out of Office replied, "but I was deposed. That position in your Majesty's Cabinet would, I think, be filled by me very creditably."

The King being greatly pleased by the applicant's manner and appearance, walked across the audience hall to his Prime Minister.

"Tell me how to make a vacancy in the Cabinet," he said.

"Appoint one," said the Prime Minister. "And permit me, Sire, to recommend the one with whom you have just been speaking."

THE LIMIT

THE King of the Faraway Islands appointed his horse prime minister and rode a man. Observing that under the new order of things the realm prospered, an Aged Statesman advised the king to turn himself out to grass and put an ox upon the throne.

"No," said the sovereign, thoughtfully, "a good principle may be pushed to an injurious extreme. True reform stops short of revolution."

AS USUAL

ANNOYED by an Irrelevant Consideration, a Point-at-issue commanded her to get out of his hearing forthwith, but the Irrelevant Consideration gathered up her skirts and trampling him into the mire went her way amidst the plaudits of the populace.

THE UNSHREWD ASSASSIN

A CONVICTED Murderer whom a Sheriff was engaged in hanging was asked if he had anything to say.

"Will it do me any good," he inquired, "to say something?"

"That," replied the Sheriff, adjusting the noose, "depends somewhat upon what you say. I thought you might perhaps put yourself into an easier frame of mind by damning the District Attorney."

"How much does he owe you?" the Murderer asked.

"You are not so shrewd as you think yourself," the Sheriff said; "I owe him fifty dollars."

"It is pretty much the same thing," said the Murderer.

"It is altogether the same thing," the Sheriff assented, springing the drop—"to you."

FABLES FROM "FUN"

(These fables appeared in the London "Fun" in 1872–73. They have been slightly revised.)

A Fox and a Duck having quarreled about the ownership of a frog, referred the matter to a Lion. After hearing a deal of argument the Lion opened his mouth to deliver judgment.

"I know what your decision is," said the Duck, interrupting. "It is that by our own showing the frog belongs to neither of us, and you will eat him yourself. Permit me to say that this is unjust, as I shall prove."

"To me," said the Fox, "it is clear that you will give the frog to the Duck and the Duck to me and take me yourself. I am not without experience of the law."

"I was about to explain," said the Lion, yawning, "that during the arguments in this case the property in dispute has hopped away. Perhaps you can procure another frog."

A Negro seeing an Ostrich began pelting him with stones. When a considerable number had been flung the Ostrich turned to and ate them.

"Pray tell me," he said, "to what virtue I am indebted for this excellent meal."

"To generosity," the Negro answered, now eager to conciliate one whom he thought miraculously gifted; "if it had not been for a charitable impulse I should have eaten those stones myself."

"My good fellow," said the Ostrich, "it seems that some of the lesser human virtues are not readily distinguishable from an imperfect digestion."

A MAN was plucking a live Goose, when the bird addressed him thus: "Suppose that you were a goose; do you think that you would relish this sort of thing?"

"Suppose that I were," said the Man; "do you think that you would like to pluck me?"

"Indeed I should!" was the natural, emphatic, but injudicious reply.

"Just so," concluded her tormentor, pulling out another handful of feathers; "that is the way that *I* feel about it."

A SHEEP making a long journey found the heat of her fleece insupportable, and seeing a flock of others in a fold, evidently in expectation, leaped in and joined them in the hope of being shorn. Perceiving the Shepherd approaching, and the other sheep huddling into a remote corner of the fold, she shouldered her way forward and said:

"Your flock is insubordinate; it is fortunate that I came along to set them an example of docility. Seeing me operated on, they will be encouraged to offer themselves."

"Thank you," said the Shepherd, "but I never kill more than one at a time. Mutton does not keep well in warm weather."

AN Oyster who had got a large pebble between the valves of his shell and was unable to get it out was lamenting his untoward fate, when a Monkey ran to him—the tide being out—and began an examination."

"You appear," said the Monkey, "to have something else in here, too. I will remove that first."

He inserted his paw and scooped out the body of the patient.

"Now," said he, devouring it, "I think you will be able to endure the pebble without inconvenience."

A Wild Horse meeting a Domestic One, taunted him with his condition of servitude. The tamed animal swore that he was as free as the wind.

"If that is so," said the other, "pray what is the office of that bit in your mouth?"

"That," was the answer, "is iron, one of the best tonics known."

"But what is the meaning of the rein attached to it?"

"That keeps it from falling from my mouth when I am too indolent to hold it."

"How about the saddle?"

"It spares me fatigue: when I am tired I mount and ride."

An Ass wandering near a village in the evening saw the light of the rising moon beyond a hill.

"Ho-ho, Master Redface," said he, "you are going to point out my long ears to the villagers, are you? I'll meet you at the crest and set my heels into you!"

So he scrambled painfully up to the crest and stood outlined against the broad disc of the unconscious luminary, a more conspicuous ass than ever before.

Laden with a grain of wheat which he had acquired with infinite toil, an Ant was breasting a current of his fellows, each of whom, as is their etiquette, insisted on stopping him, feeling him all over and shaking hands. It occurred to him that excess of ceremony is abuse of courtesy; so he laid down his burden, sat upon it, folded all his legs and smiled a smile of great grimness.

"Hello!" said his Fellow Ants, "what is the matter with you?"

"Sick of the hollow conventionalities of an effete civilization," was the rasping reply—"returned to the simplicity of primitive life."

"Ah! then we must trouble you for that grain. In the primitive life there are no rights of property."

A great white light fell upon the understanding of that rebellious insect. He rose and grappling the grain of wheat trotted away with alacrity. It was observed that he submitted with a wealth of patience to manipulation of his friends and neighbors and went long distances out of his way to shake hands with strangers on competing lines of traffic.

HAVING been taught Greek, a Parrot was puffed up with conceit. "Observe," said he, "the advantages of a classical education! I can chatter nonsense in the tongue of Plato."

"I should advise you," said his Master, quietly, "to let it be nonsense of a character somewhat different from that of some of Plato's most admired compatriots if you value the privilege of hanging at that open window. Commit no mythology, please."

A CERTAIN Magician had a Learned Pig who had lived a cleanly, gentlemanly life, achieving a wide renown and winning the hearts of the people, attending his elevating performances. But perceiving that the creature was unhappy, the Magician transformed him to a man. Straightway the man abandoned his cards, his timepiece, his musical instruments and the other devices of his profession, and betook himself to a pool of mud, wherein he inhumed himself to the tip of his nose, grunting with sodden satisfaction.

"THE Millennium is come," said a Lion to a Lamb inside the fold. "Come out and let us lie down together, as it has been foretold that we shall."

"Have you brought along the little child that is to lead us?" the Lamb asked.

"No; I thought that perhaps a child of the shepherd would serve."

"I distrust a Millennium that requires the shepherd to supply both the feast and the leader of the revel. My notion of that happy time is that it is to be a period in which mutton is unfit to eat and a lion the product of the sculptor's art."

Finding no profit in dissimulation, the Lion walked thoughtfully away and candidly dined on the village priest.

"I SAY, you," bawled a fat Ox in a stall to a lusty young Ass who was braying outside; "the like of that is not in good taste."

"In whose good taste, my adipose censor?" inquired the Ass, not too respectfully.

"Why—ah—h'm. I mean that it does not suit me. You should bellow."

"May I ask how it concerns you whether I bellow or bray, or do both, or neither?"

"I cannot tell you," said the Ox, shaking his head despondingly—"I do not at all understand the matter. I can only say that I have been used to censure all discourse that differs from my own."

"Exactly," said the Ass; "you have tried to make an art of impudence by calling preferences principles. In 'taste' you have invented a word incapable of definition to denote an idea impossible of expression, and by employing the word 'good ' or 'bad' in connection with it you indicate a merely subjective process, in terms of an objective quality. Such presumption transcends the limits of mere effrontery and passes into the boundless empyrean of pure gall!"

The bovine critic having no words to express his disapproval of this remarkable harangue, said it was in bad taste.

An Author who had wrought a book of fables (the merit whereof transcended expression) was peacefully sleeping atop of his modest literary eminence, when he was rudely roused by a throng of Critics uttering adverse judgment on the incomparable tales.

"Apparently," said he, "I have been guilty of some small degree of unconsidered wisdom, and it is a bitterness to these good folk, the which they will not abide. Ah, well, those who produce the Strasburg *pâté* and the feather pillow regard *us* as rival creators. Doubtless it is in course of nature for those who grow the pen to censure the manner of its use."

So speaking, he executed a smile a hand's-breadth in extent and resumed his airy dream of dropping ducats.

A Tortoise and an Armadillo, having quarreled, repaired to a secluded spot to vindicate their honor by an appeal to arms.

"Now, then," shouted the Tortoise shrinking into the innermost recesses of his shell, "come on!"

"Very well," assented the Armadillo, coiling up tightly in his coat of mail, "I am ready for you!"

An historian of the period obscurely alludes to the incident as foreshadowing the naval engagement of the future.

A Jackal in pursuit of a Deer was about to seize it, when an earthquake opened a broad and deep chasm between him and his prey.

"This," he said, "is a pernicious interference with the laws of Nature. I refuse to recognize any such irregularity."

So he resumed the chase, endeavoring to cross the abyss by two leaps.

ÆSOPUS EMENDATUS

JUPITER AND THE BABY SHOW

JUPITER held a baby show, open to all animals, and a Monkey entered her hideous cub for a prize, but Jupiter only laughed at her.

"It is all very well," said the Monkey, "to laugh at my offspring, but you go into any gallery of antique sculpture and look at the statues and busts of the fellows that you begot yourself."

" 'Sh! don't expose me," said Jupiter, and awarded her the first prize.

MERCURY AND THE WOODCHOPPER

A WOODCHOPPER who had dropped his ax into a deep pool besought Mercury to recover it for him. That thoughtless deity immediately plunged into the pool, which became so salivated that the trees about its margin all came loose and dropped out.

THE PENITENT THIEF

A BOY who had been taught by his Mother to steal grew to be a man and was a professional public official. One day he was taken in the act and condemned to die. While going to the place of execution he passed his Mother and said to her:

"Behold your work! If you had not taught me to steal I should not have come to this."

"Indeed!" said the Mother. "And who, pray, taught you to be detected?"

FOX AND GRAPES

A Fox, seeing some sour grapes hanging within an inch of his nose, and being unwilling to admit that there was anything he would not eat, solemnly declared that they were out of his reach.

FARMER AND FOX

A FARMER who had a deadly hatred against a certain Fox caught him and tied some tow to his tail; then carrying him to the center of his own grain-field, he set the tow on fire and let the animal go.

"Alas!" said the Farmer, seeing the result; "if that grain had not been heavily insured I might have had to dissemble my hatred of the Fox."

ARCHER AND EAGLE

AN Eagle mortally wounded by an Archer was greatly comforted to observe that the arrow was feathered with one of his own quills.

"I should have felt bad, indeed," he said, "to think that any other eagle had a hand in this."

TRUTH AND THE TRAVELER

A MAN traveling in a desert met a Woman.

"Who art thou?" asked the Man, "and why dost thou dwell in this dreadful place?"

"My name," replied the Woman, "is Truth; and I live in the desert in order to be near my worshipers when they are driven from among their fellows. They all come, sooner or later."

"Well," said the Man looking about, "the country doesn't seem to be very thickly settled hereabout."

WOLF AND LAMB

A LAMB, pursued by a Wolf, fled into the temple.

"The priest will catch you and sacrifice you," said the Wolf, "if you remain there."

"It is just as well to be sacrificed by the priest as to be eaten by you," said the Lamb.

"My friend," said the Wolf, "it pains me to see you considering so great a question from a purely selfish point of view. It is not just as well for me."

GRASSHOPPER AND ANT

ONE day in winter a hungry Grasshopper applied to an Ant for some of the food which the ants had stored.

"Why," said the Ant, "did you not store up some food for yourself, instead of singing all the time?"

"So I did," said the Grasshopper; "so I did; but you fellows broke in and carried it all away."

GOOSE AND SWAN

A CERTAIN rich man reared a Goose and a Swan, the one for his table, the other because she was reputed a good singer. One night when the Cook went to kill the Goose he got hold of the Swan instead. Thereupon the Swan, to induce him to spare her life, began to sing; but she saved him nothing but the trouble of killing her, for she died of the song.

FISHER AND FISHED

A FISHERMAN who had caught a very small Fish was putting it into his basket when it said:

"I pray you put me back into the stream, for I can be of no use to you; the gods do not eat fish."

"I am no god," said the Fisherman.

"True," said the Fish, "but as soon as Jupiter has heard of your exploit he will elevate you to the deitage. You are the only man that ever caught a small fish."

WOLVES AND DOGS

"Why should there be strife between us?" said the Wolves to the Sheep. "It is all owing to those meddlesome dogs. Dismiss them, and we shall have peace."

"You seem," replied the Sheep, "to think it an easy thing to dismiss dogs."

DAME FORTUNE AND THE TRAVELER

A weary Traveler who had lain down and fallen asleep on the brink of a deep well was discovered by Dame Fortune.

"If this fool," she said, "should have an uneasy dream and roll into the well men would say that I did it. It is painful to me to be unjustly accused, and I shall see that I am not."

So saying she rolled the man into the well.

WOLF AND SHEPHERDS

A Wolf passing a Shepherd's hut looked in and saw the shepherds dining.

"Come in," said one of them ironically, "and partake of your favorite dish, a leg of mutton."

"Thank you," said the Wolf moving away, "but you must excuse me; I have just had a saddle of shepherd."

LION, COCK AND ASS

A Lion was about to attack a braying Ass, when a Cock near by crowed shrilly and the Lion ran away. "What frightened him?" the Ass asked.

"Lions have a superstitious terror of my voice," answered the Cock, proudly.

"Well, well, well," said the Ass, shaking his head; "I should think that any animal that is afraid of your voice and doesn't mind mine must have an uncommon kind of ear."

SNAKE AND SWALLOW

A Swallow who had built her nest in a court of justice reared a fine family of young birds. One day a Snake came out of a chink in the wall and was about to eat them. The Just Judge at once issued an injunction, and making an order for their removal to his own house, ate them himself.

FAWN AND BUCK

A Fawn said to its father: "You are larger, stronger and more active than a dog, and you have sharp horns. Why do you run away when you hear one barking?"

"Because, my child," replied the Buck, "my temper is so uncertain that if I permit one of those noisy creatures to come into my presence I am likely to forget myself and do him an injury."

HEN AND VIPERS

A Hen who had patiently hatched out a brood of vipers was accosted by a Swallow, who said: "What a fool you are to give life to creatures that will reward you by destroying you."

"I am a little bit destructive myself," said the Hen, tranquilly swallowing one of the little reptiles; "and it is not an act of folly to provide oneself with the delicacies of the season."

SPENDTHRIFT AND SWALLOW

A Spendthrift, seeing a single swallow, pawned his cloak, thinking that Summer was at hand. It was.

LION AND THORN

A Lion roaming through the forest got a thorn in his foot and meeting a Shepherd asked him to remove it. The Shepherd did so and the Lion, having just surfeited himself on another shepherd, went away without harming him. Some time afterward the Shepherd was condemned on a false accusation to be cast to the lions in the amphitheatre. When they were about to devour him one of them said:

"This is the man who removed the thorn from my foot."

Hearing this, the others honorably abstained, and the claimant ate the Shepherd all by himself.

VICTOR AND VICTIM

Two Game Cocks having fought a battle, the defeated one skulked away and hid, but the victor mounted a wall and crowed lustily. This attracted the attention of a Hawk, who said:

"Behold! how pride goeth before a fall."

So he swooped down upon the boasting bird and was about to destroy him, when the vanquished Cock came out of his hiding-place and between the two the Hawk was calamitously defeated.

KITE, PIGEONS AND HAWK

SOME Pigeons exposed to the attacks of a Kite asked a Hawk to defend them. He consented, and being admitted into the cote waited for the Kite, whom he fell upon and devoured. When he was so surfeited that he could scarcely move the grateful Pigeons scratched out his eyes.

WOLF AND BABE

A FAMISHING WOLF passing the door of a cottage in the forest heard a Mother say to her Babe:

"Be quiet, or I will throw you out of the window and the wolves will get you."

So he waited all day below the window, growing more hungry all the time. But at night the Old Man, having returned from the village club, threw out both Child and Mother.

WOLF AND OSTRICH

A WOLF who in devouring a man had choked himself with a bunch of keys asked an ostrich to put her head down his throat and pull them out, which she did.

"I suppose," said the Wolf, "you expect payment for that service."

"A kind act," replied the Ostrich, "is its own reward; I have eaten the keys."

HERDSMAN AND LION

A HERDSMAN who had lost a bullock entreated the gods to bring him the thief and vowed he would sacrifice a goat to them. Just then a Lion, his jaws dripping with bullock's blood, approached the Herdsman.

"I thank you, good deities," said the Herdsman resuming his prayer, "for showing me the thief. And now if you will take him away I will stand another goat."

WAR-HORSE AND MILLER

HAVING heard that the State was about to be invaded by a hostile army, a War-horse belonging to a Colonel of the Militia offered his services to a passing Miller.

"No," said the patriotic Miller, "I will employ no one who deserts his position in the hour of danger. It is sweet to die for one's country."

Something in the sentiment sounded familiar and looking at the Miller more closely the War-horse recognized his master in disguise.

MAN AND FISH-HORN

A TRUTHFUL MAN finding a musical instrument in the road, asked the name of it and was told that it was a fish-horn. The next time he went fishing he set his nets and blew the fish-horn all day to charm the fish into them, but at nightfall there was not only no fish in his nets, but none along that part of the coast. Meeting a friend while on his way home he was asked what luck he had had.

"Well," said the Truthful Man, "the weather is not right for fishing, but it's a red-letter day for music."

HERCULES AND THE CARTER

A CARTER was driving a wagon loaded with a merchant's goods, when the wheels stuck in a rut. Thereupon he began to pray to Hercules, without other exertion.

"Indolent fellow!" said Hercules; "you ask me to help you, but will not help yourself."

So the Carter helped himself to so many of the most valuable goods that the horses easily ran away with the remainder.

HARE AND TORTOISE

A HARE having ridiculed the slow movements of a Tortoise was challenged by the latter to run a race, a Fox to go to the goal and be the judge. They got off well together, the Hare at the top of her speed, the Tortoise, who had no other intention than making his antagonist exert herself, going very leisurely. After sauntering along for some time he discovered the Hare by the wayside, apparently asleep, and seeing a chance to win pushed on as fast as he could, arriving at the goal hours afterward, suffering from extreme fatigue and claiming the victory.

"Not so," said the Fox; "the Hare was here long ago and went back to cheer you on your way."

LION AND BULL

A LION wishing to lure a Bull to a place where it would be safe to attack him said: "My friend, I have killed a fine sheep; will you come with me and partake of the mutton?"

"With pleasure," said the Bull, "as soon as you have refreshed yourself a little for the journey. Pray have some grass."

OLD MAN AND SONS

AN Old Man, afflicted with a family of contentious Sons, brought in a bundle of sticks and asked the young men to break it. After repeated efforts they confessed that it could not be done. "Behold," said the Old Man, "the advantage of unity; as long as these sticks are in alliance they are invincible, but observe how feeble they are individually."

Pulling a single stick from the bundle, he broke it easily upon the head of the eldest Son, and this he repeated until all had been served.

MAN AND EAGLE

AN Eagle was once captured by a Man, who clipped his wings and put him into the poultry yard, along with the chickens. The Eagle was much depressed in spirits by the change.

"Why should you not rather rejoice?" said the Man. "You were only an ordinary fellow as an eagle; but as an old cock you are a fowl of incomparable distinction."

MAN AND GOOSE

"SEE these valuable golden eggs," said a Man that owned a Goose. "Surely a Goose that can lay such eggs must have a gold mine inside her."

So he killed the Goose and cut her open, but found that she was just like any other goose. Moreover, on examining the eggs that she had laid he found they were just like any other eggs.

DOG AND REFLECTION

A DOG passing over a stream on a plank saw his reflection in the water. "You ugly brute!" he cried; "how dare you look at me in that insolent way?"

He made a grab in the water and getting hold of what he supposed was the other dog's lip lifted out a fine piece of meat which a butcher's boy had dropped into the stream.

WOLF AND GOAT

A Wolf saw a Goat feeding at the summit of a rock, where he could not get at her.

"Why do you stay up there in that sterile place and go hungry?" said the Wolf. "Down here where I am the broken-bottle vine cometh up as a flower, the celluloid collar blossoms as the rose and the tin-can tree brings forth after its kind."

"That is true, no doubt," said the Goat, "but how about the circus-poster crop? I hear that it failed this year down there."

The Wolf, perceiving that he was being derided, went away and resumed his duties at the doors of the poor.

MAN AND VIPER

A Man finding a frozen Viper put it into his bosom.

"The coldness of the human heart," he said with a grin, "will keep the creature in his present condition until I can reach home and revive him on the coals."

But the pleasures of hope so fired his heart that the Viper thawed, slid to the ground and, thanking the Man civilly for his hospitality, glided away.

NORTH WIND AND SUN

The Sun and the North Wind disputed which was the more powerful and agreed that he should be declared victor who could the sooner strip a traveler of his clothes. So they waited until a Traveler came by. But the Traveler had been indiscreet enough to stay over night at a summer hotel, and had no clothes.

CRAB AND SON

A LOGICAL CRAB said to his Son, "Why do you not walk straight forward? Your sidelong gait is singularly ungraceful."

"Why don't you walk straight forward yourself?" said the Son.

"Erring youth," replied the Logical Crab, "you are introducing new and irrelevant matter."

JUPITER AND THE BIRDS

JUPITER commanded all the birds to appear before him, so that he might choose the most beautiful to be their king. The ugly Jackdaw, collecting all the fine feathers that had fallen from the other birds, attached them to his own body and appeared at the examination, looking very gay. The other birds recognizing their own borrowed plumage indignantly protested and began to strip him.

"Hold!" said Jupiter; "this self-made bird has more sense than any of you. He shall be your king."

LION AND MOUSE

A LION who had caught a Mouse was about to kill him, when the Mouse said:

"If you will spare my life, I will do as much for you some day."

The Lion good-naturedly let him go. It happened shortly afterwards that the Lion was caught by some hunters and bound with cords. The Mouse, passing that way and seeing that his benefactor was helpless gnawed off his tail.

LAMB AND WOLF

A WOLF was slaking his thirst at a stream, when a Lamb left the side of his shepherd, came down the stream and passing ostentatiously round the Wolf, prepared to drink below.

"I beg you to observe," said the Lamb, "that water does not commonly run uphill. My sipping here cannot possibly defile the water where you are; so you have not the flimsiest pretext for slaying me."

"I am not aware," replied the Wolf, "that I need a pretext for liking mutton chops."

End of that small logician.

MOUNTAIN AND MOUSE

A Mountain was in labor, and the people of seven cities had descended to watch its movements and hear its groans. While they waited in breathless expectancy out came a Mouse.

"Oh, what a baby!" they cried in derision.

"I may be a baby," said the Mouse, gravely, as he passed outward through the forest of shins, "but I know tolerably well how to diagnose a volcano."

THE BELLAMY AND THE MEMBERS

The Members of a body of Socialists rose in insurrection against their Bellamy.

"Why," said they, "should we be all the time tucking you out with food when you do nothing to tuck us out?"

So, resolving to take no further action, they went away and looking backward had the satisfaction to see the Bellamy compelled to sell his own book.

CAT AND YOUTH

A Cat fell in love with a handsome Young Man and entreated Venus to change her into a woman.

"I should think," said Venus, "you might make so trifling a change without bothering me. However, be a woman."

Afterward, wishing to see if the change were complete, Venus caused a mouse to approach, whereupon the woman shrieked and made such a show of herself that the Young Man would not marry her.

FARMER AND SONS

A Farmer being about to die, and knowing that during his illness his Sons had permitted the vineyard to become overgrown with weeds while they gambled with the doctor, said to them:

"My boys, there is a great treasure buried in the vineyard. Dig in the ground until you find it."

So the Sons dug up all the weeds, and all the vines, too, and even neglected to bury the old man.

OLD SAWS WITH NEW TEETH
Certain Ancient Fables Applied to the
Life of Our Times

WOLF AND CRANE

A Rich Man wanted to tell a certain lie, but the lie was of such monstrous size that it stuck in his throat; so he employed an Editor to write it out and publish it in his paper as an editorial. But when the Editor presented his bill the Rich Man said:

"Be content—is it nothing that I refrained from advising you about investments?"

LION AND MOUSE

A Judge was awakened by the noise of a lawyer prosecuting a Thief. Rising in wrath he was about to sentence the Thief to life imprisonment when the latter said:

"I beg that you will set me free, and I will some day requite your kindness."

Pleased and flattered to be bribed, although by nothing but an empty promise, the Judge let him go. Soon afterward he found that it was more than an empty promise, for having become a Thief he was himself set free by the other, who had become a Judge.

HARE AND FROGS

THE Members of a Legislature being told that they were the meanest thieves in the world resolved to kill themselves. So they bought shrouds and laying them in a convenient place prepared to cut their throats. While they were grinding their razors some Tramps passing that way stole the shrouds.

"Let us live, my friends," said one of the Legislators; "the world is better than we thought. It contains meaner thieves than we."

BELLY AND MEMBERS

SOME Workingmen employed in a shoe factory went on a strike, saying: "Why should we continue to work to feed and clothe our employer when we have none too much to eat and wear ourselves?"

The Manufacturer, seeing that he could get no labor for a long time and finding the times pretty hard anyhow, burned down his shoe factory for the insurance and when the strikers wanted to resume work there was no work to resume. So they boycotted a tanner.

THE PIPING FISHERMAN

AN Editor who was always vaunting the purity, enterprise and fearlessness of his paper was pained to observe that he got no subscribers. One day it occurred to him to stop saying that his paper was pure and enterprising and fearless, and make it so. "If these are not good qualities," he reasoned, "it is folly to claim them."

Under the new policy he got so many subscribers that his rivals endeavored to discover the secret of his prosperity, but he kept it, and when he died it died with him.

ANTS AND GRASSHOPPER

SOME Members of a Legislature were making schedules of their wealth at the end of the session, when an Honest Miner came along and asked them to divide with him. The members of the Legislature inquired: "Why did you not acquire property of your own?"

"Because," replied the Honest Miner, "I was so busy digging out gold that I had no leisure to lay up something worth while."

Then the Members of the Legislature derided him, saying:

"If you waste your time in profitless amusement you cannot, of course, expect to share the rewards of industry."

THE DOG AND HIS REFLECTION

A STATE OFFICIAL carrying off the dome of the capitol met the Ghost of his predecessor, who had come out of his political grave to warn him that God saw him. As the place of meeting was lonely and the time midnight, the State Official set down the dome of the capitol and commanded the supposed traveler to throw up his hands. The Ghost replied that he had not eaten them, and while he was explaining the situation another State Official silently added the dome to his own collection.

LION, BEAR AND FOX

Two Thieves having stolen a piano and being unable to divide it fairly without a remainder went to law about it and continued the contest as long as either one had a dollar to bribe the Judge. When they could give no more an Honest Man came along and by a single small payment obtained a judgment and took the piano home, where his daughter used it to develop her biceps muscles, becoming a famous *pugiliste.*

WOLF AND LION

AN Indian who had been driven out of a fertile valley by a White Settler, said:

"Now that you have robbed me of my land there is nothing for me to do but issue invitations to a war-dance."

"I don't so much mind your dancing," said the White Settler, putting a fresh cartridge into his rifle, "but if you attempt to make me dance you will become a good Indian lamented by all who didn't know you. How did *you* get this land, anyhow?"

The Indian's claim was compromised for a silk hat and a tin horn.

THE ASS IN THE LION'S SKIN

A MEMBER of the State Militia stood at a street corner, scowling stormily, and the people passing that way went a long way around him, thinking of the horrors of war. But presently, in order to terrify them still more, he strode toward them, when, his sword entangling his legs, he fell upon the field of glory and the people passed over him singing their sweetest songs.

ASS AND GRASSHOPPERS

A STATESMAN heard some Laborers singing at their work and wishing to be happy too asked them what made them so.

"Honesty," replied the Laborers.

So the Statesman resolved that he too would be honest and the result was that he died of want.

THE WOLF WHO WOULD BE A LION

A FOOLISH fellow who had been told that he was a great man believed it and got himself appointed a Commissioner to the Interasylum Exposition of Preserved Idiots. At the first meeting of the Board he was mistaken for one of the exhibits and the janitor was ordered to remove him to his appropriate glass case.

"Alas!" he exclaimed as he was carried out, "why was I not content to remain where the cut of my forehead is so common that it is known as the Pacific Slope?"

KING LOG AND KING STORK

THE people being dissatisfied with a Democratic Legislature, which stole no more than they had, elected a Republican one, which not only stole all they had but exacted a promissory note for the balance due, secured by a mortgage upon their hope of death.

MILKMAID AND BUCKET

A SENATOR fell to musing as follows: "With the money which I shall get for my vote in favor of the bill to subsidize cat-ranches I can buy a kit of burglar's tools and open a bank. The profit of that enterprise will enable me to obtain a long, low, black schooner, raise a death's head-flag and engage in commerce on the high seas. From my gains in that business I can pay for the Presidency, which at $50,000 a year will give me in four years—" but it took him so long to make the calculation that the bill to subsidize cat-ranches passed without his vote and he was compelled to return to his constituents an honest man tormented with a clean conscience.

HARE AND TORTOISE

OF two writers one was brilliant but indolent; the other, though dull, industrious. They set out for the goal of fame with equal opportunities. Before they died the brilliant one was detected in seventy languages as the author of only two or three books of fiction and poetry, while the other was honored in the Bureau of Statistics of his native land as the compiler of sixteen volumes of tabulated information relating to the domestic hog.

MONKEY AND NUTS

A CERTAIN city desiring to purchase a site for a public Deformatory procured an appropriation from the Government of the country. Deeming this insufficient for purchase of the site and payment of reasonable commissions to themselves, the Men in Charge of the Matter asked for a larger sum, which was readily promised. Believing that the fountain could not be dipped dry, they applied for still more, and more yet. Wearied at last by their importunities the Government said it would be damned if it gave anything at all. So it gave nothing and was damned all the harder.

BOYS AND FROGS

SOME Editors of newspapers were engaged in diffusing general intelligence and elevating the moral sentiment of the public. They had been doing this for some time, when an Eminent Statesman stuck his head out of the pool of politics and speaking for the members of his profession said:

"My friends, I beg you will desist. I know you make a great deal of money by this kind of thing, but consider the damage you inflict upon the business of others!"

FABLES IN RHYME

THE SLEEPING LION

A Bull, the angel of the wild,
A Bull as gentle as a child,
A pleasant mannered Bull that lay
Upon a hill at break of day
And munched his cud, observed a gleam
Of crimson on the world's extreme
Where the Dawn-Spirit had released
His flaring banner in the east.
The Bull, a flame in either eye
That frightened the offending sky,
Rose, pawed the earth until his skin
Was dun with dust from tail to chin,
And lowering his horrid brows,

Roared out: "How dare you thus arouse
The sleeping lion in my breast!"
Then, like a storm from out the west,
He blindly charged, and without check,
Went o'er a cliff and broke his neck!
A Tiger, calm, serene, sedate,
Administered on his estate,
And as he turned him into chyle
Remarked with a contented smile:
"That sleeping lion in his breast
Was just an ass that needed rest."

IN DOGLAND

A Man who fared along a road
That passed a yellow Dog's abode
Incurred a paralyzing bite
From that incarnate appetite,
Creation's joy and hope and crown—
The pride and terror of the town!
The Man in anger went before
The nearest Magistrate and swore
A warrant out for the Dog's Master,
As author of the dire disaster.
Haled into court, that citizen
Employed attorneys, eight or ten,
Who as one man arose, and O,
The kind of things they said were so!
All honest souls, a crowd immense,
Were witnesses for the defense,
And when they came to testify
Of that bad plaintiff—my, O my!
Defendant rose and gravely swore
The Dog had never bit before.
"How could I know, till he transgressed,
The serpent lurking in his breast?"
And all the people cried: "That's so!
How could he know? How could he know?"

That won—Defendant left the place
On shoulders of the populace.
The miserable Plaintiff slunk
Away and soon was dead or drunk,

Tradition says not which; I think
Death is inferior to drink.
But that's irrelevant: what now
Concerns us is the bow and wow
Made by the snapdogs of that region
(Their name, tradition says, was Legion)
When, with a sound of trumpets blown,
The great decision was made known
From Sweetpotatoville to Pone.
They said, the dogs did, that the law
Was good—*pro bonos mores* (Latin
That dogs and lawyers mostly chat in).
They said, the while their bosoms burned
With ardor, that their souls discerned
"The dawn of a new era," which
They promptly "hailed" at concert pitch!

As dogs had now the legal right
To trouble Man for one free bite
'Twas voted that they would. They did:
That land, from Glorypool to Squid,
With snarl and yelp and snap of teeth
(Flashing like falchions from the sheath)
Was vocal till each cur beneath
The sun had fleshed his maiden fang
In some one of the human gang!
True, all the dogs whose heads were frosted
With age had long before exhausted
Their lawful privilege, and these
Died of chagrin among their fleas;
But there were pups enough at heel
Of every human leg to deal
Out floods of hydrophobia's sap
And wash that country from the map.

A PAIR OF OPPOSITES

A Fabulist of wide repute,
Whose laugh was loud and wit was mute—
Whose grammar had the grace of guess,
And language an initial S—
Whose tireless efforts, long sustained,
Proved him far better brawned than brained,

Once met a Toad. "My son," said he,
" 'Twould jar you to get onto me!
You're swell, but I'm the dandy guy
That slings the gilt-edged lullaby.
Dost tumble? What I'm shouting, see,
Is, you're the antithesis of Me."
"That compliment," the Toad replied,
"Is grateful to my foolish pride:
It seems to mean that though I hop
Right awkwardly I sometimes stop."
The gods, whom long the Fabulist
Had plagued (the Toad had only hissed)
Emitted loud Olympian snorts
Of joy to hear the King of Waits
Administer a mental pang
To the Protagonist of Slang.
So Jove appointed him to be
Chief Jester by divine decree,
And ne'er another joke made he.

THE DEGENERATE

Two Horses that had always chewed
The bitter grain of servitude—
Between their meals had ever felt
The bit in mouth and lash on pelt—
Once, as they drew the creaking wain,
Saw a wild Zebra of the plain,
Unknown to halter, stall or cage.
Cried one: "Good Lord! this is an age
Of miracle!" "Not so," said t'other,
"That vision is a horse-and-brother.
Degraded as he is by sin,
He has an equine soul within,
Albeit Law, with stern reproof,
Has laid on him the heavy hoof.
Those stripes but show he's 'serving time'
In punishment of some great crime."
The other thought an hour's span,
Then said: "Perhaps he stole a man."

THE VAIN CAT

Remarked a Tortoise to a Cat:
"Your speed's a thing to marvel at!
I saw you as you flitted by,
And wished I were one-half so spry."
The Cat said, humbly: "Why, indeed
I was not showing then my speed—
That was a poor performance." Then
She said exultantly (as when
The condor feels his bosom thrill
Remembering Chimborazo's hill,
And how he soared so high above,
It looked a valley, he a dove):
" 'Twould fire your very carapace
To see me with a dog in chase!"
Its snout in any kind of swill,
Pride, like a pig, will suck its fill.

THE CO-DEFENDANTS

A Jackass by a Lion chased
Had made so admirable haste
That his pursuer, far behind,
Had, long before, his hope resigned
And gone to sleep; but still poor Jack
Pressed on, nor ventured to look back.
"Why, what's the matter?" cried a Steer,
Obstructing him in his career.
"Out of the way and let us pass!"
Roared the still apprehensive Ass.
" 'Us'? Why, my friend," the Steer replied,
"I see but you, and none beside."
"I'm but the foremost," answered Jack—
"The woods are full of us 'way back.
Behold, he clawed me here and here;
See how he tore my precious ear!
Believe me, sir, your count's at fault—
No one escapes that cat's assault."
To let them limp along, the Steer
Backed off in wonder and in fear.

The Ass evanished like a flame,
But not another donkey came.
Then said the Steer: "I've saved—well done!—
All jackasses beneath the sun,
Rolled into one, rolled into one."

IN CONSEQUENCE OF APPLAUSE

"What makes you so round?"
Said an indolent Hound
To a Tiger that looked
As if he had booked
All the pilgrims of earth
For an inside berth.
Said the Tiger: "I strayed
To the edge of a glade
Where a man on a stump,
Sleek, handsome and plump,
His notions expounded
To those who surrounded
Him there with their ears
Erected like spears
For the words that he flung
From his flickering tongue."
"Yes, yes, my good cat,
But what of all that?
That statesman, I swear,
Had enough and to spare
Of the breezes that blow
Out of heaven, but, O
'Tis remarkably odd he
Could blow up your body
And make you so poddy."
"By-and-by the man stopped,
And his forehead he mopped,
And his scalp—which was bald.
Then somebody called
For three cheers—" "Hully Gee!
I'm beginning to see."
"And a tiger. That's me."

THE MONK
and
THE HANGMAN'S DAUGHTER

WRITTEN IN COLLABORATION WITH
G. A. DANZIGER

PREFACE

Many years ago—probably in 1890—Dr. Gustav Adolf Danziger brought to me in San Francisco what he said was a translation by himself of a German story by that brilliant writer, Herr Richard Voss, of Heidelberg. As Dr. Danziger had at that time a most imperfect acquaintance with the English language, he asked me to rewrite his version of Herr Voss's work for publication in this country. In reading it I was struck by what seemed to me certain possibilities of amplification, and I agreed to do the work if given a free hand by both author and translator. To this somewhat ill-considered proposal, which I supposed would make an end of the matter, I was afterward assured that the author, personally known to the translator, had assented. The result was this book, published by F. J. Schulte & Company of Chicago. Almost coincidently in point of time the publishers failed, and it was, so far as I know, never put upon the market.

Never having seen the original story, and having no skill in German anyhow, I am unable to say what liberties Dr. Danziger may have taken with his author's text; to me he professed to have taken none; yet, in recent books of his he is described on the title pages as "Author of The Monk and the Hangman's Daughter"—a statement that seems to justify, if not compel, this brief account of a matter which, though not particularly important, has given rise to more discussion than I have cared to engage in.

By a merely literary artifice the author of the German tale professed to have derived it from another writing, and in the Schulte version appeared the note following:

"The foundation of this narrative is an old manuscript originally belonging to the Franciscan monastery at Berchtesgaden, Bavaria. The manuscript was obtained from a peasant by Herr Richard Voss, of Heidelberg, from whose German version this is an adaptation."

I have always felt that this was inadequate acknowledgment of the work of Herr Voss, for whom I have the profoundest admiration. Not the least part of my motive and satisfaction in republishing lies in the opportunity that it supplies for doing justice to one to whose splendid imagination the chief credit of the tale is due. My light opinion of the credit due to any one else is attested by my retention of Dr. Danziger's name on the title page. In this version the work that came into my hands from his has been greatly altered and extended.

AMBROSE BIERCE.

WASHINGTON, D. C.,
November 29, 1906.

PUBLISHER'S NOTE

To Mr. Bierce's illuminating preface the following facts relating to "The Monk and the Hangman's Daughter" should be added:

Dr. Gustav Adolf Danziger made a rough translation of Richard Voss's "Der Mönch Von Berchtesgaden" in the German monthly magazine, *Vom Fels Zum Meer,* and turned it over to Ambrose Bierce "to copy it verbatim, for your pen will not let you write the wrong word." Beginning September 13, 1891, the story was published in the *San Francisco Examiner,* bearing the authorship, Dr. G. A. Danziger and Ambrose Bierce. Soon afterwards it was published in book form with Bierce's name preceding Danziger's on the title page. In the Neale edition of Bierce's Writings, published in 1907, the title read: by Ambrose Bierce written in collaboration with G. A. Danziger.

Ambrose Bierce's contributions to the story consist mainly of the excellent English in which he rewrote it and in its surprise ending. For these reasons, as well as for the fact that a good part of Bierce's literary reputation is based upon this tale, the story is included in the present edition of his writings.

THE MONK AND THE HANGMAN'S DAUGHTER

I

ON the first day of May in the year of our Blessed Lord 1680, the Franciscan monks Ægidius, Romanus and Ambrosius were sent by their Superior from the Christian city of Passau to the Monastery of Berchtesgaden, near Salzburg. I, Ambrosius, was the strongest and youngest of the three, being but twenty-one years of age.

The Monastery of Berchtesgaden was, we knew, in a wild and mountainous country, covered with dismal forests, which were infested with bears and evil spirits; and our hearts were filled with sadness to think what might become of us in so dreadful a place. But since it is Christian duty to obey the mandates of the Church, we did not complain, and were even glad to serve the wish of our beloved and revered Superior.

Having received the benediction, and prayed for the last time in the church of our Saint, we tied up our cowls, put new sandals on our feet, and set out, attended by the blessings of all. Although the way was long and perilous, we did not lose our hope, for hope is not only the beginning and the end of religion, but also the strength of youth and the support of age. Therefore our hearts soon forgot the sadness of parting, and rejoiced in the new and varying scenes that gave us our first real knowledge of the beauty of the earth as God has made it. The color and brilliance of the air were like the garment of the Blessed Virgin; the sun shone like the Golden Heart of the Savior, from which streameth light and life for all mankind; the dark blue canopy that hung above formed a grand and beautiful house of prayer, in which every blade of grass, every flower and living creature praised the glory of God.

As we passed through the many hamlets, villages and cities that lay along our way, the thousands of people, busy in all the vocations of life, presented to us poor monks a new and strange spectacle, which filled us with wonder and admiration. When so many churches came into view as we journeyed on, and the piety and ardor of the people were made manifest by the acclamations with which they hailed us and their alacrity in ministering to our needs, our hearts were full of gratitude and happiness. All the institutions of the Church were prosperous and wealthy, which showed that they had found favor in the sight of the good God whom we serve. The gardens and orchards of the monasteries and convents were well kept, proving the care and industry of the pious peasantry and the holy inmates of the cloisters. It was glorious to hear the peals of bells announcing the hours of the day: we actually breathed music in the air—the sweet tones were like the notes of angels singing praise to the Lord.

Wherever we went we greeted the people in the name of our patron Saint. On all sides were manifest humility and joy: women and children hastened to the wayside, crowding about us to kiss our hands and beseech a blessing. It almost seemed as if we were no longer poor servitors of God and man, but lords and masters of this whole beautiful earth. Let us, however, not grow proud in spirit, but remain humble, looking carefully into our hearts lest we deviate from the rules of our holy Order and sin against our blessed Saint.

I, Brother Ambrosius, confess with penitence and shame that my soul caught itself upon exceedingly worldly and sinful thoughts. It seemed to me that the women sought more eagerly to kiss my hands than those of my companions—which surely was not right, since I am not more holy than they; besides, am younger and less experienced and tried in the fear and commandments of the Lord. When I observed this error of the women, and saw how the maidens kept their eyes upon me, I became frightened, and wondered if I could resist should temptation accost me; and often I thought, with fear and trembling, that vows and prayer and penance alone do not make one a saint; one must be so pure in heart that temptation is unknown. Ah me!

At night we always lodged in some monastery, invariably receiving a pleasant welcome. Plenty of food and drink was set before us, and as we sat at table the monks would crowd about, asking for news of the great world of which it was our blessed privilege to see and learn so much. When our destination was learned we were usually pitied for being doomed to live in the mountain wilderness. We were told of icefields, snow-crowned mountains and tremendous rocks, roaring torrents, caves and gloomy forests; also of a lake so mysterious and terrible that there was none like it in the world. God be with us!

On the fifth day of our journey, while but a short distance beyond the city of Salzburg, we saw a strange and ominous sight. On the horizon, directly in our front, lay a bank of mighty clouds, with many gray points and patches of darker hue, and above, between them and the blue sky, a second firmament of perfect white. This spectacle greatly puzzled and alarmed us. The clouds had no movement; we watched them for hours and could see no change. Later in the afternoon, when the sun was sinking into the west, they became ablaze with light. They glowed and gleamed in a wonderful manner, and looked at times as if they were on fire!

No one can imagine our surprise when we discovered that what we had mistaken for clouds was simply earth and rocks. These then, were the mountains of which we had heard so much, and the white firmament was nothing else than the snowy summit of the range which the Lutherans say their faith can remove. I greatly doubt it.

II

When we stood at the opening of the pass leading into the mountains we were overcome with dejection; it looked like the mouth of Hell. Behind us lay the beautiful country through which we had come, and which now we were compelled to leave forever; before us frowned the mountains with their inhospitable gorges and haunted forests, forbidding to the sight and full of peril to the body and the soul. Strengthening our hearts with spirits, we entered the narrow pass in the prayer and whispering anathemas against evil name of God, and pressed forward, prepared to suffer whatever might befall.

As we proceeded cautiously on our way giant trees barred our progress and dense foliage almost shut out the light of day, the darkness being deep and chill. The sound of our footfalls and of our voices, when we dared to speak, was returned to us from the great rocks bordering the pass, with such distinctness and so many repetitions, yet withal so changed, that we could hardly believe we were not accompanied by troops of invisible beings who mocked us and made a sport of our fears. Great birds of prey, startled from their nests in the treetops and the sides of the cliffs, perched upon high pinnacles of rock and eyed us malignly as we passed; vultures and ravens croaked above us in hoarse and savage tones that made our blood run cold. Nor could our prayers and hymns give us peace; they only called forth other fowl and by their own echoes multiplied the dreadful noises that beset us. It surprised us to observe that huge trees had been plucked out of the earth by the roots and hurled down the sides of the hills, and we shuddered to think by what powerful hands this had been done. At times we passed along the edges of high precipices, and the dark chasms that yawned below were a terrible sight. A storm arose, and we were half-blinded by the fires of heaven and stunned by thunder a thousand times louder than we had ever heard. Our fears were at last worked up to so great a degree that we expected every minute to see some devil from Hell leap from behind a rock in our front, or a ferocious bear appear from the undergrowth to dispute our progress. But only deer and foxes crossed our path, and our fears were somewhat quieted to perceive that our blessed Saint was no less powerful in the mountains than on the plains below.

At length we reached the bank of a stream whose silvery waters presented a most refreshing sight. In its crystal depths between the rocks we could see beautiful golden trout as large as the carp in the pond of our monastery at Passau. Even in these wild places Heaven had provided bountifully for the fasting of the faithful.

Beneath the black pines and close to the large lichen-covered rocks bloomed rare flowers of dark blue and golden yellow. Brother Ægidius, who was as learned as pious, knew them from his herbarium and told us their names. We were delighted by the sight of various brilliant beetles and butterflies which had come out of their hiding-places after the rain. We gathered handfuls of flowers and chased the pretty winged insects, forgetting our fears and prayers, the bears and evil spirits, in the exuberance of our joy.

For many hours we had not seen a dwelling nor a human being. Deeper and deeper we penetrated the mountain region; greater and greater became the difficulties we experienced in forest and ravine, and all the horrors of the wilderness that we had already passed were repeated, but without so great an effect upon our souls, for we all perceived that the good God was preserving us for longer service to His holy will. A branch of the friendly river lay in our course, and, approaching it, we were delighted to find it spanned by a rough but substantial bridge. As we were about to cross I happened to cast my eyes to the other shore, where I saw a sight that made my blood turn cold with terror. On the opposite bank of the stream was a meadow, covered with beautiful flowers, and in the center a gallows upon which hung the body of a man! The face was turned toward us, and I could plainly distinguish the features, which, though black and distorted, showed unmistakable signs that death had come that very day.

I was upon the point of directing my companions' attention to the dreadful spectacle, when a strange incident occurred: in the meadow appeared a young girl, with long golden hair, upon which rested a wreath of blossoms. She wore a bright red dress, which seemed to me to light up the whole scene like a flame of fire. Nothing in her actions indicated fear of the corpse upon the gallows; on the contrary, she glided toward it barefooted through the grass, singing in a loud but sweet voice, and waving her arms to scare away the birds of prey that had gathered about it, uttering harsh cries and with a great buffeting of wings and snapping of beaks. At the girl's approach they all took flight, except one great vulture, which retained its perch upon the gallows and appeared to defy and threaten her. She ran close up to the obscene creature, jumping, dancing, screaming, until it, too, put out its wide wings and flapped heavily away. Then she ceased her dancing, and, taking a position at the gibbet's foot, calmly and thoughtfully looked up at the swinging body of the unfortunate man.

The maiden's singing had attracted the attention of my companions, and we all stood watching the lovely child and her strange surroundings with too much amazement to speak.

While gazing on the surprising scene, I felt a cold shiver run through my body. This is said to be a sure sign that some one has stepped upon the spot which is to be your grave. Strange to say, I felt this chill at the moment the maiden stepped under the gallows. But this only shows how the true beliefs of men are mixed up with foolish superstitions; for how could a sincere follower of Saint Franciscus possibly come to be buried beneath a gallows?

"Let us hasten," I said to my companions, "and pray for the soul of the dead."

We soon found our way to the spot, and, without raising our eyes, said prayers with great fervor; especially did I, for my heart was full of compassion for the poor sinner who hung above. I recalled the words of God, who said, "Vengeance is mine," and remembered that the dear Savior had pardoned the thief upon the cross at His side; and who knows that there were not mercy and forgiveness for this poor wretch who had died upon the gallows?

On our approach the maiden had retired a short distance, not knowing what to make of us and our prayers. Suddenly, however, in the midst of our devotions, I heard her sweet, bell-like tones exclaim: "The vulture! the vulture!" and her voice was agitated, as if she felt great fear. I looked up and saw a great gray bird above the pines, swooping downward. It showed no fear of us, our sacred calling and our pious rites. My brothers, however, were indignant at the interruption caused by the child's voice, and scolded her. But I said: "The girl is probably a relation of the dead man. Now think of it, brothers; this terrible bird comes to tear the flesh from his face and feed upon his hands and his body. It is only natural that she should cry out."

One of the brothers said: "Go to her, Ambrosius, and command her to be silent that we may pray in peace for the departed soul of this sinful man."

I walked among the fragrant flowers to where the girl stood with her eyes still fixed upon the vulture, which swung in ever narrowing circles about the gallows. Against a mass of silvery flowers on a bush by which she stood the maid's exquisite figure showed to advantage, as I wickedly permitted myself to observe. Perfectly erect and motionless, she watched my advance, though I marked a terrified look in her large, dark eyes, as if she feared that I would do her harm. Even when I was quite near her she made no movement to come forward, as women and children usually did, and kiss my hands.

"Who are you?" I said, "and what are you doing in this dreadful place all alone?"

She did not answer me, and made neither sign nor motion; so I repeated my question: "Tell me, child, what are you doing here?"

"Scaring away the vultures," she replied, in a soft, musical voice, inexpressibly pleasing.

"Are you a relation of the dead man?" I asked.

She shook her head.

"You knew him?" I continued, "and you pity his unchristian death?"

But she was again silent, and I had to renew my questioning: "What was his name, and why was he put to death? What crime did he commit?"

"His name was Nathaniel Alfinger, and he killed a man for a woman," said the maiden, distinctly and in the most unconcerned manner that it is possible to conceive, as if murder and hanging were the commonest and most uninteresting of all events. I was astounded, and gazed at her sharply, but her look was passive and calm, denoting nothing unusual.

"Did you know Nathaniel Alfinger?"

"No."

"Yet you came here to protect his corpse from the fowls?"

"Yes."

"Why do you do that service to one whom you did not know?"

"I always do so."

"How—!"

"Always when any one is hanged here I come and frighten away the birds and make them find other food. See—there is another vulture!"

She uttered a wild, high scream, threw her arms above her head, and ran across the meadow so that I thought her mad. The big bird flew away, and the maiden came quietly back to me, and, pressing her sunburnt hands upon her breast, sighed deeply, as from fatigue. With as much mildness as I could put into my voice, I asked her:

"What is your name?"

"Benedicta."

"And who are your parents?"

"My mother is dead."

"But your father—where is he?"

She was silent. Then I pressed her to tell me where she lived, for I wanted to take the poor child home and admonish her father to have better care of his daughter and not let her stray into such dreadful places again.

"Where do you live, Benedicta? I pray you tell me."

"Here."

"What! here? Ah, my child, here is only the gallows."

She pointed toward the pines. Following the direction of her finger, I saw among the trees a wretched hut which looked like a habitation more fit for animals than human beings. Then I knew better than she could have told me whose child she was.

When I returned to my companions and they asked me who the girl was, I answered: "The hangman's daughter."

III

Having commended the soul of the dead man to the intercession of the Blessed Virgin and the Holy Saints, we left the accursed spot, but as we withdrew I looked back at the lovely child of the hangman. She stood where I had left her, looking after us. Her fair white brow was still crowned with the wreath of primroses, which gave an added charm to her wonderful beauty of feature and expression, and her large, dark eyes shone like the stars of a winter midnight. My companions, to whom the hangman's daughter was a most unchristian object, reproved me for the interest that I manifested in her; but it made me sad to think this sweet and beautiful child was shunned and despised through no fault of her own. Why should she be made to suffer blame because of her father's dreadful calling? And was it not the purest Christian charity which prompted this innocent maiden to keep the vultures from the body of a fellow-creature whom in life she had not even known and who had been adjudged unworthy to live? It seemed to me a more kindly act than that of any professed Christian who bestows money upon the poor. Expressing these feelings to my companions, I found, to my sorrow, that they did not share them; on the contrary, I was called a dreamer and a fool who wished to overthrow the ancient and wholesome customs of the world. Every one, they said, was bound to execrate the class to which the hangman and his family belonged, for all who associated with such persons would surely be contaminated. I had, however, the temerity to remain steadfast in my conviction, and with due humility questioned the justice of treating such persons as criminals because they were a part of the law's machinery by which criminals were punished. Because in the church the hangman and his family had a dark corner specially set apart for them, that could not absolve us from our duty as servants of the Lord to preach the gospel of justice and mercy and give an example of Christian love and charity. But my brothers grew very angry with me, and the wilderness rang with their loud vociferations, so that I began to feel as if I were very wicked, although unable to perceive my error. I could do nothing but hope that Heaven would be more merciful to us all than we are to one another. In thinking of the maiden it gave me comfort to know that her name was Benedicta. Perhaps her parents had so named her as a means of blessing one whom no one else would ever bless.

But I must relate what a wonderful country it was into which we were now arrived. Were we not assured that all the world is the Lord's, for he made it, we might be tempted to think such a wild region the kingdom of the Evil One.

Far down below our path the river roared and foamed between great cliffs, the gray points of which seemed to pierce the very sky. On our left, as we gradually rose out of this chasm, was a black forest of pines, frightful to see, and in front of us a most formidable peak. This mountain, despite its terrors, had a comical appearance, for it was white and pointed like a fool's cap, and looked as if some one had put a flour-sack on the knave's head. After all it was nothing but snow. Snow in the middle of the glorious month of May!—surely the works of God are wonderful and almost past belief! The thought came to me that if this old mountain should shake his head the whole region would be full of flying snow.

We were not a little surprised to find that in various places along our road the forest had been cleared away for a space large enough to build a hut and plant a garden. Some of these rude dwellings stood where one would have thought that only eagles would have been bold enough to build; but there is no place, it seems, free from the intrusion of Man, who stretches out his hand for everything, even that which is in the air. When at last we arrived at our destination and beheld the temple and the house erected in this wilderness to the name and glory of our beloved Saint, our hearts were thrilled with pious emotions. Upon the surface of a pine-covered rock was a cluster of huts and houses, the monastery in the midst, like a shepherd surrounded by his flock. The church and monastery were of hewn stone, of noble architecture, spacious and comfortable.

May the good God bless our entrance into this holy place.

IV

I have now been in this wilderness for a few weeks, but the Lord, too, is here, as everywhere. My health is good, and this house of our beloved Saint is a stronghold of the Faith, a house of peace, an asylum for those who flee from the wrath of the Evil One, a rest for all who bear the burden of sorrow. Of myself, however, I cannot say so much. I am young, and although my mind is at peace, I have so little experience of the world and its ways that I feel myself peculiarly liable to error and accessible to sin. The course of my life is like a rivulet which draws its silver thread smoothly and silently through friendly fields and flowery meadows, yet knows that when the storms come and the rains fall it may become a raging torrent, defiled with earth and whirling away to the sea the wreckage attesting the madness of its passion and its power.

Not sorrow nor despair drew me away from the world into the sacred retreat of the Church, but a sincere desire to serve the Lord. My only wish is to belong to my beloved Saint, to obey the blessed mandates of the Church, and, as a servant of God, to be charitable to all mankind, whom I dearly love. The Church is, in truth, my beloved mother, for, my parents having died in my infancy I, too, might have perished without care had she not taken pity on me, fed and clothed me and reared me as her own child. And, oh, what happiness there will be for me, poor monk, when I am ordained and receive holy orders as a priest of the Most High God! Always I think and dream of it and try to prepare my soul for that high and sacred gift. I know I can never be worthy of this great happiness, but I do hope to be an honest and sincere priest, serving God and Man according to the light that is given from above. I often pray Heaven to put me to the test of temptation, that I may pass through the fire unscathed and purified in mind and soul. As it is, I feel the sovereign peace which, in this solitude, lulls my spirit to sleep, and all life's temptations and trials seem far away, like perils of the sea to one who can but faintly hear the distant thunder of the waves upon the beach.

V

Our Superior, Father Andreas, is a mild and pious gentleman. Our brothers live in peace and harmony. They are not idle, neither are they worldly nor arrogant. They are temperate, not indulging too much in the pleasures of the table—a praiseworthy moderation, for all this region, far and wide—the hills and the valleys, the river and forest, with all that they contain—belongs to the monastery. The woods are full of all kinds of game, of which the choicest is brought to our table, and we relish it exceedingly. In our monastery a drink is prepared from malt and barley—a strong, bitter drink, refreshing after fatigue, but not, to my taste, very good.

The most remarkable thing in this part of the country is the salt-mining. I am told that the mountains are full of salt—how wonderful are the works of the Lord! In pursuit of this mineral Man has penetrated deep into the bowels of the earth by means of shafts and tunnels, and brings forth the bitter marrow of the hills into the light of the sun. The salt I have myself seen in red, brown and yellow crystals. The works give employment to our peasants and their sons, with a few foreign laborers, all under the command of an overseer, who is known as the Saltmaster. He is a stern man, exercising great power, but our Superior and the brothers speak little good of him—not from any unchristian spirit, but because his actions are evil. The Saltmaster has an only son. His name is Rochus, a handsome but wild and wicked youth.

VI

The people hereabout are a proud, stubborn race. I am told that in an old chronicle they are described as decendants of the Romans, who in their day drove many tunnels into these mountains to get out the precious salt; and some of these tunnels are still in existence. From the window of my cell I can see these giant hills and the black forests which at sunset burn like great fire-brands along the crests against the sky.

The forefathers of these people (after the Romans) were, I am told, more stubborn still than they are, and continued in idolatry after all the neighboring peoples had accepted the cross of the Lord our Savior. Now, however, they bow their stiff necks to the sacred symbol and soften their hearts to receive the living truth. Powerful as they are in body, in spirit they are humble and obedient to the Word. Nowhere else did the people kiss my hand so fervently as here, although I am not a priest— an evidence of the power and victory of our glorious faith.

Physically they are strong and exceedingly handsome in face and figure, especially the young men; the elder men, too, walk as erect and proud as kings. The women have long golden hair, which they braid and twist about their heads very beautifully, and they love to adorn themselves with jewels. Some have eyes whose dark brilliancy rivals the luster of the rubies and garnets they wear about their white necks. I am told that the young men fight for the young women as stags for does. Ah, what wicked passions exist in the hearts of men! But since I know nothing of these things, nor shall ever feel such unholy emotions, I must not judge and condemn.

Lord, what a blessing is the peace with which Thou hast filled the spirits of those who are Thine own! Behold, there is no turmoil in my breast; all is calm there as in the soul of a babe which calls "Abba," dear Father. And so may it ever be.

VII

I have again seen the hangman's beautiful daughter. As the bells were chiming for mass I saw her in front of the monastery church. I had just come from the bedside of a sick man, and as my thoughts were gloomy the sight of her face was pleasant, and I should have liked to greet her, but her eyes were cast down: she did not notice me. The square in front of the church was filled with people, the men and youth on one side, on the other the women and maidens all clad in their high hats and adorned with their gold chains. They stood close together, but when the poor child approached all stepped aside, whispering and looking askance at her as if she were an accursed leper and they feared infection.

Compassion filled my breast, compelling me to follow the maiden, and, overtaking her, I said aloud: "God greet you, Benedicta."

She shrank away as if frightened, then, looking up, recognized me, seemed astonished, blushed again and again and finally hung her head in silence.

"Do you fear to speak to me?" I asked.

But she made no reply. Again I spoke to her: "Do good, obey the Lord and fear no one: then shall you be saved."

At this she drew a long sigh, and replied in a low voice, hardly more than a whisper: "I thank you, my lord."

"I am not a lord, Benedicta," I said, "but a poor servant of God, who is a gracious and kind Father to all His children, however lowly their estate. Pray to Him when your heart is heavy, and He will be near you."

While I spoke she lifted her head and looked at me like a sad child that is being comforted by its mother. And, still speaking to her out of the great compassion in my heart, I led her into the church before all the people.

But do thou, O holy Franciscus, pardon the sin that I committed during that high sacrament! For while Father Andreas was reciting the solemn words of the mass my eyes constantly wandered to the spot where the poor child knelt in a dark corner set apart for her and her father, forsaken and alone. She seemed to pray with holy zeal, and surely thou didst grace her with a ray of thy favor, for it was through thy love of mankind that thou didst become a great saint, and didst bring before the Throne of Grace thy large heart, bleeding for the sins of all the world. Then shall not I, the humblest of thy followers, have enough of thy spirit to pity this poor outcast who suffers for no sin of her own? Nay, I feel for her a peculiar tenderness, which I cannot help accepting as a sign from Heaven that I am charged with a special mandate to watch over her, to protect her, and finally to save her soul.

VIII

Our Superior has sent for me and rebuked me. He told me I had caused great ill-feeling among the brothers and the people, and asked what devil had me in possession that I should walk into church with the daughter of the public hangman.

What could I say but that I pitied the poor maiden and could not do otherwise than as I did?

"Why did you pity her?" he asked.

"Because all the people shun her," I replied, "as if she were mortal sin itself, and because she is wholly blameless. It certainly is not her fault that her father is a hangman, nor his either, since, alas, hangmen must be."

Ah, beloved Franciscus, how the Superior scolded thy poor servant for these bold words.

"And do you repent?" he demanded at the close of his reproof. But how could I repent of my compassion—incited, as I verily believe, by our beloved Saint?

On learning my obduracy, the Superior became very sad. He gave me a long lecture and put me under hard penance. I took my punishment meekly and in silence, and am now confined in my cell, fasting and chastising myself. Nor in this do I spare myself at all, for it is happiness to suffer for the sake of one so unjustly treated as the poor friendless child.

I stand at the grating of my cell, looking out at the high, mysterious mountains showing black against the evening sky. The weather being mild, I open the window behind the bars to admit the fresh air and better to hear the song of the stream below, which speaks to me with a divine companionship, gentle and consoling.

I know not if I have already mentioned that the monastery is built upon a rock high over the river. Directly under the windows of our cells are the rugged edges of great cliffs, which none can scale but at the peril of his life. Imagine, then, my astonishment when I saw a living figure lift itself up from the awful abyss by the strength of its hands, and, drawing itself across the edge, stand erect upon the very verge! In the dusk I could not make out what kind of creature it was; I thought it some evil spirit come to tempt me; so I crossed myself and said a prayer. Presently there is a movement of its arm, and something flies through the window, past my head, and lies upon the floor of my cell, shining like a white star. I bend and pick it up. It is a bunch of flowers such as I have never seen—leafless, white as snow, soft as velvet, and without fragrance. As I stand by the window, the better to see the wondrous flowers, my eyes turn again to the figure on the cliff, and I hear a sweet, low voice, which says: "I am Benedicta, and I thank you."

Ah, Heaven! it was the child, who, that she might greet me in my loneliness and penance, had climbed the dreadful rocks, heedless of the danger. She knew, then, of my punishment—knew that it was for her. She knew even the very cell in which I was confined. O holy Saint! surely she could not have known all this but from thee; and I were worse than an infidel to doubt that the feeling which I have for her signifies that a command has been laid upon me to save her.

I saw her bending over the frightful precipice. She turned a moment and waved her hand to me and disappeared. I uttered an involuntary cry—had she fallen? I grasped the iron bars of my window and shook them with all my strength, but they did not yield. In my despair I threw myself upon the floor, crying and praying to all the saints to protect the dear child in her dangerous descent if still she lived, to intercede for her unshriven soul if she had fallen. I was still kneeling when Benedicta gave me a sign of her safe arrival below. It was such a shout as these mountaineers utter in their untamed enjoyment of life—only Benedicta's shout, coming from far below in the gorge, and mingled with its own strange echoes, sounded like nothing I had ever heard from any human throat, and so affected me that I wept, and the tears fell upon the wild flowers in my hand.

IX

As a follower of Saint Franciscus, I am not permitted to own anything dear to my heart, so I have disposed of my most precious treasure; I have presented to my beloved Saint the beautiful flowers which were Benedicta's offering. They are so placed before his picture in the monastery church as to decorate the bleeding heart which he carries upon his breast as a symbol of his suffering for mankind.

I have learned the name of the flower: because of its color, and because it is finer than other flowers, it is called Edelweiss—noble white. It grows in so rare perfection only upon the highest and wildest rocks— mostly upon cliffs, over abysses many hundred feet in depth, where one false step would be fatal to him who gathers it.

These beautiful flowers, then, are the real evil spirits of this wild region: they lure many mortals to a dreadful death. The brothers here have told me that never a year passes but some shepherd, some hunter or some bold youth, attracted by these wonderful blossoms, is lost in the attempt to get them.

May God be merciful to all their souls!

X

I must have turned pale when one of the brothers reported at the supper table that upon the picture of Saint Franciscus had been found a bunch of edelweiss of such rare beauty as grows nowhere else in the country but at the summit of a cliff which is more than a thousand feet high, and overhangs a dreadful lake. The brothers tell wondrous tales of the horrors of this lake—how wild its waters and how deep, and how the most hideous specters are seen along its shores or rising out of it.

Benedicta's edelweiss, therefore, has caused great commotion and wonder, for even among the boldest hunters there are few, indeed, who dare to climb that cliff by the haunted lake. And the tender child has accomplished this feat! She has gone quite alone to that horrible place, and has climbed the almost vertical wall of the mountain to the green spot where the flowers grow with which she was moved to greet me. I doubt not that Heaven guarded her against mishap in order that I might have a visible sign and token that I am charged with the duty of her salvation.

Ah, thou poor sinless child, accurst in the eyes of the people, God hath signified His care of thee, and in my heart I feel already something of that adoration which shall be thy due when for thy purity and holiness He shall bestow upon thy relics some signal mark of His favor, and the Church shall declare thee blessed!

I have learned another thing that I will chronicle here. In this country these flowers are the sign of a faithful love: the youth presents them to his sweetheart, and the maidens decorate the hats of their lovers with them. It is clear that, in expressing her gratitude to a humble servant of the Church, Benedicta was moved, perhaps without knowing it, to signify at the same time her love of the Church itself, although, alas, she has yet too little cause.

As I ramble about here, day after day, I am becoming familiar with every path in the forest, in the dark pass, and on the slopes of the mountains.

I am often sent to the homes of the peasants, the hunters and the shepherds, to carry either medicine to the sick or consolation to the sad. The most reverend Superior has told me that as soon as I receive the holy orders I shall have to carry the sacraments to the dying, for I am the youngest and the strongest of the brothers. In these high places it sometimes occurs that a hunter or a shepherd falls from the rocks, and after some days is found, still living. It is then the duty of the priest to perform the offices of our holy religion at the bedside of the sufferer, so that the blessed Savior may be there to receive the departing soul.

That I may be worthy of such grace, may our beloved Saint keep my heart pure from every earthly passion and desire!

XI

The monastery has celebrated a great festival, and I will report all that occurred.

For many days before the event the brothers were busy preparing for it. Some decorated the church with sprays of pine and birch and with flowers.

They went with the other men and gathered the most beautiful Alpine roses they could find, and as it is midsummer they grow in great abundance. On the day before the festival the brothers sat in the garden, weaving garlands to adorn the church; even the most reverend Superior and the fathers took pleasure in our merry task. They walked beneath the trees and chatted pleasantly while encouraging the brother butler to spend freely the contents of the cellars.

The next morning was the holy procession. It was very beautiful to see, and added to the glory of our holy Church. The Superior walked under a purple silken canopy, surrounded by the worthy Fathers, and bore in his hands the sacred emblem of the crucifixion of our Savior. We brothers followed, bearing burning candles and singing psalms. Behind us came a great crowd of the people, dressed in their finest attire.

The proudest of those in the procession were the mountaineers and the salt-miners, the Saltmaster at their head on a beautiful horse adorned with costly trappings. He was a proud-looking man, with his great sword at his side and a plumed hat upon his broad, high brow. Behind him rode Rochus, his son. When we had collected in front of the gate to form a line I took special notice of that young man. I judge him to be self-willed and bold. He wore his hat on the side of his head and cast flaming glances upon the women and the maidens. He looked contemptuously upon us monks. I fear he is not a good Christian, but he is the most beautiful youth that I have ever seen: tall and slender like a young pine, with light brown eyes and golden locks.

The Saltmaster is as powerful in this region as our Superior. He is appointed by the Duke and has judicial powers in all affairs. He has even the power of life and death over those accused of murder or any other abominable crime. But the Lord has fortunately endowed him with good judgment and wisdom.

Through the village the procession moved out into the valley and down to the entrances of the great salt mines. In front of the principal mine an altar was erected, and there our Superior read high mass, while all the people knelt. I observed that the Saltmaster and his son knelt and bent their heads with visible reluctance, and this made me very sad. After the service the procession moved toward the hill called "Mount Calvary," which is still higher than the monastery, and from the top of which one has a good view of the whole country below. There the reverend Superior displayed the crucifix in order to banish the evil powers which abound in these terrible mountains; and he also said prayers and pronounced anathemas against all demons infesting the valley below. The bells chimed their praises to the Lord, and it seemed as if divine voices were ringing through the wilderness. It was all, indeed, most beautiful and good.

I looked about me to see if the child of the hangman were present, but I could not see her anywhere, and knew not whether to rejoice that she was out of reach of the insults of the people or to mourn because deprived of the spiritual strength that might have come to me from looking upon her heavenly beauty.

After the services came the feast. Upon a meadow sheltered by trees tables were spread, and the clergy and the people, the most reverend

Superior and the great Saltmaster partook of the viands served by the young men. It was interesting to see the young men make big fires of pine and maple, put great pieces of beef upon wooden spits, turn them over the coals until they were brown and then lay them before the Fathers and the mountaineers. They also boiled mountain trout and carp in large kettles. The wheaten bread was brought in immense baskets, and as to drink, there was assuredly no scarcity of that, for the Superior and the Saltmaster had each given a mighty cask of beer. Both of these monstrous barrels lay on wooden stands under an ancient oak. The boys and the Saltmaster's men drew from the cask which he had given, while that of the Superior was served by the brother butler and a number of us younger monks. In honor of Saint Franciscus I must say that the clerical barrel was of vastly greater size than that of the Saltmaster.

Separate tables had been provided for the Superior and the Fathers, and for the Saltmaster and the best of his people. The Saltmaster and Superior sat upon chairs which stood upon a beautiful carpet, and their seats were screened from the sun by a linen canopy. At the table, surrounded by their beautiful wives and daughters, sat many knights, who had come from their distant castles to share in the great festival. I helped at table. I handed the dishes and filled the goblets and was able to see how good an appetite the company had, and how they loved that brown and bitter drink. I could see also how amorously the Saltmaster's son looked at the ladies, which provoked me very much, as he could not marry them all, especially those already married.

We had music, too. Some boys from the village, who practice on various instruments in their spare moments, were the performers. Ah, how they yelled, those flutes and pipes, and how the fiddle bows danced and chirped! I do not doubt the music was very good, but Heaven has not seen fit to give me the right kind of ears.

I am sure our blessed Saint must have derived great satisfaction from the sight of so many people eating and drinking their bellies full. Heavens! how they did eat—what unearthly quantities they did away with! But that was nothing to their drinking. I firmly believe that if every mountaineer had brought along a barrel of his own he would have emptied it, all by himself. But the women seemed to dislike the beer, especially the young girls. Usually before drinking a young man would hand his cup to one of the maids, who barely touched it with her lips, and, making a grimace, turned away her face. I am not sufficiently acquainted with the ways of woman to say with certainty if this proved that at other times they were so abstemious.

After eating, the young men played at various games which exhibited their agility and strength. Holy Franciscus! what legs they have, what arms and necks! They leapt, they wrestled with one another; it was like the fighting of bears. The mere sight of it caused me to feel great fear. It seemed as if they would crush one another. But the maidens looked on, feeling neither fear nor anxiety; they giggled and appeared well pleased. It was wonderful, too, to hear the voices of these young mountaineers; they threw back their heads and shouted till the echoes rang from the mountain-sides and roared in the gorges, as if from the throats of a legion of demons.

Foremost among all was the Saltmaster's son. He sprang like a deer, fought like a fiend, and bellowed like a wild bull. Among these mountaineers he was a king. I observed that many were jealous of his strength and beauty, and secretly hated him; yet all obeyed. It was beautiful to see how this young man bent his slender body while leaping and playing in the games—how he threw up his head like a stag at gaze, shook his golden locks and stood in the midst of his fellows with flaming cheeks and sparkling eyes. How sad to think that pride and passion should make their home in so lovely a body, which seems created for the habitation of a soul that would glorify its Maker!

It was near dusk when the Superior, the Saltmaster, the Fathers and all the distinguished guests parted and retired to their homes, leaving the others at drink and dance. My duties compelled me to remain with the brother butler to serve the debauching youths with beer from the great cask. Young Rochus remained too. I do not know how it occurred, but suddenly he stood before me. His looks were dark and his manner proud.

"Are you," he said, "the monk who gave offense to the people the other day?"

I asked humbly—though beneath my monk's robe I felt a sinful anger: "What are you speaking of?"

"As if you did not know!" he said, haughtily. "Now bear in mind what I tell you; if you ever show any friendship toward that girl I shall teach you a lesson which you will not soon forget. You monks are likely to call your impertinence by the name of some virtue; but I know the trick, and will have none of it. Make a note of that, you young cowl-wearer, for your handsome face and big eyes will not save you."

With that he turned his back upon me and went away, but I heard his strong voice ringing out upon the night as he sang and shouted with the others. I was greatly alarmed to learn that this bold boy had cast his eyes upon the hangman's lovely daughter. His feeling for her was surely not honorable, or, instead of hating me for being kind to her, he would have been grateful and would have thanked me. I feared for the child, and again and again did I promise my blessed Saint that I would watch over and protect her, in obedience to the miracle which he has wrought in my breast regarding her. With that wondrous feeling to urge me on, I cannot be slack in my duty, and, Benedicta, thou shalt be saved—thy body and thy soul!

XII

Let me continue my report.

The boys threw dry brushwood into the fire so that the flames illuminated the whole meadow and shone red upon the trees. Then they laid hands upon the village maidens and began to turn and swing them round and round. Holy saints! how they stamped and turned and threw their hats in the air, kicked up their heels, and lifted the girls from the ground, as if the sturdy wenches were nothing but feather balls! They shouted and yelled as if all the evil spirits had them in possession, so that I wished a herd of swine might come, that the devils might leave these human brutes and go into the four-legged ones. The boys were quite full of the brown beer, which for its bitterness and strength is a beastly drink.

Before long the madness of intoxication broke out; they attacked one another with fists and knives, and it looked as if they would do murder. Suddenly the Saltmaster's son, who had stood looking on, leapt among them, caught two of the combatants by the hair and knocked their heads together with such force that the blood started from their noses, and I thought surely their skulls had been crushed like egg-shells; but they must have been very hard-headed, for on being released they seemed little the worse for their punishment. After much shouting and screaming, Rochus succeeded in making peace, which seemed to me, poor worm, quite heroic. The music set in again: the fiddles scraped and the pipes shrieked, while the boys, with torn clothes and scratched and bleeding faces, renewed the dance as if nothing has occurred. Truly this is a people that would gladden the heart of a Bramarbas or a Holofernes!

I had scarcely recovered from the fright which Rochus had given me, when I was made to feel a far greater one. Rochus was dancing with a tall and beautiful girl, who looked the very queen of this young king. They made such mighty leaps and dizzy turns, but at the same time so graceful, that all looked on with astonishment and pleasure. The girl had a sensuous smile on her lips and a bold look in her brown face, which seemed to say: "See! I am the mistress of his heart!" But suddenly he pushed her from him as in disgust, broke from the circle of dancers, and cried to his friends: "I am going to bring my own partner. Who will go with me?"

The tall girl, maddened by the insult, stood looking at him with the face of a demon, her black eyes burning like flames of hell! But her discomfiture amused the drunken youths, and they laughed aloud.

Snatching a fire-brand and swinging it about his head till the sparks flew in showers, Rochus cried again: "Who goes with me?" and walked rapidly away into the forest. The others, seizing fire-brands also, ran after him, and soon their voices could be heard far away, ringing out upon the night, themselves no longer seen. I was still looking in the direction which they had taken, when the tall girl whom Rochus had insulted stepped to my side and hissed something into my ear. I felt her hot breath on my cheek.

"If you care for the hangman's daughter, then hasten and save her from that drunken wretch. No woman resists him!"

God! how the wild words of that woman horrified me! I did not doubt the girl's words, but in my anxiety for the poor child I asked: "How can I save her?"

"Run and warn her, monk," the wench replied: "she will listen to you."

"But they will find her sooner than I."

"They are drunk and will not go fast. Besides, I know a path leading to the hangman's hut by a shorter route."

"Then show me and be quick!" I cried.

She glided away, motioning me to follow. We were soon in the woods, where it was so dark I could hardly see the woman's figure; but she moved as fast and her step was as sure as in the light of day. Above us we could see the torches of the boys, which showed that they had taken the longer path along the mountain-side. I heard their wild shouts, and trembled for the child. We had walked for some time in silence, having left the youths far behind, when the young woman began speaking to herself. At first I did not understand, but soon my ears caught every passionate word:

"He shall not have her! To the devil with the hangman's whelp! Every one despises her and spits at the sight of her. It is just like him—he does not care for what people think or say. Because they hate he loves. Besides, she has a pretty face. I'll make it pretty for her! I'll mark it with blood! But if she were the daughter of the devil himself he would not rest until he had her. He shall not!"

She lifted her arms and laughed wildly—I shuddered to hear her! I thought of the dark powers that live in the human breast, though I know as little of them, thank God, as a child.

At length we reached the Galgenberg, where stands the hangman's hut, and a few moments' climb brought us near the door.

"There she lives," said the girl, pointing to the hut, through the windows of which shone the yellow light of a tallow candle; "go warn her. The hangman is ill and unable to protect his daughter, even if he dared. You'd better take her away—take her to the Alpfeld on the Göll, where my father has a house. They will not look for her up there."

With that she left me and vanished in the darkness.

XIII

Looking in at the window of the hut, I saw the hangman sitting in a chair, with his daughter beside him, her hand upon his shoulder. I could hear him cough and groan, and knew that she was trying to soothe him in his pain. A world of love and sorrow was in her face, which was more beautiful than ever.

Nor did I fail to observe how clean and tidy were the room and all in it. The humble dwelling looked, indeed, like a place blessed by the peace of God. Yet these blameless persons are treated as accurst and hated like mortal sin! What greatly pleased me was an image of the Blessed Virgin on the wall opposite the window at which I stood. The frame was decorated with flowers of the field, and the mantle of the Holy Mother festooned with edelweiss.

I knocked at the door, calling out at the same time: "Do not fear; it is I—Brother Ambrosius."

It seemed to me that, on hearing my voice and name, Benedicta showed a sudden joy in her face, but perhaps it was only surprise—may the saints preserve me from the sin of pride. She came to the window and opened it.

"Benedicta," said I, hastily, after returning her greeting, "wild and drunken boys are on their way hither to take you to the dance. Rochus is with them, and says that he will fetch you to dance with him. I have come before them to assist you to escape."

At the name of Rochus I saw the blood rise into her cheeks and suffuse her whole face with crimson. Alas, I perceived that my jealous guide was right: no woman could resist that beautiful boy, not even this pious and virtuous child. When her father comprehended what I said he rose to his feet and stretched out his feeble arms as if to shield her from harm, but, although his soul was strong, his body I knew, was powerless. I said to him: "Let me take her away; the boys are drunk and know not what they do. Your resistance would only make them angry, and they might harm you both. Ah, look! See their torches; hear their boisterous voices! Hasten, Benedicta—be quick, be quick!"

Benedicta sprang to the side of the now sobbing old man and tenderly embraced him. Then she hurried from the room, and after covering my hands with kisses ran away into the woods, disappearing in the night, at which I was greatly surprised. I waited for her to return, for a few minutes, then entered the cabin to protect her father from the wild youths who, I thought, would visit their disappointment upon him.

But they did not come. I waited and listened in vain. All at once I heard shouts of joy and screams that made me tremble and pray to the blessed Saint. But the sounds died away in the distance, and I knew that the boys had retraced their steps down the Galgenberg to the meadow of the fires. The sick man and I spoke of the miracle which had changed their hearts, and we were filled with gratitude and joy. Then I returned along the path by which I had come. As I arrived near the meadow, I could hear a wilder and madder uproar than ever, and could see through the trees the glare of greater fires, with the figures of the youths and a few maids dancing in the open, their heads uncovered, their hair streaming over their shoulders, their garments disordered by the fury of their movements. They circled about the fires, wound in and out among them, showing black or red according to how the light struck them, and looking altogether like Demons of the Pit commemorating some infernal anniversary or some new torment for the damned. And, holy Savior!

there, in the midst of an illuminated space, upon which the others did not trespass, dancing by themselves and apparently forgetful of all else, were Rochus and Benedicta!

XIV

Holy Mother of God! what can be worse than the fall of an angel? I saw—I understood, then that in leaving me and her father, Benedicta had gone willingly to meet the very fate from which I had striven to save her!

"The accurst wench has run into Rochus' arms," hissed some one at my side, and, turning, I saw the tall brown girl who had been my guide, her face distorted with hate. "I wish that I had killed her. Why did you suffer her to play us this trick, you fool of a monk?"

I pushed her aside and ran toward the couple without thinking what I did. But what could I do? Even at that instant, as though to prevent my interference, though really unconscious of my presence, the drunken youths formed a circle about them, bawling their admiration and clapping their hands to mark the time.

As these two beautiful figures danced they were a lovely picture. He, tall, slender and lithe, was like a god of the heathen Greeks; while Benedicta looked like a fairy. Seen through the slight mist upon the meadows, her delicate figure, moving swiftly and swaying from side to side, seemed veiled with a web of purple and gold. Her eyes were cast modestly upon the ground; her motions, though agile, were easy and graceful; her face glowed with excitement, and it seemed as if her whole soul were absorbed in the dance. Poor, sweet child! her error made me weep, but I forgave her. Her life was so barren and joyless; why should she not love to dance? Heaven bless her! But Rochus— ah, God forgive him!

While I was looking on at all this, and thinking what it was my duty to do, the jealous girl—she is called Amula—had stood near me, cursing and blaspheming. When the boys applauded Benedicta's dancing Amula made as if she would spring forward and strangle her. But I held the furious creature back, and, stepping forward, called out: "Benedicta!"

She started at the sound of my voice, but though she hung her head a little lower she continued dancing. Amula could control her rage no longer, and rushed forward with a savage cry, trying to break into the circle. But the drunken boys prevented. They jeered at her, which maddened her the more, and she made effort after effort to reach her victim. The boys drove her away with shouts, curses and laughter. Holy Franciscus, pray for us!—when I saw the hatred in Amula's eyes a cold shudder ran through my body. God be with us! I believe the creature capable of killing the poor child with her own hands, and glorying in the deed!

I ought now to have gone home, but I remained. I thought of what might occur when the dance was over, for I had been told that the youths commonly accompanied their partners home, and I was horrified to think of Rochus and Benedicta alone together in the forest and the night.

Imagine my surprise when all at once Benedicta lifted her head, stopped dancing, and, looking kindly at Rochus, said in her sweet voice, so like the sound of silver bells:

"I thank you, sir, for having chosen me for your partner in the dance in such a knightly way."

Then bowing to the Saltmaster's son, she slipped quickly through the circle, and, before any one could know what was occurring disappeared in the black spaces of the forest. Rochus at first seemed stupefied with amazement, but when he realized that Benedicta was indeed gone he raved like a madman. He shouted: "Benedicta!" He called her endearing names; but all to no purpose—she had vanished. Then he hurried after her and wanted to search the forest with torches, but the other youths dissuaded him. Observing my presence, he turned his wrath upon me; I think if he had dared he would have struck me. He cried: "I'll make you smart for this, you miserable cowl-wearer!"

But I do not fear him. Praise be to God! Benedicta is not guilty, and I can respect her as before. Yet I tremble to think of the many perils which beset her. She is defenseless against the hate of Amula as well as against the lust of Rochus. Ah, if I could be ever at her side to watch over and protect her! But I commend her to Thee, O Lord: the poor motherless child shall surely not trust to Thee in vain.

XV

Alas! my unhappy fate!—again punished and again unable to find myself guilty.

It seems that Amula has talked about Benedicta and Rochus. The brown wench strolled from house to house telling how Rochus went to the gallows for his partner in the dance. And she added that Benedicta had acted in the most shameless manner with the drunken boys. When the people spoke to me of this I enlightened them regarding the facts, as it seemed to me my duty to do, and told all as it had occurred.

By this testimony in contradiction of one who broke the Decalogue by bearing false witness against her neighbor I have, it seems, offended the Superior. I was summoned before him and accused of defending the hangman's daughter against the statements of an honest Christian girl. I asked, meekly, what I should have done—whether I should have permitted the innocent and defenseless to be calumniated.

"Of what interest," I was asked, "can the hangman's daughter be to you? Moreover, it is a fact that she went of her own will to associate with the drunken boys."

To this I replied: "She went out of love to her father, for if the intoxi-cated youths had not found her they would have maltreated him—and she loves the old man, who is ill and helpless. Thus it happened, and thus I have testified."

But His Reverence insisted that I was wrong, and put me under severe penance. I willingly undergo it: I am glad to suffer for the sweet child. Nor will I murmur against the reverend Superior, for he is my master, against whom to rebel, even in thought, is sin. Is not obedience the foremost commandment of our great Saint for all his disciples? Ah, how I long for the priestly ordination and the holy oil! Then I shall have peace and be able to serve Heaven better and with greater acceptance.

I am troubled about Benedicta. If not confined to my cell I should go toward the Galgenberg: perhaps I should meet her. I grieve for her as if she were my sister.

Belonging to the Lord, I have no right to love anything but Him who died upon the cross for our sins—all other love is evil. O blessed Saints in Heaven! what if it be that this feeling which I have accepted as a sign and token that I am charged with the salvation of Benedicta's soul is but an earthly love? Pray for me, O dear Franciscus, that I may have the light, lest I stray into that road which leads down to Hell. Light and strength, beloved Saint, that I may know the right path, and walk therein forever!

XVI

I stand at the window of my cell. The sun sinks and the shadows creep higher on the sides of the mountains beyond the abyss. The abyss itself is filled with a mist whose billowy surface looks like a great lake. I think how Benedicta climbed out of these awful depths to fling me the edelweiss; I listen for the sound of the stones displaced by her daring little feet and plunging into the chasm below. But night after night has passed. I hear the wind among the pines; I hear the water roaring in the deeps; I hear the distant song of the nightingale; but her voice I do not hear.

Every evening the mist rises from the abyss. It forms billows; then rings; then flakes, and these rise and grow and darken until they are great clouds. They cover the hill and the valley, the tall pines and the snow-pointed mountains. They extinguish the last remaining touches of sunlight on the higher peaks, and it is night. Alas, in my soul also there is night—dark, starless and without hope of dawn!

To-day is Sunday. Benedicta was not in church—"the dark corner" remained vacant. I was unable to keep my mind upon the service, a sin for which I shall do voluntary penance.

Amula was among the other maidens, but I saw nothing of Rochus. It seemed to me that her watchful black eyes were a sufficient guard against any rival, and that in her jealousy Benedicta would find protection. God can make the basest passions serve the most worthy ends, and the reflection gave me pleasure, which, alas, was of short life.

The services being at an end, the Fathers and friars left the church slowly in procession, moving through the vestry, while the people went out at the main entrance. From the long covered gallery leading out of the vestry one has a full view of the public square of the village. As we friars, who were behind the Fathers, were in the gallery, something occurred which I shall remember even to the day of my death as an unjust deed which Heaven permitted for I know not what purpose. It seems that the Fathers must have known what was coming, for they halted in the gallery, giving us all an opportunity to look out upon the square.

I heard a confused noise of voices. It came nearer, and the shouting and yelling sounded like the approach of all the fiends of Hell. Being at the farther end of the gallery, I was unable to see what was going on in the square, so I asked a brother at a window near by what it was all about.

"They are taking a woman to the pillory," he answered.

"Who is it?"

"A girl."

"What has she done?"

"You ask a foolish question. Whom are pillories and whipping-posts for but fallen women?"

The howling mob passed farther into the square, so that I had a full view. In the front were boys, leaping, gesticulating and singing vile songs. They seemed mad with joy and made savage by the shame and pain of their fellow-creature. Nor did the maids behave much better. "Fie upon the outcast!" they cried. "See what it is to be a sinner! Thank Heaven, we are virtuous."

In the rear of these yelling boys, surrounded by this mob of screaming women and girls—O, God! how can I write it? How can I express the horror of it? In the midst of it all—she, the lovely, the sweet, the immaculate Benedicta!

O my Savior! how did I see all this, yet am still living to relate it? I must have come near to death. The gallery, the square, the people seemed whirling round and round; the earth sank beneath my feet, and, although I strained my eyes open to see, yet all was dark. But it must have been for but a short time; I recovered, and, looking down into the square, saw her again.

They had clothed her in a long gray cloak, fastened at the waist with a rope. Her head bore a wreath of straw, and on her breast, suspended by a string about the neck, was a black tablet bearing in chalk the word "Buhle"—harlot.

By the end of the rope about her waist a man led her. I looked at him closely, and—O most holy Son of God, what brutes and beasts Thou didst come to save!—it was Benedicta's father! They had compelled the poor old man to perform one of the duties of his office by leading his own child to the pillory! I learned later that he had implored the Superior on his knees not to lay this dreadful command upon him, but all in vain.

The memory of this scene can never leave me. The hangman did not remove his eyes from his daughter's face, and she frequently nodded at him and smiled. By the grace of God, the maiden smiled!

The mob insulted her, called her vile names and spat upon the ground in front of her feet. Nor was this all. Observing that she took no notice of them, they pelted her with dust and grass. This was more than the poor father could endure, and, with a faint, inarticulate moan, he fell to the ground in a swoon.

Oh, the pitiless wretches!—they wanted to lift him up and make him finish his task, but Benedicta stretched out her arm in supplication, and with an expression of so ineffable tenderness upon her beautiful face that even the brutal mob felt her gentle power and recoiled from before her, leaving the unconscious man upon the ground. She knelt and took her father's head in her lap. She whispered in his ear words of love and comfort. She stroked his gray hair and kissed his pale lips until she had coaxed him into consciousness and he had opened his eyes. Benedicta, thrice blessed Benedicta, thou surely art born to be a saint, for thou didst show a divine patience like that with which our Savior bore His cross and with it all the sins of the world!

She helped her father to rise, and smiled brightly in his face when he made out to stand. She shook the dust from his clothing, and then, still smiling and murmuring words of encouragement, handed him the rope. The boys yelled and sang, the women screamed, and the wretched old man led his innocent child to the place of shame.

XVII

When I was back again in my cell I threw myself upon the stones and cried aloud to God against the injustice and misery that I had witnessed, and against the still greater misery of which I had been spared the sight. I saw in my mind the father binding his child to the post. I saw the brutal populace dance about her with savage delight. I saw the vicious Amula spit in the pure one's face. I prayed long and earnestly that the poor child might be made strong to endure her great affliction.

Then I sat and waited. I waited for the setting of the sun, for at that time the sufferer is commonly released from the whipping-post. The minutes seemed hours, the hours eternities. The sun did not move; the day of shame was denied a night.

It was in vain that I tried to understand it all; I was stunned and dazed. Why did Rochus permit Benedicta to be so disgraced? Does he think the deeper her shame the more easily he can win her? I know not, nor do I greatly care to search out his motive. But, God help me! I myself feel her disgrace, most keenly.

And, Lord, Lord, what a light has come into the understanding of Thy servant! It has come to me like a revelation out of Heaven that my feeling for Benedicta is more and less than what I thought it. It is an earthly love—the love of a man for a woman. As first this knowledge broke into my consciousness my breath came short, my heart beat quick and hard; it seemed to me that I should suffocate. Yet such was the hardness of my heart from witnessing so terrible an injustice tolerated by Heaven, that I was unable wholly to repent. In the sudden illumination I was blinded: I could not clearly see my degree of sin. The tumult of my emotions was not altogether disagreeable; I had to confess to myself that I would not willingly forego it, even if I knew it wicked. May the Mother of Mercy intercede for me!

Even now I cannot think that in supposing myself to have a divine mandate to save the soul of Benedicta, and prepare her for a life of sanctity, I was wholly in error. This other human desire—comes it not also of God? Is it not concerned for the good of its object? And what can be a greater good than salvation of the soul?—a holy life on earth, and in Heaven eternal happiness and glory to reward it. Surely the spiritual and the carnal love are not so widely different as I have been taught to think them. They are, perhaps, not antagonistic, and are but expressions of the same will. O holy Franciscus, in this great light that has fallen about me, guide thou my steps. Show to my dazzled eyes the straight, right way to Benedicta's good!

At length the sun disappeared behind the cloister. The flakes and cloudlets gathered upon the horizon; the haze rose from the abyss and, beyond, the purple shadow climbed higher and higher the great slope of the mountain, extinguishing at last the gleam of light upon the summit. Thank God, O thank God, she is free!

XVIII

I have been very ill, but by the kind attention of the brothers am sufficiently recovered to leave my bed. It must be God's will that I live to serve Him, for certainly I have done nothing to merit His great mercy in restoring me to health. Still, I feel a yearning in my soul for a complete dedication of my poor life to Him and His service. To embrace Him and be bound up in His love are now the only aspirations that I have. As soon as the holy oil is on my brow, these hopes, I am sure, will be fulfilled, and, purged of my hopeless earthly passion for Benedicta, I shall be lifted into a new and diviner life. And it may be that then I can, without offense to Heaven or peril to my soul, watch over and protect her far better than I can now as a wretched monk.

I have been weak. My feet, like those of an infant, failed to support my body. The brothers carried me into the garden. With what gratitude I again looked upward into the blue of the sky! How rapturously I gazed upon the white peaks of the mountains and the black forests on their slopes! Every blade of grass seemed to me of special interest, and I greeted each passing insect as if it were an old acquaintance.

My eyes wander to the south, where the Galgenberg is, and I think unceasingly of the poor child of the hangman. What has become of her? Has she survived her terrible experience in the public square? What is she doing? Oh, that I were strong enough to walk to the Galgenberg! But I am not permitted to leave the monastery, and there is none of whom I dare ask her fate. The friars look at me strangely; it is as if they no longer regarded me as one of them. Why is this so? I love them, and desire to live in harmony with them. They are kind and gentle, yet they seem to avoid me as much as they can. What does it all mean?

XIX

I have been in the presence of the most reverend Superior, Father Andreas. "Your recovery was miraculous," said he. "I wish you to be worthy of such mercies, and to prepare your soul for the great blessing that awaits you. I have, therefore, my son, ordained that you leave us for a season, to dwell apart in the solitude of the mountains, for the double purpose of restoring your strength and affording you an insight into your own heart. Make a severe examination apart from any distractions, and you will perceive, I do not doubt, the gravity of your error. Pray that a divine light may be shed upon your path, that you may walk upright in the service of the Lord as a true priest and apostle, with immunity from all base passions and earthly desires."

I had not the presumption to reply. I submit to the will of His Reverence without a murmur, for obedience is a rule of our Order. Nor do I fear the wilderness, although I have heard that it is infested with wild beasts and evil spirits. Our Superior is right: the time passed in solitude will be to me a season of probation, purification and healing, of which I am doubtless in sore need. So far I have progressed in sin only; for in confession I have kept back many things. Not from the fear of punishment, but because I could not mention the name of the maiden before any other than my holy and blessed Franciscus, who alone can understand. He looks kindly down upon me from the skies, listening to my sorrow; and whatever of guilt there may be in my compassion for the innocent and persecuted child he willingly overlooks for the sake of our blessed Redeemer, who also suffered injustice and was acquainted with grief.

In the mountains it will be my duty to dig certain roots and send them to the monastery. From such roots as I am instructed to gather the Fathers distil a liquor which has become famous throughout the land, even as far, I have been told, as the great city of Munich. This liquor is so strong and so fiery with spices that after drinking it one feels a burning in his throat as if he had swallowed a flame from hell; yet it is held in high esteem everywhere by reason of its medicinal properties, it being a remedy for many kinds of ills and infirmities; and it is said to be good also for the health of the soul, though I should suppose a godly life might be equally efficacious in places where the liquor cannot be obtained. However this may be, from the sale of the liquor comes the chief revenue of the monastery.

The root from which it is chiefly made is that of an Alpine plant called *gentiana,* which grows in great abundance on the sides of the mountains. In the months of July and August the friars dig the roots and dry them by fire in the mountain cabins, and they are then packed and sent to the monastery. The Fathers have the sole right to dig the root in this region, and the secret of manufacturing the liquor is jealously guarded.

As I am to live in the high country for some time, the Superior has directed me to collect the root from time to time as I have the strength. A boy, a servant in the monastery, is to guide me to my solitary station, carrying up my provisions and returning immediately. He will come once a week to renew my supply of food and take away the roots that I shall have dug.

No time has been lost in dispatching me on my penitential errand. This very evening I have taken leave of the Superior, and, retiring to my cell, have packed my holy books, the Agnus and the Life of Saint Franciscus, in a bag. Nor have I forgotten writing-materials with which to continue my diary. These preparations made, I have fortified my soul with prayer, and am ready for any fate, even an encounter with the beasts and demons.

Beloved Saint, forgive the pain I feel in going away without having seen Benedicta, or even knowing what has become of her since that dreadful day. Thou knowest, O glorious one, and humbly do I confess, that I long to hasten to the Galgenberg, if only to get one glimpse of the hut which holds the fairest and best of her sex. Take me not, holy one, too severely to task, I beseech thee, for the weakness of my erring human heart!

XX

As I left the monastery with my young guide all was quiet within its walls; the holy brotherhood slept the sleep of peace, which had so long been denied to me. It was early dawn, and the clouds in the east were beginning to show narrow edges of gold and crimson as we ascended the path leading to the mountain. My guide, with bag upon his shoulder, led, and I followed, with my robe fastened back and a stout stick in my hand. This had a sharp iron point which might be used against wild beasts.

My guide was a light-haired, blue-eyed young fellow with a cheerful and amiable face. He evidently found a keen delight in climbing his native hills toward the high country whither we were bound. He seemed not to feel the weight of the burden that he bore; his gait was light and free, his footing sure. He sprang up the steep and rugged way like a mountain-goat.

The boy was in high spirits. He told me strange tales of ghosts and goblins, witches and fairies. These last he seemed to be very well acquainted with. He said they appeared in shining garments, with bright hair and beautiful wings, and this description agrees very nearly with what is related of them in books by certain of the Fathers. Any one to whom they take a fancy, says the boy, they are able to keep under their spell, and no one can break the enchantment, nor even the Holy Virgin. But I judge that this is true of only such as are in sin, and that the pure in heart have nothing to fear from them.

We traveled up hill and down, through forests and blooming meadows and across ravines. The mountain-streams, hastening down to the valleys, full-banked and noisy, seemed to be relating the wonderful things that they had seen and the strange adventures they had met with on their way. Sometimes the hillsides and the wood resounded with nature's various voices, calling, whispering, sighing, chanting praises to the Lord of All. Now and again we passed a mountaineer's cabin, before which played children, yellow-haired and unkempt. On seeing strangers, they ran away. But the women came forward, with infants in their arms, and asked for benedictions. They offered us milk, butter, green cheese and black bread. We frequently found the men seated in front of their huts, carving wood, mostly images of our Savior upon the cross. These are sent to the city of Munich, where they are offered for sale, bringing, I am told, considerable money and much honor to their pious makers.

At last we arrived at the shore of a lake, but a dense fog prevented a clear view of it. A clumsy little boat was found moored to the bank; my guide bade me enter it, and presently it seemed as if we were gliding through the sky in the midst of the clouds. I had never before been on the water, and felt a terrible misgiving lest we should capsize and drown. We heard nothing but the sound of the ripples against the sides of the boat. Here and there, as we advanced, some dark object became dimly visible for a moment, then vanished as suddenly as it had appeared, and we seemed gliding again through empty space. As the mist at times lifted a little, I observed great black rocks protruding from the water, and not far from shore were lying giant trees half submerged, with huge limbs that looked like the bones of some monstrous skeleton. The scene was so full of horrors that even the joyous youth was silent now, his watchful eye ever seeking to penetrate the fog in search of new dangers.

By all these signs I knew that we were crossing that fearful lake which is haunted by ghosts and demons, and I therefore commended my soul to God. The power of the Lord overcomes all evil. Scarcely had I said my prayer against the spirits of darkness, when suddenly the veil of fog was rent asunder, and like a great rose of fire the sun shone out, clothing the world in garments of color and gold!

Before this glorious eye of God the darkness fled and was no more. The dense fog, which had changed to a thin, transparent mist, lingered a little on the mountain-sides, then vanished quite away. Except in the black clefts of the hills, no vestige of it stayed. The lake was as liquid silver; the mountains were gold, bearing forests that were like flames of fire. My heart was filled with wonder and gratitude.

As our boat crept on I observed that the lake filled a long, narrow basin. On our right the cliffs rose to a great height, their tops covered with pines, but to the left and in front lay a pleasant land, where stood a large building. This was Saint Bartholomæ, the summer residence of his Reverence, Superior Andreas.

This garden spot was of no great extent: it was shut in on all sides but that upon which the lake lay by cliffs that rose a thousand feet into the air. High in the front of this awful wall was set a green meadow, which seemed like a great jewel gleaming upon the gray cloak of the mountain. My guide pointed it out as the only place in all that region where the edelweiss grew. This, then, was the very place where Benedicta had culled the lovely flowers that she had brought to me during my penance. I gazed upward to that beautiful but terrible spot with feelings that I have no words to express. The youth, his mood sympathetic with the now joyous aspect of nature, shouted and sang, but I felt the hot tears rise into my eyes and flow down upon my cheeks, and concealed my face in my cowl.

XXI

After leaving the boat we climbed the mountain. Dear Lord, nothing comes from Thy hand without a purpose and a use, but why Thou shouldst have piled up these mountains, and why Thou shouldst have covered them with so many stones, is a mystery to me, since I can see no purpose in stones, which are a blessing to neither man nor beast.

After hours of climbing we reached a spring, where I sat down, faint and foot-sore and out of breath. As I looked about me the scene fully justified all that I had been told of these high solitudes. Wherever I turned my eyes was nothing but gray, bare rocks streaked with red and yellow and brown. There were dreary wastes of stones where nothing grew—no single plant nor blade of grass—dreadful abysses filled with ice, and glittering snowfields sloping upward till they seemed to touch the sky.

Among the rocks I did, however, find a few flowers. It seemed as if the Creator of this wild and desolate region had himself found it too horrible, and, reaching down to the valleys, had gathered a handful of flowers and scattered them in the barren places. These flowers, so distinguished by the Divine hand, have bloomed with a celestial beauty that none others know. The boy pointed out the plant whose root I am to dig, as well as several strong and wholesome herbs serviceable to man, among them the golden-flowered arnica.

After an hour we continued our journey, which we pursued until I was hardly able to drag my feet along the path. At last we reached a lonely spot surrounded by great black rocks. In the center was a miserable hut of stones, with a low opening in one side for an entrance, and this, the youth told me, was to be my habitation. We entered, and my heart sank to think of dwelling in such a place. There was no furniture of any kind. A wide bench, on which was some dry Alpine grass, was to be my bed. There was a fireplace, with some wood for fuel, and a few simple cooking-utensils.

The boy took up a pan and ran away with it, and, throwing myself down in front of the hut, I was soon lost in contemplation of the wildness and terror of the place in which I was to prepare my soul for service of the Lord. The boy soon returned, bearing the pan in both hands, and on seeing me he gave a joyful shout, whose echoes sounded like a hundred voices babbling among the rocks on every side. After even so short a period of solitude I was so happy to see a human face that I came near answering his greeting with unbecoming joy. How, then, could I hope to sustain a week of isolation in that lonely spot?

When the boy placed the pan before me it was full of milk, and he brought forth from his clothing a pat of yellow butter, prettily adorned with Alpine flowers, and a cake of snow-white cheese wrapped in aromatic herbs. The sight delighted me, and I asked him, jokingly:

"Do butter and cheese, then, grow on stones up here, and have you found a spring of milk?"

"You might accomplish such a miracle," he replied, "but I prefer to hasten to the Black Lake and ask this food of the young women who live there."

He then got some flour from a kind of pantry in the hut, and, having kindled a fire on the hearth, proceeded to make a cake.

"Then we are not alone in this wilderness," I said. "Tell me where is that lake on the shore of which these generous people dwell?"

"The Black Lake," he replied, blinking his eyes, which were full of smoke, "is behind that *Kogel* yonder, and the dairy-house stands on the edge of the cliff above the water. It is a bad place. The lake reaches clear down to Hell, and you can hear, through the fissures of the rocks, the roaring and hissing of the flames and the groans of the souls. And in no other place in all this world are there so many fierce and evil spirits. Beware of it! You might fall ill there in spite of your sanctity. Milk and butter and cheese can be obtained at the Green Lake lower down; but I will tell the women to send up what you require. They will be glad to oblige you; and if you will preach them a sermon every Sunday, they will fight the very devil for you!"

After our meal, which I thought the sweetest that I had ever eaten, the boy stretched himself in the sunshine and straightway fell asleep, snoring so loudly that, tired as I was, I could hardly follow his example.

XXII

When I awoke the sun was already behind the mountains, whose tops were fringed with fire. I felt as one in a dream, but was soon recalled to my senses, and made to feel that I was alone in the wilderness by shouts of the young man in the distance. Doubtless he had pitied my condition, for, instead of disturbing me, he had gone away without taking leave, being compelled to reach the dairy on the Green Lake before nightfall. Entering the cabin, I found a fire burning lustily and a quantity of fuel piled beside it. Nor had the thoughtful youth forgotten to prepare my supper of bread and milk. He had also shaken up the grass on my hard bed, and covered it with a woolen cloth, for which I was truly grateful to him.

Refreshed by my long sleep, I remained outside the cabin till late in the evening. I said my prayers in view of the gray rocks beneath the black sky, in which the stars blinked merrily. They seemed much more brilliant up here than when seen from the valley, and it was easy to imagine that, standing on the extreme summit, one might touch them with his hands.

Many hours of that night I passed under the sky and the stars, examining my conscience and questioning my heart. I felt as if in church, kneeling before the altar and feeling the awful presence of the Lord. And at last my soul was filled with a divine peace, and as an innocent child presses its mother's breast, even so I leaned my head upon thine, O Nature, mother of us all!

XXIII

I had not before seen a dawn so glorious! The mountains were rosered, and seemed almost transparent. The atmosphere was of a silvery lucidity, and so fresh and pure that with every breath I seemed to be taking new life. The dew, heavy and white, clung to the scanty grass-blades like rain and dripped from the sides of the rocks.

It was while engaged in my morning devotions that I involuntarily became acquainted with my neighbors. All night long the marmots had squealed, greatly to my dismay, and they were now capering to and fro like hares. Overhead the brown hawks sailed in circles with an eye to the birds flitting among the bushes and the wood-mice racing along the rocks. Now and again a troop of chamois passed near, on their way to the feeding-grounds on the cliffs, and high above all I saw a single eagle rising into the sky, higher and higher, as a soul flies heavenward when purged of sin.

I was still kneeling when the silence was broken by the sound of voices. I looked about, but, although I could distinctly hear the voices and catch snatches of song, I saw no one. The sounds seemed to come from the heart of the mountain and, remembering the malevolent powers that infest the place, I repeated a prayer against the Evil One and awaited the event.

Again the singing was heard, ascending from a deep chasm, and presently I saw rising out of it three female figures. As soon as they saw me they ceased singing and uttered shrill screams. By this sign I knew them to be daughters of the earth, and thought they might be Christians, and so waited for them to approach.

As they drew near I observed that they carried baskets on their heads, and that they were tall, good-looking lasses, light-haired, brown in complexion and black-eyed. Setting their baskets upon the ground, they greeted me humbly and kissed my hands, after which they opened the baskets and displayed the good things they had brought me—milk, cream, cheese, butter and cakes.

Seating themselves upon the ground, they told me they were from the Green Lake, and said they were glad to have a "mountain brother" again, especially so young and handsome a one; and in saying so there were merry twinkles in their dark eyes and smiles on their red lips, which pleased me exceedingly.

I inquired if they were not afraid to live in the wilderness, at which they laughed, showing their white teeth. They said they had a hunter's gun in their cabin to keep off bears, and knew several powerful sentences and anathemas against demons. Nor were they very lonely, they added, for every Saturday the boys from the valley came up to hunt wild beasts, and then all made merry. I learned from them that meadows and cabins were common among the rocks, where herdsmen and herdswomen lived during the whole summer. The finest meadows, they said, belonged to the monastery, and lay but a short distance away.

The pleasant chatting of the maidens greatly delighted me, and the solitude began to be less oppressive. Having received the benediction, they kissed my hand and went away as they had come, laughing, singing and shouting in the joy of youth and health. So much I have already observed: the people in the mountains lead a better and happier life than those in the damp, deep valleys below. Also, they seem purer in heart and mind, and that may be due to their living so much nearer to Heaven, which some of the brothers say approaches more closely to the earth here than at any other place in the world excepting Rome.

XXIV

The maidens having gone, I stowed away the provisions which they had brought me, and, taking a short pointed spade and a bag, went in search of the gentiana roots. They grew in abundance, and my back soon began to ache from stooping and digging; but I continued the labor, for I desired to send a good quantity to the monastery to attest my zeal and obedience. I had gone a long distance from my cabin without observing the direction which I had taken, when suddenly I found myself on the brink of an abyss so deep and terrible that I recoiled with a cry of horror. At the bottom of this chasm, so far below my feet that I was giddy to look down, a small circular lake was visible, like the eye of a fiend. On the shore of it, near a cliff overhanging the water, stood a cabin, from the stone-weighted roof of which rose a thin column of blue smoke. About the cabin, in the narrow and sterile pasture, a few cows and sheep were grazing. What a dreadful place for a human habitation!

I was still gazing down with fear into this gulf when I was again startled: I heard a voice distinctly call a name! The sound came from behind me, and the name was uttered with so caressing sweetness that I hastened to cross myself as a protection from the wiles of the fairies with their spells and enchantments. Soon I heard the voice again, and this time it caused my heart to beat so that I was near suffocation, for it was Benedicta's! Benedicta in this wilderness, and I alone with her!

Surely I now had need of thy guidance, blessed Franciscus, to keep my feet in the path of the Divine purpose.

I turned about and saw her. She was now springing from rock to rock, looking backward and calling the name that was strange to me. When she saw that I looked at her she stood motionless. I walked to her, greeting her in the name of the Blessed Virgin, though, God forgive me! hardly able in the tumult of my emotions to articulate that holy title.

Ah, how changèd the poor child was! The lovely face was as pale as marble; the large eyes were sunken and inexpressibly sad. Her beautiful hair alone was unaltered, flowing over her shoulders like threads of gold. We stood looking at each other, silent from surprise; then I again addressed her:

"Is it, then, you, Benedicta, who live in the cabin down there by the Black Lake—near the waters of Avernus? And is your father with you?"

She made no reply, but I observed a quivering about her delicate mouth, as when a child endeavors to refrain from weeping. I repeated my question: "Is your father with you?"

She answered faintly, in a tone that was hardly more than a sigh: "My father is dead."

I felt a sudden pain in my very heart, and was for some moments unable to speak further, quite overcome by compassion. Benedicta had turned away her face to hide her tears, and her fragile frame was shaken by her sobs. I could no longer restrain myself. Stepping up to her, I took her hand in mine, and, trying to crush back into my secret heart every human desire, and address her in words of religious consolation, said:

"My child—dear Benedicta—your father is gone from you, but another Father remains who will protect you every day of your life. And as far as may accord with His holy will I, too, good and beautiful maiden, will help you to endure your great affliction. He whom you mourn is not lost; he is gone to the mercy seat, and God will be gracious to him."

But my words seemed only to awaken her sleeping grief. She threw herself upon the ground and gave way to her tears, sobbing so violently that I was filled with alarm. O Mother of Mercy! how can I bear the memory of the anguish I suffered in seeing this beautiful and innocent child overwhelmed with so great a flood of grief? I bent over her, and my own tears fell upon her golden hair. My heart urged me to lift her from the earth, but my hands were powerless to move. At length she composed herself somewhat and spoke, but as if she were talking to herself rather than to me:

"Oh, my father, my poor, heart-broken father! Yes, he is dead—they killed him—he died long ago of grief. My beautiful mother, too, died of grief—of grief and remorse for some great sin, I know not what, which he had forgiven her. He could only be compassionate and merciful. His heart was too tender to let him kill a worm or a beetle, and he was compelled to kill men. His father and his father's father had lived and died in the Galgenberg. They were hangmen all, and the awful inheritance fell to him: there was no escape, for the terrible people held him to the trade. I have heard him say that he was often tempted to kill himself, and but for me I am sure he would have done so. He could not leave me to starve, though he had to see me reviled, and at last, O Holy Virgin! publicly disgraced for that of which I was not guilty."

As Benedicta made this reference to the great injustice that she had been made to suffer her white cheeks kindled to crimson with the recollection of the shame which for her father's sake she had, at the time of it, so differently endured.

During the narrative of her grief she had partly risen and had turned her beautiful face more and more toward me as her confidence had grown; but now she veiled it with her hair, and would have turned her back but that I gently prevented her and spoke some words of comfort, though God knows my own heart was near breaking through sympathy with hers. After a few moments she resumed:

"Alas, my poor father! he was unhappy every way. Not even the comfort of seeing his child baptized was granted him. I was a hangman's daughter, and my parents were forbidden to present me for baptism; nor could any priest be found who was willing to bless me in the name of the Holy Trinity. So they gave me the name Benedicta, and blessed me themselves, over and over again.

"I was only an infant when my beautiful mother died. They buried her in unconsecrated ground. She could not go to the Heavenly Father in the mansions above, but was thrust into the flames. While she was dying my father had hastened to the Reverend Superior, imploring him to send a priest with the sacrament. His prayer was denied. No priest came, and my poor father closed her eyes himself, while his own were blind with tears of anguish for her terrible fate.

"And all alone he had to dig her grave. He had no other place than near the gallows, where he had so often buried the hanged and the accurst. With his own hands he had to place her in that unholy ground, nor could any masses be said for her suffering soul.

"I well remember how my dear father took me then to the image of the Holy Virgin and bade me kneel, and, joining my little hands, taught me to pray for my poor mother, who had stood undefended before the terrible Judge of the Dead. This I have done every morning and evening since that day, and now I pray for both; for my father also has died unshriven, and his soul is not with God, but burns in unceasing fire.

"When he was dying I ran to the Superior, just as he had done for my dear mother. I besought him on my knees. I prayed and wept and embraced his feet, and would have kissed his hand but that he snatched it away. He commanded me to go."

As Benedicta proceeded with her narrative she gained courage. She rose to her feet and stood erect, threw back her beautiful head and lifted her eyes to the heavens as if recounting her wrongs to God's high angels and ministers of doom. She stretched forth her bare arms in gestures of so natural force and grace that I was filled with astonishment, and her unstudied words came from her lips with an eloquence of which I had never before had any conception. I dare not think it inspiration, for, God forgive us all! every word was an unconscious arraignment of Him and His Holy Church; yet surely no mortal with lips untouched by a live coal from the altar ever so spake before! In the presence of this strange and gifted being I so felt my own unworth that I had surely knelt, as before a blessed saint, but that she suddenly concluded, with a pathos that touched me to tears.

"The cruel people killed him," she said, with a sob in the heart of every word. "They laid hands upon me whom he loved. They charged me falsely with a foul crime. They attired me in a garment of dishonor, and put a crown of straw upon my head, and hung about my neck the black tablet of shame. They spat upon me and reviled me, and compelled him to lead me to the pillory, where I was bound and struck with whips and stones. That broke his great, good heart, and so he died, and I am alone."

XXV

When Benedicta had finished I remained silent, for in the presence of such a sorrow what could I say? For such wounds as hers religion has no balm. As I thought of the cruel wrongs of this humble and harmless family there came into my heart a feeling of wild rebellion against the world, against the Church, against God! They were brutally unjust, horribly, devilishly unjust!—God, the Church, and the world.

Our very surroundings—the stark and soulless wilderness, perilous with precipices and bleak with everlasting snows—seemed a visible embodiment of the woful life to which the poor child had been condemned from birth; and truly this was more than fancy, for since her father's death had deprived her of even so humble a home as the hangman's hovel she had been driven to these eternal solitudes by the stress of want. But below us were pleasant villages, fertile fields, green gardens, and homes where peace and plenty abided all the year.

After a time, when Benedicta was somewhat composed, I asked her if she had any one with her for protection.

"I have none," she replied. But observing my look of pain, she added: "I have always lived in lonely, accurst places; I am accustomed to that. Now that my father is dead, there is no one who cares even to speak to me, nor any whom I care to talk with—except you." After a pause she said: "True, there is one who cares to see me, but he"—

Here she broke off, and I did not press her to explain lest it should embarrass her. Presently she said:

"I knew yesterday that you were here. A boy came for some milk and butter for you. If you were not a holy man the boy would not have come to me for your food. As it is, you cannot be harmed by the evil which attaches to everything I have or do. Are you sure, though, that you made the sign of the cross over the food yesterday?"

"Had I known that it came from you, Benedicta, that precaution would have been omitted," I answered.

She looked at me with beaming eyes, and said:

"Oh, dear sir, dear Brother!"

And both the look and the words gave me the keenest delight—as, in truth, do all this saintly creature's words and ways.

I inquired what had brought her to the cliff-top, and who the person was that I had heard her calling.

"It is no person," she answered, smiling; "it is only my goat. She has strayed away, and I was searching for her among the rocks."

Then nodding to me as if about to say farewell, she turned to go, but I detained her, saying that I would assist her to look for the goat.

We soon discovered the animal in a crevice of rock, and so glad was Benedicta to find her humble companion that she knelt by its side, put her arms about its neck and called it by many endearing names. I thought this very charming, and could not help looking upon the group with obvious admiration. Benedicta, observing it, said:

"Her mother fell from a cliff and broke her neck. I took the little one and brought it up on milk, and she is very fond of me. One who lives alone as I do values the love of a faithful animal."

When the maiden was about to leave me I gained courage to speak to her of what had been so long in my mind. I said: "It is true, is it not, Benedicta, that on the night of the festival you went to meet the drunken boys in order to save your father from harm?"

She looked at me in great astonishment. "For what other reason could you suppose I went?"

"I could not think of any other," I replied, in some confusion.

"And now, good-by, Brother," she said, moving away.

"Benedicta," I cried. She paused and turned her head.

"Next Sunday I shall preach to the dairy women at the Green Lake; will you come?"

"Oh, no, dear Brother," she replied hesitating and in low tones.

"You will not come?"

"I should like to come, but my presence would frighten away the dairy women and others whom your goodness would bring there to hear you. Your charity to me would cause you trouble. I pray you, sir, accept my thanks, but I cannot come."

"Then I shall come to you."

"Beware, O, pray, beware!"

"I shall come."

XXVI

The boy had taught me how to prepare a cake. I knew all that went to the making of it, and the right proportions, yet when I tried to make it I could not. All that I was able to make was a smoky, greasy pap, more fit for the mouth of Satan than for a pious son of the Church and follower of Saint Franciscus. My failure greatly discouraged me, yet it did not destroy my appetite; so, taking some stale bread, I dipped it in sour milk and was about to make my stomach do penance for its many sins, when Benedicta came with a basketful of good things from her dairy. Ah, the dear child! I fear that it was not with my heart only that I greeted her that blessed morning.

Observing the smoky mass in the pan, she smiled, and quietly throwing it to the birds (which may Heaven guard!) she cleansed the pan at the spring, and, returning, arranged the fire. She then prepared the material for a fresh cake. Taking two handfuls of flour, she put it into an earthen bowl, and upon the top of it poured a cup of cream. Adding a pinch of salt, she mixed the whole vigorously with her slender white hands until it became a soft, swelling dough. She next greased the pan with a piece of yellow butter, and, pouring the dough into it, placed it on the fire. When the heat had penetrated the dough, causing it to expand and rise above the sides of the pan, she deftly pierced it here and there that it should not burst, and when it was well browned she took it up and set it before me, all unworthy as I was. I invited her to share the meal with me, but she would not. She insisted, too, that I should cross myself before partaking of anything that she had brought me or prepared, lest some evil come to me because of the ban upon her; but this I would not consent to do. While I ate she culled flowers from among the rocks, and, making a wreath, hung it upon the cross in front of the cabin; after which, when I had finished, she employed herself in cleansing the dishes and arranging everything in order as it should be, so that I imagined myself far more comfortable than before, even in merely looking about me. When there was nothing more to be done, and my conscience would not permit me to invent reasons for detaining her, she went away, and O, my Savior! how dismal and dreary seemed the day when she was gone! Ah, Benedicta, Benedicta, what is this that thou hast done to me?—making that sole service of the Lord to which I am dedicated seem less happy and less holy than a herdsman's humble life here in the wilderness with thee!

XXVII

Life up here is less disagreeable than I thought. What seemed to me a dreary solitude seems now less dismal and desolate. This mountain wilderness, which at first filled me with awe, gradually reveals its benign character. It is marvelously beautiful in its grandeur, with a beauty which purifies and elevates the soul. One can read in it, as in a book, the praises of its Creator. Daily, while digging gentiana roots, I do not fail to listen to the voice of the wilderness and to compose and chasten my soul more and more.

In these mountains are no feathered songsters. The birds here utter only shrill cries. The flowers, too, are without fragrance, but wondrously beautiful, shining with the fire and gold of stars. I have seen slopes and heights here which doubtless were never trodden by any human foot. They seem to me sacred, the touch of the Creator still visible upon them, as when they came from His hand.

Game is in great abundance. Chamois are sometimes seen in such droves that the very hill-sides seem to move. There are steinbocks, veritable monsters, but as yet, thank Heaven, I have seen no bears. Marmots play about me like kittens, and eagles, the grandest creatures in this high world, nest in the cliffs to be as near the sky as they can get.

When fatigued I stretch myself on the Alpine grass, which is as fragrant as the most precious spices. I close my eyes and hear the wind whisper through the tall stems, and in my heart is peace. Blessed be the Lord!

XXVIII

Every morning the dairy women come to my cabin, their merry shouts ringing in the air and echoed from the hills. They bring fresh milk, butter and cheese, chat a little while and go away. Each day they relate something new that has occurred in the mountains or been reported from the villages below. They are joyous and happy, and look forward with delight to Sunday, when there will be divine service in the morning and a dance in the evening.

Alas, these happy people are not free of the sin of bearing false witness against their neighbor. They have spoken to me of Benedicta—called her a disgraceful wench, a hangman's daughter and (my heart rebels against its utterance) the mistress of Rochus! The pillory, they said, was made for such as she.

Hearing these maidens talk so bitterly and falsely of one whom they so little knew, it was with difficulty that I mastered my indignation. But in pity of their ignorance I reprimanded them gently and kindly. It was wrong, I said, to condemn a fellow-being unheard. It was unchristian to speak ill of any one.

They do not understand. It surprises them that I defend a person like

Benedicta—one who, as they truly say, has been publicly disgraced and has not a friend in the world.

XXIX

This morning I visited the Black Lake. It is indeed an awful and accursed place, fit for the habitation of the damned. And there lives the poor forsaken child! Approaching the cabin, I could see a fire burning on the hearth, and over it was suspended a kettle. Benedicta was seated on a low stool, looking into the flames. Her face was illuminated with a crimson glow, and I could observe heavy tear-drops on her cheeks.

Not wishing to see her secret sorrow, I hastened to make known my presence, and addressed her as gently as I could. She was startled, but when she saw who it was, smiled and blushed. She rose and came to greet me, and I began speaking to her almost at random, in order that she might recover her composure. I spoke as a brother might speak to his sister, yet earnestly, for my heart was full of compassion.

"O, Benedicta," I said, "I know your heart, and it has more love for that wild youth Rochus than for our dear and blessed Savior. I know how willingly you bore infamy and disgrace, sustained by the thought that he knew you innocent. Far be it from me to condemn you, for what is holier or purer than a maiden's love? I would only warn and save you from the consequence of having given it to one so unworthy."

She listened with her head bowed, and said nothing, but I could hear her sighs. I saw, too, that she trembled. I continued:

"Benedicta, the passion which fills your heart may prove your destruction in this life and hereafter. Young Rochus is not one who will make you his wife in the sight of God and Man. Why did he not stand forth and defend you when you were falsely accused?"

"He was not there," she said, lifting her eyes to mine; "he and his father were at Salzburg. He knew nothing till they told him."

May God forgive me if at this I felt no joy in another's acquittal of the heavy sin with which I had charged him. I stood a moment irresolute, with my head bowed, silent.

"But, Benedicta," I resumed, "will he take for a wife one whose good name has been blackened in the sight of his family and his neighbors? No, he does not seek you with an honorable purpose. O, Benedicta, confide in me. Is it not as I say?"

But she remained silent, nor could I draw from her a single word. She would only sigh and tremble; she seemed unable to speak. I saw that she was too weak to resist the temptation to love young Rochus; nay, I saw that her whole heart was bound up in him, and my soul melted with pity and sorrow—pity for her and sorrow for myself, for I felt that my power was unequal to the command that had been laid upon me. My agony was so keen that I could hardly refrain from crying out.

I went from her cabin, but did not return to my own. I wandered about the haunted shore of the Black Lake for hours, without aim or purpose.

Reflecting bitterly upon my failure, and beseeching God for greater grace and strength, it was revealed to me that I was an unworthy disciple of the Lord and a faithless son of the Church. I became more keenly conscious than I ever had been before of the earthly nature of my love for Benedicta, and of its sinfulness. I felt that I had not given my whole heart to God, but was clinging to a temporal and human hope. It was plain to me that unless my love for the sweet child should be changed to a purely spiritual affection, purified from all the dross of passion, I could never receive holy orders, but should remain always a monk and always a sinner. These reflections caused me great torment, and in my despair I cast myself down upon the earth, calling aloud to my Savior. In this my greatest trial I clung to the Cross. "Save me, O Lord!" I cried. "I am engulfed in a great passion—save me, oh, save me, or I perish forever!"

All that night I struggled and prayed and fought against the evil spirits in my soul, with their suggestions of recreancy to the dear Church whose child I am.

"The Church," they whispered, "has servants enough. You are not as yet irrevocably bound to celibacy. You can procure a dispensation from your monastic vows and remain here in the mountains, a layman. You can learn the craft of the hunter or the herdsman, and be ever near Benedicta to guard and guide her—perhaps in time to win her love from Rochus and take her for your wife."

To these temptations I opposed my feeble strength and such aid as the blessed Saint gave me in my great trial. The contest was long and agonizing, and more than once, there in the darkness and the wilderness, which rang with my cries, I was near surrender; but at the dawning of the day I became more tranquil, and peace once more filled my heart, even as the golden light filled the great gorges of the mountain where but a few moments before were the darkness and the mist. I thought then of the suffering and death of our Savior, who died for the redemption of the world, and most fervently I prayed that Heaven would grant me the great boon to die likewise, in a humbler way, even though it were for but one suffering being—Benedicta.

May the Lord hear my prayer!

XXX

The night before the Sunday on which I was to hold divine service great fires were kindled on the cliffs—a signal for the young men in the valley to come up to the mountain dairies. They came in great numbers, shouting and screaming, and were greeted with songs and shrill cries by the dairy maidens, who swung flaming torches that lit up the faces of the great rocks and sent gigantic shadows across them. It was a beautiful sight. These are indeed a happy people.

The monastery boy came in with the rest. He will remain over Sunday, and, returning, will take back the roots that I have dug. He gave me much news from the monastery. The reverend Superior is living at Saint Bartholomæ, fishing and hunting. Another thing—one which gives me great alarm—is that the Saltmaster's son, young Rochus, is in the mountains not far from the Black Lake. It seems he has a hunting-lodge on the upper cliff, and a path leads from it directly to the lake. The boy told me this, but did not observe how I trembled when hearing it. Would that an angel with a flaming sword might guard the path to the lake, and to Benedicta!

The shouting and singing continued during the whole night, and between this and the agitation in my soul I did not close my eyes. Early the next morning the boys and girls arrived in crowds from all directions. The maidens wore silken kerchiefs twisted prettily about their heads, and had decorated themselves and their escorts with flowers.

Not being an ordained priest, it was not permitted me either to read mass or to preach a sermon, but I prayed with them and spoke to them whatever my aching heart found to say. I spoke to them of our sinfulness and God's great mercy; of our harshness to one another and the Savior's love for us all; of His infinite compassion. As my words echoed from the abyss below and the heights above I felt as if I were lifted out of this world of suffering and sin and borne away on angels' wings to the radiant spheres beyond the sky! It was a solemn service, and my little congregation was awed into devotion and seemed to feel as if it stood in the Holy of Holies.

The service being concluded, I blessed the people and they quietly went away. They had not been long gone before I heard the lads send forth ringing shouts, but this did not displease me. Why should they not rejoice? Is not cheerfulness the purest praise a human heart can give?

In the afternoon I went down to Benedicta's cabin and found her at the door, making a wreath of edelweiss for the image of the Blessed Virgin, intertwining the snowy flowers with a purple blossom that looked like blood.

Seating myself beside her, I looked on at her beautiful work in silence, but in my soul was a wild tumult of emotion and a voice that cried: "Benedicta, my love, my soul, I love you more than life! I love you above all things on earth and in Heaven!"

XXXI

The Superior sent for me, and with a strange foreboding I followed his messenger down the difficult way to the lake and embarked in the boat. Occupied with gloomy reflections and presentiments of impending evil, I hardly observed that we had left the shore before the sound of merry voices apprised me of our arrival at St. Bartholomæ. On the beautiful meadow surrounding the dwelling of the Superior were a great number of people—priests, friars, mountaineers and hunters. Many were there who had come afar with large retinues of servants and boys. In the house was a great bustle—a confusion and a hurrying to and fro, as during a fair. The doors stood wide open, and people ran in and out, clamoring noisily. The dogs yelped and howled as loud as they could. On a stand under an oak was a great cask of beer, and many of the people were gathered about it, drinking. Inside the house, too, there seemed to be much drinking, for I saw many men near the windows with mighty cups in their hands.

On entering, I encountered throngs of servants carrying dishes of fish and game. I asked one of them when I could see the Superior. He answered that His Reverence would be down immediately after the meal, and I concluded to wait in the hall. The walls were hung with pictures of some large fish which had been caught in the lake. Below each picture the weight of the monster and the date of its capture, together with the name of the person taking it, were inscribed in large letters. I could not help interpreting these records—perhaps uncharitably —as intimations to all good Christians to pray for the souls of those whose names were inscribed.

After more than an hour the Superior descended the stairs. I stepped forward, saluting him humbly, as became my position. He nodded, eyed me sharply, and directed me to go to his apartment immediately after supper. This I did.

"How about your soul, my son Ambrosius?" he asked me, solemnly. "Has the Lord shown you grace? Have you endured the probation?"

Humbly, with my head bowed, I answered:

"Most reverend Father, God in my solitude has given me knowledge."

"Of what? Of your guilt?"

This I affirmed.

"Praise be to God!" exclaimed the Superior. "I knew, my son, that solitude would speak to your soul with the tongue of an angel. I have good tidings for you. I have written in your behalf to the Bishop of Salzburg. He summons you to his palace. He will consecrate you and give you holy orders in person, and you will remain in his city. Prepare yourself, for in three days you are to leave us."

The Superior looked sharply into my face again, but I did not permit him to see into my heart. I asked for his benediction, bowed and left him. Ah, then, it was for this that I was summoned! I am to go away forever. I must leave my very life behind me; I must renounce my care and protection of Benedicta. God help her and me!

XXXII

I am once more in my mountain home, but to-morrow I leave it forever. But why am I sad? Does not a great blessing await me? Have I not ever looked forward to the moment of my consecration with longing, believing it would bring me the supreme happiness of my life? And now that this great joy is almost within my grasp, I am sad beyond measure.

Can I approach the altar of the Lord with a lie on my lips? Can I receive the holy sacrament as an impostor? The holy oil upon my forehead would turn to fire and burn into my brain, and I should be forever damned.

I might fall upon my knees before the Bishop and say: "Expel me, for I do not seek after the love of Christ, nor after holy and heavenly things, but after the things of this world."

If I so spoke, I should be punished, but I could endure that without a murmur.

If only I were sinless and could rightly become a priest, I could be of great service to the poor child. I should be able to give her infinite blessings and consolations. I could be her confessor and absolve her from sin, and, if I should outlive her—which God forbid!—might by my prayers even redeem her soul from Purgatory. I could read masses for the souls of her poor dead parents, already in torment.

Above all, if I succeeded in preserving her from that one great and destructive sin for which she secretly longs; if I could take her with me and place her under thy protection, O Blessed Virgin, that would be happiness indeed.

But where is the sanctuary that would receive the hangman's daughter? I know it but too well: when I am gone from here, the Evil One, in the winning shape he has assumed, will prevail, and she will be lost in time and in eternity.

XXXIII

I have been at Benedicta's cabin.

"Benedicta," I said, "I am going away from here—away from the mountains—away from you."

She grew pale, but said nothing. For a moment I was overcome with emotion; I seemed to choke, and could not continue. Presently I said: "Poor child, what will become of you? I know that your love for Rochus is strong, and love is like a torrent which nothing can stay. There is no safety for you but in clinging to the cross of our Savior. Promise me that you will do so—do not let me go away in misery, Benedicta."

"Am I, then, so wicked?" she said, without lifting her eyes from the ground. "Can I not be trusted?"

"Ah, but, Benedicta, the enemy is strong, and you have a traitor to unbar the gates. Your own heart, poor child, will at last betray you."

"He will not harm me," she murmured. "You wrong him, sir, indeed you do."

But I knew that I did not, and was all the more concerned to judge that the wolf would use the arts of the fox. Before the sacred purity of this maiden the base passions of the youth had not dared to declare themselves. But none the less I knew that an hour would come when she would have need of all her strength, and it would fail her. I grasped her arm and demanded that she take an oath that she would throw herself into the waters of the Black Lake rather than into the arms of Rochus. But she would not reply. She remained silent, her eyes fixed upon mine with a look of sadness and reproach which filled my mind with the most melancholy thoughts, and, turning away, I left her.

XXXIV

Lord, Savior of my soul, whither hast Thou led me? Here am I in the culprit's tower, a condemned murderer, and to-morrow at sunrise I shall be taken to the gallows and hanged! For whoso slays a fellow being, he shall be slain; that is the law of God and man.

On this the last day of my life I have asked that I be permitted to write, and my prayer is granted. In the name of God and in the truth I shall now set down all that occurred.

Leaving Benedicta, I returned to my cabin, and, having packed everything, waited for the boy. But he did not come: I should have to remain in the mountains another night. I grew restless. The cabin seemed too narrow to hold me; the air too heavy and hot to sustain life. Going outside, I lay upon a rock and looked up at the sky, dark and glittering with stars. But my soul was not in the heavens; it was at the cabin by the Black Lake.

Suddenly I heard a faint, distant cry, like a human voice. I sat upright and listened, but all was still. It may have been, I thought, the note of some night-bird. I was about to lie down again, when the cry was repeated, but it seemed to come from another direction. It was the voice of Benedicta! It sounded again, and now it seemed to come from the air—from the sky above my head, and distinctly it called my name; but, O Mother of God, what anguish was in those tones!

I leapt from the rock. "Benedicta, Benedicta!" I cried aloud. There was no reply.

"Benedicta, I am coming to thee, child!"

I sprang away in the darkness, along the path to the Black Lake. I ran and leapt, stumbling and falling over rocks and stumps of trees. My limbs were bruised, my clothing was torn, but I gave no heed; Benedicta was in distress, and I alone could save and guard her. I rushed on until I reached the Black Lake. But at the cabin all was quiet; there was neither light nor sound; everything was as peaceful as a house of God.

After waiting a long time I left. The voice that I had heard calling me could not have been Benedicta's, but must have been that of some evil spirit mocking me in my great sorrow. I meant to return to my cabin, but an invisible hand directed my steps another way; and although it led me to my death, I know it to have been the hand of the Lord.

Walking on, hardly knowing whither, and unable to find the path by which I had descended, I found myself at the foot of a precipice. Here was a narrow path leading steeply upward along the face of the cliff, and I began ascending it. After I had gone up some distance I looked above, and saw outlined against the starry sky a cabin perched upon the very verge. It flashed through my mind that this was the hunting-lodge of the Saltmaster's son, and this the path by which he visited Benedicta. Merciful Father! he, Rochus, was certain to come this way; there could be no other. I would wait for him here.

I crouched in the shadow and waited, thinking what to say to him and imploring the Lord for inspiration to change his heart and turn him from his evil purpose.

Before long I heard him approaching from above. I heard the stones displaced by his foot roll down the steep slopes and leap into the lake far below. Then I prayed God that if I should be unable to soften the youth's heart he might miss his footing and fall, too, like the stones; for it would be better that he should meet a sudden and impenitent death, and his soul be lost, than that he should live to destroy the soul of an innocent girl.

Turning at an angle of the rock, he stood directly before me as, rising, I stepped into the faint light of the new moon. He knew me at once, and in a haughty tone asked me what I wanted.

I replied mildly, explaining why I had barred his way, and begging him to go back. He insulted and derided me.

"You miserable cowler," he said, "will you never cease meddling in my affairs? Because the mountain maids are so foolish as to praise your white teeth and your big black eyes, must you fancy yourself a man, and not a monk? You are no more to women than a goat!"

I begged him to desist and to listen to me. I threw myself on my knees and implored him, however he might despise me and my humble though holy station, to respect Benedicta and spare her. But he pushed me from him with his foot upon my breast. No longer master of myself, I sprang erect, and called him an assassin and a villain.

At this he pulled a dagger from his belt, saying: "I will send you to Hell!"

Quick as a flash of lightning my hand was upon his wrist. I wrested the knife from him and flung it behind me, crying: "Not with weapons, but unarmed and equal, we will fight to the death, and the Lord shall decide!"

We sprang upon each other with the fury of wild animals, and were instantly locked together with arms and hands. We struggled upward and downward along the path, with the great wall of rock on one side, and on the other the precipice, the abyss, the waters of the Black Lake! We writhed and strained for the advantage, but the Lord was against me for He permitted my enemy to overcome me and throw me down on the edge of the precipice. I was in the grasp of a strong enemy, whose eyes glowed like coals of fire. His knee was on my breast and my head hung over the edge—my life was in his hands. I thought he would push me over, but he made no attempt to do so. He held me there between life and death for a dreadful time, then said, in a low, hissing voice: "You see, monk, if I but move I can hurl you down the abyss like a stone. But I care not to take your life, for it is no impediment to me. The girl belongs to me, and to me you shall leave her; do you understand?"

With that he rose and left me, going down the path toward the lake. His footfalls had long died away in the silent night before I was able to move hand or foot. Great God! I surely did not deserve such defeat, humiliation and pain. I had but wished to save a soul, yet Heaven permitted me to be conquered by him who would destroy it!

Finally I was able to rise, although in great pain, for I was bruised by my fall, and could still feel the fierce youth's knee upon my breast and his fingers about my throat. I walked with difficulty back along the path, downward toward the lake. Wounded as I was, I would return to Benedicta's cabin and interpose my body between her and harm. But my progress was slow, and I had frequently to rest; yet it was near dawn before I gave up the effort, convinced that I should be too late to do the poor child the small service of yielding up my remnant of life in her defense.

At early dawn I heard Rochus returning, with a merry song upon his lips. I concealed myself behind a rock, though not in fear, and he passed without seeing me.

At this point there was a break in the wall of the cliff, the path crossing a great crevice that clove the mountain as by a sword-stroke from the arm of a Titan. The bottom was strewn with loose bowlders and overgrown with brambles and shrubs, through which trickled a slender stream of water fed by the melting snows above. Here I remained for three days and two nights. I heard the boy from the monastery calling my name as he traversed the path searching for me, but I made no answer. Not once did I quench my burning thirst at the brook nor appease my hunger with blackberries that grew abundantly on every side. Thus I mortified the sinful flesh, killed rebellious nature and subdued my spirit to the Lord until at last I felt myself delivered from all evil, freed from the bondage of an earthly love and prepared to devote my heart and soul and life to no woman but thee, O Blessed Virgin!

The Lord having wrought this miracle, my soul felt as light and free as if wings were lifting me to the skies. I praised the Lord in a loud voice, shouting and rejoicing till the rocks rang with the sound. I cried: "Hosanna! Hosanna!" I was now prepared to go before the altar and receive the holy oil upon my head. I was no longer myself. Ambrosius, the poor erring monk, was dead; I was an instrument in the right hand of God to execute His holy will. I prayed for the delivery of the soul of the beautiful maiden, and as I prayed, behold! there appeared to me in the splendor and glory of Heaven the Lord Himself, attended by innumerable angels, filling half the sky! A great rapture enthralled my senses; I was dumb with happiness. With a smile of ineffable benignity God spake to me:

"Because that thou hast been faithful to thy trust, and through all the trials that I have sent upon thee hast not faltered, the salvation of the sinless maiden's soul is now indeed given into thy hand."

"Thou, Lord, knowest," I replied, "that I am without the means to do this work, nor know I how it is to be done."

The Lord commanded me to rise and walk on, and, turning my face away from the glorious Presence, which filled the heart of the cloven mountain with light, I obeyed, leaving the scene of my purgation and regaining the path that led up the face of the cliff. I began the ascent, walking on and on in the splendor of the sunset, reflected from crimson clouds.

Suddenly I felt impelled to stop and look down, and there at my feet, shining red in the cloudlight, as if stained with blood, lay the sharp knife of Rochus. Now I understood why the Lord had permitted that wicked youth to conquer me, yet had moved him to spare my life. I had been reserved for a more glorious purpose. And so was placed in my hands the means to that sacred end. My God, my God, how mysterious are Thy ways!

XXXV

"You shall leave her to me." So had spoken the wicked youth while holding me between life and death at the precipice. He permitted me to live, not from Christian mercy, but because he despised my life, a trivial thing to him, not worth taking. He was sure of his prey; it did not matter if I were living or dead.

"You shall leave her to me." Oh, arrogant fool! Do you not know that the Lord holds His hand over the flowers of the field and the young birds in the nest? Leave Benedicta to you?—permit you to destroy her body and soul? Ah, you shall see how the hand of God shall be spread above her to guard and save. There is yet time—that soul is still spotless and undefiled. Forward, then, to fulfill the command of the Most High God!

I knelt upon the spot where God had given into my hand the means of her deliverance. My soul was wholly absorbed in the mission intrusted to me. My heart was in ecstasy, and I saw plainly, as in a vision, the triumphant completion of the act which I had still to do.

I arose, and, concealing the knife in my robe, retraced my steps, going downward toward the Black Lake. The new moon looked like a divine wound in the sky, as if some hand had plunged a dagger into Heaven's holy breast.

Benedicta's door was ajar, and I stood outside a long time, gazing upon the beautiful picture presented to my eyes. A bright fire on the hearth lit up the room. Opposite the fire sat Benedicta, combing her long golden hair. Unlike what it was the last time I had stood before her cabin and gazed upon it, her face was full of happiness and had a glory that I had never imagined in it. A sensuous smile played about her lips while she sang in a low, sweet voice the air of a love song of the people. Ah me! she was beautiful; she looked like a bride of Heaven. But though her voice was as that of an angel, it angered me, and I called out to her:

"What are you doing, Benedicta, so late in the evening? You sing as if you expected your lover, and arrange your hair as for a dance. It is but three days since I, your brother and only friend, left you, in sorrow and despair. And now you are as happy as a bride."

She sprang up and manifested great joy at seeing me again, and hastened to kiss my hands. But she had no sooner glanced into my face than she uttered a scream of terror and recoiled from me as if I had been a fiend from Hell!

But I approached her and asked: "Why do you adorn yourself so late in the night?—why are you so happy? Have the three days been long enough for you to fall? Are you the mistress of Rochus?"

She stood staring at me in horror. She asked: "Where have you been and why do you come? You look so ill! Sit, sir, I pray you, and rest. You are pale and you shake with cold. I will make you a warm drink and you will feel better."

She was silenced by my stern gaze. "I have not come to rest and be nursed by you," I said. "I am here because the Lord commands. Tell me why you sang."

She looked up at me with the innocent expression of a babe, and replied: "Because I had for the moment forgotten that you were going away, and I was happy."

"Happy?"

"Yes—he has been here."

"Who? Rochus?"

She nodded. "He was so good." she said. "He will ask his father to consent to see me, and perhaps take me to his great house and persuade the Reverend Superior to remove the curse from my life. Would not that be fine? But then," she added, with a sudden change of voice and manner, lowering her eyes, "perhaps you would no longer care for me. It is because I am poor and friendless."

"What! he will persuade his father to befriend you?—to take you to his home?—you, the hangman's daughter? He, this reckless youth, at war with God and God's ministers, will move the Church! O, lie, lie, lie! O Benedicta—lost, betrayed Benedicta! By your smiles and by your tears I know that you believe the monstrous promises of this infamous villain."

"Yes," she said, inclining her head as if she were making a confession of faith before the altar of the Lord, "I believe him."

"Kneel, then," I cried, "and praise the Lord for sending one of His chosen to save your soul from temporal and eternal perdition!"

At these words she trembled as in great fear.

"What do you wish me to do?" she exclaimed.

"To pray that your sins may be forgiven."

A sudden rapturous impulse seized my soul. "I am a priest," I cried, "anointed and ordained by God Himself, and in the name of the Father, and of the Son, and of the Holy Spirit, I forgive you your only sin, which is your love. I give you absolution without repentance. I free your soul from the taint of sin because you will atone for it with your blood and life."

With these words, I seized her and forced her down upon her knees. But she wanted to live; she cried and wailed. She clung to my knees and entreated and implored in the name of God and the Blessed Virgin. Then she sprang to her feet and attempted to run away. I seized her again, but she broke away from my grasp and ran to the open door, crying: "Rochus! Rochus! help, O, help!"

Springing after her, I grasped her by the shoulder, turned her half-round and plunged the knife into her breast.

I held her in my arms, pressed her against my heart and felt her warm blood upon my body. She opened her eyes and fixed upon me a look of reproach, as if I had robbed her of a life of happiness. Then her eyes slowly closed, she gave a long, shuddering sigh, her little head turned upon her shoulder, and so she died.

I wrapped the beautiful body in a white sheet, leaving the face uncovered, and laid it upon the floor. But the blood tinged the linen, so I parted her long golden hair, spreading it over the crimson roses upon her breast. As I had made her a bride of Heaven, I took from the image of the Virgin the wreath of edelweiss and placed it on Benedicta's brow; and now I remembered the edelweiss which she had once brought me to comfort me in my penance.

Then I stirred the fire, which cast upon the shrouded figure and the beautiful face a rich red light, as if God's glory had descended there to enfold her. It was caught and tangled in the golden tresses that lay upon her breast, so that they looked a mass of curling flame.

And so I left her.

XXXVI

I descended the mountain by precipitous paths, but the Lord guided my steps so that I neither stumbled nor fell into the abyss. At the dawning of the day I arrived at the monastery, rang the bell and waited until the gate was opened. The brother porter evidently thought me a fiend, for he raised a howl that aroused the whole monastery. I went straight to the room of the Superior, stood before him in my blood-stained garments, and, telling him for what deed the Lord had chosen me, informed him that I was now an ordained priest. At this they seized me, put me into the tower, and, holding court upon me, condemned me to death as if I were a murderer. O, the fools, the poor demented fools!

. . . . .

One person has come to me to-day in my dungeon, who fell upon her knees before me, kissed my hands and adored me as God's chosen instrument—Amula, the brown maiden. She alone has discovered that I have done a great and glorious deed.

I have asked Amula to chase away the vultures from my body, for Benedicta is in Heaven.

I shall soon be with her. Praise be to God! Hosanna! Amen.

. . . . .

[To this old manuscript are added the following lines in another hand: "On the fifteenth day of October, in the year of our Lord 1680, in this place, Brother Ambrosius was hanged, and on the following day his body was buried under the gallows, close to that of the girl Benedicta, whom he killed. This Benedicta, though called the hangman's daughter, was (as is now known through declarations of the youth Rochus) the bastard child of the Saltmaster by the hangman's wife. It is also veritably attested by the same youth that the maiden cherished a secret and forbidden love for him who slew her in ignorance of her passion. In all else Brother Ambrosius was a faithful servant of the Lord. Pray for him, pray for him!"]

NEGLIGIBLE TALES

A BOTTOMLESS GRAVE

MY name is John Brenwalter. My father, a drunkard, had a patent for an invention for making coffee-berries out of clay; but he was an honest man and would not himself engage in the manufacture. He was, therefore, only moderately wealthy, his royalties from his really valuable invention bringing him hardly enough to pay his expenses of litigation with rogues guilty of infringement. So I lacked many advantages en joyed by the children of unscrupulous and dishonorable parents, and had it not been for a noble and devoted mother, who neglected all my brothers and sisters and personally supervised my education, should have grown up in ignorance and been compelled to teach school. To be the favorite child of a good woman is better than gold.

When I was nineteen years of age my father had the misfortune to die. He had always had perfect health, and his death, which occurred at the dinner table without a moment's warning, surprised no one more than himself. He had that very morning been notified that a patent had been granted him for a device to burst open safes by hydraulic pressure, without noise. The Commissioner of Patents had pronounced it the most ingenious, effective and generally meritorious invention that had ever been submitted to him, and my father had naturally looked forward to an old age of prosperity and honor. His sudden death was, therefore, a deep disappointment to him; but my mother, whose piety and resignation to the will of Heaven were conspicuous virtues of her character, was apparently less affected. At the close of the meal, when my poor father's body had been removed from the floor, she called us all into an adjoining room and addressed us as follows:

"My children, the uncommon occurrence that you have just witnessed is one of the most disagreeable incidents in a good man's life, and one in which I take little pleasure, I assure you. I beg you to believe that I had no hand in bringing it about. Of course," she added, after a pause, during which her eyes were cast down in deep thought, "of course it is better that he is dead."

She uttered this with so evident a sense of its obviousness as a self-evident truth that none of us had the courage to brave her surprise by asking an explanation. My mother's air of surprise when any of us went wrong in any way was very terrible to us. One day, when in a fit of peevish temper, I had taken the liberty to cut off the baby's ear, her simple words, "John, you surprise me!" appeared to me so sharp a reproof that after a sleepless night I went to her in tears, and throwing myself at her feet, exclaimed: "Mother, forgive me for surprising you." So now we all—including the one-eared baby—felt that it would keep matters smoother to accept without question the statement that it was better, somehow, for our dear father to be dead. My mother continued:

"I must tell you, my children, that in a case of sudden and mysterious death the law requires the Coroner to come and cut the body into pieces and submit them to a number of men who, having inspected them, pronounce the person dead. For this the Coroner gets a large sum of money. I wish to avoid that painful formality in this instance; it is one which never had the approval of—of the remains. John"—here my mother turned her angel face to me—"you are an educated lad, and very discreet. You have now an opportunity to show your gratitude for all the sacrifices that your education has entailed upon the rest of us. John, go and remove the Coroner."

Inexpressibly delighted by this proof of my mother's confidence, and by the chance to distinguish myself by an act that squared with my natural disposition, I knelt before her, carried her hand to my lips and bathed it with tears of sensibility. Before five o'clock that afternoon I had removed the Coroner.

I was immediately arrested and thrown into jail, where I passed a most uncomfortable night, being unable to sleep because of the profanity of my fellow-prisoners, two clergymen, whose theological training had given them a fertility of impious ideas and a command of blasphemous language altogether unparalleled. But along toward morning the jailer, who, sleeping in an adjoining room, had been equally disturbed, entered the cell and with a fearful oath warned the reverend gentlemen that if he heard any more swearing their sacred calling would not prevent him from turning them into the street. After that they moderated their objectionable conversation, substituting an accordion, and I slept the peaceful and refreshing sleep of youth and innocence.

The next morning I was taken before the Superior Judge, sitting as a committing magistrate, and put upon my preliminary examination. I pleaded not guilty, adding that the man whom I had murdered was a notorious Democrat. (My good mother was a Republican, and from early childhood I had been carefully instructed by her in the principles of honest government and the necessity of suppressing factional opposition.) The Judge, elected by a Republican ballot-box with a sliding bottom, was visibly impressed by the cogency of my plea and offered me a cigarette.

"May it please your Honor," began the District Attorney, "I do not deem it necessary to submit any evidence in this case. Under the law of the land you sit here as a committing magistrate. It is therefore your duty to commit. Testimony and argument alike would imply a doubt that your Honor means to perform your sworn duty. That is my case."

My counsel, a brother of the deceased Coroner, rose and said: "May it please the Court, my learned friend on the other side has so well and eloquently stated the law governing in this case that it only remains for me to inquire to what extent it has been already complied with. It is true, your Honor is a committing magistrate, and as such it is your duty to commit—what? That is a matter which the law has wisely and justly left to your own discretion, and wisely you have discharged already every obligation that the law imposes. Since I have known your Honor you have done nothing but commit. You have committed embracery, theft, arson, perjury, adultery, murder—every crime in the calendar and every excess known to the sensual and depraved, including my learned friend, the District Attorney. You have done your whole duty as a committing magistrate, and as there is no evidence against this worthy young man, my client, I move that he be discharged."

An impressive silence ensued. The Judge arose, put on the black cap and in a voice trembling with emotion sentenced me to life and liberty. Then turning to my counsel he said, coldly but significantly:

"I will see you later."

The next morning the lawyer who had so conscientiously defended me against a charge of murdering his own brother—with whom he had a quarrel about some land—had disappeared and his fate is to this day unknown.

In the meantime my poor father's body had been secretly buried at midnight in the back yard of his late residence, with his late boots on and the contents of his late stomach unanalyzed. "He was opposed to display," said my dear mother, as she finished tamping down the earth above him and assisted the children to litter the place with straw; "his instincts were all domestic and he loved a quiet life."

My mother's application for letters of administration stated that she had good reason to believe that the deceased was dead, for he had not come home to his meals for several days; but the Judge of the Crowbait Court—as she ever afterward contemptuously called it—decided that the proof of death was insufficient, and put the estate into the hands of the Public Administrator, who was his son-in-law. It was found that the liabilities were exactly balanced by the assets; there was left only the patent for the device for bursting open safes without noise, by hydraulic pressure and this had passed into the ownership of the Probate Judge and the Public Administraitor—as my dear mother preferred to spell it. Thus, within a few brief months a worthy and respectable family was reduced from prosperity to crime; necessity compelled us to go to work.

In the selection of occupations we were governed by a variety of considerations, such as personal fitness, inclination, and so forth. My mother opened a select private school for instruction in the art of changing the spots upon leopard-skin rugs; my eldest brother, George Henry, who had a turn for music, became a bugler in a neighboring asylum for deaf mutes; my sister, Mary Maria, took orders for Professor Pumpernickel's Essence of Latchkeys for flavoring mineral springs, and I set up as an adjuster and gilder of crossbeams for gibbets. The other children, too young for labor, continued to steal small articles exposed in front of shops, as they had been taught.

In our intervals of leisure we decoyed travelers into our house and buried the bodies in a cellar.

In one part of this cellar we kept wines, liquors and provisions. From the rapidity of their disappearance we acquired the superstitious belief that the spirits of the persons buried there came at dead of night and held a festival. It was at least certain that frequently of a morning we would discover fragments of pickled meats, canned goods and such débris, littering the place, although it had been securely locked and barred against human intrusion. It was proposed to remove the provisions and store them elsewhere, but our dear mother, always generous and hospitable, said it was better to endure the loss than risk exposure: if the ghosts were denied this trifling gratification they might set on foot an investigation, which would overthrow our scheme of the division of labor, by diverting the energies of the whole family into the single industry pursued by me—we might all decorate the cross-beams of gibbets. We accepted her decision with filial submission, due to our reverence for her worldly wisdom and the purity of her character.

One night while we were all in the cellar—none dared to enter it alone—engaged in bestowing upon the Mayor of an adjoining town the solemn offices of Christian burial, my mother and the younger children, holding a candle each, while George Henry and I labored with a spade and pick, my sister Mary Maria uttered a shriek and covered her eyes with her hands. We were all dreadfully startled and the Mayor's obsequies were instantly suspended, while with pale faces and in trembling tones we begged her to say what had alarmed her. The younger children were so agitated that they held their candles unsteadily, and the waving shadows of our figures danced with uncouth and grotesque movements on the walls and flung themselves into the most uncanny attitudes. The face of the dead man, now gleaming ghastly in the light, and now extinguished by some floating shadow, appeared at each emergence to have taken on a new and more forbidding expression, a maligner menace. Frightened even more than ourselves by the girl's scream, rats raced in multitudes about the place, squeaking shrilly, or starred the black opacity of some distant corner with steadfast eyes, mere points of green light, matching the faint phosphorescence of decay that filled the half-dug grave and seemed the visible manifestation of that faint odor of mortality which tainted the unwholesome air. The children now sobbed and clung about the limbs of their elders, dropping their candles, and we were near being left in total darkness, except for that sinister light, which slowly welled upward from the disturbed earth and overflowed the edges of the grave like a fountain.

Meanwhile my sister, crouching in the earth that had been thrown out of the excavation, had removed her hands from her face and was staring with expanded eyes into an obscure space between two wine casks.

"There it is!—there it is!" she shrieked, pointing; "God in heaven! can't you see it?"

And there indeed it was!—a human figure, dimly discernible in the gloom—a figure that wavered from side to side as if about to fall, clutching at the wine-casks for support, had stepped unsteadily forward and for one moment stood revealed in the light of our remaining candles; then it surged heavily and fell prone upon the earth. In that moment we had all recognized the figure, the face and bearing of our father—dead these ten months and buried by our own hands!—our father indubitably risen and ghastly drunk!

On the incidents of our precipitate flight from that horrible place—on the extinction of all human sentiment in that tumultuous, mad scramble up the damp and mouldy stairs—slipping, falling, pulling one another down and clambering over one another's back—the lights extinguished, babes trampled beneath the feet of their strong brothers and hurled backward to death by a mother's arm!—on all this I do not dare to dwell. My mother, my eldest brother and sister and I escaped; the others remained below, to perish of their wounds, or of their terror—some, perhaps, by flame. For within an hour we four, hastily gathering together what money and jewels we had and what clothing we could carry, fired the dwelling and fled by its light into the hills. We did not even pause to collect the insurance, and my dear mother said on her death-bed, years afterward in a distant land, that this was the only sin of omission that lay upon her conscience. Her confessor, a holy man, assured her that under the circumstances Heaven would pardon the neglect.

About ten years after our removal from the scenes of my childhood I, then a prosperous forger, returned in disguise to the spot with a view to obtaining, if possible, some treasure belonging to us, which had been buried in the cellar. I may say that I was unsuccessful: the discovery of many human bones in the ruins had set the authorities digging for more. They had found the treasure and had kept it for their honesty. The house had not been rebuilt; the whole suburb was, in fact, a desolation. So many unearthly sights and sounds had been reported thereabout that nobody would live there. As there was none to question nor molest, I resolved to gratify my filial piety by gazing once more upon the face of my beloved father, if indeed our eyes had deceived us and he was still in his grave. I remembered, too, that he had always worn an enormous diamond ring, and never having seen it nor heard of it since his death, I had reason to think he might have been buried in it. Procuring a spade, I soon located the grave in what had been the backyard and began digging. When I had got down about four feet the whole bottom fell out of the grave and I was precipitated into a large drain, falling through a long hole in its crumbling arch. There was no body, nor any vestige of one.

Unable to get out of the excavation, I crept through the drain, and having with some difficulty removed a mass of charred rubbish and blackened masonry that choked it, emerged into what had been that fateful cellar.

All was clear. My father, whatever had caused him to be "taken bad" at his meal (and I think my sainted mother could have thrown some light upon that matter) had indubitably been buried alive. The grave having been accidentally dug above the forgotten drain, and down almost to the crown of its arch, and no coffin having been used, his struggles on reviving had broken the rotten masonry and he had fallen through, escaping finally into the cellar. Feeling that he was not welcome in his own house, yet having no other, he had lived in subterranean seclusion, a witness to our thrift and a pensioner on our providence. It was he who had eaten our food; it was he who had drunk our wine— he was no better than a thief! In a moment of intoxication, and feeling, no doubt, that need of companionship which is the one sympathetic link between a drunken man and his race, he had left his place of concealment at a strangely inopportune time, entailing the most deplorable consequences upon those nearest and dearest to him—a blunder that had almost the dignity of crime.

JUPITER DOKE, BRIGADIER-GENERAL

From the Secretary of War to the Hon. Jupiter Doke, Hardpan Cross-roads, Posey County, Illinois.

WASHINGTON, November 3, 1861.

HAVING faith in your patriotism and ability, the President has been pleased to appoint you a brigadier-general of volunteers. Do you accept?

From the Hon. Jupiter Doke to the Secretary of War.

HARDPAN, ILLINOIS, November 9, 1861.

It is the proudest moment of my life. The office is one which should be neither sought nor declined. In times that try men's souls the patriot knows no North, no South, no East, no West. His motto should be: "My country, my whole country and nothing but my country." I accept the great trust confided in me by a free and intelligent people, and with a firm reliance on the principles of constitutional liberty, and invoking the guidance of an all-wise Providence, Ruler of Nations, shall labor so to discharge it as to leave no blot upon my political escutcheon. Say to his Excellency, the successor of the immortal Washington in the Seat of Power, that the patronage of my office will be bestowed with an eye single to securing the greatest good to the greatest number, the stability of republican institutions and the triumph of the party in all elections; and to this I pledge my life, my fortune and my sacred honor. I shall at once prepare an appropriate response to the speech of the chairman of the committee deputed to inform me of my appointment, and I trust the sentiments therein expressed will strike a sympathetic chord in the public heart, as well as command the Executive approval.

From the Secretary of War to Major-General Blount Wardorg, Commanding the Military Department of Eastern Kentucky.

WASHINGTON, November 14, 1861.

I have assigned to your department Brigadier-General Jupiter Doke, who will soon proceed to Distilleryville, on the Little Buttermilk River, and take command of the Illinois Brigade at that point, reporting to you by letter for orders. Is the route from Covington by way of Bluegrass, Opossum Corners and Horsecave still infested with bushwackers, as reported in your last dispatch? I have a plan for cleaning them out.

From Major-General Blount Wardorg to the Secretary of War.

LOUISVILLE, KENTUCKY, November 20, 1861.

The name and services of Brigadier-General Doke are unfamiliar to me, but I shall be pleased to have the advantage of his skill. The route from Covington to Distilleryville *via* Opossum Corners and Horsecave

I have been compelled to abandon to the enemy, whose guerilla warfare made it possible to keep it open without detaching too many troops from the front. The brigade at Distilleryville is supplied by steamboats up the Little Buttermilk.

From the Secretary of War to Brigadier-General Jupiter Doke, Hardpan, Illinois.

WASHINGTON, November 26, 1861.

I deeply regret that your commission had been forwarded by mail before the receipt of your letter of acceptance; so we must dispense with the formality of official notification to you by a committee. The President is highly gratified by the noble and patriotic sentiments of your letter, and directs that you proceed at once to your command at Distilleryville, Kentucky, and there report by letter to Major-General Wardorg at Louisville, for orders. It is important that the strictest secrecy be observed regarding your movements until you have passed Covington, as it is desired to hold the enemy in front of Distilleryville until you are within three days of him. Then if your approach is known it will operate as a demonstration against his right and cause him to strengthen it with his left now at Memphis, Tennessee, which it is desirable to capture first. Go by way of Bluegrass, Opossum Corners and Horsecave. All officers are expected to be in full uniform when *en route* to the front.

From Brigadier-General Jupiter Doke to the Secretary of War.

COVINGTON, KENTUCKY, December 7, 1861.

I arrived yesterday at this point, and have given my proxy to Joel Briller, Esq., my wife's cousin, and a staunch Republican, who will worthily represent Posey County in field and forum. He points with pride to a stainless record in the halls of legislation, which have often echoed to his soul-stirring eloquence on questions which lie at the very foundation of popular government. He has been called the Patrick Henry of Hardpan, where he has done yeoman's service in the cause of civil and religious liberty. Mr. Briller left for Distilleryville last evening, and the standard bearer of the Democratic host confronting that stronghold of freedom will find him a lion in his path. I have been asked to remain here and deliver some addresses to the people in a local contest involving issues of paramount importance. That duty being performed, I shall in person enter the arena of armed debate and move in the direction of the heaviest firing, burning my ships behind me. I forward by this mail to his Excellency the President a request for the appointment of my son, Jabez Leonidas Doke, as postmaster at Hardpan. I would take it, sir, as a great favor if you would give the application a strong oral indorsement, as the appointment is in the line of reform. Be kind enough to inform me what are the emoluments of the office I hold in the military arm, and if they are by salary or fees. Are there any perquisites? My mileage account will be transmitted monthly.

From Brigadier-General Jupiter Doke to Major General Blount Wardorg.

DISTILLERYVILLE, KENTUCKY, January 12, 1862.

I arrived on the tented field yesterday by steamboat, the recent storms having inundated the landscape, covering, I understand, the greater part of a congressional district. I am pained to find that Joel Briller, Esq., a prominent citizen of Posey County, Illinois, and a far-seeing statesman who held my proxy, and who a month ago should have been thundering at the gates of Disunion, has not been heard from, and has doubtless been sacrificed upon the altar of his country. In him the American people lose a bulwark of freedom. I would respectfully move that you designate a committee to draw up resolutions of respect to his memory, and that the office holders and men under your command wear the usual badge of mourning for thirty days. I shall at once place myself at the head of affairs here, and am now ready to entertain any suggestions which you may make, looking to the better enforcement of the laws in this commonwealth. The militant Democrats on the other side of the river appear to be contemplating extreme measures. They have two large cannons facing this way, and yesterday morning, I am told, some of them came down to the water's edge and remained in session for some time, making infamous allegations.

From the Diary of Brigadier-General Jupiter Doke, at Distilleryville, Kentucky.

January 12, 1862.—On my arrival yesterday at the Henry Clay Hotel (named in honor of the late far-seeing statesman) I was waited on by a delegation consisting of the three colonels intrusted with the command of the regiments of my brigade. It was an occasion that will be memorable in the political annals of America. Forwarded copies of the speeches to the Posey *Maverick,* to be spread upon the record of the ages. The gentlemen composing the delegation unanimously reaffirmed their devotion to the principles of national unity and the Republican party. Was gratified to recognize in them men of political prominence and untarnished escutcheons. At the subsequent banquet, sentiments of lofty patriotism were expressed. Wrote to Mr. Wardorg at Louisville for instructions.

January 13, 1862.—Leased a prominent residence (the former incumbent being absent in arms against his country) for the term of one year, and wrote at once for Mrs. Brigadier-General Doke and the vital issues—excepting Jabez Leonidas. In the camp of treason opposite here there are supposed to be three thousand misguided men laying the ax at the root of the tree of liberty. They have a clear majority, many of our men having returned without leave to their constituents. We could probably not poll more than two thousand votes. Have advised my heads of regiments to make a canvass of those remaining, all bolters to be read out of the phalanx.

January 14, 1862.—Wrote to the President, asking for the contract to supply this command with firearms and regalia through my brother-in-law, prominently identified with the manufacturing interests of the country. Club of cannon soldiers arrived at Jayhawk, three miles back from here, on their way to join us in battle array. Marched my whole brigade to Jayhawk to escort them into town, but their chairman, mistaking us for the opposing party, opened fire on the head of the procession and by the extraordinary noise of the cannon balls (I had no conception of it!) so frightened my horse that I was unseated without a contest. The meeting adjourned in disorder and returning to camp I found that a deputation of the enemy had crossed the river in our absence and made a division of the loaves and fishes. Wrote to the President, applying for the Gubernatorial Chair of the Territory of Idaho.

From Editorial Article in the Posey, Illinois, "Maverick," January 20, 1862.

Brigadier-General Doke's thrilling account, in another column, of the

Battle of Distilleryville will make the heart of every loyal Illinoisian leap with exultation. The brilliant exploit marks an era in military history, and as General Doke says, "lays broad and deep the foundations of American prowess in arms." As none of the troops engaged, except the gallant author-chieftain (a host in himself) hails from Posey County, he justly considered that a list of the fallen would only occupy our valuable space to the exclusion of more important matter, but his account of the strategic ruse by which he apparently abandoned his camp and so inveigled a perfidious enemy into it for the purpose of murdering the sick, the unfortunate *countertempus* at Jayhawk, the subsequent dash upon a trapped enemy flushed with a supposed success, driving their terrified legions across an impassable river which precluded pursuit—all these "moving accidents by flood and field" are related with a pen of fire and have all the terrible interest of romance.

Verily, truth is stranger than fiction and the pen is mightier than the sword. When by the graphic power of the art preservative of all arts we are brought face to face with such glorious events as these, the *Maverick's* enterprise in securing for its thousands of readers the services so distinguished a contributor as the Great Captain who made the history as well as wrote it seems a matter of almost secondary importance. For President in 1864 (subject to the decision of the Republican National Convention) Brigadier-General Jupiter Doke, of Illinois!

From Major-General Blount Wardorg to Brigadier-General Jupiter Doke.

LOUISVILLE, January 22, 1862.

Your letter apprising me of your arrival at Distilleryville was delayed in transmission, having only just been received (open) through the courtesy of the Confederate department commander under a flag of truce. He begs me to assure you that he would consider it an act of cruelty to trouble you, and I think it would be. Maintain, however, a threatening attitude, but at the least pressure retire. Your position is simply an outpost which it is not intended to hold.

From Major-General Blount Wardorg to the Secretary of War.

LOUISVILLE, January 23, 1862.

I have certain information that the enemy has concentrated twenty thousand troops of all arms on the Little Buttermilk. According to your assignment, General Doke is in command of the small brigade of raw troops opposing them. It is no part of my plan to contest the enemy's advance at that point, but I cannot hold myself responsible for any reverses to the brigade mentioned, under its present commander. I think him a fool.

From the Secretary of War to Major-General Blount Wardorg.

WASHINGTON, February 1, 1862.

The President has great faith in General Doke. If your estimate of him is correct, however, he would seem to be singularly well placed where he now is, as your plans appear to contemplate a considerable sacrifice for whatever advantages you expect to gain.

From Brigadier-General Jupiter Doke to Major-General Blount Wardorg.

DISTILLERYVILLE, February 1, 1862.

To-morrow I shall remove my headquarters to Jayhawk in order to point the way whenever my brigade retires from Distilleryville, as foreshadowed by your letter of the 22d ult. I have appointed a Committee on Retreat, the minutes of whose first meeting I transmit to you. You will perceive that the committee having been duly organized by the election of a chairman and secretary, a resolution (prepared by myself) was adopted, to the effect that in case treason again raises her hideous head on this side of the river every man of the brigade is to mount a mule, the procession to move promptly in the direction of Louisville and the loyal North. In preparation for such an emergency I have for some time been collecting mules from the resident Democracy, and have on hand 2300 in a field at Jayhawk. Eternal vigilance is the price of liberty!

From Major-General Gibeon J. Buxter, C. S. A., to the Confederate Secretary of War.

BUNG STATION, KENTUCKY, February 4, 1862.

On the night of the 2d inst., our entire force, consisting of 25,000 men and thirty-two field pieces, under command of Major-General Simmons B. Flood, crossed by a ford to the north side of Little Buttermilk River at a point three miles above Distilleryville and moved obliquely down and away from the stream, to strike the Covington turnpike at Jayhawk; the object being, as you know, to capture Covington, destroy Cincinnati and occupy the Ohio Valley. For some months there had been in our front only a small brigade of undisciplined troops, apparently without a commander, who were useful to us, for by not disturbing them we could create an impression of our weakness. But the movement on Jayhawk having isolated them, I was about to detach an Alabama regiment to bring them in, my division being the leading one, when an earth-shaking rumble was felt and heard, and suddenly the head-of-column was struck by one of the terrible tornadoes for which this region is famous, and utterly annihilated. The tornado, I believe, passed along the entire length of the road back to the ford, dispersing or destroying our entire army; but of this I cannot be sure, for I was lifted from the earth insensible and blown back to the south side of the river. Continuous firing all night on the north side and the reports of such of our men as have recrossed at the ford convince me that the Yankee brigade has exterminated the disabled survivors. Our loss has been uncommonly heavy. Of my own division of 15,000 infantry, the casualties —killed, wounded, captured, and missing—are 14,994. Of General Dolliver Billow's division, 11,200 strong, I can find but two officers and a nigger cook. Of the artillery, 800 men, none has reported on this side of the river. General Flood is dead. I have assumed command of the expeditionary force, but owing to the heavy losses have deemed it advisable to contract my line of supplies as rapidly as possible. I shall push southward to-morrow morning early. The purposes of the campaign have been as yet but partly accomplished.

From Major-General Dolliver Billows, C. S. A., to the Confederate Secretary of War.

BUHAC, KENTUCKY, February 5, 1862.

. . . But during the 2d they had, unknown to us, been reinforced by fifty thousand cavalry, and being apprised of our movement by a spy, this vast body was drawn up in the darkness at Jayhawk, and as the head of our column reached that point at about 11 P. M., fell upon it with astonishing fury, destroying the division of General Buxter in an instant. General Baumschank's brigade of artillery, which was in the rear, may have escaped—I did not wait to see, but withdrew my division to the river at a point several miles above the ford, and at daylight ferried it across on two fence rails lashed together with a suspender. Its losses, from an effective strength of 11,200, are 11,199. General Buxter is dead. I am changing my base to Mobile, Alabama.

From Brigadier-General Schneddeker Baumschank, C. S. A., to the Confederate Secretary of War.

IODINE, KENTUCKY, February 6, 1862.

. . . Yoost den somdings occur, I know nod vot it vos—somdings mackneefcent, but it vas nod vor—und I finds meinselluf, afder leedle viles, in dis blace, midout a hors und mit no men und goons. Sheneral Peelows is deadt. You will blease be so goot as to resign me—I vights no more in a dam gontry vere I gets vipped und knows nod how it vos done.

Resolutions of Congress, February 15, 1862.

Resolved, That the thanks of Congress are due, and hereby tendered, to Brigadier-General Jupiter Doke and the gallant men under his command for their unparalleled feat of attacking—themselves only 2000 strong—an army of 25,000 men and utterly overthrowing it, killing 5327, making prisoners of 19,003, of whom more than half were wounded, taking 32 guns, 20,000 stand of small arms and, in short, the enemy's entire equipment.

Resolved, That for this unexampled victory the President be requested to designate a day of thanksgiving and public celebration of religious rites in the various churches.

Resolved, That he be requested, in further commemoration of the great event, and in reward of the gallant spirits whose deeds have added such imperishable lustre to the American arms, to appoint, with the advice and consent of the Senate, the following officer:
One major-general.

Statement of Mr. Hannibal Alcazar Peyton, of Jayhawk, Kentucky.

Dat wus a almighty dark night, sho', and dese yere ole eyes aint wuf shuks, but I's got a year like a sque'l, an' w'en I cotch de mummer o' v'ices I knowed dat gang b'long on de far side o' de ribber. So I jes' runs in de house an' wakes Marse Doke an' tells him: "Skin outer dis fo' yo' life!" An' de Lo'd bress my soul! ef dat man didn' go right fru de winder in his shir' tail an' break for to cross de mule patch! An' dem twenty-free hunerd mules dey jes' t'ink it is de debble hese'f wid de brandin' iron, an' dey bu'st outen dat patch like a yarthquake, an' pile inter de upper ford road, an' flash down it five deep, an' it full o' Confed'rates from en' to en'! . . .

THE WIDOWER TURMORE

THE circumstances under which Joram Turmore became a widower have never been popularly understood. I know them, naturally, for I am Joram Turmore; and my wife, the late Elizabeth Mary Turmore, is by no means ignorant of them; but although she doubtless relates them, yet they remain a secret, for not a soul has ever believed her.

When I married Elizabeth Mary Johnin she was very wealthy, otherwise I could hardly have afforded to marry, for I had not a cent, and Heaven had not put into my heart any intention to earn one. I held the Professorship of Cats in the University of Graymaulkin, and scholastic pursuits had unfitted me for the heat and burden of business or labor.

Moreover, I could not forget that I was a Turmore—a member of a family whose motto from the time of William of Normandy has been *Laborare est errare*. The only known infraction of the sacred family tradition occurred when Sir Aldebaran Turmore de Peters-Turmore, an illustrious master burglar of the seventeenth century, personally assisted at a difficult operation undertaken by some of his workmen. That blot upon our escutcheon cannot be contemplated without the most poignant mortification.

My incumbency of the Chair of Cats in the Graymaulkin University had not, of course, been marked by any instance of mean industry. There had never, at any one time, been more than two students of the Noble Science, and by merely repeating the manuscript lectures of my predecessor, which I had found among his effects (he died at sea on his way to Malta) I could sufficiently sate their famine for knowledge without really earning even the distinction which served in place of salary.

Naturally, under the straitened circumstances, I regarded Elizabeth Mary as a kind of special Providence. She unwisely refused to share her fortune with me, but for that I cared nothing; for, although by the laws of that country (as is well known) a wife has control of her separate property during her life, it passes to the husband at her death; nor can she dispose of it otherwise by will. The mortality among wives is considerable, but not excessive.

Having married Elizabeth Mary and, as it were, ennobled her by making her a Turmore, I felt that the manner of her death ought, in some sense, to match her social distinction. If I should remove her by any of the ordinary marital methods I should incur a just reproach, as one destitute of a proper family pride. Yet I could not hit upon a suitable plan.

In this emergency I decided to consult the Turmore archives, a priceless collection of documents, comprising the records of the family from the time of its founder in the seventh century of our era. I knew that among these sacred muniments I should find detailed accounts of all the principal murders committed by my sainted ancestors for forty generations. From that mass of papers I could hardly fail to derive the most valuable suggestions.

The collection contained also most interesting relics. There were patents of nobility granted to my forefathers for daring and ingenious removals of pretenders to thrones, or occupants of them; stars, crosses and other decorations attesting services of the most secret and unmentionable character; miscellaneous gifts from the world's greatest conspirators, representing an intrinsic money value beyond computation. There were robes, jewels, swords of honor, and every kind of "testimonials of esteem"; a king's skull fashioned into a wine cup; the title deeds to vast estates, long alienated by confiscation, sale, or abandonment; an illuminated breviary that had belonged to Sir Aldebaran Turmore de Peters-Turmore of accursed memory; embalmed ears of several of the family's most renowned enemies; the small intestine of a certain unworthy Italian statesman inimical to Turmores, which, twisted into a jumping rope, had served the youth of six kindred generations—mementoes and souvenirs precious beyond the appraisals of imagination, but by the sacred mandates of tradition and sentiment forever inalienable by sale or gift.

As the head of the family, I was custodian of all these priceless heirlooms, and for their safe keeping had constructed in the basement of my dwelling a strong-room of massive masonry, whose solid stone walls and single iron door could defy alike the earthquake's shock, the tireless assaults of Time, and Cupidity's unholy hand.

To this thesaurus of the soul, redolent of sentiment and tenderness, and rich in suggestions of crime, I now repaired for hints upon assassination. To my unspeakable astonishment and grief I found it empty! Every shelf, every chest, every coffer had been rifled. Of that unique and incomparable collection not a vestige remained! Yet I proved that until I had myself unlocked the massive metal door, not a bolt nor bar had been disturbed; the seals upon the lock had been intact.

I passed the night in alternate lamentation and research, equally fruitless; the mystery was impenetrable to conjecture, the pain invincible to balm. But never once throughout that dreadful night did my firm spirit relinquish its high design against Elizabeth Mary, and daybreak found me more resolute than before to harvest the fruits of my marriage. My great loss seemed but to bring me into nearer spiritual relations with my dead ancestors, and to lay upon me a new and more inevitable obedience to the suasion that spoke in every globule of my blood.

My plan of action was soon formed, and procuring a stout cord I entered my wife's bedroom, finding her, as I expected, in a sound sleep. Before she was awake, I had her bound fast, hand and foot. She was greatly surprised and pained, but heedless of her remonstrances, delivered in a high key, I carried her into the now rifled strong-room, which I had never suffered her to enter, and of whose treasures I had not apprised her. Seating her, still bound, in an angle of the wall, I passed the next two days and nights in conveying bricks and mortar to the spot, and on the morning of the third day had her securely walled in, from floor to ceiling. All this time I gave no further heed to her pleas for mercy than (on her assurance of non-resistance, which I am bound to say she honorably observed) to grant her the freedom of her limbs. The space allowed her was about four feet by six. As I inserted the last bricks of the top course, in contact with the ceiling of the strong-room, she bade me farewell with what I deemed the composure of despair, and I rested from my work, feeling that I had faithfully observed the traditions of an ancient and illustrious family. My only bitter reflection, so far as my own conduct was concerned, came of the consciousness that in the performance of my design I had labored; but this no living soul would ever know.

After a night's rest I went to the Judge of the Court of Successions and Inheritances and made a true and sworn relation of all that I had done—except that I ascribed to a servant the manual labor of building the wall. His honor appointed a court commissioner, who made a careful examination of the work, and upon his report Elizabeth Mary Turmore was, at the end of a week, formally pronounced dead. By due process of law I was put into possession of her estate, and although this was not by hundreds of thousands of dollars as valuable as my lost treasures, it raised me from poverty to affluence and brought me the respect of the great and good.

Some six months after these events strange rumors reached me that the ghost of my deceased wife had been seen in several places about the country, but always at a considerable distance from Graymaulkin. These rumors, which I was unable to trace to any authentic source, differed widely in many particulars, but were alike in ascribing to the apparition a certain high degree of apparent worldly prosperity combined with an audacity most uncommon in ghosts. Not only was the spirit attired in most costly raiment, but it walked at noonday, and even drove! I was inexpressibly annoyed by these reports, and thinking there might be something more than superstition in the popular belief that only the spirits of the unburied dead still walk the earth, I took some workmen equipped with picks and crowbars into the now long unentered strong-room, and ordered them to demolish the brick wall that I had built about the partner of my joys. I was resolved to give the body of Elizabeth Mary such burial as I thought her immortal part might be willing to accept as an equivalent to the privilege of ranging at will among the haunts of the living.

In a few minutes we had broken down the wall and, thrusting a lamp through the breach, I looked in. Nothing! Not a bone, not a lock of hair, not a shred of clothing—the narrow space which, upon my affidavit, had been legally declared to hold all that was mortal of the late Mrs. Turmore was absolutely empty! This amazing disclosure, coming upon a mind already overwrought with too much of mystery and excitement, was more than I could bear. I shrieked aloud and fell in a fit. For months afterward I lay between life and death, fevered and delirious; nor did I recover until my physician had had the providence to take a case of valuable jewels from my safe and leave the country.

The next summer I had occasion to visit my wine cellar, in one corner of which I had built the now long disused strong-room. In moving a cask of Madeira I struck it with considerable force against the partition wall, and was surprised to observe that it displaced two large square stones forming a part of the wall.

Applying my hands to these, I easily pushed them out entirely, and looking through saw that they had fallen into the niche in which I had immured my lamented wife; facing the opening which their fall left, and at a distance of four feet, was the brickwork which my own hands had made for that unfortunate gentlewoman's restraint. At this significant revelation I began a search of the wine cellar. Behind a row of casks I found four historically interesting but intrinsically valueless objects:

First, the mildewed remains of a ducal robe of state (Florentine) of the eleventh century; second, an illuminated vellum breviary with the name of Sir Aldebaran Turmore de Peters-Turmore inscribed in colors on the title page; third, a human skull fashioned into a drinking cup and deeply stained with wine; fourth, the iron cross of a Knight Commander of the Imperial Austrian Order of Assassins by Poison.

That was all—not an object having commercial value, no papers—nothing. But this was enough to clear up the mystery of the strong-room. My wife had early divined the existence and purpose of that apartment, and with the skill amounting to genius had effected an entrance by loosening the two stones in the wall.

Through that opening she had at several times abstracted the entire collection, which doubtless she had succeeded in converting into coin of the realm. When with an unconscious justice which deprives me of all satisfaction in the memory I decided to build her into the wall, by some malign fatality I selected that part of it in which were these movable stones, and doubtless before I had fairly finished my bricklaying she had removed them and, slipping through into the wine cellar, replaced them as they were originally laid. From the cellar she had easily escaped unobserved, to enjoy her infamous gains in distant parts. I have endeavored to procure a warrant, but the Lord High Baron of the Court of Indictment and Conviction reminds me that she is legally dead, and says my only course is to go before the Master in Cadavery and move for a writ of disinterment and constructive revival. So it looks as if I must suffer without redress this great wrong at the hands of a woman devoid alike of principle and shame.

THE CITY OF THE GONE AWAY

I WAS born of poor because honest parents, and until I was twenty-three years old never knew the possibilities of happiness latent in another person's coin. At that time Providence threw me into a deep sleep and revealed to me in a dream the folly of labor. "Behold," said a vision of a holy hermit, "the poverty and squalor of your lot and listen to the teachings of nature. You rise in the morning from your pallet of straw and go forth to your daily labor in the fields. The flowers nod their heads in friendly salutation as you pass. The lark greets you with a burst of song. The early sun sheds his temperate beams upon you, and from the dewy grass you inhale an atmosphere cool and grateful to your lungs. All nature seems to salute you with the joy of a generous servant welcoming a faithful master. You are in harmony with her gentlest mood and your soul sings within you. You begin your daily task at the plow, hopeful that the noonday will fulfill the promise of the morn, maturing the charms of the landscape and confirming its benediction upon your spirit.

You follow the plow until fatigue invokes repose, and seating yourself upon the earth at the end of your furrow you expect to enjoy in fulness the delights of which you did but taste.

"Alas! the sun has climbed into a brazen sky and his beams are become a torrent. The flowers have closed their petals, confining their perfume and denying their colors to the eye. Coolness no longer exhales from the grass: the dew has vanished and the dry surface of the fields repeats the fierce heat of the sky. No longer the birds of heaven salute you with melody, but the jay harshly upbraids you from the edge of the copse. Unhappy man! all the gentle and healing ministrations of nature are denied you in punishment of your sin. You have broken the First Commandment of the Natural Decalogue: you have labored!"

Awakening from my dream, I collected my few belongings, bade adieu to my erring parents and departed out of that land, pausing at the grave of my grandfather, who had been a priest, to take an oath that never again, Heaven helping me, would I earn an honest penny.

How long I traveled I know not, but I came at last to a great city by the sea, where I set up as a physician. The name of that place I do not now remember, for such were my activity and renown in my new profession that the Aldermen, moved by pressure of public opinion, altered it, and thenceforth the place was known as the City of the Gone Away. It is needless to say that I had no knowledge of medicine, but by securing the service of an eminent forger I obtained a diploma purporting to have been granted by the Royal Quackery of Charlatanic Empiricism at Hoodos, which, framed in immortelles and suspended by a bit of *crêpe* to a willow in front of my office, attracted the ailing in great numbers. In connection with my dispensary I conducted one of the largest undertaking establishments ever known, and as soon as my means permitted, purchased a wide tract of land and made it into a cemetery. I owned also some very profitable marble works on one side of the gateway to the cemetery, and on the other an extensive flower garden. My Mourner's Emporium was patronized by the beauty, fashion and sorrow of the city. In short, I was in a very prosperous way of business, and within a year was able to send for my parents and establish my old father very comfortably as a receiver of stolen goods—an act which I confess was saved from the reproach of filial gratitude only by my exaction of all the profits.

But the vicissitudes of fortune are avoidable only by practice of the sternest indigence: human foresight cannot provide against the envy of the gods and the tireless machinations of Fate. The widening circle of prosperity grows weaker as it spreads until the antagonistic forces which it has pushed back are made powerful by compression to resist and finally overwhelm. So great grew the renown of my skill in medicine that patients were brought to me from all the four quarters of the globe. Burdensome invalids whose tardiness in dying was a perpetual grief to their friends; wealthy testators whose legatees were desirous to come by their own; superfluous children of penitent parents and dependent parents of frugal children; wives of husbands ambitious to remarry and husbands of wives without standing in the courts of divorce—these and all conceivable classes of the surplus population were conducted to my dispensary in the City of the Gone Away. They came in incalculable multitudes.

Government agents brought me caravans of orphans, paupers, lunatics and all who had become a public charge. My skill in curing orphanism and pauperism was particularly acknowledged by a grateful parliament.

Naturally, all this promoted the public prosperity, for although I got the greater part of the money that strangers expended in the city, the rest went into the channels of trade, and I was myself a liberal investor, purchaser and employer, and a patron of the arts and sciences. The City of the Gone Away grew so rapidly that in a few years it had inclosed my cemetery, despite its own constant growth. In that fact lay the lion that rent me.

The Aldermen declared my cemetery a public evil and decided to take it from me, remove the bodies to another place and make a park of it. I was to be paid for it and could easily bribe the appraisers to fix a high price, but for a reason which will appear the decision gave me little joy. It was in vain that I protested against the sacrilege of disturbing the holy dead, although this was a powerful appeal, for in that land the dead are held in religious veneration. Temples are built in their honor and a separate priesthood maintained at the public expense, whose only duty is performance of memorial services of the most solemn and touching kind. On four days in the year there is a Festival of the Good, as it is called, when all the people lay by their work or business and, headed by the priests, march in procession through the cemeteries, adorning the graves and praying in the temples. However bad a man's life may be, it is believed that when dead he enters into a state of eternal and inexpressible happiness. To signify a doubt of this is an offense punishable by death. To deny burial to the dead, or to exhume a buried body, except under sanction of law by special dispensation and with solemn ceremony, is a crime having no stated penalty because no one has ever had the hardihood to commit it.

All these considerations were in my favor, yet so well assured were the people and their civic officers that my cemetery was injurious to the public health that it was condemned and appraised, and with terror in my heart I received three times its value and began to settle up my affairs with all speed.

A week later was the day appointed for the formal inauguration of the ceremony of removing the bodies. The day was fine and the entire population of the city and surrounding country was present at the imposing religious rites. These were directed by the mortuary priesthood in full canonicals. There was propitiatory sacrifice in the Temples of the Once, followed by a processional pageant of great splendor, ending at the cemetery. The Great Mayor in his robe of state led the procession. He was armed with a golden spade and followed by one hundred male and female singers, clad all in white and chanting the Hymn to the Gone Away. Behind these came the minor priesthood of the temples, all the civic authorities, habited in their official apparel, each carrying a living pig as an offering to the gods of the dead. Of the many divisions of the line, the last was formed by the populace, with uncovered heads, sifting dust into their hair in token of humility. In front of the mortuary chapel in the midst of the necropolis, the Supreme Priest stood in gorgeous vestments, supported on each hand by a line of bishops and other high dignitaries of his prelacy, all frowning with the utmost austerity. As the Great Mayor paused in the Presence, the minor clergy, the civic authorities, the choir and populace closed in and encompassed the spot. The Great Mayor, laying his golden spade at the feet of the Supreme Priest, knelt in silence.

"Why comest thou here, presumptuous mortal?" said the Supreme Priest in clear, deliberate tones. "Is it thy unhallowed purpose with this implement to uncover the mysteries of death and break the repose of the Good?"

The Great Mayor, still kneeling, drew from his robe a document with portentous seals: "Behold, O ineffable, thy servant, having warrant of his people, entreateth at thy holy hands the custody of the Good, to the end and purpose that they lie in fitter earth, by consecration duly prepared against their coming."

With that he placed in the sacerdotal hands the order of the Council of Aldermen decreeing the removal. Merely touching the parchment, the Supreme Priest passed it to the Head Necropolitan at his side, and raising his hands relaxed the severity of his countenance and exclaimed: "The gods comply."

Down the line of prelates on either side, his gesture, look and words were successively repeated. The Great Mayor rose to his feet, the choir began a solemn chant and, opportunely, a funeral car drawn by ten white horses with black plumes rolled in at the gate and made its way through the parting crowd to the grave selected for the occasion—that of a high official whom I had treated for chronic incumbency. The Great Mayor touched the grave with his golden spade (which he then presented to the Supreme Priest) and two stalwart diggers with iron ones set vigorously to work.

At that moment I was observed to leave the cemetery and the country; for a report of the rest of the proceedings I am indebted to my sainted father, who related it in a letter to me, written in jail the night before he had the irreparable misfortune to take the kink out of a rope.

As the workmen proceeded with their excavation, four bishops stationed themselves at the corners of the grave and in the profound silence of the multitude, broken otherwise only by the harsh grinding sound of spades, repeated continuously, one after another, the solemn invocations and responses from the Ritual of the Disturbed, imploring the blessed brother to forgive. But the blessed brother was not there. Full fathom two they mined for him in vain, then gave it up. The priests were visibly disconcerted, the populace was aghast, for that grave was indubitably vacant.

After a brief consultation with the Supreme Priest, the Great Mayor ordered the workmen to open another grave. The ritual was omitted this time until the coffin should be uncovered. There was no coffin, no body.

The cemetery was now a scene of the wildest confusion and dismay. The people shouted and ran hither and thither, gesticulating, clamoring, all talking at once, none listening. Some ran for spades, fire-shovels, hoes, sticks, anything. Some brought carpenters' adzes, even chisels from the marble works, and with these inadequate aids set to work upon the first graves they came to. Others fell upon the mounds with their bare hands, scraping away the earth as eagerly as dogs digging for marmots. Before nightfall the surface of the greater part of the cemetery had been upturned; every grave had been explored to the bottom and thousands of men were tearing away at the interspaces with as furious a frenzy as exhaustion would permit. As night came on torches were lighted, and in the sinister glare these frantic mortals, looking like a legion of fiends performing some unholy rite, pursued their disappointing work until they had devastated the entire area. But not a body did they find—not even a coffin.

The explanation is exceedingly simple. An important part of my income had been derived from the sale of *cadavres* to medical colleges, which never before had been so well supplied, and which, in added recognition of my services to science, had all bestowed upon me diplomas, degrees and fellowships without number. But their demand for *cadavres* was unequal to my supply: by even the most prodigal extravagances they could not consume the one-half of the products of my skill as a physician. As to the rest, I had owned and operated the most extensive and thoroughly appointed soapworks in all the country. The excellence of my "Toilet Homoline" was attested by certificates from scores of the saintliest theologians, and I had one in autograph from Badelina Fatti the most famous living soaprano.

THE MAJOR'S TALE

IN the days of the Civil War practical joking had not, I think, fallen into that disrepute which characterizes it now. That, doubtless, was owing to our extreme youth—men were much younger than now, and evermore your very young man has a boisterous spirit, running easily to horse-play. You cannot think how young the men were in the early sixties! Why, the average age of the entire Federal Army was not more than twenty-five; I doubt if it was more than twenty-three, but not having the statistics on that point (if there are any) I want to be moderate: we will say twenty-five. It is true a man of twenty-five was in that heroic time a good deal more of a man than one of that age is now; you could see that by looking at him. His face had nothing of that unripeness so conspicuous in his successor. I never see a young fellow now without observing how disagreeably young he really is; but during the war we did not think of a man's age at all unless he happened to be pretty well along in life. In that case one could not help it, for the unloveliness of age assailed the human countenance then much earlier than now; the result, I suppose, of hard service—perhaps, to some extent, of hard drink, for, bless my soul! we did shed the blood of the grape and the grain abundantly during the war. I remember thinking General Grant, who could not have been more than forty, a pretty well preserved old chap, considering his habits. As to men of middle age—say from fifty to sixty —why, they all looked fit to personate the Last of the Hittites, or the Madagascarene Methuselah, in a museum. Depend upon it, my friends, men of that time were greatly younger than men are to-day, but looked much older. The change is quite remarkable.

I said that practical joking had not then gone out of fashion. It had not, at least, in the army; though possibly in the more serious life of the civilian it had no place except in the form of tarring and feathering an occasional "copperhead." You all know, I suppose, what a "copperhead" was, so I will go directly at my story without introductory remark, as is my way.

It was a few days before the battle of Nashville. The enemy had driven us up out of northern Georgia and Alabama. At Nashville we had turned at bay and fortified, while old Pap Thomas, our commander, hurried down reinforcements and supplies from Louisville. Meantime Hood, the Confederate commander, had partly invested us and lay close enough to have tossed shells into the heart of the town. As a rule he abstained—he was afraid of killing the families of his own soldiers, I suppose, a great many of whom had lived there. I sometimes wondered what were the feelings of those fellows, gazing over our heads at their own dwellings, where their wives and children or their aged parents were perhaps suffering for the necessaries of life, and certainly (so their reasoning would run) cowering under the tyranny and power of the barbarous Yankees.

To begin, then, at the beginning, I was serving at that time on the staff of a division commander whose name I shall not disclose, for I am relating facts, and the person upon whom they bear hardest may have surviving relatives who would not care to have him traced. Our headquarters were in a large dwelling which stood just behind our line of works. This had been hastily abandoned by the civilian occupants, who had left everything pretty much as it was—had no place to store it, probably, and trusted that Heaven would preserve it from Federal cupidity and Confederate artillery. With regard to the latter we were as solicitous as they.

Rummaging about in some of the chambers and closets one evening, some of us found an abundant supply of lady-gear—gowns, shawls, bonnets, hats, petticoats and the Lord knows what; I could not at that time have named the half of it. The sight of all this pretty plunder inspired one of us with what he was pleased to call an "idea," which, when submitted to the other scamps and scapegraces of the staff, met with instant and enthusiastic approval. We proceeded at once to act upon it for the undoing of one of our comrades.

Our selected victim was an aide, Lieutenant Haberton, so to call him. He was a good soldier—as gallant a chap as ever wore spurs; but he had an intolerable weakness: he was a lady-killer, and like most of his class, even in those days, eager that all should know it. He never tired of relating his amatory exploits, and I need not say how dismal that kind of narrative is to all but the narrator. It would be dismal even if sprightly and vivacious, for all men are rivals in woman's favor, and to relate your successes to another man is to rouse in him a dumb resentment, tempered by disbelief. You will not convince him that you tell the tale for his entertainment; he will hear nothing in it but an expression of your own vanity. Moreover, as most men, whether rakes or not, are willing to be thought rakes, he is very likely to resent a stupid and unjust inference which he suspects you to have drawn from his reticence in the matter of his own adventures—namely, that he has had none. If, on the other hand, he has had no scruple in the matter and his reticence is due to lack of opportunity to talk, or of nimbleness in taking advantage of it, why, then he will be surly because you "have the floor" when he wants it himself. There are, in short, no circumstances under which a man, even from the best of motives, or no motive at all, can relate his feats of love without distinctly lowering himself in the esteem of his male auditor; and herein lies a just punishment for such as kiss and tell. In my younger days I was myself not entirely out of favor with the ladies, and have a memory stored with much concerning them which doubtless I might put into acceptable narrative had I not undertaken another tale, and if it were not my practice to relate one thing at a time, going straight away to the end, without digression.

Lieutenant Haberton was, it must be confessed, a singularly handsome man with engaging manners. He was, I suppose, judging from the imperfect view-point of my sex, what women call "fascinating." Now, the qualities which make a man attractive to ladies entail a double disadvantage. First, they are of a sort readily discerned by other men, and by none more readily than by those who lack them. Their possessor, being feared by all these, is habitually slandered by them in self-defense. To all the ladies in whose welfare they deem themselves entitled to a voice and interest they hint at the vices and general unworth of the "ladies' man" in no uncertain terms, and to their wives relate without shame the most monstrous falsehoods about him. Nor are they restrained by the consideration that he is their friend; the qualities which have engaged their own admiration make it necessary to warn away those to whom the allurement would be a peril. So the man of charming personality, while loved by all the ladies who know him well, yet not too well, must endure with such fortitude as he may the consciousness that those others who know him only "by reputation" consider him a shameless reprobate, a vicious and unworthy man—a type and example of moral depravity. To name the second disadvantage entailed by his charms: he commonly is.

In order to get forward with our busy story (and in my judgment a story once begun should not suffer impedition) it is necessary to explain that a young fellow attached to our headquarters as an orderly was notably effeminate in face and figure. He was not more than seventeen and had a perfectly smooth face and large lustrous eyes, which must have been the envy of many a beautiful woman in those days. And how beautiful the women of those days were! and how gracious! Those of the South showed in their demeanor toward us Yankees something of *hauteur*, but, for my part, I found it less insupportable than the studious indifference with which one's attentions are received by the ladies of this new generation, whom I certainly think destitute of sentiment and sensibility.

This young orderly, whose name was Arman, we persuaded—by what arguments I am not bound to say—to clothe himself in female

attire and personate a lady. When we had him arrayed to our satisfaction—and a charming girl he looked—he was conducted to a sofa
in the office of the adjutant-general. That officer was in the secret, as
indeed were all excepting Haberton and the general; within the awful
dignity hedging the latter lay possibilities of disapproval which we
were unwilling to confront.

When all was ready I went to Haberton and said: "Lieutenant, there
is a young woman in the adjutant-general's office. She is the daughter
of the insurgent gentleman who owns this house, and has, I think,
called to see about its present occupancy. We none of us know just how
to talk to her, but we think perhaps you would say about the right
thing—at least you will say things in the right way. Would you mind
coming down?"

The lieutenant would not mind; he made a hasty toilet and joined
me. As we were going along a passage toward the Presence we encountered a formidable obstacle—the general.

"I say, Broadwood," he said, addressing me in the familiar manner
which meant that he was in excellent humor, "there's a lady in Lawson's
office. Looks like a devilish fine girl—came on some errand of mercy
or justice, no doubt. Have the goodness to conduct her to my quarters.
I won't saddle you youngsters with *all* the business of this division," he
added facetiously.

This was awkward; something had to be done.

"General," I said, "I did not think the lady's business of sufficient
importance to bother you with it. She is one of the Sanitary Commission's nurses, and merely wants to see about some supplies for the
smallpox hospital where she is on duty. I'll send her in at once."

"You need not mind," said the general, moving on; "I dare say Lawson will attend to the matter."

Ah, the gallant general! how little I thought, as I looked after his
retreating figure and laughed at the success of my ruse, that within the
week he would be "dead on the field of honor!" Nor was he the only
one of our little military household above whom gloomed the shadow
of the death angel, and who might almost have heard "the beating of
his wings." On that bleak December morning a few days later, when
from an hour before dawn until ten o'clock we sat on horseback on
those icy hills, waiting for General Smith to open the battle miles
away to the right, there were eight of us. At the close of the fighting

there were three. There is now one. Bear with him yet a little while, oh, thrifty generation; he is but one of the horrors of war strayed from his era into yours. He is only the harmless skeleton at your feast and peace-dance, responding to your laughter and your footing it featly, with rattling fingers and bobbing skull—albeit upon suitable occasion, with a partner of his choosing, he might do his little dance with the best of you.

As we entered the adjutant-general's office we observed that the entire staff was there. The adjutant-general himself was exceedingly busy at his desk. The commissary of subsistence played cards with the surgeon in a bay window. The rest were in several parts of the room, reading or conversing in low tones. On a sofa in a half lighted nook of the room, at some distance from any of the groups, sat the "lady," closely veiled, her eyes modestly fixed upon her toes.

"Madam," I said, advancing with Haberton, "this officer will be pleased to serve you if it is in his power. I trust that it is."

With a bow I retired to the farther corner of the room and took part in a conversation going on there, though I had not the faintest notion what it was about, and my remarks had no relevancy to anything under the heavens. A close observer would have noticed that we were all intently watching Haberton and only "making believe" to do anything else.

He was worth watching, too; the fellow was simply an *édition de luxe* of "Turveydrop on Deportment." As the "lady" slowly unfolded her tale of grievances against our lawless soldiery and mentioned certain instances of wanton disregard of property rights—among them, as to the imminent peril of bursting our sides we partly overheard, the looting of her own wardrobe—the look of sympathetic agony in Haberton's handsome face was the very flower and fruit of histrionic art. His deferential and assenting nods at her several statements were so exquisitely performed that one could not help regretting their unsubstantial nature and the impossibility of preserving them under glass for instruction and delight of posterity. And all the time the wretch was drawing his chair nearer and nearer. Once or twice he looked about to see if we were observing, but we were in appearance blankly oblivious to all but one another and our several diversions. The low hum of our conversation, the gentle tap-tap of the cards as they fell in play and the furious scratching of the adjutant-general's pen as he turned off count-

less pages of words without sense were the only sounds heard. No—
there was another: at long intervals the distant boom of a heavy gun,
followed by the approaching rush of the shot. The enemy was amusing
himself.

On these occasions the lady was perhaps not the only member of that
company who was startled, but she was startled more than the others,
sometimes rising from the sofa and standing with clasped hands, the
authentic portrait of terror and irresolution. It was no more than
natural that Haberton should at these times reseat her with infinite
tenderness, assuring her of her safety and regretting her peril in the
same breath. It was perhaps right that he should finally possess himself
of her gloved hand and a seat beside her on the sofa; but it certainly
was highly improper for him to be in the very act of possessing himself
of *both* hands when—boom, *whiz,* BANG!

We all sprang to our feet. A shell had crashed into the house and
exploded in the room above us. Bushels of plaster fell among us. That
modest and murmurous young lady sprang erect.

"Jumping Jee-rusalem!" she cried.

Haberton, who had also risen, stood as one petrified—as a statue of
himself erected on the site of his assassination. He neither spoke, nor
moved, nor once took his eyes off the face of Orderly Arman, who
was now flinging his girl-gear right and left, exposing his charms in
the most shameless way; while out upon the night and away over the
lighted camps into the black spaces between the hostile lines rolled the
billows of our inexhaustible laughter! Ah, what a merry life it was in
the old heroic days when men had not forgotten how to laugh!

Haberton slowly came to himself. He looked about the room less
blankly; then by degrees fashioned his visage into the sickliest grin
that ever libeled all smiling. He shook his head and looked knowing.

"You can't fool *me!*" he said.

CURRIED COW

MY Aunt Patience, who tilled a small farm in the state of Michigan, had a favorite cow. This creature was not a good cow, nor a profitable one, for instead of devoting a part of her leisure to secretion of milk and production of veal she concentrated all her faculties on the study of kicking. She would kick all day and get up in the middle of the night to kick. She would kick at anything—hens, pigs, posts, loose stones, birds in the air and fish leaping out of the water; to this impartial and catholic-minded beef, all were equal—all similarly undeserving. Like old Timotheus, who "raised a mortal to the skies," was my Aunt Patience's cow; though, in the words of a later poet than Dryden, she did it "more harder and more frequently." It was pleasing to see her open a passage for herself through a populous barnyard. She would flash out, right and left, first with one hind-leg and then with the other, and would sometimes, under favoring conditions, have a considerable number of domestic animals in the air at once.

Her kicks, too, were as admirable in quality as inexhaustible in quantity. They were incomparably superior to those of the untutored kine that had not made the art a life study—mere amateurs that kicked "by ear," as they say in music. I saw her once standing in the road, professedly fast asleep, and mechanically munching her cud with a sort of Sunday morning lassitude, as one munches one's cud in a dream. Snouting about at her side, blissfully unconscious of impending danger and wrapped up in thoughts of his sweetheart, was a gigantic black hog—a hog of about the size and general appearance of a yearling rhinoceros. Suddenly, while I looked—without a visible movement on the part of the cow—with never a perceptible tremor of her frame, nor a lapse in the placid regularity of her chewing—that hog had gone away from there—had utterly taken his leave. But away toward the pale horizon a minute black speck was traversing the empyrean with the speed of a meteor, and in a moment had disappeared, without audible report, beyond the distant hills. It may have been that hog.

Currying cows is not, I think, a common practice, even in Michigan;

759

but as this one had never needed milking, of course she had to be subjected to some equivalent form of persecution; and irritating her skin with a curry-comb was thought as disagreeable an attention as a thoughtful affection could devise. At least she thought it so; though I suspect her mistress really meant it for the good creature's temporal advantage. Anyhow my aunt always made it a condition to the employment of a farm-servant that he should curry the cow every morning; but after just enough trials to convince himself that it was not a sudden spasm, nor a mere local disturbance, the man would always give notice of an intention to quit, by pounding the beast half-dead with some foreign body and then limping home to his couch. I don't know how many men the creature removed from my aunt's employ in this way, but judging from the number of lame persons in that part of the country, I should say a good many; though some of the lameness may have been taken at second-hand from the original sufferers by their descendants, and some may have come by contagion.

I think my aunt's was a faulty system of agriculture. It is true her farm labor cost her nothing, for the laborers all left her service before any salary had accrued; but as the cow's fame spread abroad through the several States and Territories, it became increasingly difficult to obtain hands; and, after all, the favorite was imperfectly curried. It was currently remarked that the cow had kicked the farm to pieces—a rude metaphor, implying that the land was not properly cultivated, nor the buildings and fences kept in adequate repair.

It was useless to remonstrate with my aunt: she would concede everything, amending nothing. Her late husband had attempted to reform the abuse in this manner, and had had the argument all his own way until he had remonstrated himself into an early grave; and the funeral was delayed all day, until a fresh undertaker could be procured, the one originally engaged having confidingly undertaken to curry the cow at the request of the widow.

Since that time my Aunt Patience had not been in the matrimonial market; the love of that cow had usurped in her heart the place of a more natural and profitable affection. But when she saw her seeds unsown, her harvests ungarnered, her fences overtopped with rank brambles and her meadows gorgeous with the towering Canada thistle she thought it best to take a partner.

When it transpired that my Aunt Patience intended wedlock there was intense popular excitement. Every adult single male became at once a marrying man. The criminal statistics of Badger county show that in that single year more marriages occurred than in any decade before or since. But none of them was my aunt's. Men married their cooks, their laundresses, their deceased wives' mothers, their enemies' sisters—married whomsoever would wed; and any man who, by fair means or courtship, could not obtain a wife went before a justice of the peace and made an affidavit that he had some wives in Indiana. Such was the fear of being married alive by my Aunt Patience.

Now, where my aunt's reflection was concerned she was, as the reader will have already surmised, a rather determined woman; and the extraordinary marrying epidemic having left but one eligible male in all that county, she had set her heart upon that one eligible male; then she went and carted him to her home. He turned out to be a long Methodist parson, named Huggins.

Aside from his unconscionable length, the Rev. Berosus Huggins was not so bad a fellow, and was nobody's fool. He was, I suppose, the most ill-favored mortal, however, in the whole northern half of America— thin, angular, cadaverous of visage and solemn out of all reason. He commonly wore a low-crowned black hat, set so far down upon his head as partly to eclipse his eyes and wholly obscure the ample glory of his ears. The only other visible article of his attire (except a brace of wrinkled cowskin boots, by which the word "polish" would have been considered the meaningless fragment of a lost language) was a tight-fitting black frock-coat, preternaturally long in the waist, the skirts of which fell about his heels, sopping up the dew. This he always wore snugly buttoned from the throat downward. In this attire he cut a tolerably spectral figure. His aspect was so conspicuously unnatural and inhuman that whenever he went into a cornfield, the predatory crows would temporarily forsake their business to settle upon him in swarms, fighting for the best seats upon his person, by way of testifying their contempt for the weak inventions of the husbandman.

The day after the wedding my Aunt Patience summoned the Rev. Berosus to the council chamber, and uttered her mind to the following intent:

"Now, Huggy, dear, I'll tell you what there is to do about the place. First, you must repair all the fences, clearing out the weeds and repressing the brambles with a strong hand. Then you will have to exterminate the Canadian thistles, mend the wagon, rip up a plow or two, and get things into ship-shape generally. This will keep you out of mischief for the better part of two years; of course you will have to give up preaching, for the present. As soon as you have—O! I forgot poor Phœbe. She—"

"Mrs. Huggins," interrupted her solemn spouse, "I shall hope to be the means, under Providence, of effecting all needful reforms in the husbandry of this farm. But the sister you mention (I trust she is not of the world's people)—have I the pleasure of knowing her? The name, indeed, sounds familiar, but—"

"Not know Phœbe!" cried my aunt, with unfeigned astonishment; "I thought everybody in Badger knew Phœbe. Why, you will have to scratch her legs, every blessed morning of your natural life!"

"I assure you, madam," rejoined the Rev. Berosus, with dignity, "it would yield me a hallowed pleasure to minister to the spiritual needs of sister Phœbe, to the extent of my feeble and unworthy ability; but, really, I fear the merely secular ministration of which you speak must be entrusted to abler and, I would respectfully suggest, female hands."

"Whyyy, youuu ooold foooool!" replied my aunt, spreading her eyes with unbounded amazement, "Phœbe is a *cow!*"

"In that case," said the husband, with unruffled composure, "it will, of course, devolve upon me to see that her carnal welfare is properly attended to; and I shall be happy to bestow upon her legs such time as I may, without sin, snatch from my strife with Satan and the Canadian thistles."

With that the Rev. Mr. Huggins crowded his hat upon his shoulders, pronounced a brief benediction upon his bride, and betook himself to the barn-yard.

Now, it is necessary to explain that he had known from the first who Phœbe was, and was familiar, from hearsay, with all her sinful traits. Moreover, he had already done himself the honor of making her a visit, remaining in the vicinity of her person, just out of range, for more than an hour and permitting her to survey him at her leisure from every point of the compass. In short, he and Phœbe had mutually reconnoitered and prepared for action.

Amongst the articles of comfort and luxury which went to make up the good parson's *dot,* and which his wife had already caused to be conveyed to his new home, was a patent cast-iron pump, about seven feet high. This had been deposited near the barn-yard, preparatory to being set up on the planks above the barn-yard well. Mr. Huggins now sought out this invention and conveying it to its destination put it into position, screwing it firmly to the planks. He next divested himself of his long gaberdine and his hat, buttoning the former loosely about the pump, which it almost concealed, and hanging the latter upon the summit of the structure. The handle of the pump, when depressed, curved outwardly between the coat-skirts, singularly like a tail, but with this inconspicuous exception, any unprejudiced observer would have pronounced the thing Mr. Huggins, looking uncommonly well.

The preliminaries completed, the good man carefully closed the gate of the barnyard, knowing that as soon as Phœbe, who was campaigning in the kitchen garden, should note the precaution she would come and jump in to frustrate it, which eventually she did. Her master, meanwhile, had laid himself, coatless and hatless, along the outside of the close board fence, where he put in the time pleasantly, catching his death of cold and peering through a knot-hole.

At first, and for some time, the animal pretended not to see the figure on the platform. Indeed she had turned her back upon it directly she arrived, affecting a light sleep. Finding that this stratagem did not achieve the success that she had expected, she abandoned it and stood for several minutes irresolute, munching her cud in a half-hearted way, but obviously thinking very hard. Then she began nosing along the ground as if wholly absorbed in a search for something that she had lost, tacking about hither and thither, but all the time drawing nearer to the object of her wicked intention. Arrived within speaking distance, she stood for a little while confronting the fraudful figure, then put out her nose toward it, as if to be caressed, trying to create the impression that fondling and dalliance were more to her than wealth, power and the plaudits of the populace—that she had been accustomed to them all her sweet young life and could not get on without them. Then she approached a little nearer, as if to shake hands, all the while maintaining the most amiable expression of countenance and executing all manner of seductive nods and winks and smiles. Suddenly she wheeled about and with the rapidity of lightning dealt out a terrible kick—a kick of inconceivable force and fury, comparable to nothing in nature but a stroke of paralysis out of a clear sky!

The effect was magical! Cows kick, not backward but sidewise. The impact which was intended to project the counterfeit theologian into the middle of the succeeding conference week reacted upon the animal herself, and it and the pain together set her spinning like a top. Such was the velocity of her revolution that she looked like a dim, circular cow, surrounded by a continuous ring like that of the planet Saturn— the white tuft at the extremity of her sweeping tail! Presently, as the sustaining centrifugal force lessened and failed, she began to sway and wabble from side to side, and finally, toppling over on her side, rolled convulsively on her back and lay motionless with all her feet in the air, honestly believing that the world had somehow got atop of her and she was supporting it at a great sacrifice of personal comfort. Then she fainted.

How long she lay unconscious she knew not, but at last she unclosed her eyes, and catching sight of the open door of her stall, "more sweet than all the landscape smiling near," she struggled up, stood wavering upon three legs, rubbed her eyes, and was visibly bewildered as to the points of the compass. Observing the iron clergyman standing fast by its faith, she threw it a look of grieved reproach and hobbled heart-broken into her humble habitation, a subjugated cow.

For several weeks Phœbe's right hind leg was swollen to a monstrous growth, but by a season of judicious nursing she was "brought round all right," as her sympathetic and puzzled mistress phrased it, or "made whole," as the reticent man of God preferred to say. She was now as tractable and inoffensive "in her daily walk and conversation" (Huggins) as a little child. Her new master used to take her ailing leg trustfully into his lap, and for that matter, might have taken it into his mouth if he had so desired. Her entire character appeared to be radically changed—so altered that one day my Aunt Patience, who, fondly as she loved her, had never before so much as ventured to touch the hem of her garment, as it were, went confidently up to her to soothe her with a pan of turnips. Gad! how thinly she spread out that good old lady upon the face of an adjacent stone wall! You could not have done it so evenly with a trowel.

A REVOLT OF THE GODS

MY father was a deodorizer of dead dogs, my mother kept the only shop for the sale of cats'-meat in my native city. They did not live happily; the difference in social rank was a chasm which could not be bridged by the vows of marriage. It was indeed an ill-assorted and most unlucky alliance; and as might have been foreseen it ended in disaster. One morning after the customary squabbles at breakfast, my father rose from the table, quivering and pale with wrath, and proceeding to the parsonage thrashed the clergyman who had performed the marriage ceremony. The act was generally condemned and public feeling ran so high against the offender that people would permit dead dogs to lie on their property until the fragrance was deafening rather than employ him; and the municipal authorities suffered one bloated old mastiff to utter itself from a public square in so clamorous an exhalation that passing strangers supposed themselves to be in the vicinity of a saw-mill. My father was indeed unpopular. During these dark days the family's sole dependence was on my mother's emporium for cats'-meat.

The business was profitable. In that city, which was the oldest in the world, the cat was an object of veneration. Its worship was the religion of the country. The multiplication and addition of cats were a perpetual instruction in arithmetic. Naturally, any inattention to the wants of a cat was punished with great severity in this world and the next; so my good mother numbered her patrons by the hundred. Still, with an unproductive husband and seventeen children she had some difficulty in making both ends cats'-meat; and at last the necessity of increasing the discrepancy between the cost price and the selling price of her carnal wares drove her to an expedient which proved eminently disastrous: she conceived the unlucky notion of retaliating by refusing to sell cats'-meat until the boycott was taken off her husband.

On the day when she put this resolution into practice the shop was thronged with excited customers, and others extended in turbulent and restless masses up four streets, out of sight. Inside there was nothing but cursing, crowding, shouting and menace. Intimidation was freely resorted to—several of my younger brothers and sisters being threatened with cutting up for the cats—but my mother was as firm as a rock, and the day was a black one for Sardasa, the ancient and sacred city that was the scene of these events. The lock-out was vigorously maintained, and seven hundred and fifty thousand cats went to bed hungry!

The next morning the city was found to have been placarded during the night with a proclamation of the Federated Union of Old Maids. This ancient and powerful order averred through its Supreme Executive Head that the boycotting of my father and the retaliatory lock-out of my mother were seriously imperiling the interests of religion. The proclamation went on to state that if arbitration were not adopted by noon that day all the old maids of the federation would strike—and strike they did.

The next act of this unhappy drama was an insurrection of cats. These sacred animals, seeing themselves doomed to starvation, held a mass-meeting and marched in procession through the streets, swearing and spitting like fiends. This revolt of the gods produced such consternation that many pious persons died of fright and all business was suspended to bury them and pass terrifying resolutions.

Matters were now about as bad as it seemed possible for them to be. Meetings among representatives of the hostile interests were held, but no understanding was arrived at that would hold. Every agreement was broken as soon as made, and each element of the discord was frantically appealing to the people. A new horror was in store.

It will be remembered that my father was a deodorizer of dead dogs, but was unable to practice his useful and humble profession because no one would employ him. The dead dogs in consequence reeked rascally. Then they struck! From every vacant lot and public dumping ground, from every hedge and ditch and gutter and cistern, every crystal rill and the clabbered waters of all the canals and estuaries—from all the places, in short, which from time immemorial have been preëmpted by dead dogs and consecrated to the uses of them and their heirs and successors forever—they trooped innumerous, a ghastly crew! Their procession was a mile in length. Midway of the town it met the procession of cats in full song. The cats instantly exalted their backs and magnified their tails; the dead dogs uncovered their teeth as in life, and erected such of their bristles as still adhered to the skin.

The carnage that ensued was too awful for relation! The light of the sun was obscured by flying fur, and the battle was waged in the darkness, blindly and regardless. The swearing of the cats was audible miles away, while the fragrance of the dead dogs desolated seven provinces.

How the battle might have resulted it is impossible to say, but when it was at its fiercest the Federated Union of Old Maids came running down a side street and sprang into the thickest of the fray. A moment later my mother herself bore down upon the warring hosts, brandishing a cleaver, and laid about her with great freedom and impartiality. My father joined the fight, the municipal authorities engaged, and the general public, converging on the battle-field from all points of the compass, consumed itself in the center as it pressed in from the circumference. Last of all, the dead held a meeting in the cemetery and resolving on a general strike, began to destroy vaults, tombs, monuments, headstones, willows, angels and young sheep in marble—everything they could lay their hands on. By nightfall the living and the dead were alike exterminated, and where the ancient and sacred city of Sardasa had stood nothing remained but an excavation filled with dead bodies and building materials, shreds of cat and blue patches of decayed dog. The place is now a vast pool of stagnant water in the center of a desert.

The stirring events of those few days constituted my industrial education, and so well have I improved my advantages that I am now Chief of Misrule to the Dukes of Disorder, an organization numbering thirteen million American workingmen.

THE BAPTISM OF DOBSHO

IT was a wicked thing to do, certainly. I have often regretted it since, and if the opportunity of doing so again were presented I should hesitate a long time before embracing it. But I was young then, and cherished a species of humor which I have since abjured. Still, when I remember the character of the people who were burlesquing and bringing into disrepute the letter and spirit of our holy religion I feel a certain satisfaction in having contributed one feeble effort toward making them ridiculous. In consideration of the little good I may have done in that way, I beg the reader to judge my conceded error as leniently as possible. This is the story.

Some years ago the town of Harding, in Illinois, experienced "a revival of religion," as the people called it. It would have been more accurate and less profane to term it a revival of Rampageanism, for the craze originated in, and was disseminated by, the sect which I will call the Rampagean communion; and most of the leaping and howling was done in that interest. Amongst those who yielded to the influence was my friend Thomas Dobsho. Tom had been a pretty bad sinner in a small way, but he went into this new thing heart and soul. At one of the meetings he made a public confession of more sins than he ever was, or ever could have been guilty of; stopping just short of statutory crimes, and even hinting, significantly, that he could tell a good deal more if he were pressed. He wanted to join the absurd communion the very evening of his conversion. He wanted to join two or three communions. In fact, he was so carried away with his zeal that some of the brethren gave me a hint to take him home; he and I occupied adjoining apartments in the Elephant Hotel.

Tom's fervor, as it happened, came near defeating its own purpose; instead of taking him at once into the fold without reference or "character," which was their usual way, the brethren remembered against him his awful confessions and put him on probation. But after a few weeks, during which he conducted himself like a decent lunatic, it was decided to baptise him along with a dozen other pretty hard cases who had been converted more recently. This sacrilegious ceremony I persuaded myself it was my duty to prevent, though I think now I erred as to the means adopted. It was to take place on a Sunday, and on the preceding Saturday I called on the head revivalist, the Rev. Mr. Swin, and craved an interview.

"I come," said I, with simulated reluctance and embarrassment, "in behalf of my friend, Brother Dobsho, to make a very delicate and unusual request. You are, I think, going to baptise him to-morrow, and I trust it will be to him the beginning of a new and better life. But I don't know if you are aware that his family are all Plungers, and that he is himself tainted with the wicked heresy of that sect. So it is. He is, as one might say in secular metaphor, 'on the fence' between their grievous error and the pure faith of your church. It would be most melancholy if he should get down on the wrong side. Although I confess with shame I have not myself embraced the truth, I hope I am not too blind to see where it lies."

"The calamity that you apprehend," said the reverend lout, after solemn reflection, "would indeed seriously affect our friend's interest and endanger his soul. I had not expected Brother Dobsho so soon to give up the good fight."

"I think sir," I replied reflectively, "there is no fear of that if the matter is skilfully managed. He is heartily with you—might I venture to say with *us?*—on every point but one. He favors immersion! He has been so vile a sinner that he foolishly fears the more simple rite of your church will not make him wet enough. Would you believe it? his uninstructed scruples on the point are so gross and materialistic that he actually suggested soaping himself as a preparatory ceremony! I believe, however, if instead of sprinkling my friend, you would pour a generous basinful of water on his head—but now that I think of it in your enlightening presence I see that such a proceeding is quite out of the question. I fear we must let matters take the usual course, trusting to our later efforts to prevent the backsliding which may result."

The parson rose and paced the floor a moment, then suggested that he'd better see Brother Dobsho, and labor to remove his error. I told him I thought not; I was sure it would not be best. Argument would only confirm him in his prejudices. So it was settled that the subject should not be broached in that quarter. It would have been bad for me if it had been.

When I reflect now upon the guile of that conversation, the falsehood of my representations and the wickedness of my motive I am almost ashamed to proceed with my narrative. Had the minister been other than an arrant humbug, I hope I should never have suffered myself to make him the dupe of a scheme so sacrilegious in itself, and prosecuted with so sinful a disregard of honor.

The memorable Sabbath dawned bright and beautiful. About nine o'clock the cracked old bell, rigged up on struts before the "meeting-house," began to clamor its call to service, and nearly the whole population of Harding took its way to the performance. I had taken the precaution to set my watch fifteen minutes fast. Tom was nervously preparing himself for the ordeal. He fidgeted himself into his best suit an hour before the time, carried his hat about the room in the most aimless and demented way and consulted his watch a hundred times. I was to accompany him to church, and I spent the time fussing about the room, doing the most extraordinary things in the most exasperating manner—in short, keeping up Tom's feverish excitement by every wicked device I could think of. Within a half hour of the real time for service I suddenly yelled out—

"O, I say, Tom; pardon me, but that head of yours is just frightful! Please *do* let me brush it up a bit!"

Seizing him by the shoulders I thrust him into a chair with his face to the wall, laid hold of his comb and brush, got behind him and went to work. He was trembling like a child, and knew no more what I was doing than if he had been brained. Now, Tom's head was a curiosity. His hair, which was remarkably thick, was like wire. Being cut rather short it stood out all over his scalp like the spines on a porcupine. It had been a favorite complaint of Tom's that he never could do anything to that head. I found no difficulty—I did something to it, though I blush to think what it was. I did something which I feared he might discover if he looked in the mirror, so I carelessly pulled out my watch, sprung it open, gave a start and shouted—

"By Jove! Thomas—pardon the oath—but we're late. Your watch is all wrong; look at mine! Here's your hat, old fellow; come along. There's not a moment to lose!"

Clapping his hat on his head, I pulled him out of the house, with actual violence. In five minutes more we were in the meeting-house with ever so much time to spare.

The services that day, I am told, were specially interesting and impressive, but I had a good deal else on my mind—was preoccupied, absent, inattentive. They might have varied from the usual profane exhibition in any respect and to any extent, and I should not have observed it. The first thing I clearly perceived was a rank of "converts" kneeling before the "altar," Tom at the left of the line. Then the Rev. Mr. Swin approached him, thoughtfully dipping his fingers into a small earthern bowl of water as if he had just finished dining. I was much affected: I could see nothing distinctly for my tears. My handkerchief was at my face—most of it inside. I was observed to sob spasmodically, and I am abashed to think how many sincere persons mistakenly followed my example.

With some solemn words, the purport of which I did not quite make out, except that they sounded like swearing, the minister stood before Thomas, gave me a glance of intelligence and then with an innocent expression of face, the recollection of which to this day fills me with remorse, spilled, as if by accident, the entire contents of the bowl on the head of my poor friend—that head into the hair of which I had sifted a prodigal profusion of Seidlitz-powders!

I confess it, the effect was magical—anyone who was present would tell you that. Tom's pow simmered—it seethed—it foamed yeastily, and slavered like a mad dog! It steamed and hissed, with angry spurts and flashes! In a second it had grown bigger than a small snowbank, and whiter. It surged, and boiled, and walloped, and overflowed, and sputtered—sent off feathery flakes like down from a shot swan! The froth poured creaming over his face, and got into his eyes. It was the most sinful shampooing of the season!

I cannot relate the commotion this produced, nor would I if I could. As to Tom, he sprang to his feet and staggered out of the house, groping his way between the pews, sputtering strangled profanity and gasping like a stranded fish. The other candidates for baptism rose also, shaking their pates as if to say, "No you don't, my hearty," and left the house in a body. Amidst unbroken silence the minister reascended the pulpit with the empty bowl in his hand, and was first to speak:

"Brethren and sisters," said he with calm, deliberate evenness of tone, "I have held forth in this tabernacle for many more years than I have got fingers and toes, and during that time I have known not guile, nor anger, nor any uncharitableness. As to Henry Barber, who put up this job on me, I judge him not lest I be judged. Let him take *that* and sin no more!"—and he flung the earthern bowl with so true an aim that it was shattered against my skull. The rebuke was not undeserved, I confess, and I trust I have profited by it.

THE RACE AT LEFT BOWER

"IT'S all very well fer you Britishers to go assin' about the country tryin' to strike the trail o' the mines you've salted down yer loose carpital in," said Colonel Jackhigh, setting his empty glass on the counter and wiping his lips with his coat sleeve; "but w'en it comes to hoss racin', w'y I've got a cayuse ken lay over all the thurrerbreds yer little mantel-ornyment of a island ever panned out—bet yer britches I have! Talk about yer Durby winners—w'y this pisen little beast o' mine'll take the bit in her teeth and show 'em the way to the horizon like she was takin' her mornin' stroll and they was tryin' to keep an eye on her to see she didn't do herself an injury—that's w'at she would! And she haint never run a race with anything spryer'n an Injun in all her life; she's a green amatoor, *she* is!"

"Oh, very well," said the Englishman with a quiet smile; "it is easy enough to settle the matter. My animal is in tolerably good condition, and if yours is in town we can have the race to-morrow for any stake you like, up to a hundred dollars."

"That's jest the figger," said the colonel; "dot it down, barkeep. But it's like slarterin' the innocents," he added, half-remorsefully, as he turned to leave; "it's bettin' on a dead sure thing—that's what it is! If my cayuse knew wa't I was about she'd go and break a laig to make the race a fair one."

So it was arranged that the race was to come off at three o'clock the next day, on the *mesa,* some distance from town. As soon as the news got abroad, the whole population of Left Bower and vicinity knocked off work and assembled in the various bars to discuss it. The English-man and his horse were general favorites, and aside from the unpopu-larity of the colonel, nobody had ever seen his "cayuse." Still the ele-ment of patriotism came in, making the betting very nearly even.

A race-course was marked off on the *mesa* and at the appointed hour every one was there except the colonel. It was arranged that each man should ride his own horse, and the Englishman, who had acquired something of the free-and-easy bearing that distinguishes the "mining sharp," was already atop of his magnificent animal, with one leg thrown carelessly across the pommel of his Mexican saddle, as he puffed his cigar with calm confidence in the result of the race. He was conscious, too, that he possessed the secret sympathy of all, even of those who had felt it their duty to bet against him. The judge, watch in hand was growing impatient, when the colonel appeared about a half-mile away, and bore down upon the crowd. Everyone was eager to inspect his mount; and such a mount as it proved to be was never before seen, even in Left Bower!

You have seen "perfect skeletons" of horses often enough, no doubt, but this animal was not even a perfect skeleton; there were bones missing here and there which you would not have believed the beast could have spared. "Little" the colonel had called her! She was not an inch less than eighteen hands high, and long out of all reasonable proportion. She was so hollow in the back that she seemed to have been bent in a machine. She had neither tail nor mane, and her neck, as long as a man, stuck straight up into the air, supporting a head without ears. Her eyes had an expression in them of downright insanity, and the muscles of her face were afflicted with periodical convulsions that drew back the corners of the mouth and wrinkled the upper lip so as to produce a ghastly grin every two or three seconds. In color she was "claybank," with great blotches of white, as if she had been pelted with small bags of flour. The crookedness of her legs was beyond all comparison, and as to her gait it was that of a blind camel walking diagonally across innumerable deep ditches. Altogether she looked like the crude result of Nature's first experiment in equifaction.

As this libel on all horses shambled up to the starting post there was a general shout; the sympathies of the crowd changed in the twinkling of an eye! Everyone wanted to bet on her, and the Englishman himself was only restrained from doing so by a sense of honor. It was growing late, however, and the judge insisted on starting them. They got off very well together, and seeing the mare was unconscionably slow the Englishman soon pulled his animal in and permitted the ugly thing to pass him, so as to enjoy a back view of her. That sealed his fate. The course had been marked off in a circle of two miles in circumference and some twenty feet wide, the limits plainly defined by little furrows. Before the animals had gone a half mile both had been permitted to settle down into a comfortable walk, in which they continued three-fourths of the way round the ring. Then the Englishman thought it time to whip up and canter in.

But he didn't. As he came up alongside the "Lightning Express," as the crowd had begun to call her, that creature turned her head diagonally backward and let fall a smile. The encroaching beast stopped as if he had been shot! His rider plied whip, and forced him again forward upon the track of the equine hag, but with the same result.

The Englishman was now alarmed; he struggled manfully with rein and whip and shout, amidst the tremendous cheering and inextinguishable laughter of the crowd, to force his animal past, now on this side, now on that, but it would not do. Prompted by the fiend in the concavity of her back, the unthinkable quadruped dropped her grins right and left with such seasonable accuracy that again and again the competing beast was struck "all of a heap" just at the moment of seeming success. And, finally, when by a tremendous spurt his rider endeavored to thrust him by, within half a dozen lengths of the winning post, the incarnate nightmare turned squarely about and fixed upon him a portentous stare—delivering at the same time a grimace of such prodigious ghastliness that the poor thoroughbred, with an almost human scream of terror, wheeled about, and tore away to the rear with the speed of the wind, leaving the colonel an easy winner in twenty minutes and ten seconds.

THE FAILURE OF HOPE & WANDEL

From Mr. Jabez Hope, in Chicago, to Mr. Pike Wandel, of New Orleans, December 2, 1877.

I will not bore you, my dear fellow, with a narrative of my journey from New Orleans to this polar region. It is cold in Chicago, believe me, and the Southron who comes here, as I did, without a relay of noses and ears will have reason to regret his mistaken economy in arranging his outfit.

To business. Lake Michigan is frozen stiff. Fancy, O child of a torrid clime, a sheet of anybody's ice, three hundred miles long, forty broad, and six feet thick! It sounds like a lie, Pikey dear, but your partner in the firm of Hope & Wandel, Wholesale Boots and Shoes, New Orleans, is never known to fib. My plan is to collar that ice. Wind up the present business and send on the money at once. I'll put up a warehouse as big as the Capitol at Washington, store it full and ship to your orders as the Southern market may require. I can send it in planks for skating floors, in statuettes for the mantel, in shavings for juleps, or in solution for ice cream and general purposes. It is a big thing!

I inclose a thin slip as a sample. Did you ever see such charming ice?

From Mr. Pike Wandel, of New Orleans, to Mr. Jabez Hope, in Chicago, December 24, 1877.

Your letter was so abominably defaced by blotting and blurring that it was entirely illegible. It must have come all the way by water. By the aid of chemicals and photography, however, I have made it out. But you forgot to inclose the sample of ice.

I have sold off everything (at an alarming sacrifice, I am sorry to say) and inclose draft for net amount. Shall begin to spar for orders at once. I trust everything to you—but, I say, has anybody tried to grow ice in *this* vicinity? There is Lake Ponchartrain, you know.

From Mr. Jabez Hope, in Chicago, to Mr. Pike Wandel, of New Orleans, February 27, 1878.

Wannie dear, it would do you good to see our new warehouse for the ice. Though made of boards, and run up rather hastily, it is as pretty as a picture, and cost a deal of money, though I pay no ground rent. It is about as big as the Capitol at Washington. Do you think it ought to have a steeple? I have it nearly filled—fifty men cutting and storing, day and night—awful cold work! By the way, the ice, which when I wrote you last was ten feet thick, is now thinner. But don't you worry; there is plenty.

Our warehouse is eight or ten miles out of town, so I am not much bothered by visitors, which is a relief. Such a giggling, sniggering lot you never saw!

It seems almost too absurdly incredible, Wannie, but do you know I believe this ice of ours gains in coldness as the warm weather comes on! I do, indeed, and you may mention the fact in the advertisements.

From Mr. Pike Wandel, of New Orleans, to Mr. Jabez Hope, in Chicago, March 7, 1878.

All goes well. I get hundreds of orders. We shall do a roaring trade as "The New Orleans and Chicago Semperfrigid Ice Company." But you have not told me whether the ice is fresh or salt. If it is fresh it won't do for cooking, and if it is salt it will spoil the mint juleps.

Is it as cold in the middle as the outside cuts are?

From Mr. Jabez Hope, from Chicago, to Mr. Pike Wandel, of New Orleans, April 3, 1878.

Navigation on the Lakes is now open, and ships are thick as ducks. I'm afloat, *en route* for Buffalo, with the assets of the New Orleans and Chicago Semperfrigid Ice Company in my vest pocket. We are busted out, my poor Pikey—we are to fortune and to fame unknown. Arrange a meeting of the creditors and don't attend.

Last night a schooner from Milwaukee was smashed into matchwood on an enormous mass of floating ice—the first berg ever seen in these waters. It is described by the survivors as being about as big as the Capitol of Washington. One-half of that iceberg belongs to you, Pikey.

The melancholy fact is, I built our warehouse on an unfavorable site, about a mile out from the shore (on the ice, you understand), and when the thaw came—O my God, Wannie, it was the saddest thing you ever saw in all your life! You will be *so* glad to know I was not in it at the time.

What a ridiculous question you ask me. My poor partner, you don't seem to know very much about the ice business.

PERRY CHUMLY'S ECLIPSE

THE spectroscope is a singularly beautiful and delicate instrument, consisting, essentially, of a prism of glass, which, decomposing the light of any heavenly body to which the instrument is directed, presents a spectrum, or long bar of color. Crossing this are narrow, dark and bright lines produced by the gases of metals in combustion, whereby the celestial orb's light is generated. From these dark and bright lines, therefore, we ascertain all that is worth knowing about the composition of the sun and stars.

Now Ben had made some striking discoveries in spectroscopic analysis at his private garden observatory, and had also an instrument of superior power and capacity, invented, or at least much improved, by himself; and this instrument it was that he and I were arranging for an examination of the comet then flaming in the heavens. William sat by apparently uninterested. Finally we had our arrangements for an observation completed, and Ben said: "Now turn her on."

"That reminds me," said William, "of a little story about Perry Chumly, who—"

"For the sake of science, William," I interrupted, laying a hand on his arm, "I must beg you not to relate it. The comet will in a few minutes be behind the roof of yonder lodging house. We really have no time for the story."

"No," said Ben, "time presses; and, anyhow, I've heard it before."

"This Perry Chumly," resumed William, "believed himself a born astronomer, and always kept a bit of smoked glass. He was particularly great on solar eclipses. I have known him to sit up all night looking out for one."

Ben had now got the spectroscope trained skyward to suit him, and in order to exclude all irrelevant light had let down the window-blind on the tube of it. The spectrum of the comet came out beautifully—a long bar of color crossed with a lovely ruling of thin dark and bright lines, the sight of which elicited from us an exclamation of satisfaction.

"One day," continued William from his seat at another window, "some one told Perry Chumly there would be an eclipse of the sun that afternoon at three o'clock. Now Perry had recently read a story about some men who in exploring a deep cañon in the mountains had looked up from the bottom and seen the stars shining at midday. It occurred to him that this knowledge might be so utilized as to give him a fine view of the eclipse, and enable him at the same time to see what the stars would appear to think about it."

"*This,*" said Ben, pointing to one of the dark lines in the cometic spectrum, "*this* is produced by the vapor of carbon in the nucleus of the heavenly visitant. You will observe that it differs but slightly from the lines that come of volatilized iron. Examined with this magnifying glass"—adjusting that instrument to his eye—"it will probably show—by Jove!" he ejaculated, after a nearer view, "it isn't carbon at all. *It is* MEAT!"

"Of course," proceeded William, "of course Perry Chumly did not have any cañon, so what did the fellow do but let himself down with his arms and legs to the bottom of an old well, about thirty feet deep! And, with the cold water up to his middle, and the frogs, pollywogs and aquatic lizards quarreling for the cosy corners of his pockets, there he stood, waiting for the sun to appear in the field of his 'instrument' and be eclipsed."

"Ben, you are joking," I remarked with some asperity; "you are taking liberties with science, Benjamin. It *can't* be meat, you know."

"I tell you it *is* though," was his excited reply; "it is just *meat,* I tell you! And this other line, which at first I took for sodium, is *bone*—bone, sir, or I'm an asteroid! I never saw the like; that comet must be densely peopled with butchers and horse-knackers!"

"When Perry Chumly had waited a long time," William went on to say, "looking up and expecting every minute to see the sun, it began to get into his mind, somehow, that the bright, circular opening above his head—the mouth of the well—*was* the sun, and that the black disk of the moon was all that was needed to complete the expected phenomenon. The notion soon took complete possession of his brain, so that he forgot where he was and imagined himself standing on the surface of the earth."

I was now scrutinizing the cometic spectrum very closely, being particularly attracted by a thin, faint line, which I thought Ben had overlooked.

"Oh, that is nothing," he explained; "that's a mere local fault arising from conditions peculiar to the medium through which the light is transmitted—the atmosphere of this neighborhood. It is whisky. This other line, though, shows the faintest imaginable trace of soap; and these uncertain, wavering ones are caused by some effluvium not in the comet itself, but in the region beyond it. I am compelled to pronounce it tobacco smoke. I will now tilt the instrument so as to get the spectrum of the celestial wanderer's tail. Ah! there we have it. Splendid!"

"Now this old well," said William, "was near a road, along which was traveling a big and particularly hideous Negro."

"See here, Thomas," exclaimed Ben, removing the magnifying glass from his eye and looking me earnestly in the face, "If I were to tell you that the *coma* of this eccentric heavenly body is really hair, as its name implies, would you believe it?"

"No, Ben, I certainly should not."

"Well, I won't argue the matter; there are the lines—they speak for themselves. But now that I look again, you are not entirely wrong: there is a considerable admixture of jute, moss, and I think tallow. It certainly is most remarkable! Sir Isaac Newton—"

"That big nigger," drawled William, "felt thirsty, and seeing the mouth of the well thought there was perhaps a bucket in it. So he ventured to creep forward on his hands and knees and look in over the edge."

Suddenly our spectrum vanished, and a very singular one of a quite different appearance presented itself in the same place. It was a dim spectrum, crossed by a single broad bar of pale yellow.

"Ah!" said Ben, "our waif of the upper deep is obscured by a cloud; let us see what the misty veil is made of."

He took a look at the spectrum with his magnifying glass, started back, and muttered: "Brown linen, by thunder!"

"You can imagine the rapture of Perry Chumly," pursued the indefatigable William, "when he saw, as he supposed, the moon's black disk encroaching upon the body of the luminary that had so long riveted his gaze. But when that obscuring satellite had thrust herself so far forward that the eclipse became almost annular, and he saw her staring down upon a darkened world with glittering white eyes and a double row of flashing teeth, it is perhaps not surprising that he vented a scream of terror, fainted and collapsed among his frogs! As for the big nigger, almost equally terrified by this shriek from the abyss, he executed a precipitate movement which only the breaking of his neck prevented from being a double back-somersault, and lay dead in the weeds with his tongue out and his face the color of a cometic spectrum. We laid them in the same grave, poor fellows, and on many a still summer evening afterward I strayed to the lonely little church-yard to listen to the smothered requiem chanted by the frogs that we had neglected to remove from the pockets of the lamented astronomer.

"And, now," added William, taking his heels from the window, "as you can not immediately resume your spectroscopic observations on that red-haired chamber-maid in the dormer-window, who pulled down the blind when I made a mouth at her, I move that we adjourn."

A PROVIDENTIAL INTIMATION

MR. ALGERNON JARVIS, of San Francisco, got up cross. The world of Mr. Jarvis had gone wrong with him overnight, as one's world is likely to do when one sits up till morning with jovial friends, to watch it, and he was prone to resentment. No sooner, therefore, had he got himself into a neat, fashionable suit of clothing than he selected his morning walking-stick and sallied out upon the town with a vague general determination to attack something. His first victim would naturally have been his breakfast; but singularly enough, he fell upon this with so feeble an energy that he was himself beaten—to the grieved astonishment of the worthy *rôtisseur,* who had to record his hitherto puissant patron's maiden defeat. Three or four cups of *café noir* were the only captives that graced Mr. Jarvis' gastric chariot-wheels that morning.

He lit a long cigar and sauntered moodily down the street, so occupied with schemes of universal retaliation that his feet had it all their own way; in consequence of which, their owner soon found himself in the billiard-room of the Occidental Hotel. Nobody was there, but Mr.

Jarvis was a privileged person; so, going to the marker's desk, he took out a little box of ivory balls, spilled them carelessly over a table and languidly assailed them with a long stick.

Presently, by the merest chance, he executed a marvelous stroke. Waiting till the astonished balls had resumed their composure, he gathered them up, replacing them in their former position. He tried the stroke again, and, naturally, did not make it. Again he placed the balls, and again he badly failed. With a vexed and humiliated air he once more put the indocile globes into position, leaned over the table and was upon the point of striking, when there sounded a solemn voice from behind: "Bet you two bits you don't make it!"

Mr. Jarvis erected himself; he turned about and looked at the speaker, whom he found to be a stranger—one that most persons would prefer should remain a stranger. Mr. Jarvis made no reply. In the first place, he was a man of aristocratic taste, to whom a wager of "two bits" was simply vulgar. Secondly, the man who had proffered it evidently had not the money. Still it is annoying to have one's skill questioned by one's social inferiors, particularly when one has doubts of it oneself, and is otherwise ill-tempered. So Mr. Jarvis stood his cue against the table, laid off his fashionable morning-coat, resumed his stick, spread his fine figure upon the table with his back to the ceiling and took deliberate aim.

At this point Mr. Jarvis drops out of this history, and is seen no more forever. Persons of the class to which he adds lustre are sacred from the pen of the humorist; they are ridiculous but not amusing. So now we will dismiss this uninteresting young aristocrat, retaining merely his outer shell, the fashionable morning-coat, which Mr. Stenner, the gentleman, who had offered the wager, has quietly thrown across his arm and is conveying away for his own advantage.

An hour later Mr. Stenner sat in his humble lodgings at North Beach, with the pilfered garment upon his knees. He had already taken the opinion of an eminent pawnbroker on its value, and it only remained to search the pockets. Mr. Stenner's notions concerning gentlemen's coats were not so clear as they might have been. Broadly stated, they were that these garments abounded in secret pockets crowded with a wealth of bank notes interspersed with gold coins. He was therefore disappointed when his careful quest was rewarded with only a delicately perfumed handkerchief, upon which he could not hope to obtain a loan of more than ten cents; a pair of gloves too small for use and a bit of paper that was not a cheque. A second look at this, however, inspired hope. It was about the size of a flounder, ruled in wide lines, and bore in conspicuous characters the words, "Western Union Telegraph Company." Immediately below this interesting legend was much other printed matter, the purport of which was that the company did not hold itself responsible for the verbal accuracy of "the following message," and did not consider itself either morally or legally bound to forward or deliver it, nor, in short, to render any kind of service for the money paid by the sender.

Unfamiliar with telegraphy, Mr. Stenner naturally supposed that a message subject to these hard conditions must be one of not only grave importance, but questionable character. So he determined to decipher it at that time and place. In the course of the day he succeeded in so doing. It ran as follows, omitting the date and the names of persons and places, which were, of course, quite illegible:

"Buy Sally Meeker!"

Had the full force of this remarkable adjuration burst upon Mr. Stenner all at once it might have carried him away, which would not have been so bad a thing for San Francisco; but as the meaning had to percolate slowly through a dense dyke of ignorance, it produced no other immediate effect than the exclamation, "Well, I'll be bust!"

In the mouths of some persons this form of expression means a great deal. On the Stenner tongue it signified the hopeless nature of the Stenner mental confusion.

It must be confessed—by persons outside a certain limited and sordid circle—that the message lacks amplification and elaboration; in its terse, bald diction there is a ghastly suggestion of traffic in human flesh, for which in California there is no market since the abolition of slavery and the importation of thoroughbred beeves. If woman suffrage had been established all would have been clear; Mr. Stenner would at once have understood the kind of purchase advised; for in political transactions he had very often changed hands himself. But it was all a muddle, and resolving to dismiss the matter from his thoughts, he went to bed thinking of nothing else; for many hours his excited imagination would do nothing but purchase slightly damaged Sally Meekers by the bale, and retail them to itself at an enormous profit.

Next day, it flashed upon his memory who Sally Meeker was—a racing mare! At this entirely obvious solution of the problem he was over-come with amazement at his own sagacity. Rushing into the street he purchased, not Sally Meeker, but a sporting paper—and in it found the notice of a race which was to come off the following week; and, sure enough, there it was:

"Budd Doble enters g. g. Clipper; Bob Scotty enters b. g. Lightnin'; Staley Tupper enters s. s. Upandust; Sim Salper enters b. m. Sally Meeker."

It was clear now; the sender of the dispatch was "in the know." Sally Meeker was to win, and her owner, who did not know it, had offered her for sale. At that supreme moment Mr. Stenner would willingly have been a rich man! In fact he resolved to be. He at once betook him to Vallejo, where he had lived until invited away by some influential citizens of the place. There he immediately sought out an industrious friend who had an amiable weakness for draw poker, and in whom Mr. Stenner regularly encouraged that passion by going up against him every payday and despoiling him of his hard earnings. He did so this time, to the sum of one hundred dollars.

No sooner had he raked in his last pool and refused his friend's ap-peal for a trifling loan wherewith to pay for breakfast than he bought a check on the Bank of California, enclosed it in a letter containing merely the words "Bi Saly Meker," and dispatched it by mail to the only clergyman in San Francisco whose name he knew. Mr. Stenner had a vague notion that all kinds of business requiring strict honesty and fidelity might be profitably intrusted to the clergy; otherwise what was the use of religion? I hope I shall not be accused of disrespect to the cloth in thus bluntly setting forth Mr. Stenner's estimate of the parsons, inasmuch as I do not share it.

This business off his mind, Mr. Stenner unbent in a week's revelry; at the end of which he worked his passage down to San Francisco to secure his winnings on the race, and take charge of his peerless mare. It will be observed that his notions concerning races were somewhat confused; his experience of them had hitherto been confined to that branch of the business requiring, not technical knowledge but manual dexterity. In short, he had done no more than pick the pockets of the spectators. Arrived at San Francisco he was hastening to the dwelling of his clerical agent, when he met an acquaintance, to whom he put the triumphant question, "How about Sally Meeker?"

"Sally Meeker? Sally Meeker?" was the reply. "Oh, you mean the hoss? Why she's gone up the flume. Broke her neck the first heat. But ole Sim Salper is never a-goin' to fret hisself to a shadder about it. He struck it pizen in the mine she was named a'ter and the stock's gone up from nothin' out o' sight. You couldn't tech that stock with a ten-foot pole!"

Which was a blow to Mr. Stenner. He saw his error; the message in the coat had evidently been sent to a broker, and referred to the stock of the "Sally Meeker" mine. And he, Stenner, was a ruined man!

Suddenly a great, monstrous, misbegotten and unmentionable oath rolled from Mr. Stenner's tongue like a cannon shot hurled along an uneven floor! Might it not be that the Rev. Mr. Boltright had also misunderstood the message, and had bought, not the mare, but the stock? The thought was electrical: Mr. Stenner ran—he flew! He tarried not at walls and the smaller sort of houses, but went through or over them! In five minutes he stood before the good clergyman—and in one more had asked, in a hoarse whisper, if he had bought any "Sally Meeker."

"My good friend," was the bland reply—"my fellow traveler to the bar of God, it would better comport with your spiritual needs to inquire what you should do to be saved. But since you ask me, I will confess that having received what I am compelled to regard as a Providential intimation, accompanied with the secular means of obedience, I did put up a small margin and purchase largely of the stock you mention. The venture, I am constrained to state, was not wholly unprofitable."

Unprofitable? The good man had made a square twenty-five thousand dollars on that small margin! To conclude—he has it yet.

MR. SWIDDLER'S FLIP-FLAP

JEROME BOWLES (said the gentleman called Swiddler) was to be hanged on Friday, the ninth of November, at five o'clock in the afternoon. This was to occur at the town of Flatbroke, where he was then in prison. Jerome was my friend, and naturally I differed with the jury that had convicted him as to the degree of guilt implied by the conceded fact that he had shot an Indian without direct provocation. Ever since his trial I had been endeavoring to influence the Governor of the State to grant a pardon; but public sentiment was against me, a fact which I attributed partly to the innate pigheadness of the people, and partly to the recent establishment of churches and schools which had corrupted the primitive notions of a frontier community. But I labored hard and unremittingly by all manner of direct and indirect means during the whole period in which Jerome lay under sentence of death; and on the very morning of the day set for the execution, the Governor sent for me, and saying "he did not purpose being worried by my importunities all winter," handed me the document which he had so often refused.

Armed with the precious paper, I flew to the telegraph office to send a dispatch to the Sheriff at Flatbroke. I found the operator locking the door of the office and putting up the shutters. I pleaded in vain; he said he was going to see the hanging, and really had no time to send my message. I must explain that Flatbroke was fifteen miles away; I was then at Swan Creek, the State capital.

The operator being inexorable, I ran to the railroad station to see how soon there would be a train for Flatbroke. The station man, with cool and polite malice, informed me that all the employees of the road had been given a holiday to see Jerome Bowles hanged, and had already gone by an early train; that there would be no other train till the next day.

I was now furious, but the station man quietly turned me out, locking the gates. Dashing to the nearest livery stable, I ordered a horse. Why prolong the record of my disappointment? Not a horse could I get in that town; all had been engaged weeks before to take people to the hanging. So everybody said, at least, though I now know there was a rascally conspiracy to defeat the ends of mercy, for the story of the pardon had got abroad.

It was now ten o'clock. I had only seven hours in which to do my fifteen miles afoot; but I was an excellent walker and thoroughly angry; there was no doubt of my ability to make the distance, with an hour to spare. The railway offered the best chance; it ran straight as a string across a level, treeless prairie, whereas the highway made a wide detour by way of another town.

I took to the track like a Modoc on the war path. Before I had gone a half-mile I was overtaken by "That Jim Peasley," as he was called in Swan Creek, an incurable practical joker, loved and shunned by all who knew him. He asked me as he came up if I were "going to the show." Thinking it was best to dissemble, I told him I was, but said nothing of my intention to stop the performance; I thought it would be a lesson to That Jim to let him walk fifteen miles for nothing, for it was clear that he was going, too. Still, I wished he would go on ahead or drop behind. But he could not very well do the former, and would not do the latter; so we trudged on together.

It was a cloudy day and very sultry for that time of the year. The railway stretched away before us, between its double row of telegraph poles, in rigid sameness, terminating in a point at the horizon. On either hand the disheartening monotony of the prairie was unbroken.

I thought little of these things, however, for my mental exaltation was proof against the depressing influence of the scene. I was about to save the life of my friend—to restore a crack shot to society. Indeed I scarcely thought of That Jim, whose heels were grinding the hard gravel close behind me, except when he saw fit occasionally to propound the sententious, and I thought derisive, query, "Tired?" Of course I was, but I would have died rather than confess it.

We had gone in this way, about half the distance, probably, in much less than half the seven hours, and I was getting my second wind, when That Jim again broke the silence.

"Used to bounce in a circus, didn't you?"

This was quite true! in a season of pecuniary depression I had once put my legs into my stomach—had turned my athletic accomplishments to financial advantage. It was not a pleasant topic, and I said nothing. That Jim persisted.

"Wouldn't like to do a feller a somersault now, eh?"

The mocking tongue of this jeer was intolerable; the fellow evidently considered me "done up," so taking a short run I clapped my hands to my thighs and executed as pretty a flip-flap as ever was made without a spring-board! At the moment I came erect with my head still spinning, I felt That Jim crowd past me, giving me a twirl that almost sent me off the track. A moment later he had dashed ahead at a tremendous pace, laughing derisively over his shoulder as if he had done a remarkably clever thing to gain the lead.

I was on the heels of him in less than ten minutes, though I must confess the fellow could walk amazingly. In half an hour I had run past him, and at the end of the hour, such was my slashing gait, he was a mere black dot in my rear, and appeared to be sitting on one of the rails, thoroughly used up.

Relieved of Mr. Peasley, I naturally began thinking of my poor friend in the Flatbroke jail, and it occurred to me that something might happen to hasten the execution. I knew the feeling of the country against him, and that many would be there from a distance who would naturally wish to get home before nightfall. Nor could I help admitting to myself that five o'clock was an unreasonably late hour for a hanging. Tortured with these fears, I unconsciously increased my pace with every step, until it was almost a run. I stripped off my coat and flung it away, opened my collar, and unbuttoned my waistcoat. And at last, puffing and steaming like a locomotive engine, I burst into a thin crowd of idlers on the outskirts of the town, and flourished the pardon crazily above my head, yelling, "Cut him down!—cut him down!"

Then, as every one stared in blank amazement and nobody said anything, I found time to look about me, marveling at the oddly familiar appearance of the town. As I looked, the houses, streets, and everything seemed to undergo a sudden and mysterious transposition with reference to the points of the compass, as if swinging round on a pivot; and like one awakened from a dream I found myself among accustomed scenes. To be plain about it, I was back again in Swan Creek, as right as a trivet!

It was all the work of That Jim Peasley. The designing rascal had provoked me to throw a confusing somersault, then bumped against me, turning me half round, and started on the back track, thereby inciting me to hook it in the same direction. The cloudy day, the two lines of telegraph poles, one on each side of the track, the entire sameness of the landscape to the right and left—these had all conspired to prevent my observing that I had put about.

When the excursion train returned from Flatbroke that evening the passengers were told a little story at my expense. It was just what they needed to cheer them up a bit after what they had seen; for that flip-flap of mine had broken the neck of Jerome Bowles seven miles away!

THE LITTLE STORY

DRAMATIS PERSONÆ—*A Supernumerary Editor.*
A Probationary Contributor.

SCENE—*"The Expounder" Office.*

PROBATIONARY CONTRIBUTOR—Editor in?

SUPERNUMERARY EDITOR—Dead.

P. C.—The gods favor me. (*Produces roll of manuscript.*) Here is a little story, which I will read to you.

S. E.—O, O!

P. C.—(*Reads.*) "It was the last night of the year—a naughty, noxious, offensive night. In the principal street of San Francisco"—

S. E.—Confound San Francisco!

P. C.—It had to be somewhere. (*Reads.*)
"In the principal street of San Francisco stood a small female orphan, marking time like a volunteer. Her little bare feet imprinted cold kisses on the paving-stones as she put them down and drew them up alternately. The chilling rain was having a good time with her scalp, and toyed soppily with her hair—her own hair. The night-wind shrewdly searched her tattered garments, as if it had suspected her of smuggling. She saw crowds of determined-looking persons grimly ruining themselves in toys and confectionery for the dear ones at home, and she wished she was in a position to ruin a little—just a little. Then, as the happy throng sped by her with loads of things to make the children sick, she leaned against an iron lamp-post in front of a bake-shop and turned on the wicked envy. She thought, poor thing, she would like to be a cake—for this little girl was very hungry indeed. Then she tried again, and thought she would like to be a tart with smashed fruit inside; then she would be warmed over every day and nobody would eat her. For the child was cold as well as hungry. Finally, she tried quite hard, and

thought she could be very well content as an oven; for then she would be kept always hot, and bakers would put all manner of good things into her with a long shovel."

S. E.—I've read that somewhere.

P. C.—Very likely. This little story has never been rejected by any paper to which I have offered it. It gets better, too, every time I write it. When it first appeared in *Veracity* the editor said it cost him a hundred subscribers. Just mark the improvement! (*Reads.*)

"The hours glided by—except a few that froze to the pavement—until midnight. The streets were now deserted, and the almanac having predicted a new moon about this time, the lamps had been conscientiously extinguished. Suddenly a great globe of sound fell from an adjacent church-tower, and exploded on the night with a deep metallic boom. Then all the clocks and bells began ringing-in the New Year—pounding and banging and yelling and finishing off all the nervous invalids left over from the preceding Sunday. The little orphan started from her dream, leaving a small patch of skin on the frosted lamp-post, clasped her thin blue hands and looked upward, 'with mad disquietude,' "—

S. E.—In *The Monitor* it was "with covetous eyes."

P. C.—I know it; hadn't read Byron then. Clever dog, Byron. (*Reads.*) "Presently a cranberry tart dropped at her feet, apparently from the clouds."

S. E.—How about those angels?

P. C.—The editor of *Good Will* cut 'em out. He said San Francisco was no place for them; and I don't believe—

S. E.—There, there! Never mind. Go on with the little story.

P. C.—(*Reads.*) "As she stopped to take the tart a veal sandwich came whizzing down, and cuffed one of her ears. Next a wheaten loaf made her dodge nimbly, and then a broad ham fell flat-footed at her toes. A sack of flour burst in the middle of the street; a side of bacon impaled itself on an iron hitching-post. Pretty soon a chain of sausages fell in a circle around her, flattening out as if a roadroller had passed over them. Then there was a lull—nothing came down but dried fish, cold puddings and flannel under-clothing; but presently her wishes began to take effect again, and a quarter of beef descended with terrific momentum upon the top of the little orphan's head."

S. E.—How did the editor of *The Reasonable Virtues* like that quarter of beef?

P. C.—Oh, he swallowed it like a little man, and stuck in a few dressed pigs of his own. I've left them out, because I don't want outsiders altering the Little Story. (*Reads.*)

"One would have thought that ought to suffice; but not so. Bedding, shoes, firkins of butter, mighty cheeses, ropes of onions, quantities of loose jam, kegs of oysters, titanic fowls, crates of crockery and glassware, assorted house-keeping things, cooking ranges, and tons of coal poured down in broad cataracts from a bounteous heaven, piling themselves above that infant to a depth of twenty feet. The weather was more than two hours in clearing up; and as late as half-past three a ponderous hogshead of sugar struck at the corner of Clay and Kearney Streets, with an impact that shook the peninsula like an earthquake and stopped every clock in town.

"At daybreak the good merchants arrived upon the scene with shovels and wheelbarrows, and before the sun of the new year was an hour old, they had provided for all of these provisions—had stowed them away in their cellars, and nicely arranged them on their shelves, ready for sale to the deserving poor."

S. E.—And the little girl—what became of *her?*

P. C.—You mustn't get ahead of the Little Story. (*Reads.*)

"When they had got down to the wicked little orphan who had not been content with her lot some one brought a broom, and she was carefully swept and smoothed out. Then they lifted her tenderly, and carried her to the coroner. That functionary was standing in the door of his office, and with a deprecatory wave of his hand, he said to the man who was bearing her:

" 'There, go away, my good fellow; there was a man here three times yesterday trying to sell me just such a map.' "

THE PARENTICIDE CLUB

MY FAVORITE MURDER

HAVING murdered my mother under circumstances of singular atrocity, I was arrested and put upon my trial, which lasted seven years. In charging the jury, the judge of the Court of Acquittal remarked that it was one of the most ghastly crimes that he had ever been called upon to explain away.

At this, my attorney rose and said:

"May it please your Honor, crimes are ghastly or agreeable only by comparison. If you were familiar with the details of my client's previous murder of his uncle you would discern in his later offense (if offense it may be called) something in the nature of tender forbearance and filial consideration for the feelings of the victim. The appalling ferocity of the former assassination was indeed inconsistent with any hypothesis but that of guilt; and had it not been for the fact that the honorable judge before whom he was tried was the president of a life insurance company that took risks on hanging, and in which my client held a policy, it is hard to see how he could decently have been acquitted. If your Honor would like to hear about it for instruction and guidance of your Honor's mind, this unfortunate man, my client, will consent to give himself the pain of relating it under oath."

The district attorney said: "Your Honor, I object. Such a statement would be in the nature of evidence, and the testimony in this case is closed. The prisoner's statement should have been introduced three years ago, in the spring of 1881."

"In a statutory sense," said the judge, "you are right, and in the Court of Objections and Technicalities you would get a ruling in your favor. But not in a Court of Acquittal. The objection is overruled."

"I except," said the district attorney.

"You cannot do that," the judge said. "I must remind you that in order to take an exception you must first get this case transferred for a time to the Court of Exceptions on a formal motion duly supported by affidavits. A motion to that effect by your predecessor in office was denied by me during the first year of this trial. Mr. Clerk, swear the prisoner."

The customary oath having been administered, I made the following statement, which impressed the judge with so strong a sense of the comparative triviality of the offense for which I was on trial that he made no further search for mitigating circumstances, but simply instructed the jury to acquit, and I left the court, without a stain upon my reputation:

"I was born in 1856 in Kalamakee, Mich., of honest and reputable parents, one of whom Heaven has mercifully spared to comfort me in my later years. In 1867 the family came to California and settled near Nigger Head, where my father opened a road agency and prospered beyond the dreams of avarice. He was a reticent, saturnine man then, though his increasing years have now somewhat relaxed the austerity of his disposition, and I believe that nothing but his memory of the sad event for which I am now on trial prevents him from manifesting a genuine hilarity.

"Four years after we had set up the road agency an itinerant preacher came along, and having no other way to pay for the night's lodging that we gave him, favored us with an exhortation of such power that, praise God, we were all converted to religion. My father at once sent for his brother, the Hon. William Ridley of Stockton, and on his arrival turned over the agency to him, charging him nothing for the franchise nor plant—the latter consisting of a Winchester rifle, a sawed-off shotgun, and an assortment of masks made out of flour sacks. The family then moved to Ghost Rock and opened a dance house. It was called 'The Saints' Rest Hurdy-Gurdy,' and the proceedings each night began with prayer. It was there that my now sainted mother, by her grace in the dance, acquired the *sobriquet* of 'The Bucking Walrus.'

"In the fall of '75 I had occasion to visit Coyote, on the road to Mahala, and took the stage at Ghost Rock. There were four other passengers. About three miles beyond Nigger Head, persons whom I identified as my Uncle William and his two sons held up the stage. Finding nothing in the express box, they went through the passengers. I acted a most honorable part in the affair, placing myself in line with the others, holding up my hands and permitting myself to be deprived of forty dollars and a gold watch. From my behavior no one could have suspected that I knew the gentlemen who gave the entertainment. A few days later, when I went to Nigger Head and asked for the return of my money and watch my uncle and cousins swore they knew nothing of the matter, and they affected a belief that my father and I had done the job ourselves in dishonest violation of commercial good faith. Uncle William even threatened to retaliate by starting an opposition dance house at Ghost Rock. As 'The Saints' Rest' had become rather unpopular, I saw that this would assuredly ruin it and prove a paying enterprise, so I told my uncle that I was willing to overlook the past if he would take me into the scheme and keep the partnership a secret from my father. This fair offer he rejected, and I then perceived that it would be better and more satisfactory if he were dead.

"My plans to that end were soon perfected, and communicating them to my dear parents I had the gratification of receiving their approval. My father said he was proud of me, and my mother promised that although her religion forbade her to assist in taking human life I should have the advantage of her prayers for my success. As a preliminary measure looking to my security in case of detection I made an application for membership in that powerful order, the Knights of Murder, and in due course was received as a member of the Ghost Rock commandery. On the day that my probation ended I was for the first time permitted to inspect the records of the order and learn who belonged to it—all the rites of initiation having been conducted in masks. Fancy my delight when, in looking over the roll of membership, I found the third name to be that of my uncle, who indeed was junior vice-chancellor of the order! Here was an opportunity exceeding my wildest dreams—to murder I could add insubordination and treachery. It was what my good mother would have called 'a special Providence.'

"At about this time something occurred which caused my cup of joy, already full, to overflow on all sides, a circular cataract of bliss. Three men, strangers in that locality, were arrested for the stage robbery in which I had lost my money and watch. They were brought to trial and, despite my efforts to clear them and fasten the guilt upon three of the most respectable and worthy citizens of Ghost Rock, convicted on the clearest proof. The murder would now be as wanton and reasonless as I could wish.

"One morning I shouldered my Winchester rifle, and going over to my uncle's house, near Nigger Head, asked my Aunt Mary, his wife, if he were at home, adding that I had come to kill him. My aunt replied with her peculiar smile that so many gentleman called on that errand and were afterward carried away without having performed it that I must excuse her for doubting my good faith in the matter. She said I did not look as if I would kill anybody, so, as a proof of good faith I leveled my rifle and wounded a Chinaman who happened to be passing the house. She said she knew whole families that could do a thing of that kind, but Bill Ridley was a horse of another color. She said, however, that I would find him over on the other side of the creek in the sheep lot; and she added that she hoped the best man would win.

"My Aunt Mary was one of the most fair-minded women that I have ever met.

"I found my uncle down on his knees engaged in skinning a sheep. Seeing that he had neither gun nor pistol handy I had not the heart to shoot him, so I approached him, greeted him pleasantly and struck him a powerful blow on the head with the butt of my rifle. I have a very good delivery and Uncle William lay down on his side, then rolled over on his back, spread out his fingers and shivered. Before he could recover the use of his limbs I seized the knife that he had been using and cut his hamstrings. You know, doubtless, that when you sever the *tendo Achillis* the patient has no further use of his leg; it is just the same as if he had no leg. Well, I parted them both, and when he revived he was at my service. As soon as he comprehended the situation, he said:

" 'Samuel, you have got the drop on me and can afford to be generous. I have only one thing to ask of you, and that is that you carry me to the house and finish me in the bosom of my family.'

"I told him I thought that a pretty reasonable request and I would do so if he would let me put him into a wheat sack; he would be easier to carry that way and if we were seen by the neighbors *en route* it would cause less remark. He agreed to that, and going to the barn I got a sack. This, however, did not fit him; it was too short and much wider than he; so I bent his legs, forced his knees up against his breast and got him into it that way, tying the sack above his head. He was a heavy man and I had all that I could do to get him on my back, but I staggered along for some distance until I came to a swing that some of the children had suspended to the branch of an oak. Here I laid him down and sat upon him to rest, and the sight of the rope gave me a happy inspiration. In twenty minutes my uncle, still in the sack, swung free to the sport of the wind.

"I had taken down the rope, tied one end tightly about the mouth of the bag, thrown the other across the limb and hauled him up about five feet from the ground. Fastening the other end of the rope also about the mouth of the sack, I had the satisfaction to see my uncle converted into a large, fine pendulum. I must add that he was not himself entirely aware of the nature of the change that he had undergone in his relation to the exterior world, though in justice to a good man's memory I ought to say that I do not think he would in any case have wasted much of my time in vain remonstrance.

"Uncle William had a ram that was famous in all that region as a fighter. It was in a state of chronic constitutional indignation. Some deep disappointment in early life had soured its disposition and it had declared war upon the whole world. To say that it would butt anything accessible is but faintly to express the nature and scope of its military activity: the universe was its antagonist; its methods that of a projectile. It fought like the angels and devils, in mid-air, cleaving the atmosphere like a bird, describing a parabolic curve and descending upon its victim at just the exact angle of incidence to make the most of its velocity and weight. Its momentum, calculated in foot-tons, was something incredible. It had been seen to destroy a four year old bull by a single impact upon that animal's gnarly forehead. No stone wall had ever been known to resist its downward swoop; there were no trees tough enough to stay it; it would splinter them into matchwood and defile their leafy honors in the dust. This irascible and implacable brute—this incarnate thunderbolt—this monster of the upper deep, I had seen reposing in the shade of an adjacent tree, dreaming dreams of conquest and glory. It was with a view to summoning it forth to the field of honor that I suspended its master in the manner described.

"Having completed my preparations, I imparted to the avuncular pendulum a gentle oscillation, and retiring to cover behind a contiguous rock, lifted up my voice in a long rasping cry whose diminishing final note was drowned in a noise like that of a swearing cat, which emanated from the sack. Instantly that formidable sheep was upon its feet and had taken in the military situation at a glance. In a few moments it had approached, stamping, to within fifty yards of the swinging foeman, who, now retreating and anon advancing, seemed to invite the fray. Suddenly I saw the beast's head drop earthward as if depressed by the weight of its enormous horns; then a dim, white, wavy streak of sheep prolonged itself from that spot in a generally horizontal direction to within about four yards of a point immediately beneath the enemy. There it struck sharply upward, and before it had faded from my gaze at the place whence it had set out I heard a horrid thump and a piercing scream, and my poor uncle shot forward, with a slack rope higher than the limb to which he was attached. Here the rope tautened with a jerk, arresting his flight, and back he swung in a breathless curve to the other end of his arc. The ram had fallen, a heap of indistinguishable legs, wool and horns, but pulling itself together and dodging as its antagonist swept downward it retired at random, alternately shaking its head and stamping its fore-feet. When it had backed about the same distance as that from which it had delivered the assault it paused again, bowed its head as if in prayer for victory and again shot forward, dimly visible as before—a prolonging white streak with monstrous undulations, ending with a sharp ascension. Its course this time was at a right angle to its former one, and its impatience so great that it struck the enemy before he had nearly reached the lowest point of his arc. In consequence he went flying round and round in a horizontal circle whose radius was about equal to half the length of the rope, which I forgot to say was nearly twenty feet long. His shrieks, *crescendo* in approach and *diminuendo* in recession, made the rapidity of his revolution more obvious to the ear than to the eye. He had evidently not yet been struck in a vital spot. His posture in the sack and the distance from the ground at which he hung compelled the ram to operate upon his lower extremities and the end of his back. Like a plant that has struck its root into some poisonous mineral, my poor uncle was dying slowly upward.

"After delivering its second blow the ram had not again retired. The fever of battle burned hot in its heart; its brain was intoxicated with the wine of strife. Like a pugilist who in his rage forgets his skill and fights ineffectively at half-arm's length, the angry beast endeavored to reach its fleeting foe by awkward vertical leaps as he passed overhead, sometimes, indeed, succeeding in striking him feebly, but more frequently overthrown by its own misguided eagerness. But as the impetus was exhausted and the man's circles narrowed in scope and diminished in speed, bringing him nearer to the ground, these tactics produced better results, eliciting a superior quality of screams, which I greatly enjoyed.

"Suddenly, as if the bugles had sung truce, the ram suspended hostilities and walked away, thoughtfully wrinkling and smoothing its great aquiline nose, and occasionally cropping a bunch of grass and slowly munching it. It seemed to have tired of war's alarms and resolved to beat the sword into a plowshare and cultivate the arts of peace. Steadily it held its course away from the field of fame until it had gained a distance of nearly a quarter of a mile. There it stopped and stood with its rear to the foe, chewing its cud and apparently half asleep. I observed, however, an occasional slight turn of its head, as if its apathy were more affected than real.

"Meantime Uncle William's shrieks had abated with his motion, and nothing was heard from him but long, low moans, and at long intervals my name, uttered in pleading tones exceedingly grateful to my ear. Evidently the man had not the faintest notion of what was being done to him, and was inexpressibly terrified. When Death comes cloaked in mystery he is terrible indeed. Little by little my uncle's oscillations diminished, and finally he hung motionless. I went to him and was about to give him the *coup de grâce,* when I heard and felt a succession of smart shocks which shook the ground like a series of light earthquakes, and turning in the direction of the ram, saw a long cloud of dust approaching me with inconceivable rapidity and alarming effect! At a distance of some thirty yards away it stopped short, and from the near end of it rose into the air what I at first thought a great white bird. Its ascent was so smooth and easy and regular that I could not realize its extraordinary celerity, and was lost in admiration of its grace. To this day the impression remains that it was a slow, deliberate movement, the ram—for it was that animal—being upborne by some power other than its own impetus, and supported through the successive stages of its flight with infinite tenderness and care. My eyes followed its progress through the air with unspeakable pleasure, all the greater by contrast with my former terror of its approach by land. Onward and upward the noble animal sailed, its head bent down almost between its knees, its fore-feet thrown back, its hinder legs trailing to rear like the legs of a soaring heron.

"At a height of forty or fifty feet, as fond recollection presents it to view, it attained its zenith and appeared to remain an instant stationary; then, tilting suddenly forward without altering the relative position of its parts, it shot downward on a steeper and steeper course with augmenting velocity, passed immediately above me with a noise like the rush of a cannon shot and struck my poor uncle almost squarely on the top of the head! So frightful was the impact that not only the man's neck was broken, but the rope too; and the body of the deceased, forced against the earth, was crushed to pulp beneath the awful front of that meteoric sheep! The concussion stopped all the clocks between Lone Hand and Dutch Dan's, and Professor Davidson, a distinguished authority in matters seismic, who happened to be in the vicinity, promptly explained that the vibrations were from north to southwest.

"Altogether, I cannot help thinking that in point of artistic atrocity my murder of Uncle William has seldom been excelled."

OIL OF DOG

MY name is Boffer Bings. I was born of honest parents in one of the humbler walks of life, my father being a manufacturer of dog-oil and my mother having a small studio in the shadow of the village church, where she disposed of unwelcome babes. In my boyhood I was trained to habits of industry; I not only assisted my father in procuring dogs for his vats, but was frequently employed by my mother to carry away the débris of her work in the studio. In performance of this duty I sometimes had need of all my natural intelligence for all the law officers of the vicinity were opposed to my mother's business. They were not elected on an opposition ticket, and the matter had never been made a political issue; it just happened so. My father's business of making dog-oil was, naturally, less unpopular, though the owners of missing dogs sometimes regarded him with suspicion, which was reflected, to some extent, upon me. My father had, as silent partners, all the physicians of the town, who seldom wrote a prescription which did not contain what they were pleased to designate as *Ol. can.* It is really the most valuable medicine ever discovered. But most persons are unwilling to make personal sacrifices for the afflicted, and it was evident that many of the fattest dogs in town had been forbidden to play with me—a fact which pained my young sensibilities, and at one time came near driving me to become a pirate.

Looking back upon those days, I cannot but regret, at times, that by indirectly bringing my beloved parents to their death I was the author of misfortunes profoundly affecting my future.

One evening while passing my father's oil factory with the body of a foundling from my mother's studio I saw a constable who seemed to be closely watching my movements. Young as I was, I had learned that a constable's acts, of whatever apparent character, are prompted by the most reprehensible motives, and I avoided him by dodging into the oilery by a side door which happened to stand ajar. I locked it at once and was alone with my dead. My father had retired for the night. The only light in the place came from the furnace, which glowed a deep, rich crimson under one of the vats, casting ruddy reflections on the walls. Within the cauldron the oil still rolled in indolent ebullition, occasionally pushing to the surface a piece of dog. Seating myself to wait for the constable to go away, I held the naked body of the foundling in my lap and tenderly stroked its short, silken hair. Ah, how beautiful it was! Even at that early age I was passionately fond of children, and as I looked upon this cherub I could almost find it in my heart to wish that the small, red wound upon its breast—the work of my dear mother—had not been mortal.

It had been my custom to throw the babes into the river which nature had thoughtfully provided for the purpose, but that night I did not dare to leave the oilery for fear of the constable. "After all," I said to myself, "it cannot greatly matter if I put it into this cauldron. My father will never know the bones from those of a puppy, and the few deaths which may result from administering another kind of oil for the incomparable *ol. can.* are not important in a population which increases so rapidly." In short, I took the first step in crime and brought myself untold sorrow by casting the babe into the cauldron.

The next day, somewhat to my surprise, my father, rubbing his hands with satisfaction, informed me and my mother that he had obtained the finest quality of oil that was ever seen; that the physicians to whom he had shown samples had so pronounced it. He added that he had no knowledge as to how the result was obtained; the dogs had been treated in all respects as usual, and were of an ordinary breed. I deemed it my duty to explain—which I did, though palsied would have been my tongue if I could have foreseen the consequences. Bewailing their previous ignorance of the advantages of combining their industries, my parents at once took measures to repair the error. My mother removed her studio to a wing of the factory building and my duties in connection with the business ceased; I was no longer required to dispose of the bodies of the small superfluous, and there was no need of alluring dogs to their doom, for my father discarded them altogether, though they still had an honorable place in the name of the oil. So suddenly thrown into idleness, I might naturally have been expected to become vicious and dissolute, but I did not. The holy influence of my dear mother was ever about me to protect me from the temptations which beset youth, and my father was a deacon in a church. Alas, that through my fault these estimable persons should have come to so bad an end!

Finding a double profit in her business, my mother now devoted herself to it with a new assiduity. She removed not only superfluous and unwelcome babes to order, but went out into the highways and byways, gathering in children of a larger growth, and even such adults as she could entice to the oilery. My father, too, enamored of the superior quality of oil produced, purveyed for his vats with diligence and zeal. The conversion of their neighbors into dog-oil became, in short, the one passion of their lives—an absorbing and overwhelming greed took possession of their souls and served them in place of a hope in Heaven —by which, also, they were inspired.

So enterprising had they now become that a public meeting was held and resolutions passed severely censuring them. It was intimated by the chairman that any further raids upon the population would be met in a spirit of hostility. My poor parents left the meeting brokenhearted, desperate and, I believe, not altogether sane. Anyhow, I deemed it prudent not to enter the oilery with them that night, but slept outside in a stable.

At about midnight some mysterious impulse caused me to rise and peer through a window into the furnace-room, where I knew my father now slept. The fires were burning as brightly as if the following day's harvest had been expected to be abundant. One of the large cauldrons was slowly "walloping" with a mysterious appearance to self-restraint, as if it bided its time to put forth its full energy. My father was not in bed; he had risen in his nightclothes and was preparing a noose in a strong cord. From the looks which he cast at the door of my mother's bedroom I knew too well the purpose that he had in mind. Speechless and motionless with terror, I could do nothing in prevention or warning. Suddenly the door of my mother's apartment was opened, noiselessly, and the two confronted each other, both apparently surprised. The lady, also, was in her night clothes, and she held in her right hand the tool of her trade, a long, narrow-bladed dagger.

She, too, had been unable to deny herself the last profit which the unfriendly action of the citizens and my absence had left her. For one instant they looked into each other's blazing eyes and then sprang together with indescribable fury. Round and round the room they struggled, the man cursing, the woman shrieking, both fighting like demons—she to strike him with the dagger, he to strangle her with his great bare hands. I know not how long I had the unhappiness to observe this disagreeable instance of domestic infelicity, but at last, after a more than usually vigorous struggle, the combatants suddenly moved apart.

My father's breast and my mother's weapon showed evidences of contact. For another instant they glared at each other in the most unamiable way; then my poor, wounded father, feeling the hand of death upon him, leaped forward, unmindful of resistance, grasped my dear mother in his arms, dragged her to the side of the boiling cauldron, collected all his failing energies, and sprang in with her! In a moment, both had disappeared and were adding their oil to that of the committee of citizens who had called the day before with an invitation to the public meeting.

Convinced that these unhappy events closed to me every avenue to an honorable career in that town, I removed to the famous city of Otumwee, where these memoirs are written with a heart full of remorse for a heedless act entailing so dismal a commercial disaster.

AN IMPERFECT CONFLAGRATION

EARLY one June morning in 1872 I murdered my father—an act which made a deep impression on me at the time. This was before my marriage, while I was living with my parents in Wisconsin. My father and I were in the library of our home, dividing the proceeds of a burglary which we had committed that night. These consisted of household goods mostly, and the task of equitable division was difficult. We got on very well with the napkins, towels and such things, and the silverware was parted pretty nearly equally, but you can see for yourself that when you try to divide a single music-box by two without a remainder you will have trouble. It was that music-box which brought disaster and disgrace upon our family. If we had left it my poor father might now be alive.

It was a most exquisite and beautiful piece of workmanship—inlaid with costly woods and carven very curiously. It would not only play a great variety of tunes, but would whistle like a quail, bark like a dog, crow every morning at daylight whether it was wound up or not, and break the Ten Commandments. It was this last mentioned accomplishment that won my father's heart and caused him to commit the only dishonorable act of his life, though possibly he would have committed more if he had been spared: he tried to conceal that music-box from me, and declared upon his honor that he had not taken it, though I know very well that, so far as he was concerned, the burglary had been undertaken chiefly for the purpose of obtaining it.

My father had the music-box hidden under his cloak; we had worn cloaks by way of disguise. He had solemnly assured me that he did not take it. I knew that he did, and knew something of which he was evidently ignorant; namely, that the box would crow at daylight and betray him if I could prolong the division of profits till that time. All occurred as I wished: as the gaslight began to pale in the library and the shape of the windows was seen dimly behind the curtains, a long cock-a-doodle-doo came from beneath the old gentleman's cloak, followed by a few bars of an aria from *Tannhauser,* ending with a loud click. A small hand-axe, which we had used to break into the unlucky house, lay between us on the table; I picked it up. The old man seeing that further concealment was useless took the box from under his cloak and set it on the table. "Cut it in two if you prefer that plan," said he; "I tried to save it from destruction."

He was a passionate lover of music and could himself play the concertina with expression and feeling.

I said: "I do not question the purity of your motive: it would be presumptuous in me to sit in judgment on my father. But business is business, and with this axe I am going to effect a dissolution of our partnership unless you will consent in all future burglaries to wear a bell-punch."

"No," he said, after some reflection, "no, I could not do that; it would look like a confession of dishonesty. People would say that you distrusted me."

I could not help admiring his spirit and sensitiveness; for a moment I was proud of him and disposed to overlook his fault, but a glance at the richly jeweled music-box decided me, and, as I said, I removed the old man from this vale of tears. Having done so, I was a trifle uneasy. Not only was he my father—the author of my being—but the body would be certainly discovered. It was now broad daylight and my mother was likely to enter the library at any moment. Under the circumstances, I thought it expedient to remove her also, which I did. Then I paid off all the servants and discharged them.

That afternoon I went to the chief of police, told him what I had done and asked his advice. It would be very painful to me if the facts became publicly known. My conduct would be generally condemned; the newspapers would bring it up against me if ever I should run for office. The chief saw the force of these considerations; he was himself an assassin of wide experience. After consulting with the presiding judge of the Court of Variable Jurisdiction he advised me to conceal the bodies in one of the bookcases, get a heavy insurance on the house and burn it down. This I proceeded to do.

In the library was a book-case which my father had recently purchased of some cranky inventor and had not filled. It was in shape and size something like the old-fashioned "ward-robes" which one sees in bed-rooms without closets, but opened all the way down, like a woman's night-dress. It had glass doors. I had recently laid out my parents and they were now rigid enough to stand erect; so I stood them in this book-case, from which I had removed the shelves. I locked them in and tacked some curtains over the glass doors. The inspector from the insurance office passed a half-dozen times before the case without suspicion.

That night, after getting my policy, I set fire to the house and started through the woods to town, two miles away, where I managed to be found about the time the excitement was at its height. With cries of apprehension for the fate of my parents, I joined the rush and arrived at the fire some two hours after I had kindled it. The whole town was there as I dashed up. The house was entirely consumed, but in one end of the level bed of glowing embers, bolt upright and uninjured, was that book-case! The curtains had burned away, exposing the glass-doors, through which the fierce, red light illuminated the interior. There stood my dear father "in his habit as he lived," and at his side the partner of his joys and sorrows. Not a hair of them was singed, their clothing was intact. On their heads and throats the injuries which in the accomplishment of my designs I had been compelled to inflict were conspicuous. As in the presence of a miracle, the people were silent; awe and terror had stilled every tongue. I was myself greatly affected.

Some three years later, when the events herein related had nearly faded from my memory, I went to New York to assist in passing some counterfeit United States bonds. Carelessly looking into a furniture store one day, I saw the exact counterpart of that book-case. "I bought it for a trifle from a reformed inventor," the dealer explained. "He said it was fireproof, the pores of the wood being filled with alum under hydraulic pressure and the glass made of asbestos. I don't suppose it is really fireproof—you can have it at the price of an ordinary book-case."

"No," I said, "if you cannot warrant it fireproof I won't take it"— and I bade him good morning.

I would not have had it at any price: it revived memories that were exceedingly disagreeable.

THE HYPNOTIST

BY those of my friends who happen to know that I sometimes amuse myself with hypnotism, mind reading and kindred phenomena, I am frequently asked if I have a clear conception of the nature of whatever principle underlies them. To this question I always reply that I neither have nor desire to have. I am no investigator with an ear at the key-hole of Nature's workshop, trying with vulgar curiosity to steal the secrets of her trade. The interests of science are as little to me as mine seem to have been to science.

Doubtless the phenomena in question are simple enough, and in no way transcend our powers of comprehension if only we could find the clew; but for my part I prefer not to find it, for I am of a singularly romantic disposition, deriving more gratification from mystery than from knowledge. It was commonly remarked of me when I was a child that my big blue eyes appeared to have been made rather to look into than look out of—such was their dreamful beauty, and in my frequent periods of abstraction, their indifference to what was going on. In those peculiarities they resembled, I venture to think, the soul which lies behind them, always more intent upon some lovely conception which it has created in its own image than concerned about the laws of nature and the material frame of things. All this, irrelevant and egotistic as it may seem, is related by way of accounting for the meagreness of the light that I am able to throw upon a subject that has engaged so much of my attention, and concerning which there is so keen and general a curiosity. With my powers and opportunities, another person might doubtless have an explanation for much of what I present simply as narrative.

My first knowledge that I possessed unusual powers came to me in my fourteenth year, when at school. Happening one day to have forgotten to bring my noon-day luncheon, I gazed longingly at that of a small girl who was preparing to eat hers. Looking up, her eyes met mine and she seemed unable to withdraw them. After a moment of hesitancy she came forward in an absent kind of way and without a word surrendered her little basket with its tempting contents and walked away. Inexpressibly pleased, I relieved my hunger and destroyed the basket. After that I had not the trouble to bring a luncheon for myself: that little girl was my daily purveyor; and not infrequently in satisfying my simple need from her frugal store I combined pleasure and profit by constraining her attendance at the feast and making misleading proffer of the viands, which eventually I consumed to the last fragment. The girl was always persuaded that she had eaten all herself; and later in the day her tearful complaints of hunger surprised the teacher, entertained the pupils, earned for her the sobriquet of Greedy-Gut and filled me with a peace past understanding.

A disagreeable feature of this otherwise satisfactory condition of things was the necessary secrecy: the transfer of the luncheon, for example, had to be made at some distance from the madding crowd, in a wood; and I blush to think of the many other unworthy subterfuges entailed by the situation. As I was (and am) naturally of a frank and open disposition, these became more and more irksome, and but for the reluctance of my parents to renounce the obvious advantages of the new *régime* I would gladly have reverted to the old. The plan that I finally adopted to free myself from the consequences of my own powers excited a wide and keen interest at the time, and that part of it which consisted in the death of the girl was severely condemned, but it is hardly pertinent to the scope of this narrative.

For some years afterward I had little opportunity to practice hypnotism; such small essays as I made at it were commonly barren of other recognition than solitary confinement on a bread-and-water diet; sometimes, indeed, they elicited nothing better than the cat-o'-nine-tails. It was when I was about to leave the scene of these small disappointments that my one really important feat was performed.

I had been called into the warden's office and given a suit of civilian's clothing, a trifling sum of money and a great deal of advice, which I am bound to confess was of a much better quality than the clothing. As I was passing out of the gate into the light of freedom I suddenly turned and looking the warden gravely in the eye, soon had him in control.

"You are an ostrich," I said.

At the post-mortem examination the stomach was found to contain a great quantity of indigestible articles mostly of wood or metal. Stuck fast in the œsophagus and constituting, according to the Coroner's jury, the immediate cause of death, one door-knob.

I was by nature a good and affectionate son, but as I took my way into the great world from which I had been so long secluded I could not help remembering that all my misfortunes had flowed like a stream from the niggard economy of my parents in the matter of school luncheons; and I knew of no reason to think they had reformed.

On the road between Succotash Hill and South Asphyxia is a little open field which once contained a shanty known as Pete Gilstrap's Place, where that gentleman used to murder travelers for a living. The death of Mr. Gilstrap and the diversion of nearly all the travel to another road occurred so nearly at the same time that no one has ever been able to say which was cause and which effect. Anyhow, the field was now a desolation and the Place had long been burned. It was while going afoot to South Asphyxia, the home of my childhood, that I found both my parents on their way to the Hill. They had hitched their team and were eating luncheon under an oak tree in the center of the field. The sight of the luncheon called up painful memories of my school days and roused the sleeping lion in my breast. Approaching the guilty couple, who at once recognized me, I ventured to suggest that I share their hospitality.

"Of this cheer, my son," said the author of my being, with characteristic pomposity, which age had not withered, "there is sufficient but for two. I am not, I hope, insensible to the hunger-light in your eyes, but—"

My father has never completed that sentence; what he mistook for hunger-light was simply the earnest gaze of the hypnotist. In a few seconds he was at my service. A few more sufficed for the lady, and the dictates of a just resentment could be carried into effect. "My former father," I said, "I presume that it is known to you that you and this lady are no longer what you were?"

"I have observed a certain subtle change," was the rather dubious reply of the old gentleman; "it is perhaps attributable to age."

"It is more than that," I explained; "it goes to character—to species. You and the lady here are, in truth, two *broncos*—wild stallions both, and unfriendly."

"Why, John," exclaimed my dear mother, "you don't mean to say that I am—"

"Madam," I replied, solemnly, fixing my eyes again upon hers, "you are."

Scarcely had the words fallen from my lips when she dropped upon her hands and knees, and backing up to the old man squealed like a demon and delivered a vicious kick upon his shin! An instant later he was himself down on all-fours, headed away from her and flinging his feet at her simultaneously and successively. With equal earnestness but inferior agility, because of her hampering body-gear, she plied her own. Their flying legs crossed and mingled in the most bewildering way; their feet sometimes meeting squarely in midair, their bodies thrust forward, falling flat upon the ground and for a moment helpless. On recovering themselves they would resume the combat, uttering their frenzy in the nameless sounds of the furious brutes which they believed themselves to be—the whole region rang with their clamor! Round and round they wheeled, the blows of their feet falling "like lightnings from the mountain cloud." They plunged and reared backward upon their knees, struck savagely at each other with awkward descending blows of both fists at once, and dropped again upon their hands as if unable to maintain the upright position of the body. Grass and pebbles were torn from the soil by hands and feet; clothing, hair, faces inexpressibly defiled with dust and blood. Wild, inarticulate screams of rage attested the delivery of the blows; groans, grunts and gasps their receipt. Nothing more truly military was ever seen at Gettysburg or Waterloo: the valor of my dear parents in the hour of danger can never cease to be to me a source of pride and gratification. At the end of it all two battered, tattered, bloody and fragmentary vestiges of mortality attested the solemn fact that the author of the strife was an orphan.

Arrested for provoking a breach of the peace, I was, and have ever since been, tried in the Court of Technicalities and Continuances whence, after fifteen years of proceedings, my attorney is moving heaven and earth to get the case taken to the Court of Remandment for New Trials.

Such are a few of my principal experiments in the mysterious force or agency known as hypnotic suggestion. Whether or not it could be employed by a bad man for an unworthy purpose I am unable to say.